OXFORD
UNIVERSITY PRESS

ASPIRE
SUCCEED
PROGRESS

Complete
Mathematics
for Cambridge IGCSE®

Fifth Edition

Extended

David Rayner
Ian Bettison
Mathew Taylor

OXFORD
UNIVERSITY PRESS

Great Clarendon Street, Oxford, OX2 6DP, United Kingdom

Oxford University Press is a department of the University of Oxford.
It furthers the University's objective of excellence in research, scholarship, and education by publishing worldwide. Oxford is a registered trade mark of Oxford University Press in the UK and in certain other countries

British Library Cataloguing in Publication Data
Data available

978-0-19-842507-6

1 3 5 7 9 10 8 6 4 2

Paper used in the production of this book is a natural, recyclable product made from wood grown in sustainable forests. The manufacturing process conforms to the environmental regulations of the country of origin.

Printed in Italy by L.E.G.O. SpA

Acknowledgements
The publishers would like to thank the following for permissions to use copyright material:

® IGCSE is the registered trademark of Cambridge Assessment International Education.

Past paper examination material reproduced by permission of Cambridge Assessment International Education.

Cambridge Assessment International Education bears no responsibility for the example answers to questions taken from its past question papers which are contained in this publication.

p1: DeAgostini/Getty Images; **p15:** patrimonio designs ltd/ Shutterstock; **p16:** EvgenySHCH/Shutterstock; **p19:** NPeter/ Shutterstock; **p24:** Eric Isselee/Shutterstock; **p25:** Don Bendickson/Shutterstock; **p29:** Mike Flippo/Shutterstock; **p29:** Leena Robinson/Shutterstock; **p31:** TonyV3112/ Shutterstock; **p33:** Supertrooper/Shutterstock; **p35:** T-Design/Shutterstock; **p37:** Tomasz Kubis/Shutterstock; **p39:** Joerg Beuge/Shutterstock; **p57:** Everett - Art/ Shutterstock; **p57:** beerlogoff/Shutterstock; **p58:** Stas Moroz/Shutterstock; **p61:** Celso Diniz/Shutterstock; **p83:** Alberto Loyo/Shutterstock; **p84:** UnderTheSea/Shutterstock; **p95:** Gts/Shutterstock; **p102:** Roger Viollet Collection/ Getty Images; **p118:** Paul Broadbent/Shutterstock; **p133:** Offscreen/Shutterstock; **p146:** EvgenySHCH/Shutterstock; **p171:** SCIENCE SOURCE/SCIENCE PHOTO LIBRARY; **p182:** LifetimeStock/Shutterstock; **p184:** rangizzz/Shutterstock; **p184:** Christopher Elwell/Shutterstock; **p198:** acceptphoto/ Shutterstock; **p199:** Blend Images/Shutterstock; **p200:** Tish1/Shutterstock; **p206:** NEW YORK PUBLIC LIBRARY/ SCIENCE PHOTO LIBRARY; **p216:** Eric Cote/Shutterstock; **p236:** SCIENCE PHOTO LIBRARY; **p249:** Ezume Images/ Shutterstock; **p262:** Kraiwut_K/Shutterstock; **p270:** Bettmann/Getty Images; **p277:** Crystal Image/Shutterstock; **p278:** Ruslan Kudrin/Shutterstock; **p306:** Bettmann/ Getty Images; **p338:** DeAgostini/Getty Images; **p362:** Natali Zakharova/Shutterstock; **p365:** WHITE RABBIT83/ Shutterstock; **p366:** Sebastian Studio/Shutterstock; **p368:** sanjungtion/Shutterstock; **p371:** NagyG/Shutterstock; **p381:** EMILIO SEGRE VISUAL ARCHIVES/AMERICAN INSTITUTE OF PHYSICS/SCIENCE PHOTO LIBRARY; **p389:** Monkey Business Images/Shutterstock; **p398:** Vlademareous/Shutterstock; **p399:** chotwit piyapramote/Shutterstockpiyapramote/ Shutterstock

Cover image: Shutterstock

Although we have made every effort to trace and contact all copyright holders before publication this has not been possible in all cases. If notified, the publisher will rectify any errors or omissions at the earliest opportunity.

Links to third party websites are provided by Oxford in good faith and for information only. Oxford disclaims any responsibility for the materials contained in any third party website referenced in this work.

Contents

Access your support website for extra homework questions and exam revision material
www.oxfordsecondary.com/9780198425076

Cambridge IGCSE®
Mathematics 0580: Extended

Syllabus topic		Page numbers in student book
E1: Number		
E1.1	Identify and use natural numbers, integers (positive, negative and zero), prime numbers, square numbers, common factors and common multiples, rational and irrational numbers (e.g. π, $\sqrt{2}$), real numbers, reciprocals.	7–9
E1.2	Use language, notation and Venn diagrams to describe sets and represent relationships between sets. Definition of sets e.g. $A = \{x: x$ is a natural number$\}$, $B = \{(x, y): y = mx + c\}$, $C = \{x: a \leqslant x \leqslant b\}$, $D = \{a, b, c, ...\}$	280–289
E1.3	Calculate with squares, square roots, cubes and cube roots and other powers and roots of numbers.	3, 8
E1.4	Use directed numbers in practical situations.	56
E1.5	Use the language and notation of simple vulgar and decimal fractions and percentages in appropriate contexts. Recognise equivalence and convert between these forms.	4–7
E1.6	Order quantities by magnitude and demonstrate familiarity with the symbols $=$, $\neq$, $>$, $<$, $\geqslant$, $\leqslant$	4, 7, 194
E1.7	Understand the meaning of indices (fractional, negative and zero) and use the rules of indices. Use the standard form $A \times 10^n$ where n is a positive or negative integer, and $1 \leqslant A < 10$.	19–21, 44–45
E1.8	Use the four rules for calculations with whole numbers, decimals and fractions (including mixed numbers and improper fractions), including correct ordering of operations and use of brackets.	2–3
E1.9	Make estimates of numbers, quantities and lengths, give approximations to specified number of significant figures and decimal places and round off answers to reasonable accuracy in the context of a given problem.	14, 18–19
E1.10	Give appropriate upper and lower bounds for data given to a specified accuracy. Obtain appropriate upper and lower bounds to solutions of simple problems given data to a specified accuracy.	15–18
E1.11	Demonstrate an understanding of ratio and proportion. Increase and decrease a quantity by a given ratio. Calculate average speed. Use common measures of rate.	21–24, 26–27, 36–39
E1.12	Calculate a given percentage of a quantity. Express one quantity as a percentage of another. Calculate percentage increase or decrease. Carry out calculations involving reverse percentages.	28–32
E1.13	Use a calculator efficiently. Apply appropriate checks of accuracy.	42–46
E1.14	Calculate times in terms of the 24-hour and 12-hour clock. Read clocks, dials and timetables.	40
E1.15	Calculate using money and convert from one currency to another.	24–25

E1.16	Use given data to solve problems on personal and household finance involving earnings, simple interest and compound interest. Extract data from tables and charts.	32–35
E1.17	Use exponential growth and decay in relation to population and finance.	9
E2: Algebra and graphs		
E2.1	Use letters to express generalised numbers and express basic arithmetic processes algebraically. Substitute numbers for words and letters in formulae. Construct and transform complicated formulae and equations.	59–63, 176–183
E2.2	Manipulate directed numbers. Use brackets and extract common factors. Expand products of algebraic expressions. Factorise where possible expressions of the form: $ax + bx + kay + kby$, $a^2x^2 - b^2y^2$, $a^2 + 2ab + b^2$, $ax^2 + bx + c$.	57–59, 64–67, 84–87
E2.3	Manipulate algebraic fractions. Factorise and simplify rational expressions.	173–176
E2.4	Use and interpret positive, negative and zero indices. Use and interpret fractional indices. Use the rules of indices.	189–193
E2.5	Derive and solve simple linear equations in one unknown. Derive and solve simultaneous linear equations in two unknowns. Derive and solve simultaneous equations, involving one linear and one quadratic. Derive and solve quadratic equations by factorisation, completing the square and by use of the formula. Derive and solve simple linear inequalities.	67–84, 87–97, 193–196
E2.6	Represent inequalities graphically and use this representation in the solution of simple linear programming problems.	196–202
E2.7	Continue a given number sequence. Recognise patterns in sequences including the term-to-term rule and relationships between different sequences. Find the nth term of sequences.	10–14
E2.8	Express direct and inverse proportion in algebraic terms and use this form of expression to find unknown quantities.	183–189
E2.9	Use function notation, e.g. $f(x) = 3x - 5$, $f : x \rightarrow 3x - 5$, to describe simple functions. Find inverse functions $f^{-1}(x)$. Form composite functions as defined by $gf(x) = g(f(x))$.	246, 305–310
E2.10	Interpret and use graphs in practical situations including travel graphs and conversion graphs. Draw graphs from given data. Apply the idea of rate of change to easy kinematics involving distance–time and speed–time graphs, acceleration and deceleration. Calculate distance travelled as area under a linear speed–time graph.	247, 249–255, 260–266
E2.11	Construct tables of values and draw graphs for functions of the form ax^n (and simple sums of these) and functions of the form $ax^b + c$. Solve associated equations approximately, including finding and determining roots by graphical methods. Draw and interpret graphs representing exponential growth and decay problems. Recognise, sketch and interpret graphs of functions.	250, 255–260
E2.12	Estimate gradients of curves by drawing tangents.	247–250
E2.13	Understand the idea of a derived function. Use the derivatives of functions of the form ax^n, and simple sums of not more than three of these. Apply differentiation to gradients and turning points (stationary points). Discriminate between maxima and minima by any method.	266–271

	E3: Coordinate geometry	
E3.1	Demonstrate familiarity with Cartesian coordinates in two dimensions.	239
E3.2	Find the gradient of a straight line. Calculate the gradient of a straight line from the coordinates of two points on it.	241–242
E3.3	Calculate the length and the coordinates of the midpoint of a straight line from the coordinates of its end points.	241–242
E3.4	Interpret and obtain the equation of a straight-line graph.	239–240, 243–244
E3.5	Determine the equation of a straight line parallel to a given line.	244
E3.6	Find the gradient of parallel and perpendicular lines.	245–246
	E4: Geometry	
E4.1	Use and interpret the geometrical terms: point, line, parallel, bearing, right angle, acute, obtuse and reflex angles, perpendicular, similarity and congruence. Use and interpret vocabulary of triangles, quadrilaterals, circles, polygons and simple solid figures including nets.	140, 144, 147, 153, 156, 158, 162, 167
E4.2	Measure and draw lines and angles. Construct a triangle given the three sides using ruler and pair of compasses only.	166–167
E4.3	Read and make scale drawings.	219–220
E4.4	Calculate lengths of similar figures. Use the relationships between areas of similar triangles, with corresponding results for similar figures and extension to volumes and surface areas of similar solids.	147–156
E4.5	Use the basic congruence criteria for triangles (SSS, ASA, SAS, RHS).	156–157
E4.6	Recognise rotational and line symmetry (including order of rotational symmetry) in two dimensions. Recognise symmetry properties of the prism (including cylinder) and the pyramid (including cone). Use the following symmetry properties of circles: • equal chords are equidistant from the centre • the perpendicular bisector of a chord passes through the centre • tangents from an external point are equal in length.	144–147, 162–164
E4.7	Calculate unknown angles using the following geometrical properties: • angles at a point • angles at a point on a straight line and intersecting straight lines • angles formed within parallel lines • angle properties of triangles and quadrilaterals • angle properties of regular polygons • angle in a semicircle • angle between tangent and radius of a circle • angle properties of irregular polygons • angle at the centre of a circle is twice the angle at the circumference • angles in the same segment are equal • angles in opposite segments are supplementary; cyclic quadrilaterals.	137–141, 158–165

E5: Mensuration		
E5.1	Use current units of mass, length, area, volume and capacity in practical situations and express quantities in terms of larger or smaller units.	105, 119, 128
E5.2	Carry out calculations involving the perimeter and area of a rectangle, triangle, parallelogram and trapezium and compound shapes derived from these.	104–108
E5.3	Carry out calculations involving the circumference and area of a circle. Solve problems involving the arc length and sector area as fractions of the circumference and area of a circle.	108–117
E5.4	Carry out calculations involving the surface area and volume of a cuboid, prism and cylinder. Carry out calculations involving the surface area and volume of a sphere, pyramid and cone.	118–127
E5.5	Carry out calculations involving the areas and volumes of compound shapes.	122, 126, 127
E6: Trigonometry		
E6.1	Interpret and use three-figure bearings.	216–218
E6.2	Apply Pythagoras' theorem and the sine, cosine and tangent ratios for acute angles to the calculation of a side or of an angle of a right-angled triangle. Solve trigonometrical problems in two dimensions involving angles of elevation and depression. Know that the perpendicular distance from a point to a line is the shortest distance to the line.	141–143, 208–216
E6.3	Recognise, sketch and interpret graphs of simple trigonometric functions. Graph and know the properties of trigonometric functions. Solve simple trigonometric equations for values between 0° and 360°.	222–224
E6.4	Solve problems using the sine and cosine rules for any triangle and the formula area of triangle = ½ ab sin C.	225–231, 106–107
E6.5	Solve simple trigonometrical problems in three dimensions including angle between a line and a plane.	220–222
E7: Matrices and transformations		
E7.1	Describe a translation by using a vector represented by e.g. $\begin{pmatrix} x \\ y \end{pmatrix}$, $\overrightarrow{AB}$ or **a**. Add and subtract vectors. Multiply a vector by a scalar.	289–299
E7.2	Reflect simple plane figures. Rotate simple plane figures through multiples of 90°. Construct given translations and enlargements of simple plane figures. Recognise and describe reflections, rotations, translations and enlargements.	310–324
E7.3	Calculate the magnitude of a vector $\begin{pmatrix} x \\ y \end{pmatrix}$ as $\sqrt{x^2+y^2}$. Represent vectors by directed line segments. Use the sum and difference of two vectors to express given vectors in terms of two coplanar vectors. Use position vectors.	299–304

E8: Probability		
E8.1	Calculate the probability of a single event as either a fraction, decimal or percentage.	366–370
E8.2	Understand and use the probability scale from 0 to 1.	366–370
E8.3	Understand that the probability of an event occurring = 1 − the probability of the event not occurring.	366–370
E8.4	Understand relative frequency as an estimate of probability. Expected frequency of outcomes.	370–371
E8.5	Calculate the probability of simple combined events, using possibility diagrams, tree diagrams and Venn diagrams.	373–381
E8.6	Calculate conditional probability using Venn diagrams, tree diagrams and tables.	381–383
E9: Statistics		
E9.1	Collect, classify and tabulate statistical data.	337–338, 358–359
E9.2	Read, interpret and draw simple inferences from tables and statistical diagrams. Compare sets of data using tables, graphs and statistical measures. Appreciate restrictions on drawing conclusions from given data.	359–361
E9.3	Construct and interpret bar charts, pie charts, pictograms, stem-and-leaf diagrams, simple frequency distributions, histograms with equal and unequal intervals and scatter diagrams.	332–343, 349–354
E9.4	Calculate the mean, median, mode and range for individual and discrete data and distinguish between the purposes for which they are used.	344–347
E9.5	Calculate an estimate of the mean for grouped and continuous data. Identify the modal class from a grouped frequency distribution.	348–349
E9.6	Construct and use cumulative frequency diagrams. Estimate and interpret the median, percentiles, quartiles and inter-quartile range. Construct and interpret box-and-whisker plots.	354–359
E9.7	Understand what is meant by positive, negative and zero correlation with reference to a scatter diagram.	350–353
E9.8	Draw, interpret and use lines of best fit by eye.	351, 353–354

Introduction

About this book

This revised 5th edition is designed to provide the best preparation for your Cambridge IGCSE examination, and has been completely updated for the latest Mathematics 0580 and 0980 extended/core syllabus.

Finding your way around

To get the most out of this book when studying or revising, use the:

- **Contents list** to help you find the appropriate units.
- **Index** to find key words so you can turn to any concept straight away.

Exercises and exam-style questions

There are thousands of questions in this book, providing ample opportunities to practise the skills and techniques required in the exam.

- **Worked examples and comprehensive exercises** are one of the main features of the book. The examples show you the important skills and techniques required. The exercises are carefully graded, starting from the basics and going up to exam standard, allowing you to practise the skills and techniques.
- **Revision exercises** at the end of each unit allow you to bring together all your knowledge on a particular topic.
- **Examination-style exercises** at the end of each unit consist of questions from past Cambridge IGCSE papers.
- **Examination-style papers:** there are two papers, corresponding to the papers you will take at the end of your course: Paper 2 and Paper 4. They give you the opportunity to practise for the real thing.
- **Revision section:** Unit 12 contains multiple-choice questions to provide an extra opportunity to revise.
- **Answers to numerical problems** are at the end of the book so you can check your progress.

Investigations

Unit 11 provides many opportunities for you to explore the world of mathematical problem-solving through investigations, puzzles and games.

Links to curriculum content

At the start of each unit you will find a list of objectives that are covered in the unit. These objectives are drawn from the Extended section of the Cambridge IGCSE syllabus.

What's on the website?

The support website contains a wealth of material to help solidify your understanding of the Cambridge IGCSE Mathematics course, and to aid revision for your examinations.

All this material can be found online, at www.oxfordsecondary.com/9780198425076

1   Number

Karl Friedrich Gauss (1777–1855) thought by many to have been the greatest all-round mathematician of all time. He considered that his finest discovery was the method for constructing a regular seventeen-sided polygon. This was not of the slightest use outside the world of mathematics, but was a great achievement of the human mind. Gauss would not have understood the modern view held by many that mathematics must somehow be 'useful' to be worthy of study.

E1.1   Identify and use natural numbers, integers (positive, negative and zero), prime numbers, square and cube numbers, common factors and common multiples, rational and irrational numbers (e.g. π, $\sqrt{2}$), real numbers, reciprocals.

E1.3   Calculate with squares, square roots, cubes and cube roots and other powers and roots of numbers.

E1.5   Use the language and notation of simple vulgar and decimal fractions and percentages in appropriate contexts. Recognise equivalence and convert between these forms.

E1.7   Use the standard form $A \times 10^n$ where n is a positive or negative integer, and $1 \leqslant A < 10$.

E1.8   Use the four rules for calculations with whole numbers, decimals and fractions (including mixed numbers and improper fractions), including correct ordering of operations and use of brackets.

E1.9   Make estimates of numbers, quantities and lengths, give approximations to specified numbers of significant figures and decimal places and round off answers to reasonable accuracy in the context of a given problem.

E1.10   Give appropriate upper and lower bounds for data given to a specified accuracy. Obtain appropriate upper and lower bounds to solutions of simple problems given data to a specified accuracy.

E1.11   Demonstrate an understanding of ratio and proportion. Increase and decrease a quantity by a given ratio. Calculate average speed. Use common measures of rate.

E1.12   Calculate a given percentage of a quantity. Express one quantity as a percentage of another. Calculate percentage increase or decrease. Carry out calculations involving reverse percentages.

E1.13   Use a calculator efficiently. Apply appropriate checks of accuracy.

E1.14   Calculate times in terms of the 24-hour and 12-hour clock. Read clocks, dials and timetables.

E1.15   Calculate using money and convert from one currency to another.

E1.16   Use given data to solve problems on personal and household finance involving earnings, simple interest and compound interest. Extract data from tables and charts.

E1.17   Use exponential growth and decay in relation to population and finance.

E2.7   Continue a given number sequence. Recognise patterns in sequences including the term-to-term rule and relationships between different sequences. Find the nth term of sequences.

1.1 Arithmetic

Decimals

Example

Evaluate:

a) $7.6 + 19$ **b)** $3.4 - 0.24$ **c)** 7.2×0.21

d) $0.84 \div 0.2$ **e)** $3.6 \div 0.004$

· ·

a)
$$\begin{array}{r} 7.6 \\ + 19.0 \\ \hline 26.6 \end{array}$$

b)
$$\begin{array}{r} 3.40 \\ - 0.24 \\ \hline 3.16 \end{array}$$

c)
$$\begin{array}{r} 7.2 \\ \times 0.21 \\ \hline 72 \\ 1440 \\ \hline 1.512 \end{array}$$
No decimal points in the working, '3 figures after the points in the question *and* therefore in the answer'.

d) $0.84 \div 0.2 = 8.4 \div 2$

$$2\overline{)8.4} \quad \begin{array}{l} 4.2 \end{array}$$
Multiply both numbers by 10 so that we can divide by a whole number.

e) $3.6 \div 0.004 = 3600 \div 4$
$$= 900$$

Exercise 1

Evaluate the following without a calculator:

1. $7.6 + 0.31$ **2.** $15 + 7.22$ **3.** $7.004 + 0.368$ **4.** $0.06 + 0.006$

5. $4.2 + 42 + 420$ **6.** $3.84 - 2.62$ **7.** $11.4 - 9.73$ **8.** $4.61 - 3$

9. $17 - 0.37$ **10.** $8.7 + 19.2 - 3.8$ **11.** $25 - 7.8 + 9.5$ **12.** $3.6 - 8.74 + 9$

13. $20.4 - 20.399$ **14.** 2.6×0.6 **15.** 0.72×0.04 **16.** 27.2×0.08

17. 0.1×0.2 **18.** $(0.01)^2$ **19.** 2.1×3.6 **20.** 2.31×0.34

21. 0.36×1000 **22.** $0.34 \times 100\,000$ **23.** $3.6 \div 0.2$ **24.** $0.592 \div 0.8$

25. $0.1404 \div 0.06$ **26.** $3.24 \div 0.002$ **27.** $0.968 \div 0.11$ **28.** $600 \div 0.5$

29. $0.007 \div 4$ **30.** $2640 \div 200$ **31.** $1100 \div 5.5$ **32.** $(11 + 2.4) \times 0.06$

33. $(0.4)^2 \div 0.2$ **34.** $77 \div 1000$ **35.** $(0.3)^2 \div 100$ **36.** $(0.1)^4 \div 0.01$

37. $\dfrac{92 \times 4.6}{2.3}$ **38.** $\dfrac{180 \times 4}{36}$ **39.** $\dfrac{0.55 \times 0.81}{4.5}$ **40.** $\dfrac{63 \times 600 \times 0.2}{360 \times 7}$

Exercise 2

1. A maths teacher bought 40 calculators at $8.20 each and a number of other calculators costing $2.95 each. In all she spent $387. How many of the cheaper calculators did she buy?

2. At a temperature of 20 °C the common amoeba reproduces by splitting in half every 24 hours. If we start with a single amoeba how many will there be after **(a)** 8 days **(b)** 16 days?

3. Copy and complete.

$$3^2 + 4^2 + 12^2 = 13^2$$

$$5^2 + 6^2 + 30^2 = 31^2$$

$$6^2 + 7^2 + \quad = \quad$$

$$x^2 + \quad + \quad = \quad$$

You can find out about square numbers on page 7.

4. Find all the missing digits in these multiplications.

   a)
   ```
     5*
     9×
   ----
   **6
   ```

   b)
   ```
     *7
     *×
   ----
   4*6
   ```

   c)
   ```
     5*
     *×
   ----
   1*4
   ```

5. Pages 6 and 27 are on the same (double) sheet of a newspaper. What are the page numbers on the opposite side of the sheet? How many pages are there in the newspaper altogether?

6. Use the numbers 1, 2, 3, 4, 5, 6, 7, 8, 9 once each and in their natural order to obtain an answer of 100. You may use only the operations +, −, ×, ÷.

7. The ruler below has eleven marks and can be used to measure lengths from one unit to twelve units.

   Design a ruler which can be used to measure all the lengths from one unit to twelve units but this time put the minimum possible number of marks on the ruler.

8. Each packet of washing powder carries a token and four tokens can be exchanged for a free packet. How many free packets will I receive if I buy 64 packets?

9. Put three different numbers in the circles so that when you add the numbers at the end of each line you always get a square number.

10. Put four different numbers in the circles so that when you add the numbers at the end of each line you always get a square number.

11. A group of friends share a bill for $13.69 equally between them. How many were in the group?

Fractions

Common fractions are added or subtracted from one another directly only when they have a common denominator. Find the lowest common multiple of the two denominators to find the lowest common denominator.

Example

Evaluate:

a) $\dfrac{3}{4}+\dfrac{2}{5}$ **b)** $2\dfrac{3}{8}-1\dfrac{5}{12}$ **c)** $\dfrac{2}{5}\times\dfrac{6}{7}$ **d)** $2\dfrac{2}{5}\div 6$

The order of operations follows the BIDMAS rule:

Brackets then

Indices then

Divide then

Multiply then

Add then

Subtract.

a) $\dfrac{3}{4}+\dfrac{2}{5}=\dfrac{15}{20}+\dfrac{8}{20}$

$=\dfrac{23}{20}$

$=1\dfrac{3}{20}$

b) $2\dfrac{3}{8}-1\dfrac{5}{12}=\dfrac{19}{8}-\dfrac{17}{12}$

$=\dfrac{57}{24}-\dfrac{34}{24}$

$=\dfrac{23}{24}$

c) $\dfrac{2}{5}\times\dfrac{6}{7}=\dfrac{12}{35}$

d) $2\dfrac{2}{5}\div 6=\dfrac{12}{5}\div\dfrac{6}{1}$

$=\dfrac{\overset{2}{\cancel{12}}}{5}\times\dfrac{1}{\underset{1}{\cancel{6}}}=\dfrac{2}{5}$

Exercise 3

Evaluate and simplify your answer.

1. $\dfrac{3}{4}+\dfrac{4}{5}$ **2.** $\dfrac{1}{3}+\dfrac{1}{8}$ **3.** $\dfrac{5}{6}+\dfrac{6}{9}$ **4.** $\dfrac{3}{4}-\dfrac{1}{3}$ **5.** $\dfrac{3}{5}-\dfrac{1}{3}$

6. $\dfrac{1}{2}-\dfrac{2}{5}$ **7.** $\dfrac{2}{3}\times\dfrac{4}{5}$ **8.** $\dfrac{1}{7}\times\dfrac{5}{6}$ **9.** $\dfrac{5}{8}\times\dfrac{12}{13}$ **10.** $\dfrac{1}{3}\div\dfrac{4}{5}$

11. $\dfrac{3}{4}\div\dfrac{1}{6}$ **12.** $\dfrac{5}{6}\div\dfrac{1}{2}$ **13.** $\dfrac{3}{8}+\dfrac{1}{5}$ **14.** $\dfrac{3}{8}\times\dfrac{1}{5}$ **15.** $\dfrac{3}{8}\div\dfrac{1}{5}$

16. $1\dfrac{3}{4}-\dfrac{2}{3}$ **17.** $1\dfrac{3}{4}\times\dfrac{2}{3}$ **18.** $1\dfrac{3}{4}\div\dfrac{2}{3}$ **19.** $3\dfrac{1}{2}+2\dfrac{3}{5}$ **20.** $3\dfrac{1}{2}\times 2\dfrac{3}{5}$

21. $3\dfrac{1}{2}\div 2\dfrac{3}{5}$ **22.** $\left(\dfrac{3}{4}-\dfrac{2}{3}\right)\div\dfrac{3}{4}$ **23.** $\left(\dfrac{3}{5}+\dfrac{1}{3}\right)\times\dfrac{5}{7}$ **24.** $\dfrac{\dfrac{3}{8}-\dfrac{1}{5}}{\dfrac{7}{10}-\dfrac{2}{3}}$ **25.** $\dfrac{\dfrac{2}{3}+\dfrac{1}{3}}{\dfrac{3}{4}-\dfrac{1}{3}}$

26. Arrange the fractions in order of size:

a) $\dfrac{7}{12},\dfrac{1}{2},\dfrac{2}{3}$ **b)** $\dfrac{3}{4},\dfrac{2}{3},\dfrac{5}{6}$ **c)** $\dfrac{1}{3},\dfrac{17}{24},\dfrac{5}{8},\dfrac{3}{4}$ **d)** $\dfrac{5}{6},\dfrac{8}{9},\dfrac{11}{12}$

27. Find the fraction which is mid-way between the two fractions given:

a) $\dfrac{2}{5}, \dfrac{3}{5}$ b) $\dfrac{5}{8}, \dfrac{7}{8}$ c) $\dfrac{2}{3}, \dfrac{3}{4}$ d) $\dfrac{1}{3}, \dfrac{4}{9}$ e) $\dfrac{4}{15}, \dfrac{1}{3}$ f) $\dfrac{3}{8}, \dfrac{11}{24}$

28. In the equation below all the asterisks stand for the same number. What is the number?

$$\left[\dfrac{*}{*} - \dfrac{*}{6} = \dfrac{*}{30}\right]$$

29. When it hatches from its egg, the shell of a certain crab is 1 cm across. When fully grown the shell is approximately 10 cm across. Each new shell is one-third bigger than the previous one. How many shells does a fully grown crab have during its life?

30. Glass A contains 100 ml of water and glass B contains 100 ml of juice.

A 10 ml spoonful of juice is taken from glass B and mixed thoroughly with the water in glass A. A 10 ml spoonful of the mixture from A is returned to B. Is there now more juice in the water or more water in the juice?

Fractions and decimals

A decimal is simply a fraction expressed in tenths, hundredths, etc.

Example 1

Change

a) $\dfrac{7}{8}$ to a decimal b) 0.35 to a fraction c) $\dfrac{1}{3}$ to a decimal

....

a) $\dfrac{7}{8}$, divide 8 into 7 b) $0.35 = \dfrac{35}{100} = \dfrac{7}{20}$ c) $\dfrac{1}{3}$, divide 3 into 1

$\dfrac{7}{8} = 0.875$ $\quad 8\overline{)7.000}^{\,0.875}$ $\dfrac{1}{3} = 0.\dot{3}\ \left(0.3 \text{ recurring}\right)$ $3\overline{)1.0^10^10^1000}^{\,0.3\,3\,3\,3}$

Example 2

a) Convert $0.\dot{7}$ to a fraction.

This recurring decimal has *one place* recursion so we multiply it by 10 and set out our working as follows:

$$10 \times: \quad 7.77777\ldots \ [1]$$
$$1 \times: \quad 0.77777\ldots \ [2]$$
$$[1] - [2]: \quad 9 \times: \quad 7.00000\ldots$$
Therefore: $\quad 1 \times: \quad \dfrac{7}{9}$

b) Convert $0.\dot{2}\dot{3}$ to a fraction.

Here we have *two place* recursion so we multiply it by 100:

$$100 \times: \quad 23.232323\ldots \ [1]$$
$$1 \times: \quad 0.232323\ldots \ [2]$$
$$[1] - [2]: \quad 99 \times: \quad 23.000000\ldots$$
Therefore: $\quad 1 \times: \quad \dfrac{23}{99}$

Exercise 4

In questions **1** to **24**, change the fractions to decimals.

1. $\dfrac{1}{4}$
2. $\dfrac{2}{5}$
3. $\dfrac{4}{5}$
4. $\dfrac{3}{4}$
5. $\dfrac{1}{2}$
6. $\dfrac{3}{8}$

7. $\dfrac{9}{10}$
8. $\dfrac{5}{8}$
9. $\dfrac{5}{12}$
10. $\dfrac{1}{6}$
11. $\dfrac{2}{3}$
12. $\dfrac{5}{6}$

13. $\dfrac{2}{7}$
14. $\dfrac{3}{7}$
15. $\dfrac{4}{9}$
16. $\dfrac{5}{11}$
17. $1\dfrac{1}{5}$
18. $2\dfrac{5}{8}$

19. $2\dfrac{1}{3}$
20. $1\dfrac{7}{10}$
21. $2\dfrac{3}{16}$
22. $2\dfrac{2}{7}$
23. $2\dfrac{6}{7}$
24. $3\dfrac{19}{100}$

In questions **25** to **40**, change the decimals to fractions and simplify.

25. 0.2
26. 0.7
27. 0.25
28. 0.45

29. 0.36
30. 0.52
31. 0.125
32. 0.625

33. 0.84
34. 2.35
35. 3.95
36. 1.05

37. 3.2
38. 0.27
39. 0.007
40. 0.000 11

Evaluate, giving the answer to 2 decimal places:

41. $\dfrac{1}{4} + \dfrac{1}{3}$
42. $\dfrac{2}{3} + 0.75$
43. $\dfrac{8}{9} - 0.24$
44. $\dfrac{7}{8} + \dfrac{5}{9} + \dfrac{2}{11}$

45. $\dfrac{1}{3} \times 0.2$
46. $\dfrac{5}{8} \times \dfrac{1}{4}$
47. $\dfrac{8}{11} \div 0.2$
48. $\left(\dfrac{4}{7} - \dfrac{1}{3}\right) \div 0.4$

Arrange the numbers in order of size (smallest first).

49. $\dfrac{1}{3}, 0.33, \dfrac{4}{15}$ **50.** $\dfrac{2}{7}, 0.3, \dfrac{4}{9}$ **51.** $0.71, \dfrac{7}{11}, 0.705$ **52.** $\dfrac{4}{13}, 0.3, \dfrac{5}{18}$

Convert the following recurring decimals to fractions.

53. $0.\dot{6}$ **54.** $0.\dot{4}$ **55.** $0.\dot{1}\dot{2}$ **56.** $0.4\dot{3}$

57. $0.1\dot{3}\dot{4}$ **58.** $0.\dot{7}3\dot{1}$ **59.** $0.2\dot{5}$ **60.** $0.6\dot{1}\dot{7}$

1.2 Number facts and sequences

Number facts

- An *integer* is a positive or negative whole number or zero, e.g. 2, −3, …

- A *prime* number is divisible only by itself and by 1, e.g. 2, 3, 5, 7, 11, 13, …

- The *multiples* of 12 are 12, 24, 36, 48, …

- The *factors* of 12 are 1, 2, 3, 4, 6, 12.

- A *square number* is the result of multiplying a number by itself, e.g. $5 \times 5 = 25$, so 25 is a square number.

- A *cube number* is the result of multiplying a number by itself twice, e.g. $5 \times 5 \times 5 = 125$, so 125 is a cube number.

- *Indices* are used as a neat way of writing products.
  $2^4 = 2 \times 2 \times 2 \times 2 = 16$ [2 to the power 4]
  $3^5 = 3 \times 3 \times 3 \times 3 \times 3 = 243$ [3 to the power 5]

- The *reciprocal* of a number is the result of dividing 1 by that number.
  The reciprocal of 4 is $\dfrac{1}{4}$.   [In index form, this is written as 4^{-1}]
  In general, the reciprocal of n is $\dfrac{1}{n}$. This can be written as n^{-1}.

Example

Find the Highest Common Factor (HCF) and Lowest Common Multiple (LCM) of 80 and 50.
First write both 80 and 50 as the product of prime factors.

$80 = 2 \times 40 = 2 \times 2 \times 20 = 2 \times 2 \times 2 \times 10 = 2 \times 2 \times 2 \times 2 \times 5 = 2^4 \times 5$

$50 = 2 \times 25 = 2 \times 5 \times 5 = 2 \times 5^2$

The HCF is found by looking at the prime factorisation and examining the elements that are in *both* numbers. 80 and 50 both have a 2 and a 5 in the prime factorisation so the HCF is $2 \times 5 = 10$.

The LCM is found by taking the HCF and multiplying it by the bits in each prime factorisation that are *left over*. For 80, we do not use 2^3 for the HCF and for 50 we do not use a 5.
So the LCM $= \text{HCF} \times 2^3 \times 5 = 10 \times 8 \times 5 = 400$.

Exercise 5

1. Which of the following are prime numbers?

   3, 11, 15, 19, 21, 23, 27, 29, 31, 37, 39, 47, 51, 59, 61, 67, 72, 73, 87, 99

2. Write down the first five multiples of the following numbers:

   a) 4   **b)** 6   **c)** 10   **d)** 11   **e)** 20

3. Write down the first six multiples of 4 and of 6. What are the first two *common* multiples of 4 and 6? [i.e. multiples of both 4 and 6]

4. Write down the first six multiples of 3 and of 5. What is the lowest common multiple of 3 and 5?

5. Write down all the factors of the following:

   a) 6   **b)** 9   **c)** 10   **d)** 15   **e)** 24   **f)** 32

6. **a)** Is 263 a prime number?

   By how many numbers do you need to divide 263 so that you can find out?

   b) Is 527 a prime number?

   c) Suppose you used a computer to find out if 1147 was a prime number. Which numbers would you tell the computer to divide by?

7. Make six prime numbers using the digits 1, 2, 3, 4, 5, 6, 7, 8, 9 once each.

8. Write the following numbers as the product of prime factors:

   a) 24   **b)** 60   **c)** 90

   d) 144   **e)** 1000   **f)** 880

9. Find the Highest Common Factor of

   a) 24 and 60   **b)** 90 and 144   **c)** 60 and 1000

   d) 24 and 880   **e)** 90 and 1000   **f)** 24, 60 and 144

10. Find the Lowest Common Multiple of

    a) 24 and 60   **b)** 60 and 90   **c)** 144 and 1000

    b) 24 and 880   **d)** 90 and 1000   **f)** 24 and 1000

11. Work out without a calculator:

    a) 4^2 **b)** 6^2 **c)** 10^2 **d)** 3^3 **e)** 10^3

12. Use the $\boxed{x^2}$ button on the calculator to work out:

    a) 9^2 **b)** 21^2 **c)** 1.2^2 **d)** 0.2^2 **e)** 3.1^2

    f) 100^2 **g)** 25^2 **h)** 8.7^2 **i)** 0.9^2 **j)** 81.4^2

13. Find the areas of these squares.

a)

2.1 cm

2.1 cm

b)

0.6 cm

0.6 cm

c)

14 m

14 m

14. A scientist has a dish containing 10^9 germs.

One day later there are 10 times as many germs.
How many germs are in the dish now?

15. A field has 2^8 daisies growing on the grass.

A cow eats half of the daisies.
How many daisies are left?

In questions **16** to **20**, work out the value of the number given, both as a fraction and as a decimal.

16. 2^{-1} **17.** 10^{-1} **18.** 5^{-1} **19.** 4^{-1} **20.** 8^{-1}

Rational and irrational numbers

- A rational number can always be written exactly in the form $\frac{a}{b}$ where a and b are whole numbers.

$\frac{3}{7}$	$1\frac{1}{2} = \frac{3}{2}$	$5.14 = \frac{257}{50}$	$0.\dot{6} = \frac{2}{3}$

  All these are rational numbers.

- An irrational number cannot be written in the form $\frac{a}{b}$.

  $\sqrt{2}, \sqrt{5}, \pi, \sqrt[3]{2}$ are all irrational numbers.

- In general $\sqrt{n}$ is irrational unless n is a square number.

In this triangle the length of the hypotenuse is *exactly* $\sqrt{5}$. On a calculator, $\sqrt{5} = 2.236068$. This value of $\sqrt{5}$ is *not* exact and is correct to only 6 decimal places.

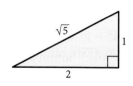

Exercise 6

1. Which of the following numbers are rational?

a) $\dfrac{\pi}{2}$ **b)** $\sqrt{5}$ **c)** $\left(\sqrt{17}\right)^2$ **d)** $\sqrt{3}$

e) 3.14   **f)** $\dfrac{\sqrt{12}}{\sqrt{3}}$ **g)** π^2 **h)** $3^{-1}+3^{-2}$

i) $7^{-\frac{1}{2}}$ **j)** $\dfrac{22}{7}$ **k)** $\sqrt{2}+1$ **l)** $\sqrt{2.25}$

2. a) Write down any rational number between 4 and 6.

   b) Write down any irrational number between 4 and 6.

   c) Find a rational number between $\sqrt{2}$ and $\sqrt{3}$.

   d) Write down any rational number between π and $\sqrt{10}$.

3. a) For each shape state whether the *perimeter* is rational or irrational.

   b) For each shape state whether the *area* is rational or irrational.

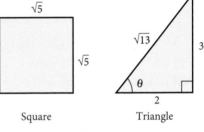

Square   Triangle

4. The diagram shows a circle of radius 3 cm drawn inside a square. Write down the exact value of the following and state whether the answer is rational or not:

   a) the circumference of the circle

   b) the diameter of the circle

   c) the area of the square

   d) the area of the circle

   e) the shaded area.

5. Think of two *irrational* numbers x and y such that $\dfrac{x}{y}$ is a *rational* number.

6. Explain the difference between a rational number and an irrational number.

7. a) Is it possible to multiply a rational number and an irrational number to give an answer which is rational?

   b) Is it possible to multiply two irrational numbers together to give a rational answer?

   c) If either or both are possible, give an example.

Sequences, the nth term

Look at the sequence which starts 2, 5, 8, 11, …

Wherever we are in the sequence, to get the next term we add 3 to the current term. Therefore, we say that the *term-to-term rule* for this sequence is 'add 3'.

Exercise 7

Write down each sequence and find the next two numbers.

For questions **1** to **4**, also state the term-to-term rule.

1. 2, 6, 10, 14
2. 2, 9, 16, 23
3. 95, 87, 79, 71
4. 13, 8, 3, −2
5. 7, 9, 12, 16
6. 20, 17, 13, 8
7. 1, 2, 4, 7, 11
8. 1, 2, 4, 8
9. 55, 49, 42, 34
10. 10, 8, 5, 1
11. −18, −13, −9, −6
12. 120, 60, 30, 15
13. 27, 9, 3, 1
14. 162, 54, 18, 6
15. 2, 5, 11, 20
16. 1, 4, 20, 120
17. 2, 3, 1, 4, 0
18. 720, 120, 24, 6

Look at the sequence which starts 5, 9, 13, 17, …

What is the 10th number in the sequence?

What is the nth number in the sequence? [n stands for any whole number.]

Is there a formula so that we can easily find the 50th or 100th number in the sequence?

The 1st term in the sequence is $(4 \times 1) + 1 = 5$

The 2nd term in the sequence is $(4 \times 2) + 1 = 9$

The 10th term in the sequence is $(4 \times 10) + 1 = 41$

The 50th term in the sequence is $(4 \times 50) + 1 = 201$

The 1000th term in the sequence is $(4 \times 1000) + 1 = 4001$

The nth term in the sequence is $(4 \times n) + 1 = 4n + 1$

Exercise 8

1. Write down each sequence and select the correct formula for the nth term from the list given.

   $\boxed{11n}$ $\boxed{10n}$ $\boxed{2n}$ $\boxed{n^2}$ $\boxed{10^n}$ $\boxed{3n}$ $\boxed{100n}$ $\boxed{n^3}$

   a) 2, 4, 6, 8, …
   b) 10, 20, 30, 40, …
   c) 3, 6, 9, 12, …
   d) 11, 22, 33, 44, …
   e) 100, 200, 300, 400, …
   f) $1^2, 2^2, 3^2, 4^2, \ldots$
   g) 10, 100, 1000, 10 000, …
   h) $1^3, 2^3, 3^3, 4^3, \ldots$

2. Look at the sequence: 5, 8, 13, 20, …

   Decide which of the following is the correct expression for the nth term of the sequence.

   $\boxed{4n + 1}$ $\qquad$ $\boxed{3n + 2}$ $\qquad$ $\boxed{n^2 + 4}$

3. Write down the first five terms of the sequence whose nth term is $2n + 7$.

4. Write down the first five terms of the sequence whose nth term is

   a) $n + 2$ b) $5n$ c) $10n - 1$ d) $100 - 3n$ e) $\dfrac{1}{n}$ f) n^2

Finding the nth term

- In an *arithmetic* sequence the difference between successive terms is always the same number.

  Here are some arithmetic sequences: A 5, 7, 9, 11, 13

  B 12, 32, 52, 72, 92

  C 20, 17, 14, 11, 8

- The expression for the nth term of an arithmetic sequence is always of the form $an + b$.

  The *difference* between successive terms is equal to the number a.

  The number b can be found by looking at the terms.

  Look at sequences A, B and C above.

  For sequence A, the nth term $= 2n + b$ [the terms go up by 2]

  For sequence B, the nth term $= 20n + b$ [the terms go up by 20]

  For sequence C, the nth term $= -3n + b$ [the terms go up by -3]

  Look at each sequence and find the value of b in each case.

  For example in sequence A: when $n = 1$, $2 \times 1 + b = 5$

  $$\text{so } b = 3$$

  The nth term in sequence A is $2n + 3$.

Exercise 9

In questions **1** to **18** find a formula for the nth term of the sequence.

1. 5, 9, 13, 17, …

2. 7, 10, 13, 16, …

3. 4, 9, 14, 19, …

4. 6, 10, 14, 18, …

5. 5, 8, 11, 14, …

6. 25, 22, 19, 16, …

7. 5, 10, 15, 20, …

8. 2, 4, 8, 16, 32, …

9. $(1 \times 3), (2 \times 4), (3 \times 5),$ …

10. $\dfrac{1}{2}, \dfrac{2}{3}, \dfrac{3}{4}, \dfrac{4}{5},$ …

11. 7, 14, 21, 28, …

12. 1, 4, 9, 16, 25, …

13. $\dfrac{5}{1^2}, \dfrac{5}{2^2}, \dfrac{5}{3^2}, \dfrac{5}{4^2},$ …

14. $\dfrac{3}{1}, \dfrac{4}{2}, \dfrac{5}{3}, \dfrac{6}{4},$ …

15. 3, 7, 11, 15, …

16. 5, 7, 9, 11, …

17. 7, 5, 3, 1, …

18. $-5, -1, 3, 7,$ …

19. Write down each sequence and then find the nth term.

    a)   8, 10, 12, 14, 16, …

    b)   3, 7, 11, 15, …

    c)   8, 13, 18, 23, …

20. Write down each sequence and write the *n*th term.

    a)   11, 19, 27, 35, …

    b) $2\frac{1}{2}, 4\frac{1}{2}, 6\frac{1}{2}, 8\frac{1}{2}, \cdots$

    c)   −7, −4, −1, 2, 5, …

21. Here is a sequence of shapes made from sticks

Shape number: $n = 1$ $n = 2$ $n = 3$
Number of sticks: 4   7   10

The number of sticks makes the sequence 4, 7, 10, 13, …

    a)   Find an expression for the *n*th term in the sequence.

    b)   How many sticks are there in shape number 1000?

Example

The sequence 1, 4, 9, 16, 25, … does not have a common difference between terms but is the sequence of *square numbers*. We can write $t = n^2$. This is a *quadratic* sequence.

Find the *n*th term of the following sequence: 3, 6, 11, 18, …
We see that each term is 2 more than n^2 so the *n*th term formula is $t = n^2 + 2$.
Find the *n*th term of the following sequence: 3, 8, 15, 24, …
The difference goes up by 2 each time so the sequence is related to n^2. Subtract n^2 from each term: 2, 4, 6, 8, …
This sequence has *n*th term $2n$ so the complete sequence has *n*th term $t = n^2 + 2n$.
Find the *n*th term of this sequence: 2, 4, 8, 16, …
Notice each term *doubles* the previous one. This type of sequence is called an *exponential* sequence.
The *n*th term is $t = 2^n$.

Exercise 10

Find an expression for the *n*th term of each sequence.

1. 4, 7, 12, 19, . . .   **2.** 2, 8, 18, 32, . . .

3. 0, 3, 8, 15, . . .   **4.** 0.5, 2, 4.5, 8, . . .

5. −6, −3, 2, 9, . . .   **6.** −1, −4, −9, −16, . . .

7. 0, −3, −8, −15, . . .   **8.** 5, 12, 21, 32, . . .

9. 1, 6, 15, 28, . . .   **10.** 3, 9, 17, 27, . . .

11. 2, 9, 28, 65, ...

12. 2, 16, 54, 128, ...

Write out the sequence of *cube* numbers and compare.

13. −1, 6, 25, 62, ...

14. 1, 3, 7, 15, ...

Write out the sequence of 2^n and compare.

15. 3, 9, 27, 81, ...

1.3 Approximations and estimation

Example

a) 7.8126 = 8 to the nearest whole number.

   ↑ This figure is '5 or more'.

b) 7.8126 = 7.81 to three significant figures.

    ↑ This figure is not '5 or more'.

c) 7.8126 = 7.813 to three decimal places.

     ↑ This figure is '5 or more'.

d) 0.078 126 = 0.0781 to three significant figures.

   ↑ 7 is the first significant figure.

e) 3596 = 3600 to two significant figures.

  ↑ This figure is '5 or more'.

Exercise 11

Write the following numbers correct to:

a) the nearest whole number   **b)** three significant figures   **c)** two decimal places.

1. 8.174	**2.** 19.617	**3.** 20.041	**4.** 0.814 52	**5.** 311.14
6. 0.275	**7.** 0.007 47	**8.** 15.62	**9.** 900.12	**10.** 3.555
11. 5.454	**12.** 20.961	**13.** 0.0851	**14.** 0.5151	**15.** 3.071

Write the following numbers correct to one decimal place.

16. 5.71   **17.** 0.7614   **18.** 11.241   **19.** 0.0614   **20.** 0.0081   **21.** 11.12

Measurements and bounds

Measurement is approximate

Example 1

A length is measured as 145 cm to the nearest cm.

The actual length could be anything from 144.5 cm to 145.49999 … cm using the normal convention which is to round up a figure of 5 or more. Clearly 145.49999 … is effectively 145.5 and we say the *upper bound* is 145.5.

The *lower bound* is 144.5.

As an inequality we can write 144.5 ⩽ length < 145.5

The upper limit often causes confusion. We use 145.5 as the upper bound simply because it is *inconvenient* to work with 145.49999 …

Example 2

When measuring the length of a page in a book, you might say the length is 246 mm to the nearest mm.

In this case the actual length could be anywhere from 245.5 mm to 246.5 mm. We write 'length is between 245.5 mm and 246.5 mm'.

Example 3

a) If you say your mass is 57 kg to the nearest kg, your mass could actually be anything from 56.5 kg to 57.5 kg.

The 'unit' is 1 so 'half a unit' is 0.5.

b) If your brother's mass was measured on more sensitive scales and the result was 57.2 kg, his actual mass could be from 57.15 kg to 57.25 kg.

The 'unit' is 0.1 so 'half a unit' is 0.05.

c) The mass of a butterfly might be given as 0.032 g. The actual mass could be from 0.0315 g to 0.0325 g.

The 'unit' is 0.001 so 'half a unit' is 0.0005.

Here are some further examples:

Measurement	Lower bound	Upper bound
The diameter of a CD is 12 cm to the nearest cm.	11.5 cm	12.5 cm
The mass of a coin is 6.2 g to the nearest 0.1 g.	6.15 g	6.25 g
The length of a fence is 330 m to the nearest 10 m.	325 m	335 m

Exercise 12

1. In a DIY store the height of a door is given as 195 cm to the nearest cm. Write down the upper bound for the height of the door.

2. A vet measures the mass of a goat at 37 kg to the nearest kg. What is the least possible mass of the goat?

3. A farmer's scales measure mass to the nearest 0.1 kg. What is the upper bound for the mass of a chicken which the scales say has a mass of 3.2 kg?

4. A surveyor using a laser beam device can measure distances to the nearest 0.1m. What is the least possible length of a warehouse which he measures at 95.6 m?

5. In the county sports Stefan was timed at 28.6 s for the 200 m. What is the upper bound for the time she could have taken?

6. Copy and complete the table.

	Measurement	Lower bound	Upper bound
a)	temperature in a fridge = 2 °C to the nearest degree		
b)	mass of an acorn = 2.3 g to 1 d.p.		
c)	length of telephone cable = 64 m to the nearest m		
d)	time taken to run 100 m = 13.6 s to the nearest 0.1 s		

7. The length of a telephone is measured as 193 mm, to the nearest mm. The length lies between:

A	B	C
192 and 194 mm	192.5 and 193.5 mm	188 and 198 mm

8. The mass of a suitcase is 35 kg, to the nearest kg. The mass lies between:

A	B	C
30 and 40 kg	34 and 36 kg	34.5 and 35.5 kg

9. Adra and Leila each measure a different worm and they both say that their worm is 11 cm long to the nearest cm.

   a) Does this mean that both worms are the same length?

   b) If not, what is the maximum possible difference in the length of the two worms?

10. To the nearest cm, the length l of a stapler is 12 cm. As an inequality we can write $11.5 \leqslant l < 12.5$.

For parts **(a)** to **(j)** you are given a measurement. Write the possible values using an inequality as above.

a) mass = 17 kg   (2 s.f.)   **b)** $d = 256$ km   (3 s.f.)

c) length = 2.4 m   (1 d.p.)   **d)** $m = 0.34$ grams   (2 s.f.)

e) $v = 2.04$ m/s   (2 d.p.)   **f)** $x = 12.0$ cm   (1 d.p.)

g) $T = 81.4\,^\circ$C   (1 d.p.)   **h)** $M = 0.3$ kg   (1 s.f.)

i) mass = 0.7 tonnes   (1 s.f.)   **j)** $n = 52\,000$ (nearest thousand)

11. A card measuring 11.5 cm long (to the nearest 0.1 cm) is to be posted in an envelope which is 12 cm long (to the nearest cm). Can you guarantee that the card will fit inside the envelope? Explain your answer.

11.5 cm   12 cm

Exercise 13

1. The sides of the triangle are measured correct to the nearest cm.

  a) Write down the upper bounds for the lengths of the three sides.

  b) Work out the maximum possible perimeter of the triangle.

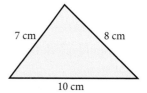

7 cm   8 cm

10 cm

2. The dimensions of a photo are measured correct to the nearest cm. Work out the minimum possible area of the photo.

9 cm

6 cm

3. In this question the value of a is either exactly 4 or 5, and the value of b is either exactly 1 or 2. Work out:

  a) the maximum value of $a + b$ **b)** the minimum value of $a + b$

  c) the maximum value of ab **d)** the maximum value of $a - b$

  e) the minimum value of $a - b$ **f)** the maximum value of $\dfrac{a}{b}$

  g) the minimum value of $\dfrac{a}{b}$ **h)** the maximum value of $a^2 - b^2$.

4. If $p = 7$ cm and $q = 5$ cm, both to the nearest cm, find:

  a) the largest possible value of $p + q$

  b) the smallest possible value of $p + q$

  c) the largest possible value of $p - q$

  d) the largest possible value of $\dfrac{p^2}{q}$.

5. If $a = 3.1$ and $b = 7.3$, correct to one decimal place, find the largest possible value of:

i) $a + b$ ii) $b - a$

6. If $x = 5$ and $y = 7$ to one significant figure, find the largest and smallest possible values of:

i) $x + y$ ii) $y - x$ iii) $\dfrac{x}{y}$

7. In the diagram, ABCD and EFGH are rectangles with AB = 10 cm, BC = 7 cm, EF = 7 cm and FG = 4 cm, all figures accurate to the nearest cm.
Find the largest possible value of the shaded area.

8. When a voltage V is applied to a resistance R the power consumed P is given by $P = \dfrac{V^2}{R}$.

If you measure V as 12.2 and R as 2.6, correct to 1 d.p., calculate the smallest possible value of P.

Estimation

You should check that the answer to a calculation is 'about the right size'.

Example

Estimate the value of $\dfrac{57.2 \times 110}{2.146 \times 46.9}$, correct to one significant figure.

We have approximately, $\dfrac{60 \times 100}{2 \times 50} \approx 60$

On a calculator the value is 62.52 (to 4 significant figures).

Exercise 14

In this exercise there are 25 questions, each followed by three possible answers.
Decide (by estimating) which answer is correct.

1. 7.2×9.8 [52.16, 98.36, 70.56]

2. 2.03×58.6 [118.958, 87.848, 141.116]

3. 23.4×19.3 [213.32, 301.52, 451.62]

4. 313×107.6 [3642.8, 4281.8, 33 678.8]

5. 6.3×0.098 [0.6174, 0.0622, 5.98]

6. 1200×0.89 [722, 1068, 131]

7. 0.21×93 [41.23, 9.03, 19.53]

8. 88.8×213 [18 914.4, 1693.4, 1965.4]

9. 0.04×968 [38.72, 18.52, 95.12]

10. 0.11×0.089 [0.1069, 0.095 9, 0.009 79]

11. $13.92 \div 5.8$ [0.52, 4.2, 2.4]

12. $105.6 \div 9.6$ [8.9, 11, 15]

13. $8405 \div 205$ [4.6, 402, 41]

14. $881.1 \div 99$ [4.5, 8.9, 88]

15. $4.183 \div 0.89$ [4.7, 48, 51]

16. $6.72 \div 0.12$ [6.32, 21.2, 56]

17. $20.301 \div 1010$ [0.0201, 0.211, 0.0021]

18. $0.288\ 96 \div 0.0096$ [312, 102.1, 30.1]

19. $0.143 \div 0.11$ [2.3, 1.3, 11.4]

20. $159.65 \div 515$ [0.11, 3.61, 0.31]

21. $(5.6 - 0.21) \times 39$ [389.21, 210.21, 20.51]

22. $\dfrac{17.5 \times 42}{2.5}$ [294, 504, 86]

23. $(906 + 4.1) \times 0.31$ [473.21, 282.131, 29.561]

24. $\dfrac{543 + 472}{18.1 + 10.9}$ [65, 35, 85]

25. $\dfrac{112.2 \times 75.9}{6.9 \times 5.1}$ [242, 20.4, 25.2]

1.4 Standard form

When dealing with either very large or very small numbers, it is not convenient to write them out in full in the normal way. It is better to use standard form. Most calculators represent large and small numbers in this way.

The number $a \times 10^n$ is in standard form when $1 \leqslant a < 10$ and n is a positive or negative integer.

> ### Example
> Write the following numbers in standard form:
>
> a) $2000 = 2 \times 1000 = 2 \times 10^3$
>
> b) $150 = 1.5 \times 100 = 1.5 \times 10^2$
>
> c) $0.0004 = 4 \times \dfrac{1}{10\,000} = 4 \times 10^{-4}$

Exercise 15

Write the following numbers in standard form:

1. 4000	**2.** 500	**3.** 70 000	**4.** 60	**5.** 2400
6. 380	**7.** 46 000	**8.** 46	**9.** 900 000	**10.** 2560
11. 0.007	**12.** 0.0004	**13.** 0.0035	**14.** 0.421	**15.** 0.000 055
16. 0.01	**17.** 564 000	**18.** 19 million		

19. The population of China is estimated at 1100 000 000. Write this in standard form.

20. The mass of a hydrogen atom is 0.000 000 000 000 000 000 000 001 67 grams. Write this mass in standard form.

21. The area of the surface of the Earth is about 510 000 000 km². Express this in standard form.

22. An atom is 0.000 000 000 25 cm in diameter. Write this in standard form.

23. Avogadro's number is 602 300 000 000 000 000 000 000. Express this in standard form.

24. The speed of light is 300 000 km/s. Express this speed in cm/s in standard form.

1 km = 1000 m
1 m = 100 cm

25. A very rich man leaves his fortune of 3.6×10^8 to be divided equally between his 100 grandchildren. How much does each child receive? Give the answer in standard form.

Example

Work out $1500 \times 8\,000\,000$.

$$1500 \times 8\,000\,000 = \left(1.5 \times 10^3\right) \times \left(8 \times 10^6\right)$$
$$= 12 \times 10^9$$
$$= 1.2 \times 10^{10}$$

Notice that we multiply the numbers and the powers of 10 separately.

Exercise 16

In questions **1** to **12** give the answer in standard form.

1. 5000×3000	**2.** $60\,000 \times 5000$	**3.** $0.000\,07 \times 400$	**4.** $0.0007 \times 0.000\,01$
5. $8000 \div 0.004$	**6.** $(0.002)^2$	**7.** 150×0.0006	**8.** $0.000\,033 \div 500$
9. $0.007 \div 20\,000$	**10.** $(0.0001)^4$	**11.** $(2000)^3$	**12.** $0.005\,92 \div 8000$

13. If $a = 512 \times 10^2$ $b = 0.478 \times 10^6$ $c = 0.0049 \times 10^7$

arrange a, b and c in order of size (smallest first).

14. If the number 2.74×10^{15} is written out in full, how many zeros follow the 4?

15. If the number 7.31×10^{-17} is written out in full, how many zeros would there be between the decimal point and the first significant figure?

16. If $x = 2 \times 10^5$ and $y = 3 \times 10^{-3}$ correct to one significant figure, find the greatest and least possible values of:

> The limits of accuracy of 2 to one significant figure are 1.5 to 2.5.

   i) xy **ii)** $\dfrac{x}{y}$

17. Oil flows through a pipe at a rate of 40 m³/s. How long will it take to fill a tank of volume 1.2×10^5 m³?

18. Given that $L = 2\sqrt{\dfrac{a}{k}}$, find the value of L in standard form when $a = 4.5 \times 10^{12}$ and $k = 5 \times 10^7$.

19. a) The number 10 to the power 100 is called a 'Googol'. If it takes $\dfrac{1}{5}$ second to write a zero and $\dfrac{1}{10}$ second to write a 'one', how long would it take to write the number 100 'Googols' in full?

   b) The number 10 to the power of a 'Googol' is called a 'Googolplex'. Using the same speed of writing, how long in years would it take to write 1 'Googolplex' in full?

1.5   Ratio and proportion

The word 'ratio' is used to describe a fraction. If the *ratio* of a boy's height to his father's height is $4:5$, then he is $\dfrac{4}{5}$ as tall as his father.

Example 1

Change the ratio $2:5$ into the form

a) $1:n$ **b)** $m:1$

a) $2:5 = 1:\dfrac{5}{2}$ **b)** $2:5 = \dfrac{2}{5}:1$

           $= 1:2.5$ $= 0.4:1$

Example 2

Divide \$60 between two people A and B in the ratio $5:7$.

Consider \$60 as 12 equal parts (i.e. $5 + 7$). Then A receives 5 parts and B receives 7 parts.

$\therefore$ A receives $\dfrac{5}{12}$ of \$60 $= \$25$

     B receives $\dfrac{7}{12}$ of \$60 $= \$35$

Example 3

Divide 200 kg in the ratio $1:3:4$.

The parts are $\frac{1}{8}$, $\frac{3}{8}$ and $\frac{4}{8}$ (of 200 kg). i.e. 25 kg, 75 kg and 100 kg.

Exercise 17

In questions **1** to **8** express the ratios in the form $1:n$.

1. $2:6$	**2.** $5:30$	**3.** $2:100$	**4.** $5:8$
5. $4:3$	**6.** $8:3$	**7.** $22:550$	**8.** $45:360$

In questions **9** to **12** express the ratios in the form $n:1$.

9. $12:5$	**10.** $5:2$	**11.** $4:5$	**12.** $2:100$

In questions **13** to **18** divide the quantity in the ratio given.

13. $40; (3:5)$	**14.** $120; (3:7)$	**15.** 250 m; $(14:11)$
16. $117; (2:3:8)$	**17.** 180 kg; $(1:5:6)$	**18.** 184 minutes; $(2:3:3)$

19. When $143 is divided in the ratio $2:4:5$, what is the difference between the largest share and the smallest share?

20. Divide 180 kg in the ratio $1:2:3:4$.

21. Divide $4000 in the ratio $2:5:5:8$.

22. If $\frac{5}{8}$ of the children in a school are boys, what is the ratio of boys to girls?

23. A man and a woman share a prize of $1000 between them in the ratio $1:4$. The woman shares her part between herself, her mother and her daughter in the ratio $2:1:1$. How much does her daughter receive?

24. A man and a woman share a sum of money in the ratio $3:2$. If the sum of money is doubled, in what ratio should they divide it so that the man still receives the same amount?

25. In a herd of x cattle, the ratio of the number of bulls to cows is $1:6$. Find the number of bulls in the herd in terms of x.

26. If $x:3 = 12:x$, calculate the positive value of x.

27. If $y:18 = 8:y$, calculate the positive value of y.

28. $400 is divided between Kas, Jaspar and Jae so that Kas has twice as much as Jaspar and Jaspar has three times as much as Jae. How much does Jaspar receive?

29. A cake of mass 550 g has three dry ingredients: flour, sugar and raisins. There is twice as much flour as sugar and one and a half times as much sugar as raisins. How much flour is there?

30. A brother and sister share out their collection of 5000 stamps in the ratio 5:3. The brother then shares his stamps with two friends in the ratio 3:1:1, keeping most for himself. How many stamps do each of his friends receive?

Proportion

The majority of problems where proportion is involved are usually solved by finding the value of a unit quantity.

<table>
<tr><td>

Example 1

If a wire of length 2 metres costs $10, find the cost of a wire of length 35 cm.

          200 cm costs 1000 cents

$\therefore$ 1 cm costs $\frac{1000}{200}$ cents $= 5$ cents

$\therefore$ 35 cm costs 5×35 cents $= 175$ cents

                      $= \$1.75$

</td><td>

Chapter 5 covers these ideas of **direct** and **inverse** proportion using algebraic methods.

</td></tr>
</table>

Example 2

Eight men can dig a hole in 4 hours. How long will it take five men to dig the same size hole?

8 men take 4 hours

1 man would take 32 hours

5 men would take $\frac{32}{5}$ hours $= 6$ hours 24 minutes.

Exercise 18

1. Five cans of cola cost $1.20. Find the cost of seven cans.

2. A man earns $140 in a 5-day week. What is his pay for 3 days?

3. Three people build a wall in 10 days. How long would it take five people?

4. Nine fruit juice bottles contain $4\frac{1}{2}$ litres of fruit juice between them. How much juice do five bottles hold?

5. A car uses 10 litres of petrol in 75 km. How far will it go on 8 litres?

6. A wire 11 cm long has a mass of 187 g. What is the mass of 7 cm of this wire?

7. A shopkeeper can buy 36 toys for $20.52. What will he pay for 120 toys?

8. A ship has sufficient food to supply 600 passengers for 3 weeks. How long would the food last for 800 people?

9. The cost of a phone call lasting 3 minutes 30 seconds was 52.5 cents. At this rate, what was the cost of a call lasting 5 minutes 20 seconds?

10. 80 machines can produce 4800 identical pens in 5 hours. At this rate
    a) how many pens would one machine produce in one hour?
    b) how many pens would 25 machines produce in 7 hours?

11. Three men can build a wall in 10 hours. How many men would be needed to build the wall in $7\frac{1}{2}$ hours?

12. If it takes 6 men 4 days to dig a hole 3 metres deep, how long will it take 10 men to dig a hole 7 metres deep?

13. Find the cost of 1 km of pipe at 7 cents for every 40 cm.

14. A wheel turns through 90 revolutions per minute.
    How many degrees does it turn through in 1 second?

15. Find the cost of 200 grams of flour at $6 per kilogram.

16. The height of One Kansas City Place is 623 feet. Express this height to the nearest metre using 1 m = 3.281 feet.

17. A floor is covered by 800 tiles measuring 10 cm². How many square tiles of side 8 cm would be needed to cover the same floor?

18. A battery has enough energy to operate eight toy bears for 21 hours. For how long could the battery operate 15 toy bears?

19. An engine has enough fuel to operate at full power for 20 minutes. For how long could the engine operate at 35% of full power?

20. A large drum, when full, contains 260 kg of oil of density 0.9 g/cm³. What mass of petrol, of density 0.84 g/cm³, can be contained in the drum?

21. A wall can be built by 6 men working 8 hours per day in 5 days. How many days will it take 4 men to build the wall if they work only 5 hours per day?

Foreign exchange

Money is changed from one currency into another using the method of proportion.

Exchange rate for US dollars ($):

Country	Rate of exchange
Argentina (pesos)	$1 = 3.79 ARS
Australia (dollar)	$1 = 1.13 AUD
Euro (euros)	$1 = €0.70 EUR
India (rupees)	$1 = 46.50 INR
Japan (yen)	$1 = 91.20 JPY
Kuwait (dinar)	$1 = 0.29 KWD
UK (pounds)	$1 = £0.63 GBP

Convert:

a) $22.50 to dinars

b) €300 to dollars.

a) $1 = 0.29 dinars (KWD)

   so $22.5 = 0.29 × 22.50 KWD

         = 6.53 KWD

b) €0.70 = $1

   so $€1 = \dfrac{1}{0.70}$

   so $€300 = \dfrac{1}{0.70} × 300$

         $= 428.57

Exercise 19

Give your answers correct to two decimal places. Use the exchange rates given in the table.

1. Change the number of dollars into the foreign currency stated.

   a) $20 [euros]   **b)** $70 [pounds]   **c)** $200 [pesos]

   d) $1.50 [rupees]   **e)** $2.30 [yen]   **f)** 90c [dinars]

2. Change the amount of foreign currency into dollars.

   a) €500   **b)** £2500   **c)** 7.50 rupees

   d) 900 dinars   **e)** 125.24 pesos   **f)** 750 AUD

3. A CD costs £9.50 in London and $9.70 in Chicago. How much cheaper, in British money, is the CD when bought in the US?

4. An MP3 player costs €20.46 in Spain and £12.60 in the UK. Which is the cheaper in dollars, and by how much?

5. The monthly rent of a flat in New Delhi is 32 860 rupees. How much is this in euros?

6. A Persian kitten is sold in several countries at the prices given below.

   Kuwait   150 dinars

   France   550 euros

   Japan   92 000 yen

   Write out in order a list of the prices converted into GBP.

7. An Australian man on holiday in Germany finds that his wallet contains 700 AUD. If he changes the money at a bank how many euros will he receive?

Map scales

You can use proportion to work out map scales. First you need to know these metric equivalents:

1 km = 1000 m	km means kilometre
1 m = 100 cm	m means metre
1 cm = 10 mm	cm means centimetre
	mm means millimetre

Example

A map is drawn to a scale of 1 to 50 000. Calculate:

a) the length of a road which appears as 3 cm long on the map

b) the length on the map of a lake which is 10 km long.

....

a) 1 cm on the map is equivalent to 50 000 cm on the Earth.

$\therefore$ 1 cm $\equiv$ 50 000 cm

$\therefore$ 1 cm $\equiv$ 500 m

$\therefore$ 1 cm $\equiv$ 0.5 km

so 3 cm $\equiv$ 3 × 0.5 km = 1.5 km.

The road is 1.5 km long.

b)   0.5 km $\equiv$ 1 cm

$\therefore$ 1 km $\equiv$ 2 cm

$\therefore$ 10 km $\equiv$ 2 × 10 cm

= 20 cm

The lake appears 20 cm long on the map.

Exercise 20

1. Find the actual length represented on a drawing by

  a)   14 cm   **b)**   3.2 cm

  c)   0.71 cm   **d)**   21.7 cm

when the scale is 1 cm to 5 m.

2. Find the length on a drawing that represents

  a)   50 m   **b)**   35 m

  c)   7.2 m   **d)**   28.6 m

when the scale is 1 cm to 10 m.

3. If the scale is 1 : 10 000, what length will 45 cm on the map represent:

  a)   in cm   **b)**   in m   **c)**   in km?

4. On a map of scale 1 : 100 000, the distance between De'aro and Debeka is 12.3 cm. What is the actual distance in km?

5. On a map of scale 1 : 15 000, the distance between Noordwijk aan Zee and Katwijk aan Zee is 31.4 cm. What is the actual distance in km?

6. If the scale of a map is 1 : 10 000, what will be the length on this map of a road which is 5 km long?

7. The distance from Hong Kong to Shenzhen is 32 km. How far apart will they be on a map of scale 1 : 50 000?

8. The 17th hole at the famous St Andrews golf course is 420 m in length. How long will it appear on a plan of the course of scale 1 : 8000?

An area involves two dimensions multiplied together and hence the scale is multiplied *twice*.

For example, if the linear scale is $\frac{1}{100}$, then the area scale is $\frac{1}{100} \times \frac{1}{100} = \frac{1}{10\,000}$.

You can use a diagram to help:

If a scale is 1 : 50 000

then 2 cm ≡ 1km

An area of 6 cm² can be thought of as:

3 cm

| 6 cm² | 2 cm

so the equivalent area using the scale is:

1.5 km

| 1.5 km² | 1 km w

Exercise 21

1. The scale of a map is 1 : 1000. What are the actual dimensions of a rectangle which appears as 4 cm by 3 cm on the map? What is the area on the map in cm²? What is the actual area in m²?

2. The scale of a map is 1 : 100. What area does 1 cm² on the map represent? What area does 6 cm² represent?

3. The scale of a map is 1 : 20 000. What area does 8 cm² represent?

4. The scale of a map is 1 : 1000. What is the area, in cm², on the map of a lake of area 5000 m²?

5. The scale of a map is 1 cm to 5 km. A farm is represented by a rectangle measuring 1.5 cm by 4 cm. What is the actual area of the farm?

6. On a map of scale 1 cm to 250 m the area of a car park is 3 cm². What is the actual area of the car park in hectares? (1 hectare = 10 000 m²)

7. The area of the playing surface at the Olympic Stadium in Beijing is $\frac{3}{5}$ of a hectare. What area will it occupy on a plan drawn to a scale of 1 : 500?

8. On a map of scale 1 : 20 000 the area of a forest is 50 cm². On another map the area of the forest is 8 cm². Find the scale of the second map.

1.6 Percentages

Percentages are simply a convenient way of expressing fractions or decimals. '50% of $60' means $\frac{50}{100}$ of $60, or more simply $\frac{1}{2}$ of $60. Percentages are used very frequently in everyday life and are misunderstood by a large number of people. What are the implications if 'inflation falls from 10% to 8%'? Does this mean prices will fall?

> ## Example
> a) Change 80% to a fraction.
>
> b) Change $\frac{3}{8}$ to a percentage.
>
> c) Change 8% to a decimal.
>
> ....
>
> a) $80\% = \frac{80}{100} = \frac{4}{5}$
>
> b) $\frac{3}{8} = \left(\frac{3}{8} \times \frac{100}{1}\right)\% = 37\frac{1}{2}\%$
>
> c) $8\% = \frac{8}{100} = 0.08$

Exercise 22

1. Change to fractions:

   a) 60%   **b)** 24%   **c)** 35%   **d)** 2%

2. Change to percentages:

   a) $\frac{1}{4}$ **b)** $\frac{1}{10}$ **c)** $\frac{7}{8}$

   d) $\frac{1}{3}$ **e)** 0.72   **f)** 0.31

3. Change to decimals:

   a) 36%   **b)** 28%   **c)** 7%

   d) 13.4%   **e)** $\frac{3}{5}$ **f)** $\frac{7}{8}$

4. Arrange in order of size (smallest first):

   a) $\frac{1}{2}$; 45%; 0.6   **b)** 0.38; $\frac{6}{16}$; 4%

   c) 0.111; 11%; $\frac{1}{9}$ **d)** 32%; 0.3; $\frac{1}{3}$

5. The following are marks obtained in various tests. Convert them to percentages.

   a) 17 out of 20   **b)** 31 out of 40   **c)** 19 out of 80

   d) 112 out of 200   **e)** $2\frac{1}{2}$ out of 25   **f)** $7\frac{1}{2}$ out of 20

Example 1

A car costing $2400 is reduced in price by 10%. Find the new price.

$$10\% \text{ of } \$2400 = \frac{10}{100} \times \frac{2400}{1}$$
$$= \$240$$

New price of car $= \$(2400 - 240)$
$$= \$2160$$

Example 2

After a price increase of 10% a television set costs $286.

What was the price before the increase?

The price before the increase is 100%.

$\therefore$ 110% of old price $= \$286$

$\therefore$ 1% of old price $= \$\dfrac{286}{110}$

$\therefore$ 100% of old price $= \$\dfrac{286}{110} \times \dfrac{100}{1}$

      Old price of TV $= \$260$

Exercise 23

1. Calculate:

   a) 30% of $50   **b)** 45% of 2000 kg

   c) 4% of $70   **d)** 2.5% of 5000 people

2. In a sale, a jacket costing $40 is reduced by 20%. What is the sale price?

3. The charge for a telephone call costing 12 cents is increased by 10%. What is the new charge?

4. In peeling potatoes 4% of the mass of the potatoes is lost as 'peel'. How much is left for use from a bag containing 55 kg?

5. Work out, to the nearest cent:

   a) 6.4% of $15.95

   b) 11.2% of $192.66

   c) 8.6% of $25.84

   d) 2.9% of $18.18

6. Find the total bill:

   5 golf clubs at $18.65 each

   60 golf balls at $16.50 per dozen

   1 pair of golf shoes at $75.80

   Sales tax at 15% is added to the total cost.

7. In 2015 a club has 250 members who each pay $95 annual subscription. In 2016 the membership increases by 4% and the annual subscription is increased by 6%. What is the total income from subscriptions in 2016?

8. In Thailand the population of a town is 48 700 men and 41 600 women. What percentage of the total population are men?

9. In South Korea there are 21 280 000 licensed vehicles on the road. Of these, 16 486 000 are private cars. What percentage of the licensed vehicles are private cars?

10. A quarterly telephone bill consists of $19.15 rental plus 4.7 cents for each dialled unit. Tax is added at 15%. What is the total bill for Bryndis who used 915 dialled units?

11. 70% of Hassan's collection of goldfish died. If he has 60 survivors, how many did he have originally?

12. The average attendance at Parma football club fell by 7% in 2015. If 2030 fewer people went to matches in 2015, how many went in 2014?

13. When heated an iron bar expands by 0.2%. If the increase in length is 1 cm, what is the original length of the bar?

14. In the last two weeks of a sale, prices are reduced first by 30% and then by a *further* 40% of the new price. What is the final sale price of a shirt which originally cost $15?

15. During a Grand Prix car race, the tyres on a car are reduced in mass by 3%. If their mass is 388 kg at the end of the race, what was their mass at the start?

16. Over a period of 6 months, a colony of rabbits increases in number by 25% and then by a further 30%. If there were originally 200 rabbits in the colony, how many were there at the end?

17. A television costs $270.25 including 15% tax. How much of the cost is tax?

18. The cash price for a car was $7640. Gurtaj bought the car on the following terms: 'A deposit of 20% of the cash price and 36 monthly payments of $191.60'. Calculate the total amount Gurtaj paid.

Percentage increase or decrease

In the next exercise use the formulae:

$$\text{percentage profit} = \frac{\text{actual profit}}{\text{original price}} \times \frac{100}{1}$$

$$\text{percentage loss} = \frac{\text{actual loss}}{\text{original price}} \times \frac{100}{1}$$

Example 1

A radio is bought for $16 and sold for $20. What is the percentage profit?

$$\text{actual profit} = \$4$$

$$\therefore \quad \text{percentage profit} = \frac{4}{16} \times \frac{100}{1} = 25\%$$

The radio is sold at a 25% profit.

Example 2

A car is sold for $2280, at a loss of 5% on the cost price. Find the cost price.

Do *not* calculate 5% of $2280!
The loss is 5% of the cost price.

$$\therefore \quad 95\% \text{ of cost price} = \$2280$$

$$1\% \text{ of cost price} = \$\frac{2280}{95}$$

$$\therefore \quad 100\% \text{ of cost price} = \$\frac{2280}{95} \times \frac{100}{1}$$

$$\text{cost price} = \$2400$$

Exercise 24

1. The first figure is the cost price and the second figure is the selling price.
   Calculate the percentage profit or loss in each case.

   a) $20, $25
   b) $400, $500
   c) $60, $54

   d) $9000, $10 800
   e) $460, $598
   f) $512, $550.40

   g) $45, $39.60
   h) 50c, 23c

   > c is the symbol for cents.
   > 100c = $1

2. A car dealer buys a car for $500, and then sells it for $640. What is the percentage profit?

3. A damaged carpet which cost $180 when new, is sold for $100. What is the percentage loss?

4. During the first four weeks of her life, a baby girl increases her mass from 3.2 kg to 4.7 kg. What percentage increase does this represent? (Give your answer to 3 s.f.)

5. When tax is added to the cost of a lipstick, its price increases from $16.50 to $18.48. What is the rate at which tax is charged?

6. The price of a sports car is reduced from $30 000 to $28 400. What percentage reduction is this?

7. Find the *cost* price of the following:
   a) selling price $55, profit 10%
   b) selling price $558, profit 24%
   c) selling price $680, loss 15%
   d) selling price $11.78, loss 5%

8. A sari is sold for $60 thereby making a profit of 20% on the cost price. What was the cost price?

9. A pair of jeans is sold for $15, thereby making a profit of 25% on the cost price. What was the cost price?

10. A book is sold for $5.40, at a profit of 8% on the cost price. What was the cost price?

11. A can of worms is sold for 48c, incurring a loss of 20%. What was the cost price?

12. A car was sold for $1430, thereby making a loss of 35% on the cost price. What was the cost price?

13. If an employer reduces the working week from 40 hours to 35 hours, with no loss of weekly pay, calculate the percentage increase in the hourly rate of pay.

14. The rental for a television set changed from $80 per year to $8 per month. What is the percentage increase in the yearly rental?

15. A greengrocer sells a melon at a profit of $37\frac{1}{2}$% on the price he pays for it. What is the ratio of the cost price to the selling price?

16. Given that $G = ab$, find the percentage increase in G when both a and b increase by 10%.

17. Given that $T = \dfrac{kx}{y}$, find the percentage increase in T when k, x and y all increase by 20%.

Simple interest

When a sum of money P is invested for T years at R% interest per annum (each year), then the interest gained I is given by:

$$I = \frac{P \times R \times T}{100}$$

This is known as simple interest.

Example

Joel invests $400 for 6 months at 5% per annum.

Work out the simple interest gained.

$P = \$400$ $R = 5$ $T = 0.5$ (6 months is half a year)

so $I = \dfrac{400 \times 5 \times 0.5}{100}$

      $I = \$10$

Exercise 25

1. Calculate:

   a) the simple interest on $1200 for 3 years at 6% per annum

   b) the simple interest on $700 at 8.25% per annum for 2 years

   c) the length of time for $5000 to earn $1000 if invested at 10% per annum

   d) the length of time for $400 to earn $160 if invested at 8% per annum.

2. Khalid invests $6750 at 8.5% per annum. How much interest
   has he earned and what is the total amount in his account after 4 years?

3. Petra invests $10 800. After 4 years she has earned $3240 in interest.
   At what annual rate of interest did she invest her money?

Compound interest

Suppose a bank pays a fixed interest of 10% on money in deposit accounts.
A man puts $500 in the bank.

After one year he has

    $500 + 10\%$ of $500 = \$550$

After two years he has

    $550 + 10\%$ of $550 = \$605$

      [Check that this is $1.10^2 \times 500$]

After three years he has

    $605 + 10\%$ of $605 = \$665.50$

      [Check that this is $1.10^3 \times 500$]

In general after n years the money in the bank will be $\$(1.10^n \times 500)$

Exercise 26

1. A bank pays interest of 9% on money in deposit accounts. Carme puts $2000 in the bank. How much has she after
   a) one year, **b)** two years, **c)** three years?

2. A bank pays interest of 11%. Mamuru puts $5000 in the bank. How much has he after **a)** one year, **b)** three years, **c)** five years?

3. A student gets a grant of $10 000 a year. Assuming her grant is increased by 7% each year, what will her grant be in four years time?

4. Isoke's salary in 2015 is $30 000 per year. Every year her salary is increased by 5%.

   In 2016 her salary will be $\qquad$ $30\,000 \times 1.05 = \$31\,500$

   In 2017 her salary will be $\qquad$ $30\,000 \times 1.05 \times 1.05 = \$33\,075$

   In 2018 her salary will be $30\,000 \times 1.05 \times 1.05 \times 1.05 = \$34\,728.75$

   And so on.

   a) What will her salary be in 2019?

   b) What will her salary be in 2021?

5. The rental price of a dacha was $9000. At the end of each month the price is increased by 6%.

   a) Find the price of the house after 1 month.

   b) Find the price of the house after 3 months.

   c) Find the price of the house after 10 months.

6. Assuming an average inflation rate of 8%, work out the probable cost of the following items in 10 years:

   a) motor bike $6500

   b) iPod $340

   c) car $50 000.

7. A new scooter is valued at $15 000. At the end of each year its value is reduced by 15% of its value at the start of the year. What will it be worth after 3 years?

8. The population of an island increases by 10% each year. After how many years will the original population be doubled?

9. A bank pays interest of 11% on $6000 in a deposit account. After how many years will the money have trebled?

10. A tree grows in height by 21% per year. It is 2 m tall after one year. After how many more years will the tree be over 20 m tall?

11. Which is the better investment over ten years:

$20 000 at 12% compound interest

or $30 000 at 8% compound interest?

Income tax

> **Example**
>
> Workers generally pay tax on their earnings. Sometimes they are entitled to a *tax free* allowance before paying a percentage tax on the rest of their earnings.
>
> Vivien earns $42 000 per year and she gets a tax free allowance of $6000. If she pays 20% tax on the next $30 000 and 40% on the rest, how much tax does she pay in total?
>
> $42 000 − $6000 = $36 000
>
> 20% of $30 000 = $30 000 ÷ 5 = $6000
>
> $36 000 − $30 000 = $6000
>
> 40% of $6000 = $6000 × 0.4 = $2400
>
> Total tax = $6000 + $2400 = $8400

Exercise 27

1. Tomas earns $37 000 per year. He gets a tax free allowance of $8000 and pays 25% tax on the rest.

   How much tax will he pay in a year?

2. Juliette earns $4500 per month. She gets a tax free allowance of $10 000 per year and pays tax at 20% on the rest. How much tax will she pay in a year?

3. Elise gets a tax free allowance of $6000 and pays tax at 25% on the next $20 000. She pays tax at a rate of 30% on the rest. If she earns $72 000 per year, how much tax must she pay?

4. Johan earns $650 per week and works 48 weeks a year. If he gets a tax free allowance of $8000, pays tax at a rate of 10% on the next $10 000 and 20% on the rest, how much tax will he pay in a year?

1.7 Speed, distance and time

Calculations involving these three quantities are simpler when the speed is *constant*. The formulae connecting the quantities are as follows:

a) distance = speed × time

b) speed = $\dfrac{\text{distance}}{\text{time}}$

c) time = $\dfrac{\text{distance}}{\text{speed}}$

A helpful way of remembering these formulae is to write the letters D, S and T in a triangle, thus:

to find D, cover D and we have ST

to find S, cover S and we have $\dfrac{D}{T}$

to find T, cover T and we have $\dfrac{D}{S}$

Great care must be taken with the units in these questions.

Example 1

A man is running at a speed of 8 km/h for a distance of 5200 metres. Find the time taken in minutes.

5200 metres $= 5.2$ km

time taken in hours $= \left(\dfrac{D}{S}\right) = \dfrac{5.2}{8}$

$= 0.65$ hours

time taken in minutes $= 0.65 \times 60$

$= 39$ minutes

Example 2

Change the units of a speed of 54 km/h into metres per second.

54 km/hour $= 54\,000$ metres/hour

$= \dfrac{54\,000}{60}$ metres/minute

$= \dfrac{54\,000}{60 \times 60}$ metres/second

$= 15$ m/s

Exercise 28

1. Find the time taken for the following journeys:
   a) 100 km at a speed of 40 km/h
   b) 250 miles at a speed of 80 miles per hour
   c) 15 metres at a speed of 20 cm/s (answer in seconds)
   d) 10^4 metres at a speed of 2.5 km/h.

2. Change the units of the following speeds as indicated:
   a) 72 km/h into m/s
   b) 108 km/h into m/s
   c) 300 km/h into m/s
   d) 30 m/s into km/h
   e) 22 m/s into km/h
   f) 0.012 m/s into cm/s
   g) 9000 cm/s into m/s
   h) 600 miles/day into miles per hour
   i) 2592 miles/day into miles per second.

3. Find the speeds of the bodies which move as follows:
   a) a distance of 600 km in 8 hours
   b) a distance of 31.64 km in 7 hours
   c) a distance of 136.8 m in 18 seconds
   d) a distance of 4×10^4 m in 10^{-2} seconds
   e) a distance of 5×10^5 cm in 2×10^{-3} seconds
   f) a distance of 10^8 mm in 30 minutes (in km/h)
   g) a distance of 500 m in 10 minutes (in km/h).

4. Find the distance travelled (in metres) in the following:
   a) at a speed of 55 km/h for 2 hours
   b) at a speed of 40 km/h for $\frac{1}{4}$ hour
   c) at a speed of 338.4 km/h for 10 minutes
   d) at a speed of 15 m/s for 5 minutes
   e) at a speed of 14 m/s for 1 hour
   f) at a speed of 4×10^3 m/s for 2×10^{-2} seconds
   g) at a speed of 8×10^5 cm/s for 2 minutes.

5. A car travels 60 km at 30 km/h and then a further 180 km at 160 km/h.
   Find:
   a) the total time taken
   b) the average speed for the whole journey.

6. A cyclist travels 25 kilometres at 20 km/h and then a further 80 kilometres at 25 km/h.
Find:

a) the total time taken

b) the average speed for the whole journey.

7. A swallow flies at a speed of 50 km/h for 3 hours and then at a speed of 40 km/h for a further 2 hours. Find the average speed for the whole journey.

8. A runner ran two laps around a 400 m track. She completed the first lap in 50 seconds and then decreased her speed by 5% for the second lap. Find:

a) her speed on the first lap

b) her speed on the second lap

c) her total time for the two laps

d) her average speed for the two laps.

9. An airliner flies 2000 km at a speed of 1600 km/h and then returns due to bad weather at a speed of 1000 km/h. Find the average speed for the whole trip.

10. A train travels from A to B, a distance of 100 km, at a speed of 20 km/h. If it had gone two and a half times as fast, how much earlier would it have arrived at B?

11. Two men running towards each other at 4 m/s and 6 m/s respectively are one kilometre apart. How long will it take before they meet?

12. A car travelling at 90 km/h is 500 m behind another car travelling at 70 km/h in the same direction. How long will it take the first car to catch the second?

13. How long is a train which passes a signal in twenty seconds at a speed of 108 km/h?

14. A train of length 180 m approaches a tunnel of length 620 m. How long will it take the train to pass completely through the tunnel at a speed of 54 km/h?

15. An earthworm of length 15 cm is crawling along at 2 cm/s. An ant overtakes the worm in 5 seconds. How fast is the ant walking?

16. A train of length 100 m is moving at a speed of 50 km/h. A horse is running alongside the train at a speed of 56 km/h. How long will it take the horse to overtake the train?

17. A car completes a journey at an average speed of 40 km/h. At what speed must it travel on the return journey if the average speed for the complete journey (out and back) is 60 km/h?

Example

Speed is a common measure of *rate*. A speed given in kilometres *per* hour tells us how many kilometres we travel in one hour. Other common measures of rate include litres *per* minute, when filling a bath with water, for example, and kilowatt hours *per* day when measuring energy consumption.

Exercise 29

1. Find the following rates in the units given:
   a) 4 litres in 5 minutes (litres per minute)
   b) 12 litres in 45 minutes (litres per hour)
   c) 78 litres in 12 minutes (litres per hour)
   d) 800 kilowatt hours in 2 months (kilowatt hours per year)
   e) 12 kilowatt hours in 3 days (kilowatt hours per year).

2. Find the time taken (in minutes) to fill the following containers:
   a) a 3 litre bowl at a rate of 2 litres per minute
   b) a 30 litre bucket at a rate of 0.2 litres per second
   c) a 120 litre hot water tank at a rate of 80 litres per hour
   d) a 300 ml beaker at a rate of 0.5 litres per hour.

3. A bath is filled with 80 litres of water in 6 minutes. Find the rate at which it is being filled.

4. A typical household uses 4600 kilowatt hours of energy in a year. Find the rate at which the household uses energy in kilowatt hours per day.

5. Water is dripping from a tap at a rate of 5 millilitres per second. How long will it take, in minutes, to fill a bowl with a capacity of 2.5 litres?

6. A rain butt with a capacity of 60 litres fills completely with water each day.
   a) Find the rate of fill in millilitres per hour.
   b) A gardener can use all of the water to hose his garden in 15 minutes. Find the rate of flow of the water from the hose in millilitres per second.

1.8 Mixed problems

Exercise 30

1. Fill in the blank spaces in the table so that each row contains equivalent values.

Fraction	Decimal	Percentage
	0.28	
		64%
$\frac{5}{8}$		

2. An engine pulls four identical carriages. The engine is $\frac{2}{3}$ the length of a carriage and the total length of the train is 86.8 m. Find the length of the engine.

3. A cake is made from the ingredients listed below.

    500 g flour, 450 g butter, 470 g sugar,

    1.8 kg mixed fruit, 4 eggs (70 g each)

   The cake loses 12% of its mass during cooking.
   What is its final mass?

4. Abdul left his home at 7.35 a.m. and drove at an average speed of 45 km/h arriving at the airport at 8.50 a.m. How far is his home from the airport?

5. Tuwile's parents have agreed to lend him 60% of the cost of buying a car. If Tuwile still has to find $328 himself, how much does the car cost?

6. Which bag of potatoes is the better value:

   Bag A, 6 kg for $4.14 or

   Bag B, 2·5 kg for $1.80?

7. An aeroplane was due to take off from Madrid airport at 18:42 but it was 35 min late. During the flight, thanks to a tail wind, the plane made up the time and in fact landed 16 min before its scheduled arrival time of 00:05. (Assume that the plane did not cross any time zones on its journey.)

   a) What time did the aeroplane take off?

   b) What time did it land?

8. A 20 cent coin is 1.2 mm thick. What is the value of a pile of 20 cent coins which is 21.6 cm high?

9. Work out $\frac{3}{5} + 0.12 + 6\%$ of 10.

Exercise 31

1. Find the distance travelled by light in one hour, given that the speed of light is 300 000 kilometres per second.

   Give the answer in kilometres in standard form.

2. When the lid is left off an ink bottle, the ink evaporates at a rate of 2.5×10^{-6} cm³/s. A full bottle contains 36 cm³ of ink. How long, to the nearest day, will it take for all the ink to evaporate?

3. Convert 3.35 hours into hours and minutes.

4. When I think of a number, multiply it by 6 and subtract 120, my answer is −18. What was my original number?

5. The cost of advertising in a local paper for one week is:

   > 28 cents per word plus 75 cents

   a) What is the cost of an advertisement of 15 words for one week?

   b) What is the greatest number of words in an advertisement costing up to $8 for one week?

   c) If an advertisement is run for two weeks, the cost for the second week is reduced by 30%. Calculate the total cost for an advertisement of 22 words for two weeks.

6. Bronze is made up of zinc, tin and copper in the ratio $1:4:95$. A bronze statue contains 120 g of tin. Find the quantities of the other two metals required and the total mass of the statue.

Exercise 32

1. In the diagram $\frac{5}{6}$ of the circle is shaded and $\frac{2}{3}$ of the triangle is shaded. What is the ratio of the area of the circle to the area of the triangle?

   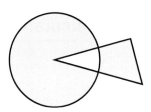

2. Find the exact answer to the following by first working out a rough answer and then using the information given.

   Do *not* use a calculator.

   a) If $142.3 \times 98.5 = 14\,016.55$ find $140.1655 \div 14.23$

   b) If $76.2 \times 8.6 = 655.32$ find $6553.2 \div 86$

   c) If $22.3512 \div 0.268 = 83.4$ find 8340×26.8

   d) If $1.6781 \div 17.3 = 0.097$ find 9700×0.173

3. A sales manager reports an increase of 28% in sales this year compared to last year.

   The increase was $70 560.

   What were the sales last year?

4. Small cubes of side 1 cm are stuck together to form a large cube of side 4 cm. Opposite faces of the large cube are painted the same colour, but adjacent faces are different colours. The three colours used are red, blue and green.

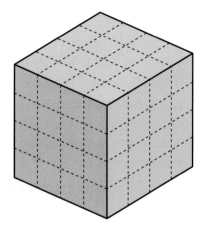

  a) How many small cubes have just one red and one green face?

  b) How many small cubes are painted on one face only?

  c) How many small cubes have one red, one green and one blue face?

  d) How many small cubes have no faces painted?

5. A bullet travels at a speed of 3×10^4 cm/s. Work out the length of time in seconds taken for the bullet to hit a target 54 m away.

6. A sewing machine cost $162.40 after a price increase of 16%. Find the price before the increase.

7. To get the next number in a sequence you double the previous number and subtract two.

The fifth number in the sequence is 50.

Find the first number.

8. A code uses 1 for A, 2 for B, 3 for C and so on up to 26 for Z. Coded words are written without spaces to confuse the enemy, so 18 could be AH or R. Decode the following message.

208919 919 1 2251825 199121225 31545

9. A coach can take 47 passengers. How many coaches are needed to transport 1330 passengers?

1.9 Calculator

In this book, the keys are described thus:

| EXP | numbers in standard form (e.g $\boxed{4}$ $\boxed{\text{EXP}}$ $\boxed{7}$ is 4×10^7)

$\boxed{+}$ add $\boxed{\sqrt{}}$ square root

$\boxed{-}$ subtract $\boxed{x^2}$ square

$\boxed{\times}$ multiply $\boxed{1/x}$ reciprocal

$\boxed{\div}$ divide $\boxed{\wedge}$ or $\boxed{y^x}$ raise number y to the power x

$\boxed{=}$ equals $\boxed{(}\,\boxed{)}$ brackets

Using the $\boxed{\text{ANS}}$ button

The $\boxed{\text{ANS}}$ button can be used as a 'short term memory'.
It holds the answer from the previous calculation.

Example

Evaluate the following to 4 significant figures:

a) $\dfrac{5}{1.2 - 0.761}$

b) $\left(\dfrac{1}{0.084}\right)^4$

c) $\sqrt[3]{[3.2 \times (1.7 - 1.64)]}$

$\cdots\cdots\cdots\cdots\cdots\cdots\cdots\cdots\cdots\cdots\cdots\cdots\cdots\cdots\cdots\cdots\cdots\cdots$

a) Find the bottom line first.

$\boxed{5}\;\boxed{\div}\;\boxed{(}\;\boxed{1.2}\;\boxed{-}\;\boxed{0.761}\;\boxed{)}\;\boxed{=}$

or

$\boxed{1.2}\;\boxed{-}\;\boxed{0.761}\;\boxed{\text{EXE}}\;\boxed{5}\;\boxed{\div}\;\boxed{\text{ANS}}\;\boxed{\text{EXE}}$

The calculator reads 11.38952164

∴ Answer = 11.39 (to four sig. fig.)

Note: The $\boxed{\text{EXE}}$ button works the same as the $\boxed{=}$ button.

b) $\left(\dfrac{1}{0.084}\right)^4$

$\boxed{1}\;\boxed{\div}\;\boxed{0.084}\;\boxed{=}\;\boxed{\wedge}\;\boxed{4}\;\boxed{=}$ or $\boxed{0.084}\;\boxed{1/x}\;\boxed{y^x}\;\boxed{4}\;\boxed{=}$

Answer 20 090 (to 4 s.f.)

c) $\sqrt[3]{[3.2(1.7 - 1.64)]}$

$\boxed{3.2}\;\boxed{\times}\;\boxed{(}\;\boxed{1.7}\;\boxed{-}\;\boxed{1.64}\;\boxed{)}\;\boxed{=}\;\boxed{\sqrt[3]{}}\;\boxed{\text{ANS}}\;\boxed{=}$

or

$\boxed{1.7}\;\boxed{-}\;\boxed{1.64}\;\boxed{=}\;\boxed{\times}\;\boxed{3.2}\;\boxed{=}$

$\boxed{y^x}\;\boxed{0.333\,333}\;\boxed{=}$

Answer 0.5769 (to 4 s.f.)

Note: To find a cube root, raise to the power $\frac{1}{3}$, or as a decimal 0.333 ...

Exercise 33

Use a calculator to evaluate the following, giving the answers to 4 significant figures:

1. $\dfrac{7.351 \times 0.764}{1.847}$

2. $\dfrac{0.0741 \times 14\,700}{0.746}$

3. $\dfrac{0.0741 \times 9.61}{23.1}$

4. $\dfrac{417.8 \times 0.008\,41}{0.073\,24}$

5. $\dfrac{8.41}{7.601 \times 0.008\,47}$

6. $\dfrac{4.22}{1.701 \times 5.2}$

7. $\dfrac{9.61}{17.4 \times 1.51}$

8. $\dfrac{8.71 \times 3.62}{0.84}$

9. $\dfrac{0.76}{0.412 - 0.317}$

10. $\dfrac{81.4}{72.6 + 51.92}$

11. $\dfrac{111}{27.4 + 2960}$

12. $\dfrac{27.4 + 11.61}{5.9 - 4.763}$

13. $\dfrac{6.51 - 0.1114}{7.24 + 1.653}$

14. $\dfrac{5.71 + 6.093}{9.05 - 5.77}$

15. $\dfrac{0.943 - 0.788}{1.4 - 0.766}$

16. $\dfrac{2.6}{1.7} + \dfrac{1.9}{3.7}$

17. $\dfrac{8.06}{5.91} - \dfrac{1.594}{1.62}$

18. $\dfrac{4.7}{11.4 - 3.61} + \dfrac{1.6}{9.7}$

19. $\dfrac{3.74}{1.6 \times 2.89} - \dfrac{1}{0.741}$

20. $\dfrac{1}{7.2} - \dfrac{1}{14.6}$

21. $\dfrac{1}{0.961} \times \dfrac{1}{0.412}$

22. $\dfrac{1}{7} + \dfrac{1}{13} - \dfrac{1}{8}$

23. $4.2\left(\dfrac{1}{5.5} - \dfrac{1}{7.6}\right)$

24. $\sqrt{(9.61 + 0.1412)}$

25. $\sqrt{\left(\dfrac{8.007}{1.61}\right)}$

26. $(1.74 + 9.611)^2$

27. $\left(\dfrac{1.63}{1.7 - 0.911}\right)^2$

28. $\left(\dfrac{9.6}{2.4} - \dfrac{1.5}{0.74}\right)^2$

29. $\sqrt{\left(\dfrac{4.2 \times 1.611}{9.83 \times 1.74}\right)}$

30. $(0.741)^3$

31. $(1.562)^5$

32. $(0.32)^3 + (0.511)^4$

33. $(1.71 - 0.863)^6$

34. $\left(\dfrac{1}{0.971}\right)^4$

35. $3\sqrt{(4.714)}$

36. $\sqrt[3]{(0.9316)}$

37. $\sqrt[3]{\left(\dfrac{4.114}{7.93}\right)}$

38. $\sqrt[4]{(0.8145 - 0.799)}$

39. $\sqrt[5]{(8.6 \times 9.71)}$

40. $\sqrt[3]{\left(\dfrac{1.91}{4.2 - 3.766}\right)}$

41. $\left(\dfrac{1}{7.6} - \dfrac{1}{18.5}\right)^3$

42. $\dfrac{\sqrt{(4.79)} + 1.6}{9.63}$

43. $\dfrac{(0.761)^2 - \sqrt{(4.22)}}{1.96}$

44. $\sqrt[3]{\left(\dfrac{1.74 \times 0.761}{0.0896}\right)}$

Example

Work out the following to 4 significant figures.

a) $2 \times 10^5 - 1.734 \times 10^4$

b) $(3.6 \times 10^{-4})^2$

. . . .

a) $\boxed{2}$ $\boxed{\text{EXP}}$ $\boxed{5}$ $\boxed{-}$ $\boxed{1.734}$ $\boxed{\text{EXP}}$ $\boxed{4}$

Answer 182 700 (to 4 s.f.)

b) $\boxed{3.6}$ $\boxed{\text{EXP}}$ $\boxed{-}$ $\boxed{4}$ $\boxed{x^2}$

Answer 1.296×10^{-7}

Exercise 34

1. $\left(\dfrac{8.6 \times 1.71}{0.43}\right)^3$

2. $\dfrac{9.61 - \sqrt{(9.61)}}{9.61^2}$

3. $\dfrac{9.6 \times 10^4 \times 3.75 \times 10^7}{8.88 \times 10^6}$

4. $\dfrac{8.06 \times 10^{-4}}{1.71 \times 10^{-6}}$

5. $\dfrac{3.92 \times 10^{-7}}{1.884 \times 10^{-11}}$

6. $\left(\dfrac{1.31 \times 2.71 \times 10^5}{1.91 \times 10^4}\right)^5$

7. $\left(\dfrac{1}{9.6} - \dfrac{1}{9.99}\right)^{10}$

8. $\dfrac{\sqrt[3]{86.6}}{\sqrt[4]{4.71}}$

9. $\dfrac{23.7 \times 0.0042}{12.48 - 9.7}$

10. $\dfrac{0.482 + 1.6}{0.024 \times 1.83}$

11. $\dfrac{8.52 - 1.004}{0.004 - 0.0083}$

12. $\dfrac{1.6 - 0.476}{2.398 \times 41.2}$

13. $\left(\dfrac{2.3}{0.791}\right)^{7}$

14. $\left(\dfrac{8.4}{28.7 - 0.47}\right)^{3}$

15. $\left(\dfrac{5.114}{7.332}\right)^{5}$

16. $\left(\dfrac{4.2}{2.3} + \dfrac{8.2}{0.52}\right)^{3}$

17. $\dfrac{1}{8.2^2} - \dfrac{3}{19^2}$

18. $\dfrac{100}{11^3} + \dfrac{100}{12^3}$

19. $\dfrac{7.3 - 4.291}{2.6^2}$

20. $\dfrac{9.001 - 8.97}{0.95^3}$

21. $\dfrac{10.1^2 + 9.4^2}{9.8}$

22. $(3.6 \times 10^{-8})^2$

23. $(8.24 \times 10^4)^3$

24. $(2.17 \times 10^{-3})^3$

25. $(7.095 \times 10^{-6})^{\frac{1}{3}}$

26. $3\sqrt{\left(\dfrac{4.7}{2.3^2}\right)}$

Checking answers

Here are five calculations, followed by sensible checks.

a) $22.2 \boxed{\div} 6 = 3.7$ check $3.7 \boxed{\times} 6 = 22.2$

b) $31.7 \boxed{-} 4.83 = 26.87$ check $26.87 \boxed{+} 4.83 = 31.7$

c) $42.8 \boxed{\times} 30 = 1284$ check $1284 \boxed{\div} 30 = 42.8$

d) $\sqrt{17} = 4.1231$ check 4.1231^2

e) $3.7 + 17.6 + 13.9$ check $13.9 + 17.6 + 3.7$ (add in reverse order)

Calculations can also be checked by rounding numbers to a given number of significant figures.

f) $\dfrac{6.1 \times 32.6}{19.3} = 10.3 \, (\text{to 3 s.f.})$

Check this answer by rounding each number to one significant figure and estimating.

$$\dfrac{6.1 \times 32.6}{19.3} \approx \dfrac{6 \times 30}{20} = \dfrac{180}{20} = 9$$

'$\approx$' means 'approximately equal to'

This is close to 10.3

so the actual answer probably is 10.3

Exercise 35

1. Use a calculator to work out the following then check the answers as indicated.

a) $92.5 \times 20 = \boxed{}$ Check $\boxed{} \div 20 = \boxed{}$

b) $14 \times 328 = \boxed{}$ Check $\boxed{} \div 328 = \boxed{}$

c) $63 - 12.6 = \boxed{}$ Check $\boxed{} + 12.6 = \boxed{}$

d) $221.2 \div 7 = \boxed{}$ Check $\boxed{} \times 7 = \boxed{}$

e) $384.93 \div 9.1 = \boxed{}$ Check $\boxed{} \times 9.1 = \boxed{}$

f) $13.71 + 25.8 = \boxed{}$ Check $\boxed{} - 25.8 = \boxed{}$

g) $95.4 \div 4.5 = \boxed{}$ Check $\boxed{} \times 4.5 = \boxed{}$

h) $8.2 + 3.1 + 19.6 + 11.5 = \boxed{}$ Check $11.5 + 19.6 + 3.1 + 8.2 = \boxed{}$

i) $\sqrt{39} = \boxed{}$ Check $\boxed{}^2 = 39$

j) $3.17 + 2.06 + 8.4 + 16 = \boxed{}$ Check $16 + 8.4 + 2.06 + 3.17 = \boxed{}$

2. The numbers below are rounded to one significant figure to *estimate* the answer to each calculation. Match each question below to the correct estimated answer.

A $\boxed{21.9 \times 1.01}$ P $\boxed{10}$

B $\boxed{\dfrac{19.82^2}{(18.61 + 22.3)}}$ Q $\boxed{5}$

C $\boxed{7.8 \times 1.01}$ R $\boxed{0.5}$

D $\boxed{\dfrac{\sqrt{98.7}}{8.78 + 11.43}}$ S $\boxed{8}$

E $\boxed{\dfrac{21.42 + 28.6}{18.84 - 8.99}}$ T $\boxed{20}$

3. Do *not* use a calculator.

$281 \times 36 = 10\,116$

Work out

a) $10\,116 \div 36$ **b)** $10\,116 \div 281$ **c)** 28.1×3.6

4. Mavis is paid a salary of $49\,620 per year. Work out a rough estimate for her weekly pay.
(Give your answer correct to one significant figure.)

5. In 2011, the population of France was 61 278 514 and the population of Greece was 9 815 972. Roughly how many times bigger is the population of France compared to the population of Greece?

Round the numbers to one significant figure.

6. *Estimate,* correct to one significant figure:

a) $41.56 \div 7.88$

b) $\dfrac{5.13 \times 18.777}{0.952}$

c) $\dfrac{1}{5}$ of £14 892

d) $\dfrac{0.0974 \times \sqrt{104}}{1.03}$

e) 52% of 0.394 kg

f) $\dfrac{6.84^2 + 0.983}{5.07^2}$

g) $\dfrac{2848.7 + 1024.8}{51.2 - 9.98}$

h) $\dfrac{2}{3}$ of £3124

i) $18.13 \times (3.96^2 + 2.07^2)$

Revision exercise 1A

1. Evaluate, without a calculator:

a) $148 \div 0.8$

b) $0.024 \div 0.000\ 16$

c) $(0.2)^2 \div (0.1)^3$

d) $2 - \dfrac{1}{2} - \dfrac{1}{3} - \dfrac{1}{4}$

e) $1\dfrac{3}{4} \times 1\dfrac{3}{5}$

f) $\dfrac{1\frac{1}{6}}{1\frac{2}{3} + 1\frac{1}{4}}$

2. On each bounce, a ball rises to $\dfrac{4}{5}$ of its previous height. To what height will it rise after the third bounce, if dropped from a height of 250 cm?

3. A man spends $\dfrac{1}{3}$ of his salary on accommodation and $\dfrac{2}{5}$ of the remainder on food. What fraction is left for other purposes?

4. $a = \dfrac{1}{2}$, $b = \dfrac{1}{4}$. Which one of the following has the greatest value?

i) ab

ii) $a + b$

iii) $\dfrac{a}{b}$

iv) $\dfrac{b}{a}$

v) $(ab)^2$

5. Express 0.054 73:

a) correct to three significant figures

b) correct to three decimal places

c) in standard form.

6. Evaluate $\dfrac{2}{3} + \dfrac{4}{7}$, correct to three decimal places.

7. Evaluate the following and give the answer in standard form:

a) $3600 \div 0.00012$

b) $\dfrac{3.33 \times 10^4}{9 \times 10^{-1}}$

c) $(30\ 000)^3$

8. a) $143 is divided in the ratio $2:3:6$; calculate the smallest share.

b) A prize is divided between three people X, Y and Z. If the ratio of X's share to Y's share is $3:1$ and Y's share to Z's share is $2:5$, calculate the ratio of X's share to Z's share.

c) If $a:3 = 12:a$, calculate the positive value of a.

9. Labour costs, totalling $47.25, account for 63% of a car repair bill. Calculate the total bill.

10. a) Convert to percentages:

i) 0.572

ii) $\dfrac{7}{8}$

b) Express 2.6 kg as a percentage of 6.5 kg.

c) In selling a red herring for 92c, a fishmonger makes a profit of 15%. Find the cost price of the fish.

11. The length of a rectangle is decreased by 25% and the width is increased by 40%. Calculate the percentage change in the area of the rectangle.

12. a) What sum of money, invested at 9% interest per year, is needed to provide an income of $45 per year?

b) A particle increases its speed from 8×10^5 m/s to 1.1×10^6 m/s. What is the percentage increase?

13. A family on holiday in France exchanged $450 for euros when the exchange rate was 1.41 euros to the dollar. They spent 500 euros and then changed the rest back into dollars, by which time the exchange rate had become 1.46 euros to the dollar. How much did the holiday cost?   (Answer in dollars.)

14. Given that

$$t = 2\pi\sqrt{\left(\frac{l}{g}\right)},$$

find the value of t, to three significant figures, when $l = 2.31$ and $g = 9.81$

15. A map is drawn to a scale of $1:10\ 000$. Find:

   a) the distance between two railway stations which appear on the map 24 cm apart

   b) the area, in square kilometres, of a lake which has an area of $100\ cm^2$ on the map.

16. A map is drawn to a scale of $1:2000$. Find:

   a) the actual distance between two points, which appear 15 cm apart on the map

   b) the length on the map of a road, which is 1.2 km in length

   c) the area on the map of a field, with an actual area of $60\ 000\ m^2$.

17. a) On a map, the distance between two points is 16 cm. Calculate the scale of the map if the actual distance between the points is 8 km.

   b) On another map, two points appear 1.5 cm apart and are in fact 60 km apart. Calculate the scale of the map.

18. a) A house is bought for $20 000 and sold for $24 400. What is the percentage profit?

   b) A piece of fish, initially of mass 2.4 kg, is cooked and subsequently has mass 1.9 kg. What is the percentage loss in mass?

   c) An article is sold at a 6% loss for $225.60. What was the cost price?

19. a) Convert into metres per second:

   i) 700 cm/s   ii) 720 km/h

   iii) 18 km/h

   b) Convert into kilometres per hour:

   i) 40 m/s   ii) 0.6 m/s

20. a) Calculate the speed (in metres per second) of a slug which moves a distance of 30 cm in 1 minute.

   b) Calculate the time taken for a bullet to travel 8 km at a speed of 5000 m/s.

   c) Calculate the distance flown, in a time of four hours, by a pigeon which flies at a speed of 12 m/s.

21. A motorist travelled 200 km in five hours. Her average speed for the first 100 km was 50 km/h. What was her average speed for the second 100 kilometres?

22. 1   3   8   9   10

From these numbers, write down:

   a) the prime number

   b) a multiple of 5

   c) two square numbers

   d) two factors of 32.

   e) Find two numbers m and n from the list such that $m = \sqrt{n}$ and $n = \sqrt{81}$.

   f) If each of the numbers in the list can be used once, find p, q, r, s, t such that $(p + q)r = 2(s + t) = 36$.

23. The value of t is given by

$$t = 2\pi\sqrt{\left(\frac{2.31^2 + 0.9^2}{2.31 \times 9.81}\right)}.$$

Without using a calculator, and using suitable approximate values for the numbers in the formula, find an estimate for the value of t. (To earn the marks in this question you must show the various stages of your working.)

24. Throughout his life Baichu's heart has beat at an average rate of 72 beats per minute. Baichu is sixty years old. How many times has his heart beat during his life? Give the answer in standard form correct to 2 significant figures.

25. Estimate the answer correct to one significant figure. Do not use a calculator.

    a) $(612 \times 52) \div 49.2$

    b) $(11.7 + 997.1) \times 9.2$

    c) $\sqrt{\left(\dfrac{91.3}{10.1}\right)}$

    d) $\pi\sqrt{5.2^2 + 18.2}$

26. Evaluate the following using a calculator: (give answers to 4 s.f.)

    a) $\dfrac{0.74}{0.81 \times 1.631}$

    b) $\sqrt{\left(\dfrac{9.61}{8.34 - 7.41}\right)}$

    c) $\left(\dfrac{0.741}{0.8364}\right)^4$

    d) $\dfrac{8.4 - 7.642}{3.333 - 1.735}$

27. Evaluate the following and give the answers to 3 significant figures:

    a) $\sqrt[3]{(9.61 \times 0.0041)}$

    b) $\left(\dfrac{1}{9.5} - \dfrac{1}{11.2}\right)^3$

    c) $\dfrac{15.6 \times 0.714}{0.0143 \times 12}$

    d) $\sqrt[4]{\left(\dfrac{1}{5 \times 10^3}\right)}$

28. The edges of a cube are all increased by 10%. What is the percentage increase in the volume?

29. Write down the reciprocals of the following numbers.

    a) 20   b) $\dfrac{1}{3}$ c) 0.4   d) 1.5

30. The number of cells in a bacterial culture doubles every hour.

    At the end of the first hour there are 2^6 cells. How many cells will there be at the end of the third hour?

Examination-style exercise 1B

1. Calculate $\dfrac{5^2}{2^5}$

    (a) giving your answer as a fraction, [1]

    (b) giving your answer as a decimal. [1]

Cambridge IGCSE Mathematics 0580
Paper 2 Q1 June 2005

2. Work out the exact value of $1 + \dfrac{2}{4 + \dfrac{8}{16 + 32}}$. [2]

3. Write down

    (a) an irrational number, [1]

    (b) a prime number between 60 and 70. [1]

Cambridge IGCSE Mathematics 0580
Paper 2 Q9 June 2007

4. At 05:06 Mr Ho bought 850 fish at a fish market for $2.62 each.

95 minutes later he sold them all to a supermarket for $2.86 each.

    (a) What was the time when he sold the fish? [1]

    (b) Calculate his total profit. [1]

Cambridge IGCSE Mathematics 0580
Paper 21 Q3 June 2009

5. Write down the next term in each of the following sequences.

    (a) 8.2, 6.2, 4.2, 2.2, 0.2, ... [1]

    (b) 1, 3, 6, 10, 15, ... [1]

Cambridge IGCSE Mathematics 0580
Paper 2 Q4 November 2005

6. (a) The formula for the nth term of the sequence 2, 15, 48, 110, 210, ...

    is $\dfrac{n(n+1)(3n-1)}{2}$.

    Find the 9th term. [1]

    (b) The nth term of the sequence 12, 19, 28, 39, 52, ... is $(n+2)^2+3$.

    Write down the formula for the nth term of the sequence
19, 26, 35, 46, 59, ... [1]

7. To raise money for charity, Jalaj walks 22 km, correct to the nearest kilometre, every day for 5 days.

    (a) Copy and complete the statement below for the distance,
d km, he walks in one day .... $\leqslant d$ km < .... [2]

    (b) He raises $1.60 for every kilometre that he walks.

    Calculate the least amount of money that he raises
at the end of the 5 days. [1]

Cambridge IGCSE Mathematics 0580
Paper 2 Q7 June 2005

8. The distance between Singapore and Sydney is 6300 km correct to the nearest 100 km.

A businessman travelled from Singapore to Sydney and then back to Singapore.

He did this six times in a year.

Between what limits is the total distance he travelled?

Write your answer as ....km ≤ total distance travelled < ....km. [2]

Cambridge IGCSE Mathematics 0580
Paper 2 Q9 June 2006

9. A rectangle has sides of length 6.1 cm and 8.1 cm correct to one decimal place.

   Calculate the upper bound for the area of the rectangle as accurately as possible. [2]

Cambridge IGCSE Mathematics 0580
Paper 21 Q7 November 2008

10. In 2005 there were 9 million bicycles in Beijing, correct to the nearest million.

    The average distance travelled by each bicycle in one day was 6.5 km correct to one decimal place.

    Work out the upper bound for the **total** distance travelled by all the bicycles in one day. [2]

Cambridge IGCSE Mathematics 0580
Paper 21 Q6 June 2009

11. The mass of the Earth is $\frac{1}{95}$ of the mass of the planet Saturn.

    The mass of the Earth is 5.97×10^{24} kilograms.

    Calculate the mass of the planet Saturn, giving your answer in standard form, correct to 2 significant figures. [3]

Cambridge IGCSE Mathematics 0580
Paper 2 Q10 November 2005

12. Maria, Carolina and Pedro receive $800 from their grandmother in the ratio

    Maria : Carolina : Pedro = 7 : 5 : 4.

    (a) Calculate how much money each receives. [3]

    (b) Maria spends $\frac{2}{7}$ of her money and then invests the rest for two years at 5% per year simple interest.

    How much money does Maria have at the end of the two years? [3]

    (c) Carolina spends all of her money on a hi-fi set and two years later sells it at a loss of 20%.

    How much money does Carolina have at the end of the two years? [2]

    (d) Pedro spends some of his money and at the end of the two years he has $100.

    Write down and simplify the ratio of the amounts of money Maria, Carolina and Pedro have at the end of the two years. [2]

(e) Pedro invests his $100 for two years at a rate of 5% per year **compound interest**.

Calculate how much money he has at the end of these two years. [2]

Cambridge IGCSE Mathematics 0580
Paper 4 Q1 November 2006

13. In 2004 Colin had a salary of $7200.

(a) This was an increase of 20% on his salary in 2002.

Calculate his salary in 2002. [2]

(b) In 2006 his salary increased to $8100.

Calculate the percentage increase from 2004 to 2006. [2]

Cambridge IGCSE Mathematics 0580
Paper 2 Q16 June 2006

14. A student played a computer game 500 times and won 370 of these games.

He then won the next x games and lost none.

He has now won 75% of the games he has played.

Find the value of x. [4]

Cambridge IGCSE Mathematics 0580
Paper 21 Q17 June 2008

15.

NORTH EASTERN BANK
SAVINGS ACCOUNT
5% Per Year
Simple Interest

SOUTH WESTERN BANK
SAVINGS ACCOUNT
4.9% Per Year
Compound Interest

Kalid and his brother have $2000 each to invest for 3 years.

(a) North Eastern Bank advertises savings with **simple** interest at 5% per year.

Kalid invests his money in this bank.

How much money will he have at the end of 3 years? [2]

(b) South Western Bank advertises savings with **compound** interest at 4.9% per year.

Kalid's brother invests his money in this bank.

At the end of 3 years, how much **more** money will he have than Kalid? [3]

Cambridge IGCSE Mathematics 0580
Paper 2 Q22 June 2007

16. Use your calculator to work out

(a) $\sqrt{(7 + 6 \times 243^{0.2})}$, [1]

(b) $2 - \tan 30° \times \tan 60°$. [1]

Cambridge IGCSE Mathematics 0580
Paper 2 Q3 November 2006

17. Hassan sells fruit and vegetables at the market.

(a) The mass of fruit and vegetables he sells is in the ratio
   fruit : vegetables = 5 : 7.

   Hassan sells 1.33 **tonnes** of vegetables.

   How many **kilograms** of fruit does he sell? [3]

(b) The amount of money Hassan receives from selling fruit
   and vegetables is in the ratio fruit : vegetables = 9 : 8.

   Hassan receives a **total** of $765 from selling fruit and vegetables.

   Calculate how much Hassan receives from selling fruit. [2]

(c) Calculate the average price of Hassan's fruit, in dollars per kilogram. [2]

(d) i) Hassan sells oranges for $0.35 per kilogram.

      He reduces this price by 40%

      Calculate the new price per kilogram. [2]

    ii) The price of $0.35 per kilogram of oranges is an increase
       of 25% on the previous day's price.

       Calculate the previous day's price. [2]

Cambridge IGCSE Mathematics 0580
Paper 4 Q1 June 2005

18. (a) The scale of a map is 1 : 20 000 000.

   On the map, the distance between Cairo and Addis Ababa is 12 cm.

   i) Calculate the distance, in kilometres, between Cairo and Addis Ababa. [2]

   ii) On the map the area of a desert region is 13 square centimetres.

      Calculate the actual area of this desert region, in square kilometres. [2]

(b) i) The actual distance between Cairo and Khartoum is 1580 km.

      On a different map this distance is represented by 31.6 cm.

      Calculate, in the form $1 : n$, the scale of this map. [2]

   ii) A plane flies the 1580 km from Cairo to Khartoum.

      It departs from Cairo at 1155 and arrives in Khartoum at 1403.

      Calculate the average speed of the plane, in kilometres per hour. [4]

Cambridge IGCSE Mathematics 0580
Paper 4 Q1 June 2007

19. $1 + 2 + 3 + 4 + 5 + \ldots + n = \dfrac{n(n+1)}{2}$

(a) i) Show that this formula is true for the sum of the first 8 natural numbers. [2]

   ii) Find the sum of the first 400 natural numbers. [1]

(b) i) Show that $2 + 4 + 6 + 8 + \cdots + 2n = n(n+1)$. [1]

   ii) Find the sum of the first 200 even numbers. [1]

   iii) Find the sum of the first 200 odd numbers. [1]

(c) i) Use the formula at the beginning of the question to find the sum of the first $2n$ natural numbers. [1]

   ii) Find a formula, in its simplest form, for

      $1 + 3 + 5 + 7 + 9 + \cdots + (2n - 1)$.

      Show your working. [2]

Cambridge IGCSE Mathematics 0580
Paper 4 Q10 November 2008

20. Each year a school organises a concert.

(a) i) In 2004 the cost of organising the concert was $385.

   In 2005 the cost was 10% less than in 2004.

   Calculate the cost in 2005. [2]

   ii) The cost of $385 in 2004 was 10% more than the cost in 2003.

   Calculate the cost in 2003. [2]

(b) i) In 2006 the number of tickets sold was 210.

   The ratio Number of adult tickets : Number of student tickets was $23 : 19$.

   How many adult tickets were sold? [2]

   ii) Adult tickets were $2.50 each and student tickets were $1.50 each.

   Calculate the **total** amount **received** from selling the tickets. [2]

   iii) In 2006 the cost of organising the concert was $410.

   Calculate the percentage profit in 2006. [2]

(c) In 2007, the number of tickets sold was again 210.

   Adult tickets were $2.60 each and student tickets were $1.40 each.

   The total amount received from selling the 210 tickets was $480.

   How many student tickets were sold? [4]

Cambridge IGCSE Mathematics 0580
Paper 4 Q1 November 2007

21. Water flows into a tank at a rate of 3 litres per minute.

(a) If the tank fills completely in 450 seconds, what is the capacity of the tank in ml? [2]

A hole is drilled in the bottom of the tank. Water flows out of the hole at a rate of 60 ml per second.

(b) How long will the tank take to drain completely if the flow of water **in** continues at the same rate? [2]

2 Algebra 1

Isaac Newton (1642–1727) is thought by many to have been one of the greatest intellects of all time. He went to Trinity College Cambridge in 1661 and by the age of 23 he had made three major discoveries: the nature of colours, the calculus and the law of gravitation. He used his version of the calculus to give the first satisfactory explanation of the motion of the Sun, the Moon and the stars. Because he was extremely sensitive to criticism, Newton was always very secretive, but he was eventually persuaded to publish his discoveries in 1687.

E1.4 Use directed numbers in practical situations.

E2.1 Use letters to express generalised numbers and express basic arithmetic processes algebraically. Substitute numbers for words and letters in complicated formulae.

E2.2 Manipulate directed numbers. Use brackets and extract common factors. Expand products of algebraic expressions. Factorise where possible expressions of the form:

$ax + bx + kay + kby$

$a^2x^2 - b^2y^2$

$a^2 + 2ab + b^2$

$ax^2 + bx + c$

E2.5 Derive and solve simple linear equations in one unknown.

Derive and solve simultaneous linear equations in two unknowns.

Derive and solve simultaneous equations, involving one linear and one quadratic.

Derive and solve quadratic equations by factorisation, completing the square or by use of the formula.

2.1 Negative numbers

- If the weather is very cold and the temperature is 3 degrees below zero, it is written −3°.
- If a golfer is 5 under par for his round, the scoreboard will show −5.
- On a bank statement if someone is $55 overdrawn [or 'in the red'] it would appear as −$55.

The above are examples of the use of negative numbers.

An easy way to begin calculations with negative numbers is to think about changes in temperature:

a) Suppose the temperature is −2° and it rises by 7°.

The new temperature is 5°.

We can write −2 + 7 = 5.

b) Suppose the temperature is −3° and it falls by 6°.

The new temperature is −9°.

We can write −3 − 6 = −9.

Exercise 1

In Questions **1** to **12** move up or down the thermometer to find the new temperature.

1. The temperature is +8° and it falls by 3°.

2. The temperature is −8° and it rises by 4°.

3. The temperature is +4° and it falls by 5°.

4. The temperature is −3° and it rises by 7°.

5. The temperature is +2° and it falls by 6°.

6. The temperature is +4° and it rises by 8°.

7. The temperature is −1° and it falls by 6°.

8. The temperature is +9° and it falls by 14°.

9. The temperature is −5° and it rises by 1°.

10. The temperature is −13° and it rises by 13°.

11. Some land in Bangladesh is below sea level.

Here are the heights, above sea level, of five villages.

A 1 m   **B** −4 m   **C** 21 m   **D** −2 m   **E** −1.5 m

a) Which village is safest from flooding?

b) Which village is most at risk from serious flooding?

12. A diver is below the surface of the water at −15 m. He dives down by 6 m, then rises 4 m.

Where is he now?

2.2 Directed numbers

To add two directed numbers with the same sign, find the sum of the numbers and give the answer the same sign.

> **Example 1**
>
> $+3 + (+5) = +3 + 5 = +8$
>
> $-7 + (-3) = -7 - 3 = -10$
>
> $-9.1 + (-3.1) = -9.1 - 3.1 = -12.2$
>
> $-2 + (-1) + (-5) = (-2 - 1) - 5$
>
> $\qquad\qquad\qquad\quad = -3 - 5$
>
> $\qquad\qquad\qquad\quad = -8$

To add two directed numbers with different signs, find the difference between the numbers and give the answer the sign of the larger number.

> **Example 2**
>
> $+7 + (-3) = +7 - 3 = +4$
>
> $+9 + (-12) = +9 - 12 = -3$
>
> $-8 + (+4) = -8 + 4 = -4$

To subtract a directed number, change its sign and add.

> **Example 3**
>
> $+7 - (+5) = +7 - 5 = +2$
>
> $+7 - (-5) = +7 + 5 = +12$
>
> $-8 - (+4) = -8 - 4 = -12$
>
> $-9 - (-11) = -9 + 11 = +2$

Exercise 2

1. $+7 + (+6)$
2. $+11 + (+200)$
3. $-3 + (-9)$
4. $-7 + (-24)$
5. $-5 + (-61)$
6. $+0.2 + (+5.9)$
7. $+5 + (+4.1)$
8. $-8 + (-27)$
9. $+17 + (+1.7)$
10. $-2 + (-3) + (-4)$
11. $-7 + (+4)$
12. $+7 + (-4)$
13. $-9 + (+7)$
14. $+16 + (-30)$
15. $+14 + (-21)$
16. $-7 + (+10)$
17. $-19 + (+200)$
18. $+7.6 + (-9.8)$
19. $-1.8 + (+10)$
20. $-7 + (+24)$
21. $+7 - (+5)$
22. $+9 - (+15)$
23. $-6 - (+9)$
24. $-9 - (+5)$

25. $+8 - (+10)$

26. $-19 - (-7)$

27. $-10 - (+70)$

28. $-5.1 - (+8)$

29. $-0.2 - (+4)$

30. $+5.2 - (-7.2)$

31. $-4 + (-3)$

32. $+6 - (-2)$

33. $+8 + (-4)$

34. $-4 - (+6)$

35. $+7 - (-4)$

36. $+6 + (-2)$

37. $+10 - (+30)$

38. $+19 - (+11)$

39. $+4 + (-7) + (-2)$

40. $-3 - (+2) + (-5)$

41. $-17 - (-1) + (-10)$

42. $-5 + (-7) - (+9)$

43. $+9 + (-7) - (-6)$

44. $-7 - (-8)$

45. $-10.1 + (-10.1)$

46. $-75 - (-25)$

47. $-204 - (+304)$

48. $-7 + (-11) - (+11)$

49. $+17 - (+17)$

50. $-6 + (-7) - (+8)$

51. $+7 + (-7.1)$

52. $-11 - (-4) + (+3)$

53. $-2 - (-8.7)$

54. $+7 + (-11) + (+5)$

55. $-610 + (-240)$

56. $-7 - (-3) - (-8)$

57. $+9 - (-6) + (-9)$

58. $-1 - (-5) + (-8)$

59. $-2.1 + (-9.9)$

60. $-47 - (-16)$

When two directed numbers with the same sign are multiplied together, the answer is positive.

- $+7 \times (+3) = +21$
- $-6 \times (-4) = +24$

When two directed numbers with different signs are multiplied together, the answer is negative.

- $-8 \times (+4) = -32$
- $+7 \times (-5) = -35$
- $-3 \times (+2) \times (+5) = -6 \times (+5) = -30$

When dividing directed numbers, the rules are the same as in multiplication.

- $-70 \div (-2) = +35$
- $+12 \div (-3) = -4$
- $-20 \div (+4) = -5$

Exercise 3

1. $+2 \times (-4)$

2. $+7 \times (+4)$

3. $-4 \times (-3)$

4. $-6 \times (-4)$

5. $-6 \times (-3)$

6. $+5 \times (-7)$

7. $-7 \times (-7)$

8. $-4 \times (+3)$

9. $+0.5 \times (-4)$

10. $-1\frac{1}{2} \times (-6)$

11. $-8 \div (+2)$

12. $+12 \div (+3)$

13. $+36 \div (-9)$

14. $-40 \div (-5)$

15. $-70 \div (-1)$

16. $-56 \div (+8)$

17. $-\frac{1}{2} \div (-2)$

18. $-3 \div (+5)$

19. $+0.1 \div (-10)$

20. $-0.02 \div (-100)$

21. $-11 \times (-11)$

22. $-6 \times (-1)$

23. $+12 \times (-50)$

24. $-\frac{1}{2} \div \left(+\frac{1}{2}\right)$

25. $-600 \div (+30)$

26. $-5.2 \div (+2)$

27. $+7 \times (-100)$

28. $-6 \div \left(-\frac{1}{3}\right)$

29. $100 \div (-0.1)$ **30.** -8×-80 **31.** $-3 \times (-2) \times (-1)$ **32.** $+3 \times (-7) \times (+2)$

33. $+0.4 \div (-1)$ **34.** $-16 \div (+40)$ **35.** $+0.2 \times (-1000)$ **36.** $-7 \times (-5) \times (-1)$

37. $-14 \div (+7)$ **38.** $-7 \div (-14)$ **39.** $+1\frac{1}{4} \div (-5)$ **40.** $-6 \times \left(-\frac{1}{2}\right) \times (-30)$

Exercise 4

1. $-7 + (-3)$ **2.** $-6 - (-7)$ **3.** $-4 \times (-3)$ **4.** $-4 \times (+7)$

5. $4 - (+6)$ **6.** $-4 \times (-4)$ **7.** $+6 \div (-2)$ **8.** $+8 - (-6)$

9. $-7 \times (+4)$ **10.** $-8 \div (-2)$ **11.** $+10 \div (-60)$ **12.** (-3^2)

13. $40 - (+70)$ **14.** $-6 \times (-4)$ **15.** $(-1)^5$ **16.** $-8 \div (+4)$

17. $+10 \times (-3)$ **18.** $-7 \times (-1)$ **19.** $+10 + (-7)$ **20.** $+12 - (-4)$

21. $+100 + (-7)$ **22.** $-60 \times (-40)$ **23.** $-20 \div (-2)$ **24.** $(-1)^{20}$

25. $6 - (+10)$ **26.** $-6 \times (+4) \times (-2)$ **27.** $+8 \div (-8)$ **28.** $0 \times (-6)$

29. $(-2)^3$ **30.** $+100 - (-70)$ **31.** $+18 \div (-6)$ **32.** $(-1)^{12}$

33. $-6 - (-7)$ **34.** $(-2)^2 + (-4)$ **35.** $+8 - (-7)$ **36.** $+7 + (-2)$

37. $-6 \times (+0.4)$ **38.** $-3 \times (-6) \times (-10)$ **39.** $(-2)^2 + (+1)$ **40.** $+6 - (+1000)$

41. $(-3)^2 - 7$ **42.** $-12 \div \frac{1}{4}$ **43.** $-30 \div -\frac{1}{2}$ **44.** $5 - (+7) + (-0.5)$

45. $(-2)^5$ **46.** $0 \div \left(-\frac{1}{5}\right)$ **47.** $(-0.1)^2 \times (-10)$ **48.** $3 - (+19)$

49. $2.1 + (-6.4)$ **50.** $\left(-\frac{1}{2}\right)^2 \div (-4)$

2.3 Formulae

When a calculation is repeated many times it is often helpful to use a formula. Publishers use a formula to work out the selling price of a book based on the production costs and the expected sales of the book.

Exercise 5

1. The final speed v of a car is given by the formula $v = u + at$.

[u = initial speed, a = acceleration, t = time taken]

Find v when $u = 15$ m/s, $a = 0.2$ m/s^2, $t = 30$ s.

2. The time period T of a simple pendulum is given by the formula $T = 2\pi \sqrt{\left(\frac{l}{g}\right)}$,

where l is the length of the pendulum and g is the gravitational acceleration.

Find T when $l = 0.65$ m, $g = 9.81$ m/s^2 and $\pi = 3.142$.

3. The total surface area A of a cone is related to the radius r and the slant height l by the formula $A = \pi r(r + l)$.
Find A when $r = 7$ cm and $l = 11$ cm.

4. The sum S of the squares of the integers from 1 to n is given by $S = \frac{1}{6}n(n+1)(2n+1)$. Find S when $n = 12$.

5. The acceleration a of a train is found using the formula $a = \dfrac{v^2 - u^2}{2s}$.
Find a when $v = 20$ m/s, $u = 9$ m/s and $s = 2.5$ m.

6. Einstein's famous equation relating energy, mass and the speed of light is $E = mc^2$. Find E when $m = 0.0001$ kg and $c = 3 \times 10^8$ m/s.

7. The distance s travelled by an accelerating rocket is given by $s = ut + \frac{1}{2}at^2$. Find s when $u = 3$ m/s, $t = 100$ s and $a = 0.1$ m/s².

8. Find a formula for the area of the shape below, in terms of a, b and c.

You can find out more about area in Unit 3 on page 104.

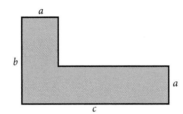

9. Find a formula for the length of the shaded part below, in terms of p, q and r.

10. A fish lays brown eggs or white eggs and it likes to lay them in a certain pattern. Each brown egg is surrounded by six white eggs. Here there are 3 brown eggs and 14 white eggs.

   a) How many eggs does it lay altogether if it lays 200 brown eggs?

   b) How many eggs does it lay altogether if it lays n brown eggs?

11. In the diagrams below the rows of green tiles are surrounded by white tiles.

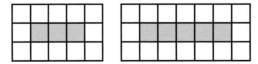

Find a formula for the number of white tiles which would be needed to surround a row of n green tiles.

Example

When $a = 3$, $b = -2$, $c = 5$, find the value of:

a) $3a + b$ b) $ac + b^2$ c) $\dfrac{a+c}{b}$ d) $a(c - b)$

....

a) $3a + b$
$= (3 \times 3) + (-2)$
$= 9 - 2$
$= 7$

b) $ac + b^2$
$= (3 \times 5) + (-2)^2$
$= 15 + 4$
$= 19$

c) $\dfrac{a+c}{b}$
$= \dfrac{3+5}{-2}$
$= \dfrac{8}{-2}$
$= -4$

d) $a(c - b)$
$= 3[5 - (-2)]$
$= 3(7)$
$= 21$

Notice that working *down* the page is easier to follow.

Exercise 6

Evaluate the following:

For questions **1** to **12**, $a = 3$, $c = 2$, $e = 5$.

1. $3a - 2$ **2.** $4c + e$ **3.** $2c + 3a$ **4.** $5e - a$

5. $e - 2c$ **6.** $e - 2a$ **7.** $4c + 2e$ **8.** $7a - 5e$

9. $c - e$ **10.** $10a + c + e$ **11.** $a + c - e$ **12.** $a - c - e$

For questions **13** to **24**, $h = 3$, $m = -2$, $t = -3$.

13. $2m - 3$ **14.** $4t + 10$ **15.** $3h - 12$ **16.** $6m + 4$

17. $9t - 3$ **18.** $4h + 4$ **19.** $2m - 6$ **20.** $m + 2$

21. $3h + m$ **22.** $t - h$ **23.** $4m + 2h$ **24.** $3t - m$

For questions **25** to **36**, $x = -2$, $y = -1$, $k = 0$.

25. $3x + 1$ **26.** $2y + 5$ **27.** $6k + 4$ **28.** $3x + 2y$

29. $2k + x$ **30.** xy **31.** xk **32.** $2xy$

33 $2(x + k)$ **34.** $3(k + y)$ **35.** $5x - y$ **36.** $3k - 2x$

$2x^2$ means $2(x^2)$.

$(2x)^2$ means 'work out $2x$ and *then* square it'.

$-7x$ means $-7(x)$.

$-x^2$ means $-1(x^2)$.

Example

When $x = -2$, find the value of:

a) $2x^2 - 5x$

b) $(3x)^2 - x^2$

....

a) $2x^2 - 5x = 2(-2)^2 - 5(-2)$

$\qquad = 2(4) + 10$

$\qquad = 18$

b) $(3x)^2 - x^2 = (3 \times -2)^2 - 1(-2)^2$

$\qquad = (-6)^2 - 1(4)$

$\qquad = 36 - 4$

$\qquad = 32$

Exercise 7

If $x = -3$ and $y = 2$, evaluate the following:

1. x^2

2. $3x^2$

3. y^2

4. $4y^2$

5. $(2x)^2$

6. $2x^2$

7. $10 - x^2$

8. $10 - y^2$

9. $20 - 2x^2$

10. $20 - 3y^2$

11. $5 + 4x$

12. $x^2 - 2x$

13. $y^2 - 3x^2$

14. $x^2 - 3y$

15. $(2x)^2 - y^2$

16. $4x^2$

17. $(4x)^2$

18. $1 - x^2$

19. $y - x^2$

20. $x^2 + y^2$

21. $x^2 - y^2$

22. $2 - 2x^2$

23. $(3x)^2 + 3$

24. $11 - xy$

25. $12 + xy$

26. $(2x)^2 - (3y)^2$

27. $2 - 3x^2$

28. $y^2 - x^2$

29. $x^2 + y^3$

30. $\dfrac{x}{y}$

31. $10 - 3x$

32. $2y^2$

33. $25 - 3y$

34. $(2y)^2$

35. $-7 + 3x$

36. $-8 + 10y$

37. $(xy)^2$

38. xy^2

39. $-7 + x^2$

40. $17 + xy$

41. $-5 - 2x^2$

42. $10 - (2x)^2$

43. $x^2 + 3x + 5$

44. $2x^2 - 4x + 1$

45. $\dfrac{x^2}{y}$

Example

When $a = -2$, $b = 3$, $c = -3$, evaluate:

a) $\dfrac{2a(b^2 - a)}{c}$

b) $\sqrt{(a^2 + b^2)}$

....

a) $(b^2 - a) = 9 - (-2)$

$\qquad = 11$

$\therefore \dfrac{2a(b^2 - a)}{c} = \dfrac{2 \times (-2) \times (11)}{-3}$

$\qquad = 14\dfrac{2}{3}$

b) $a^2 + b^2 = (-2)^2 + (3)^2$

$\qquad = 4 + 9$

$\qquad = 13$

$\therefore \sqrt{(a^2 + b^2)} = \sqrt{13}$

Exercise 8

Evaluate the following:

In questions **1** to **16**, $a = 4$, $b = -2$, $c = -3$.

1. $a(b + c)$

2. $a^2(b - c)$

3. $2c(a - c)$

4. $b^2(2a + 3c)$

5. $c^2(b - 2a)$

6. $2a^2(b + c)$

7. $2(a + b + c)$

8. $3c(a - b - c)$

9. $b^2 + 2b + a$

10. $c^2 - 3c + a$

11. $2b^2 - 3b$

12. $\sqrt{(a^2 + c^2)}$

13. $\sqrt{(ab + c^2)}$

14. $\sqrt{(c^2 - b^2)}$

15. $\dfrac{b^2}{a} + \dfrac{2c}{b}$

16. $\dfrac{c^2}{b} + \dfrac{4b}{a}$

In questions **17** to **32**, $k = -3$, $m = 1$, $n = -4$.

17. $k^2(2m - n)$

18. $5m\sqrt{(k^2 + n^2)}$

19. $\sqrt{(kn + 4m)}$

20. $kmn(k^2 + m^2 + n^2)$

21. $k^2m^2(m - n)$

22. $k^2 - 3k + 4$

23. $m^3 + m^2 + n^2 + n$

24. $k^3 + 3k$

25. $m(k^2 - n^2)$

26. $m\sqrt{(k - n)}$

27. $100k^2 + m$

28. $m^2(2k^2 - 3n^2)$

29. $\dfrac{2k + m}{k - n}$

30. $\dfrac{kn - k}{2m}$

31. $\dfrac{3k + 2m}{2n - 3k}$

32. $\dfrac{k + m + n}{k^2 + m^2 + n^2}$

In questions **33** to **48**, $w = -2$, $x = 3$, $y = 0$, $z = -\dfrac{1}{2}$.

33. $\dfrac{w}{z} + x$

34. $\dfrac{w + x}{z}$

35. $y\left(\dfrac{x + z}{w}\right)$

36. $x^2(z + wy)$

37. $x\sqrt{(x + wz)}$

38. $w^2\sqrt{(z^2 + y^2)}$

39. $2(w^2 + x^2 + y^2)$

40. $2x(w - z)$

41. $\dfrac{z}{w} + x$

42. $\dfrac{z + w}{x}$

43. $\dfrac{x + w}{z^2}$

44. $\dfrac{y^2 - w^2}{xz}$

45. $z^2 + 4z + 5$

46. $\dfrac{1}{w} + \dfrac{1}{z} + \dfrac{1}{x}$

47. $\dfrac{4}{z} + \dfrac{10}{w}$

48. $\dfrac{yz - xw}{xz - w}$

49. Find $K = \sqrt{\left(\dfrac{a^2 + b^2 + c^2 - 2c}{a^2 + b^2 + 4c}\right)}$ if $a = 3$, $b = -2$, $c = -1$.

50. Find $W = \dfrac{kmn(k + m + n)}{(k + m)(k + n)}$ if $k = \frac{1}{2}$, $m = -\frac{1}{3}$, $n = \frac{1}{4}$.

2.4 Brackets and simplifying

A term outside a bracket multiplies each of the terms inside the bracket. This is the *distributive law*.

Example 1

$3(x - 2y) = 3x - 6y$

Example 2

$2x(x - 2y + z) = 2x^2 - 4xy + 2xz$

Example 3

$7y - 4(2x - 3) = 7y - 8x + 12$

In general:
like terms can be added

x's can be added to x's

y's can be added to y's

x^2's can be added to x^2's

But they must not be mixed.

Example 4

$2x + 3y + 3x^2 + 2y - x = x + 5y + 3x^2$

Example 5

$$7x + 3x(2x - 3) = 7x + 6x^2 - 9x$$
$$= 6x^2 - 2x$$

Exercise 9

Simplify as far as possible:

1. $3x + 4y + 7y$

2. $4a + 7b - 2a + b$

3. $3x - 2y + 4y$

4. $2x + 3x + 5$

5. $7 - 3x + 2 + 4x$

6. $5 - 3y - 6y - 2$

7. $5x + 2y - 4y - x^2$

8. $2x^2 + 3x + 5$

9. $2x - 7y - 2x - 3y$

10. $4a + 3a^2 - 2a$

11. $7a - 7a^2 + 7$

12. $x^2 + 3x^2 - 4x^2 + 5x$

13. $\dfrac{3}{a} + b + \dfrac{7}{a} - 2b$

14. $\dfrac{4}{x} - \dfrac{7}{y} + \dfrac{1}{x} + \dfrac{2}{y}$

15. $\dfrac{m}{x} + \dfrac{2m}{x}$

16. $\dfrac{5}{x} - \dfrac{7}{x} + \dfrac{1}{2}$

17. $\dfrac{3}{a} + b + \dfrac{2}{a} + 2b$

18. $\dfrac{n}{4} - \dfrac{m}{3} - \dfrac{n}{2} + \dfrac{m}{3}$

19. $x^3 + 7x^2 - 2x^3$

20. $(2x)^2 - 2x^2$

21. $(3y)^2 + x^2 - (2y)^2$

22. $(2x)^2 - (2y)^2 - (4x)^2$

23. $5x - 7x^2 - (2x)^2$

24. $\dfrac{3}{x^2} + \dfrac{5}{x^2}$

Remove the brackets and collect like terms:

25. $3x + 2(x + 1)$

26. $5x + 7(x - 1)$

27. $7 + 3(x - 1)$

28. $9 - 2(3x - 1)$

29. $3x - 4(2x + 5)$

30. $5x - 2x(x - 1)$

31. $7x + 3x(x - 4)$

32. $4(x - 1) - 3x$

33. $5x(x + 2) + 4x$

34. $3x(x - 1) - 7x^2$

35. $3a + 2(a + 4)$

36. $4a - 3(a - 3)$

37. $3ab - 2a(b - 2)$

38. $3y - y(2 - y)$

39. $3x - (x + 2)$

40. $7x - (x - 3)$

41. $5x - 2(2x + 2)$

42. $3(x - y) + 4(x + 2y)$

43. $x(x - 2) + 3x(x - 3)$

44. $3x(x + 4) - x(x - 2)$

45. $y(3y - 1) - (3y - 1)$

46. $7(2x + 2) - (2x + 2)$

47. $7b(a + 2) - a(3b + 3)$

48. $3(x - 2) - (x - 2)$

Two brackets

Example 1

$(x + 5)(x + 3) = x(x + 3) + 5(x + 3)$

$\qquad\qquad\qquad = x^2 + 3x + 5x + 15$

$\qquad\qquad\qquad = x^2 + 8x + 15$

Example 2

$(2x - 3)(4y + 3) = 2x(4y + 3) - 3(4y + 3)$

$\qquad\qquad\qquad\quad = 8xy + 6x - 12y - 9$

Example 3

$3(x + 1)(x - 2) = 3\,[x\,(x - 2) + 1\,(x - 2)]$

$\qquad\qquad\qquad = 3\,[x^2 - 2x + x - 2]$

$\qquad\qquad\qquad = 3x^2 - 3x - 6$

Exercise 10

Remove the brackets and simplify:

1. $(x + 1)(x + 3)$

2. $(x + 3)(x + 2)$

3. $(y + 4)(y + 5)$

4. $(x - 3)(x + 4)$

5. $(x + 5)(x - 2)$

6. $(x - 3)(x - 2)$

7. $(a - 7)(a + 5)$

8. $(z + 9)(z - 2)$

9. $(x - 3)(x + 3)$

10. $(k - 11)(k + 11)$

11. $(2x + 1)(x - 3)$

12. $(3x + 4)(x - 2)$

13. $(2y - 3)(y + 1)$

14. $(7y - 1)(7y + 1)$

15. $(3x - 2)(3x + 2)$

16. $(3a + b)(2a + b)$ **17.** $(3x + y)(x + 2y)$ **18.** $(2b + c)(3b - c)$

19. $(5x - y)(3y - x)$ **20.** $(3b - a)(2a + 5b)$ **21.** $2(x - 1)(x + 2)$

22. $3(x - 1)(2x + 3)$ **23.** $4(2y - 1)(3y + 2)$ **24.** $2(3x + 1)(x - 2)$

25. $4(a + 2b)(a - 2b)$ **26.** $x(x - 1)(x - 2)$ **27.** $2x(2x - 1)(2x + 1)$

28. $3y(y - 2)(y + 3)$ **29.** $x(x + y)(x + z)$ **30.** $3z(a + 2m)(a - m)$

Be careful with an expression like $(x - 3)^2$. It is not $x^2 - 9$ or even $x^2 + 9$.

$$(x - 3)^2 = (x - 3)(x - 3)$$
$$= x(x - 3) - 3(x - 3)$$
$$= x^2 - 6x + 9$$

Another common mistake occurs with an expression like $4 - (x - 1)^2$.

$$4 - (x - 1)^2 = 4 - 1(x - 1)(x - 1)$$
$$= 4 - 1(x^2 - 2x + 1)$$
$$= 4 - x^2 + 2x - 1$$
$$= 3 + 2x - x^2$$

Exercise 11

Remove the brackets and simplify:

1. $(x + 4)^2$ **2.** $(x + 2)^2$ **3.** $(x - 2)^2$

4. $(2x + 1)^2$ **5.** $(y - 5)^2$ **6.** $(3y + 1)^2$

7. $(x + y)^2$ **8.** $(2x + y)^2$ **9.** $(a - b)^2$

10. $(2a - 3b)^2$ **11.** $3(x + 2)^2$ **12.** $(3 - x)^2$

13. $(3x + 2)^2$ **14.** $(a - 2b)^2$ **15.** $(x + 1)^2 + (x + 2)^2$

16. $(x - 2)^2 + (x + 3)^2$ **17.** $(x + 2)^2 + (2x + 1)^2$ **18.** $(y - 3)^2 + (y - 4)^2$

19. $(x + 2)^2 - (x - 3)^2$ **20.** $(x - 3)^2 - (x + 1)^2$ **21.** $(y - 3)^2 - (y + 2)^2$

22. $(2x + 1)^2 - (x + 3)^2$ **23.** $3(x + 2)^2 - (x + 4)^2$ **24.** $2(x - 3)^2 - 3(x + 1)^2$

Three brackets

To expand three sets of brackets, first expand one pair and then multiply this result by the third bracket.

Example

$$(x + 1)(x + 2)(x + 3) = [x(x + 2) + 1(x + 2)](x + 3)$$
$$= [x^2 + 2x + x + 2](x + 3)$$
$$= (x^2 + 3x + 2)(x + 3)$$
$$= x(x^2 + 3x + 2) + 3(x^2 + 3x + 2)$$
$$= x^3 + 3x^2 + 2x + 3x^2 + 9x + 6$$
$$= x^3 + 6x^2 + 11x + 6$$

Exercise 12

Remove the brackets and simplify:

1. $(x+2)(x-3)(x-4)$
2. $(x-1)(x+2)(x-5)$
3. $(x+6)(x-3)(x+5)$
4. $(2x-1)(x+1)(x-1)$
5. $(3x+1)(2x+1)(x-2)$
6. $(x+2)(4x-3)(2x+3)$
7. $(6x-5)(2x+7)(3x-8)$
8. $(x+1)^2(x-4)$
9. $(x-3)(x-2)^2$
10. $(x-1)(2x+3)^2$
11. $(x-1)^3$
12. $(3x+2)^3$
13. $(x-2)^3-(x+1)^3$
14. $(x+3)^3-(x-4)^3$
15. $(2x+1)^3+3(x+1)^3$

2.5 Linear equations

- If the x term is negative, add an x term with a positive coefficient to both sides of the equation.

> **Example 1**
>
> $$4 - 3x = 2$$
> $$4 = 2 + 3x$$
> $$2 = 3x$$
> $$\frac{2}{3} = x$$

- If there are x terms on both sides, collect them on one side.

> **Example 2**
>
> $$2x - 7 = 5 - 3x$$
> $$2x + 3x = 5 + 7$$
> $$5x = 12$$
> $$x = \frac{12}{5} = 2\frac{2}{5}$$

- If there is a fraction in the x term, multiply out to simplify the equation.

> **Example 3**
>
> $$\frac{2x}{3} = 10$$
> $$2x = 30$$
> $$x = \frac{30}{2} = 15$$

Exercise 13

Solve the following equations:

1. $2x - 5 = 11$
2. $3x - 7 = 20$
3. $2x + 6 = 20$
4. $5x + 10 = 60$

5. $8 = 7 + 3x$
6. $12 = 2x - 8$
7. $-7 = 2x - 10$
8. $3x - 7 = -10$

9. $12 = 15 + 2x$
10. $5 + 6x = 7$
11. $\dfrac{x}{5} = 7$
12. $\dfrac{x}{10} = 13$

13. $7 = \dfrac{x}{2}$
14. $\dfrac{x}{2} = \dfrac{1}{3}$
15. $\dfrac{3x}{2} = 5$
16. $\dfrac{4x}{5} = -2$

17. $7 = \dfrac{7x}{3}$
18. $\dfrac{3}{4} = \dfrac{2x}{3}$
19. $\dfrac{5x}{6} = \dfrac{1}{4}$
20. $-\dfrac{3}{4} = \dfrac{3x}{5}$

21. $\dfrac{x}{2} + 7 = 12$
22. $\dfrac{x}{3} - 7 = 2$
23. $\dfrac{x}{5} - 6 = -2$
24. $4 = \dfrac{x}{2} - 5$

25. $10 = 3 + \dfrac{x}{4}$
26. $\dfrac{a}{5} - 1 = -4$
27. $100x - 1 = 98$
28. $7 = 7 + 7x$

29. $\dfrac{x}{100} + 10 = 20$
30. $1000x - 5 = -6$
31. $-4 = -7 + 3x$
32. $2x + 4 = x - 3$

33. $x - 3 = 3x + 7$
34. $5x - 4 = 3 - x$
35. $4 - 3x = 1$
36. $5 - 4x = -3$

37. $7 = 2 - x$
38. $3 - 2x = x + 12$
39. $6 + 2a = 3$
40. $a - 3 = 3a - 7$

41. $2y - 1 = 4 - 3y$
42. $7 - 2x = 2x - 7$
43. $7 - 3x = 5 - 2x$
44. $8 - 2y = 5 - 5y$

45. $x - 16 = 16 - 2x$
46. $x + 2 = 3.1$
47. $-x - 4 = -3$
48. $-3 - x = -5$

49. $-\dfrac{x}{2} + 1 = -\dfrac{1}{4}$
50. $-\dfrac{3}{5} + \dfrac{x}{10} = -\dfrac{1}{5} - \dfrac{x}{5}$

Example

$x - 2(x - 1) = 1 - 4(x + 1)$

$x - 2x + 2 = 1 - 4x - 4$

$x - 2x + 4x = 1 - 4 - 2$

$3x = -5$

$x = -\dfrac{5}{3}$

Exercise 14

Solve the following equations:

1. $x + 3(x + 1) = 2x$
2. $1 + 3(x - 1) = 4$

3. $2x - 2(x + 1) = 5x$
4. $2(3x - 1) = 3(x - 1)$

5. $4(x - 1) = 2(3 - x)$
6. $4(x - 1) - 2 = 3x$

7. $4(1 - 2x) = 3(2 - x)$
8. $3 - 2(2x + 1) = x + 17$

9. $4x = x - (x - 2)$

10. $7x = 3x - (x + 20)$

11. $5x - 3(x - 1) = 39$

12. $3x + 2(x - 5) = 15$

13. $7 - (x + 1) = 9 - (2x - 1)$

14. $10x - (2x + 3) = 21$

15. $3(2x + 1) + 2(x - 1) = 23$

16. $5(1 - 2x) - 3(4 + 4x) = 0$

17. $7x - (2 - x) = 0$

18. $3(x + 1) = 4 - (x - 3)$

19. $3y + 7 + 3(y - 1) = 2(2y + 6)$

20. $4(y - 1) + 3(y + 2) = 5(y - 4)$

21. $4x - 2(x + 1) = 5(x + 3) + 5$

22. $7 - 2(x - 1) = 3(2x - 1) + 2$

23. $10(2x + 3) - 8(3x - 5) + 5(2x - 8) = 0$

24. $2(x + 4) + 3(x - 10) = 8$

25. $7(2x - 4) + 3(5 - 3x) = 2$

26. $10(x + 4) - 9(x - 3) - 1 = 8(x + 3)$

27. $5(2x - 1) - 2(x - 2) = 7 + 4x$

28. $6(3x - 4) - 10(x - 3) = 10(2x - 3)$

29. $3(x - 3) - 7(2x - 8) - (x - 1) = 0$

30. $5 + 2(x + 5) = 10 - (4 - 5x)$

31. $6x + 30(x - 12) = 2\left(x - 1\frac{1}{2}\right)$

32. $3\left(2x - \frac{2}{3}\right) - 7(x - 1) = 0$

33. $5(x - 1) + 17(x - 2) = 2x + 1$

34. $6(2x - 1) + 9(x + 1) = 8\left(x - 1\frac{1}{4}\right)$

35. $7(x + 4) - 5(x + 3) + (4 - x) = 0$

36. $0 = 9(3x + 7) - 5(x + 2) - (2x - 5)$

37. $10(2.3 - x) - 0.1(5x - 30) = 0$

38. $8\left(2\frac{1}{2}x - \frac{3}{4}\right) - \frac{1}{4}(1 - x) = \frac{1}{2}$

39. $(6 - x) - (x - 5) - (4 - x) = -\dfrac{x}{2}$

40. $10\left(1 - \dfrac{x}{10}\right) - (10 - x) - \dfrac{1}{100}(10 - x) = 0.05$

Example

$$(x + 3)^2 = (x + 2)^2 + 3^2$$
$$(x + 3)(x + 3) = (x + 2)(x + 2) + 9$$
$$x^2 + 6x + 9 = x^2 + 4x + 4 + 9$$
$$6x + 9 = 4x + 13$$
$$2x = 4$$
$$x = 2$$

Exercise 15

Solve the following equations:

1. $x^2 + 4 = (x + 1)(x + 3)$

2. $x^2 + 3x = (x + 3)(x + 1)$

3. $(x + 3)(x - 1) = x^2 + 5$

4. $(x + 1)(x + 4) = (x - 7)(x + 6)$

5. $(x - 2)(x + 3) = (x - 7)(x + 7)$

6. $(x - 5)(x + 4) = (x + 7)(x - 6)$

7. $2x^2 + 3x = (2x - 1)(x + 1)$

8. $(2x - 1)(x - 3) = (2x - 3)(x - 1)$

9. $x^2 + (x + 1)^2 = (2x - 1)(x + 4)$

10. $x(2x + 6) = 2(x^2 - 5)$

11. $(x + 1)(x - 3) + (x + 1)^2 = 2x(x - 4)$

12. $(2x + 1)(x - 4) + (x - 2)^2 = 3x(x + 2)$

13. $(x + 2)^2 - (x - 3)^2 = 3x - 11$

14. $x(x - 1) = 2(x - 1)(x + 5) - (x - 4)^2$

15. $(2x + 1)^2 - 4(x - 3)^2 = 5x + 10$

16. $2(x + 1)^2 - (x - 2)^2 = x(x - 3)$

17. The area of the rectangle shown exceeds the area of the square by 2 cm². Find x.

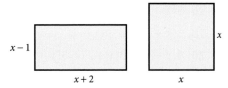

18. The area of the square exceeds the area of the rectangle by 13 m². Find y.

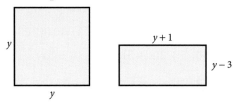

19. The area of the square is half the area of the rectangle. Find x.

When solving equations involving fractions, multiply both sides of the equation by a suitable number or letter to eliminate the fractions.

Example 1

$\dfrac{5}{x} = 2$

$5 = 2x$ (multiply both sides by x)

$\dfrac{5}{2} = x$

Example 2

$$\frac{x+3}{4} = \frac{2x-1}{3} \qquad \dots(A)$$

$$12\,\frac{(x+3)}{4} = 12\,\frac{(2x-1)}{3} \qquad \text{(multiply both sides by 12)}$$

$$\therefore \quad 3(x+3) = 4(2x-1) \qquad \dots(B)$$

$$3x+9 = 8x-4$$

$$13 = 5x$$

$$\frac{13}{5} = x$$

$$x = 2\frac{3}{5}$$

Note: It is possible to go straight from line (A) to line (B) by 'cross-multiplying'.

Example 3

$$\frac{5}{(x-1)} + 2 = 12$$

$$\frac{5}{(x-1)} = 10$$

$$5 = 10(x-1)$$

$$5 = 10x - 10$$

$$15 = 10x$$

$$\frac{15}{10} = x$$

$$x = 1\frac{1}{2}$$

Exercise 16

Solve the following equations:

1. $\dfrac{7}{x} = 21$

2. $30 = \dfrac{6}{x}$

3. $\dfrac{5}{x} = 3$

4. $\dfrac{9}{x} = -3$

5. $11 = \dfrac{5}{x}$

6. $-2 = \dfrac{4}{x}$

7. $\dfrac{x}{4} = \dfrac{3}{2}$

8. $\dfrac{x}{3} = 1\frac{1}{4}$

9. $\dfrac{x+1}{3} = \dfrac{x-1}{4}$

10. $\dfrac{x+3}{2} = \dfrac{x-4}{5}$

11. $\dfrac{2x-1}{3} = \dfrac{x}{2}$

12. $\dfrac{3x+1}{5} = \dfrac{2x}{3}$

13. $\dfrac{8-x}{2} = \dfrac{2x+2}{5}$

14. $\dfrac{x+2}{7} = \dfrac{3x+6}{5}$

15. $\dfrac{1-x}{2} = \dfrac{3-x}{3}$

16. $\dfrac{2}{x-1} = 1$

17. $\dfrac{x}{3} + \dfrac{x}{4} = 1$

18. $\dfrac{x}{3} + \dfrac{x}{2} = 4$

19. $\dfrac{x}{2} - \dfrac{x}{5} = 3$

20. $\dfrac{x}{3} = 2 + \dfrac{x}{4}$

21. $\dfrac{5}{x-1} = \dfrac{10}{x}$

22. $\dfrac{12}{2x-3} = 4$

23. $2 = \dfrac{18}{x+4}$

24. $\dfrac{5}{x+5} = \dfrac{15}{x+7}$

25. $\dfrac{9}{x} = \dfrac{5}{x-3}$

26. $\dfrac{4}{x-1} = \dfrac{10}{3x-1}$

27. $\dfrac{-7}{x-1} = \dfrac{14}{5x+2}$

28. $\dfrac{4}{x+1} = \dfrac{7}{3x-2}$

29. $\dfrac{x+1}{2} + \dfrac{x-1}{3} = \dfrac{1}{6}$

30. $\dfrac{1}{3}(x+2) = \dfrac{1}{5}(3x+2)$

31. $\dfrac{1}{2}(x-1) - \dfrac{1}{6}(x+1) = 0$

32. $\dfrac{1}{4}(x+5) - \dfrac{2x}{3} = 0$

33. $\dfrac{4}{x} + 2 = 3$

34. $\dfrac{6}{x} - 3 = 7$

35. $\dfrac{9}{x} - 7 = 1$

36. $-2 = 1 + \dfrac{3}{x}$

37. $4 - \dfrac{4}{x} = 0$

38. $5 - \dfrac{6}{x} = -1$

39. $7 - \dfrac{3}{2x} = 1$

40. $4 + \dfrac{5}{3x} = -1$

41. $\dfrac{9}{2x} - 5 = 0$

42. $\dfrac{x-1}{5} - \dfrac{x-1}{3} = 0$

43. $\dfrac{x-1}{4} - \dfrac{2x-3}{5} = \dfrac{1}{20}$

44. $\dfrac{4}{1-x} = \dfrac{3}{1+x}$

45. $\dfrac{x+1}{4} - \dfrac{x}{3} = \dfrac{1}{12}$

46. $\dfrac{2x+1}{8} - \dfrac{x-1}{3} = \dfrac{5}{24}$

2.6 Problems solved by linear equations

a) Let the unknown quantity be x (or any other letter) and state the units (where appropriate).

b) Express the given statement in the form of an equation.

c) Solve the equation for x and give the answer in *words*.
(Do not finish by just writing '$x = 3$'.)

d) Check your solution using the problem (not your equation).

Example 1

The sum of three consecutive whole numbers is 78. Find the numbers.

a) Let the smallest number be x; then the other numbers are $(x + 1)$ and $(x + 2)$.

b) Form an equation:

$x + (x + 1) + (x + 2) = 78$

c) Solve: $3x = 75$

$x = 25$

In words:

The three numbers are 25, 26 and 27.

d) Check: $25 + 26 + 27 = 78$

Example 2

The length of a rectangle is three times the width. If the perimeter is 36 cm, find the width.

a) Let the width of the rectangle be x cm.

Then the length of the rectangle is $3x$ cm.

b) Form an equation.

$x + 3x + x + 3x = 36$

c) Solve: $8x = 36$

$$x = \frac{36}{8}$$

$x = 4.5$

In words:

The width of the rectangle is 4.5 cm.

d) Check: If width = 4.5 cm

length = 13.5 cm

perimeter = 36 cm

Exercise 17

Solve each problem by forming an equation. The first questions are easy but should still be solved using an equation, in order to practise the method:

1. The sum of three consecutive numbers is 276. Find the numbers.

2. The sum of four consecutive numbers is 90. Find the numbers.

3. The sum of three consecutive odd numbers is 177. Find the numbers.

4. Find three consecutive even numbers which add up to 1524.

5. When a number is doubled and then added to 13, the result is 38. Find the number.

6. When a number is doubled and then added to 24, the result is 49. Find the number.

7. When 7 is subtracted from three times a certain number, the result is 28. What is the number?

8. The sum of two numbers is 50. The second number is five times the first. Find the numbers.

9. Two numbers are in the ratio $1:11$ and their sum is 15. Find the numbers.

10. The length of a rectangle is twice the width.
    If the perimeter is 20 cm, find the width.

11. The width of a rectangle is one third of the length.
    If the perimeter is 96 cm, find the width.

12. If AB is a straight line, find x.

13. If the perimeter of the triangle is 22 cm, find the length of the shortest side.

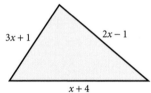

14. If the perimeter of the rectangle is 34 cm, find x.

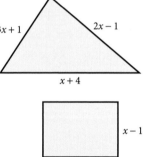

15. The difference between two numbers is 9.
    Find the numbers, if their sum is 46.

16. The three angles in a triangle are in the ratio $1:3:5$. Find them.

17. The three angles in a triangle are in the ratio $3:4:5$. Find them.

18. The product of two consecutive odd numbers is 10 more than the square of the smaller number. Find the smaller number.

19. The product of two consecutive even numbers is 12 more than the square of the smaller number. Find the numbers.

20. The sum of three numbers is 66. The second number is twice the first and six less than the third. Find the numbers.

21. The sum of three numbers is 28. The second number is three times the first and the third is 7 less than the second. What are the numbers?

22. David's mass is 5 kg less than John's, who in turn is 8 kg lighter than Paul. If their total mass is 197 kg, how heavy is each person?

23. Nilopal is 2 years older than Devjan who is 7 years older than Sucha. If their combined age is 61 years, find the age of each person.

24. Kimiya has four times as many marbles as Ramneet. If Kimiya gave 18 to Ramneet they would have the same number. How many marbles has each?

25. Mukat has five times as many books as Usha. If Mukat gave 16 books to Usha, they would each have the same number. How many books did each girl have?

26. The result of trebling a number is the same as adding 12 to it. What is the number?

27. Find the area of the rectangle if the perimeter is 52 cm.

28. The result of multiplying a number by 3 and subtracting 5 is the same as doubling the number and adding 9. What is the number?

29. Two girls have $76 between them. If the first gave the second $7 they would each have the same amount of money. How much did each girl have?

30. A tennis racket costs $12 more than a hockey stick. If the price of the two is $31, find the cost of the tennis racket.

Example

A man goes out at 16:42 and arrives at a post box, 6 km away, at 17:30. He walked part of the way at 5 km/h and then, realising the time, he ran the rest of the way at 10 km/h. How far did he have to run?

- Let the distance he ran be x km. Then the distance he walked $= (6 - x)$ km.

- Time taken to walk $(6 - x)$ km at 5 km/h $= \dfrac{(6 - x)}{5}$ hours.

  Time taken to run x km at 10 km/h $= \dfrac{x}{10}$ hours.

  Total time taken $= 48$ minutes

  $$= \frac{4}{5} \text{ hour}$$

  $$\therefore \quad \frac{(6 - x)}{5} + \frac{x}{10} = \frac{4}{5}$$

- Multiply by 10:

  $$2(6 - x) + x = 8$$
  $$12 - 2x + x = 8$$
  $$4 = x$$

  He ran a distance of 4 km.

- Check:

Time to run 4 km $= \dfrac{4}{10} = \dfrac{2}{5}$ hour.

Time to walk 2 km $= \dfrac{2}{5}$ hour.

Total time taken $= \left(\dfrac{2}{5} + \dfrac{2}{5} \right)$h $= \dfrac{4}{5}$h.

Exercise 18

1. Every year a man is paid $500 more than the previous year. If he receives $17 800 over four years, what was he paid in the first year?

2. Samir buys x cans of soda at 30 cents each and $(x + 4)$ cans of soda at 35 cents each. The total cost was $3.35. Find x.

3. The length of a straight line ABC is 5 m.
   If AB$:$BC $= 2:5$, find the length of AB.

4. The opposite angles of a cyclic quadrilateral are $(3x + 10)°$ and $(2x + 20)°$. Find the angles.

   Opposite angles of a cyclic quadrilateral add to 180°.

5. The interior angles of a hexagon are in the ratio $1:2:3:4:5:9$. Find the angles. This is an example of a concave hexagon. Try to sketch the hexagon.

   Interior angles of a hexagon add to 720°.

6. A man is 32 years older than his son. Ten years ago he was three times as old as his son was then. Find the present age of each.

7. Mahmoud runs to a marker and back in 15 minutes. His speed on the way to the marker is 5 m/s and his speed on the way back is 4 m/s. Find the distance to the marker.

8. A car completes a journey in 10 minutes. For the first half of the distance the speed was 60 km/h and for the second half the speed was 40 km/h. How far is the journey?

9. A lemming runs from a point A to a cliff at 4 m/s, jumps over the edge at B and falls to C at an average speed of 25 m/s. If the total distance from A to C is 500 m and the time taken for the journey is 41 seconds, find the height BC of the cliff.

10. A bus is travelling with 48 passengers. When it arrives at a stop, x passengers get off and 3 get on. At the next stop half the passengers get off and 7 get on. There are now 22 passengers. Find x.

11. A bus is travelling with 52 passengers. When it arrives at a stop, y passengers get off and 4 get on. At the next stop one-third of the passengers get off and 3 get on. There are now 25 passengers. Find y.

12. Mr Lee left his fortune to his 3 sons, 4 daughters and his wife. Each son received twice as much as each daughter and his wife received $6000, which was a quarter of the money. How much did each son receive?

13. In a regular polygon with n sides each interior angle is $180 - \dfrac{360}{n}$ degrees. How many sides does a polygon have if each interior angle is $156°$?

14. A sparrow flies to see a friend at a speed of 4 km/h. His friend is out, so the sparrow immediately returns home at a speed of 5 km/h. The complete journey took 54 minutes. How far away does his friend live?

15. Consider the equation $an^2 = 182$ where a is any number between 2 and 5 and n is a positive integer. What are the possible values of n?

16. Consider the equation $\dfrac{k}{x} = 12$ where k is any number between 20 and 65 and x is a positive integer. What are the possible values of x?

2.7 Simultaneous equations

To find the value of two unknowns in a problem, *two* different equations must be given that relate the unknowns to each other. These two equations are called *simultaneous* equations.

Substitution method

This method is used when one equation contains a unit quantity of one of the unknowns, as in equation [2] of the example below.

Example

$3x - 2y = 0$ ... [1]

$2x + y = 7$ ... [2]

a) Label the equations so that the working is made clear.

b) In *this* case, write y in terms of x from equation [2].

c) Substitute this expression for y into equation [1] and solve to find x.

d) Find y from equation [2] using this value of x.

$2x + y = 7$ ... [2]

$y = 7 - 2x$

Substituting into [1]

$$3x - 2(7 - 2x) = 0$$
$$3x - 14 + 4x = 0$$
$$7x = 14$$
$$x = 2$$

Substituting into [2]

$$2 \times 2 + y = 7$$
$$y = 3$$

The solutions are $x = 2$, $y = 3$.

These values of x and y are the only pair which simultaneously satisfy *both* equations.

Exercise 19

Use the substitution method to solve the following:

1. $2x + y = 5$
$x + 3y = 5$

2. $x + 2y = 8$
$2x + 3y = 14$

3. $3x + y = 10$
$x - y = 2$

4. $2x + y = -3$
$x - y = -3$

5. $4x + y = 14$
$x + 5y = 13$

6. $x + 2y = 1$
$2x + 3y = 4$

7. $2x + y = 5$
$3x - 2y = 4$

8. $2x + y = 13$
$5x - 4y = 13$

9. $7x + 2y = 19$
$x - y = 4$

10. $b - a = -5$
$a + b = -1$

11. $a + 4b = 6$
$8b - a = -3$

12. $a + b = 4$
$2a + b = 5$

13. $3m = 2n - 6\frac{1}{2}$
$4m + n = 6$

14. $2w + 3x - 13 = 0$
$x + 5w - 13 = 0$

15. $x + 2(y - 6) = 0$
$3x + 4y = 30$

16. $2x = 4 + z$
$6x - 5z = 18$

17. $3m - n = 5$
$2m + 5n = 7$

18. $5c - d - 11 = 0$
$4d + 3c = -5$

It is useful at this point to revise the operations of addition and subtraction with negative numbers.

Example

Simplify:

a) $-7 + -4 = -7 - 4 = -11$

b) $-3x + (-4x) = -3x - 4x = -7x$

c) $4y - (-3y) = 4y + 3y = 7y$

d) $3a + (-3a) = 3a - 3a = 0$

Exercise 20

Evaluate:

1. $7 + (-6)$
2. $8 + (-11)$
3. $5 - (+7)$
4. $6 - (-9)$
5. $-8 + (-4)$
6. $-7 - (-4)$
7. $10 + (-12)$
8. $-7 - (+4)$
9. $-10 - (+11)$
10. $-3 - (-4)$
11. $4 - (+4)$
12. $8 - (-7)$
13. $-5 - (+5)$
14. $-7 - (-10)$
15. $16 - (+10)$
16. $-7 - (+4)$
17. $-6 - (-8)$
18. $10 - (+5)$
19. $-12 + (-7)$
20. $7 + (-11)$

Simplify:

21. $3x + (-2x)$
22. $4x + (-7x)$
23. $6x - (+2x)$
24. $10y - (+6y)$
25. $6y - (-3y)$
26. $7x + (-4x)$
27. $-5x + (-3x)$
28. $-3x - (-7x)$
29. $5x - (+3x)$
30. $-7y - (-10y)$

Elimination method

Use this method when the first method is unsuitable (some prefer to use it for every question).

> **Example 1**
>
> $x + 2y = 8$ ... [1]
>
> $2x + 3y = 14$ ... [2]
>
> **a)** Label the equations so that the working is made clear.
>
> **b)** Choose an unknown in one of the equations and multiply the equations by a factor or factors so that this unknown has the same coefficient in both equations.
>
> **c)** Eliminate this unknown from the two equations by adding or subtracting them, then solve for the remaining unknown.
>
> **d)** Substitute into the first equation and solve for the eliminated unknown.
>
> $\qquad\qquad x + 2y = 8$ ... [1]
>
> $[1] \times 2 \quad 2x + 4y = 16$ ... [3]
>
> $\qquad\qquad 2x + 3y = 14$ ... [2]

Subtract [2] from [3]

$y = 2$

Substituting into [1]

$x + 2 \times 2 = 8$

$x = 8 - 4$

$x = 4$

The solutions are $x = 4$, $y = 2$.

Example 2

$$2x + 3y = 5 \qquad \qquad \text{... [1]}$$
$$5x - 2y = -16 \qquad \qquad \text{... [2]}$$

$[1] \times 5 \qquad 10x + 15y = 25 \qquad \qquad \text{... [3]}$

$[2] \times 2 \qquad 10x - 4y = -32 \qquad \qquad \text{... [4]}$

$[3] - [4] \quad 15y - (-4y) = 25 - (-32)$

$$19y = 57$$

$$y = 3$$

Substitute into [1]

$2x + 3 \times 3 = 5$

$2x = 5 - 9 = -4$

$x = -2$

The solutions are $x = -2$, $y = 3$.

Exercise 21

Use the elimination method to solve the following:

1. $2x + 5y = 24$
$4x + 3y = 20$

2. $5x + 2y = 13$
$2x + 6y = 26$

3. $3x + y = 11$
$9x + 2y = 28$

4. $x + 2y = 17$
$8x + 3y = 45$

5. $3x + 2y = 19$
$x + 8y = 21$

6. $2a + 3b = 9$
$4a + b = 13$

7. $2x + 3y = 11$
$3x + 4y = 15$

8. $3x + 8y = 27$
$4x + 3y = 13$

9. $2x + 7y = 17$
$5x + 3y = -1$

10. $5x + 3y = 23$
$2x + 4y = 12$

11. $7x + 5y = 32$
$3x + 4y = 23$

12. $3x + 2y = 4$
$4x + 5y = 10$

13. $3x + 2y = 11$
    $2x - y = -3$

14. $3x + 2y = 7$
    $2x - 3y = -4$

15. $x + 2y = -4$
    $3x - y = 9$

16. $5x - 7y = 27$
    $3x - 4y = 16$

17. $3x - 2y = 7$
    $4x + y = 13$

18. $x - y = -1$
    $2x - y = 0$

19. $y - x = -1$
    $3x - y = 5$

20. $x - 3y = -5$
    $2y + 3x + 4 = 0$

21. $x + 3y - 7 = 0$
    $2y - x - 3 = 0$

22. $3a - b = 9$
    $2a + 2b = 14$

23. $3x - y = 9$
    $4x - y = -14$

24. $x + 2y = 4$
    $3x + y = 9\frac{1}{2}$

25. $2x - y = 5$
    $\dfrac{x}{4} + \dfrac{y}{3} = 2$

26. $3x - y = 17$
    $\dfrac{x}{5} + \dfrac{y}{2} = 0$

27. $3x - 2y = 5$
    $\dfrac{2x}{3} + \dfrac{y}{2} = -\dfrac{7}{9}$

28. $2x = 11 - y$
    $\dfrac{x}{5} - \dfrac{y}{4} = 1$

29. $4x - 0.5y = 12.5$
    $3x + 0.8y = 8.2$

30. $0.4x + 3y = 2.6$
    $x - 2y = 4.6$

2.8 Problems solved by simultaneous equations

Example

A motorist buys 24 litres of petrol and 5 litres of oil for \$10.70, while another motorist buys 18 litres of petrol and 10 litres of oil for \$12.40. Find the cost of 1 litre of petrol and 1 litre of oil at this garage.

Let cost of 1 litre of petrol be x cents.

Let cost of 1 litre of oil be y cents.

We have, $24x + 5y = 1070$ ... [1]

$\qquad\qquad 18x + 10y = 1240$ ... [2]

a) Multiply [1] by 2,

$\qquad 48x + 10y = 2140$ ... [3]

b) Subtract [2] from [3],

$\qquad 30x = 900$

$\qquad\quad x = 30$

c) Substitute $x = 30$ into equation [2]

$\qquad 18(30) + 10y = 1240$

$\qquad\qquad 10y = 1240 - 540$

$\qquad\qquad 10y = 700$

$\qquad\qquad\; y = 70$

1 litre of petrol costs 30 cents, and 1 litre of oil costs 70 cents.

Exercise 22

Solve each problem by forming a pair of simultaneous equations:

1. Find two numbers with a sum of 15 and a difference of 4.

2. Twice one number added to three times another gives 21. Find the numbers, if the difference between them is 3.

3. The average of two numbers is 7, and three times the difference between them is 18. Find the numbers.

4. The line, with equation $y + ax = c$, passes through the points (1, 5) and (3, 1). Find a and c.

> For the point (1, 5) put $x = 1$ and $y = 5$ into $y + ax = c$, etc.

5. The line $y = mx + c$ passes through (2, 5) and (4, 13). Find m and c.

6. The curve $y = ax^2 + bx$ passes through (2, 0) and (4, 8). Find a and b.

7. A gardener buys fifty carrot seeds and twenty lettuce seeds for $1.10 and her mother buys thirty carrot seeds and forty lettuce seeds for $1.50. Find the cost of one carrot seed and one lettuce seed.

8. A shop owner can buy either two televisions and three DVD players for $1750 or four televisions and one DVD player for $1250. Find the cost of one of each.

9. Half the difference between two numbers is 2. The sum of the greater number and twice the smaller number is 13. Find the numbers.

10. A bird can lay either white or brown eggs. Three white eggs and two brown eggs have a mass of 13 grams, while five white eggs and four brown eggs have a mass of 24 grams. Find the mass of a brown egg and of a white egg.

11. A tortoise makes a journey in two parts; it can either walk at 4 cm/s or crawl at 3 cm/s. If the tortoise walks the first part and crawls the second, it takes 110 seconds. If it crawls the first part and walks the second, it takes 100 seconds. Find the lengths of the two parts of the journey.

12. A cyclist completes a journey of 500 m in 22 seconds, part of the way at 10 m/s and the remainder at 50 m/s. How far does she travel at each speed?

13. A bag contains forty coins, all of them either 2 cent or 5 cent coins. If the value of the money in the bag is $1.55, find the number of each kind.

14. A slot machine takes only 10 cent and 50 cent coins and contains a total of twenty-one coins altogether. If the value of the coins is $4.90, find the number of coins of each value.

15. Thirty tickets were sold for a concert, some at 60 cents and the rest at $1. If the total raised was $22, how many had the cheaper tickets?

16. The wage bill for five male and six female workers is $6700, while the bill for eight men and three women is $6100. Find the wage for a man and the wage for a woman.

17. A fish can swim at 14 m/s in the direction of the current and at 6 m/s against it. Find the speed of the current and the speed of the fish in still water.

18. If the numerator and denominator of a fraction are both decreased by 1 the fraction becomes $\frac{2}{3}$. If the numerator and denominator are both increased by 1 the fraction becomes $\frac{3}{4}$. Find the original fraction.

19. The denominator of a fraction is 2 more than the numerator. If both denominator and numerator are increased by 1 the fraction becomes $\frac{2}{3}$. Find the original fraction.

20. In three years' time a pet mouse will be as old as his owner was four years ago. Their present ages total 13 years. Find the age of each now.

21. Find two numbers where three times the smaller number exceeds the larger by 5 and the sum of the numbers is 11.

22. A straight line passes through the points (2, 4) and (−1, −5). Find its equation.

23. A spider can walk at a certain speed and run at another speed. If she walks for 10 seconds and runs for 9 seconds she travels 85 m. If she walks for 30 seconds and runs for 2 seconds she travels 130 m. Find her speeds of walking and running.

24. A wallet containing $40 has three times as many $1 notes as $5 notes. Find the number of each kind.

25. At the present time a man is four times as old as his son. Six years ago he was 10 times as old. Find their present ages.

26. A submarine can travel at 25 knots with the current and at 16 knots against it. Find the speed of the current and the speed of the submarine in still water.

27. The curve $y = ax^2 + bx + c$ passes through the points (1, 8), (0, 5) and (3, 20). Find the values of a, b and c and hence the equation of the curve.

28. The curve $y = ax^2 + bx + c$ passes through the points (1, 4), (−2, 19) and (0, 5). Find the equation of the curve.

29. The curve $y = ax^2 + bx + c$ passes through $(1, 8)$, $(-1, 2)$ and $(2, 14)$. Find the equation of the curve.

30. The curve $y = ax^2 + bx + c$ passes through $(2, 5)$, $(3, 12)$ and $(-1, -4)$. Find the equation of the curve.

2.9 Factorising

Earlier in this section we expanded expressions such as $x(3x - 1)$ to give $3x^2 - x$.

The reverse of this process is called *factorising*.

Example

Factorise: **a)** $4x + 4y$ **b)** $x^2 + 7x$ **c)** $3y^2 - 12y$ **d)** $6a^2b - 10ab^2$

a) 4 is common to $4x$ and $4y$.

$\therefore 4x + 4y = 4(x + y)$

b) x is common to x^2 and $7x$.

$\therefore x^2 + 7x = x(x + 7)$

The factors are x and $(x + 7)$.

c) $3y$ is common.

$\therefore 3y^2 - 12y = 3y(y - 4)$

d) $2ab$ is common.

$\therefore 6a^2b - 10ab^2 = 2ab(3a - 5b)$

Exercise 23

Factorise the following expressions completely:

1. $5a + 5b$ **2.** $7x + 7y$ **3.** $7x + x^2$ **4.** $y^2 + 8y$

5. $2y^2 + 3y$ **6.** $6y^2 - 4y$ **7.** $3x^2 - 21x$ **8.** $16a - 2a^2$

9. $6c^2 - 21c$ **10.** $15x - 9x^2$ **11.** $56y - 21y^2$ **12.** $ax + bx + 2cx$

13. $x^2 + xy + 3xz$ **14.** $x^2y + y^3 + z^2y$ **15.** $3a^2b + 2ab^2$ **16.** $x^2y + xy^2$

17. $6a^2 + 4ab + 2ac$ **18.** $ma + 2bm + m^2$ **19.** $2kx + 6ky + 4kz$ **20.** $ax^2 + ay + 2ab$

21. $x^2k + xk^2$ **22.** $a^3b + 2ab^2$ **23.** $abc - 3b^2c$ **24.** $2a^2e - 5ae^2$

25. $a^3b + ab^3$ **26.** $x^3y + x^2y^2$ **27.** $6xy^2 - 4x^2y$ **28.** $3ab^3 - 3a^3b$

29. $2a^3b + 5a^2b^2$ **30.** $ax^2y - 2ax^2z$ **31.** $2abx + 2ab^2 + 2a^2b$ **32.** $ayx + yx^3 - 2y^2x^2$

Example 1

Factorise $ah + ak + bh + bk$.

a) Divide into pairs, $ah + ak + bh + bk$.

b) a is common to the first pair.

b is common to the second pair.

$a(h + k) + b(h + k)$

c) $(h + k)$ is common to both terms.

Thus we have $(h + k)(a + b)$

Example 2

Factorise $6mx - 3nx + 2my - ny$.

a) $6mx - 3nx + 2my - ny$

b) $= 3x(2m - n) + y(2m - n)$

c) $= (2m - n)(3x + y)$

Exercise 24

Factorise the following expressions:

1. $ax + ay + bx + by$
2. $ay + az + by + bz$
3. $xb + xc + yb + yc$
4. $xh + xk + yh + yk$
5. $xm + xn + my + ny$
6. $ah - ak + bh - bk$
7. $ax - ay + bx - by$
8. $am - bm + an - bn$
9. $hs + ht + ks + kt$
10. $xs - xt + ys - yt$
11. $ax - ay - bx + by$
12. $xs - xt - ys + yt$
13. $as - ay - xs + xy$
14. $hx - hy - bx + by$
15. $am - bm - an + bn$
16. $xk - xm - kz + mz$
17. $2ax + 6ay + bx + 3by$
18. $2ax + 2ay + bx + by$
19. $2mh - 2mk + nh - nk$
20. $2mh + 3mk - 2nh - 3nk$
21. $6ax + 2bx + 3ay + by$
22. $2ax - 2ay - bx + by$
23. $x^2a + x^2b + ya + yb$
24. $ms + 2mt^2 - ns - 2nt^2$

Quadratic expressions

Example 1

Factorise $x^2 + 6x + 8$.

a) Find two numbers which multiply to give 8 and add up to 6. In this case the numbers are 4 and 2.

b) Put these numbers into brackets.

So $x^2 + 6x + 8 = (x + 4)(x + 2)$

Example 2

Factorise **a)** $x^2 + 2x - 15$

 b) $x^2 - 6x + 8$

a) Two numbers which multiply to give -15 and add up to $+2$ are -3 and 5.

$\therefore x^2 + 2x - 15 = (x - 3)(x + 5)$

b) Two numbers which multiply to give $+8$ and add up to -6 are -2 and -4.

$\therefore x^2 - 6x + 8 = (x - 2)(x - 4)$

Exercise 25

Factorise the following:

1. $x^2 + 7x + 10$
2. $x^2 + 7x + 12$
3. $x^2 + 8x + 15$
4. $x^2 + 10x + 21$
5. $x^2 + 8x + 12$
6. $y^2 + 12y + 35$
7. $y^2 + 11y + 24$
8. $y^2 + 10y + 25$
9. $y^2 + 15y + 36$
10. $a^2 - 3a - 10$
11. $a^2 - a - 12$
12. $z^2 + z - 6$
13. $x^2 - 2x - 35$
14. $x^2 - 5x - 24$
15. $x^2 - 6x + 8$
16. $y^2 - 5y + 6$
17. $x^2 - 8x + 15$
18. $a^2 - a - 6$
19. $a^2 + 14a + 45$
20. $b^2 - 4b - 21$
21. $x^2 - 8x + 16$
22. $y^2 + 2y + 1$
23. $y^2 - 3y - 28$
24. $x^2 - x - 20$
25. $x^2 - 8x - 240$
26. $x^2 - 26x + 165$
27. $y^2 + 3y - 108$
28. $x^2 - 49$
29. $x^2 - 9$
30. $x^2 - 16$

Example

Factorise $3x^2 + 13x + 4$.

a) Find two numbers which multiply to give 12 (3×4) and add up to 13. In this case the numbers are 1 and 12.

b) Split the '13x' term $3x^2 + x + 12x + 4$

c) Factorise in pairs $x(3x + 1) + 4(3x + 1)$

d) $(3x + 1)$ is common $(3x + 1)(x + 4)$

Exercise 26

Factorise the following:

1. $2x^2 + 5x + 3$
2. $2x^2 + 7x + 3$
3. $3x^2 + 7x + 2$
4. $2x^2 + 11x + 12$
5. $3x^2 + 8x + 4$
6. $2x^2 + 7x + 5$
7. $3x^2 - 5x - 2$
8. $2x^2 - x - 15$
9. $2x^2 + x - 21$
10. $3x^2 - 17x - 28$
11. $6x^2 + 7x + 2$
12. $12x^2 + 23x + 10$
13. $3x^2 - 11x + 6$
14. $3y^2 - 11y + 10$
15. $4y^2 - 23y + 15$
16. $6y^2 + 7y - 3$
17. $6x^2 - 27x + 30$
18. $10x^2 + 9x + 2$
19. $6x^2 - 19x + 3$
20. $8x^2 - 10x - 3$
21. $12x^2 + 4x - 5$
22. $16x^2 + 19x + 3$
23. $4a^2 - 4a + 1$
24. $12x^2 + 17x - 14$
25. $15x^2 + 44x - 3$
26. $48x^2 + 46x + 5$
27. $64y^2 + 4y - 3$
28. $120x^2 + 67x - 5$
29. $9x^2 - 1$
30. $4a^2 - 9$

The difference of two squares

$$x^2 - y^2 = (x - y)(x + y)$$

Remember this result.

Example

Factorise **a)** $4a^2 - b^2$ **b)** $3x^2 - 27y^2$

....

a) $4a^2 - b^2 = (2a)^2 - b^2$
$$= (2a - b)(2a + b)$$

b) $3x^2 - 27y^2 = 3\left(x^2 - 9y^2\right)$
$$= 3\left[x^2 - (3y)^2\right]$$
$$= 3(x - 3y)(x + 3y)$$

Exercise 27

Factorise the following:

1. $y^2 - a^2$

2. $m^2 - n^2$

3. $x^2 - t^2$

4. $y^2 - 1$

5. $x^2 - 9$

6. $a^2 - 25$

7. $x^2 - \dfrac{1}{4}$

8. $x^2 - \dfrac{1}{9}$

9. $4x^2 - y^2$

10. $a^2 - 4b^2$

11. $25x^2 - 4y^2$

12. $9x^2 - 16y^2$

13. $x^2 - \dfrac{y^2}{4}$

14. $9m^2 - \dfrac{4}{9}n^2$

15. $16t^2 - \dfrac{4}{25}s^2$

16. $4x^2 - \dfrac{z^2}{100}$

17. $x^3 - x$

18. $a^3 - ab^2$

19. $4x^3 - x$

20. $8x^3 - 2xy^2$

21. $12x^3 - 3xy^2$

22. $18m^3 - 8mn^2$

23. $5x^2 - 1\dfrac{1}{4}$

24. $50a^3 - 18ab^2$

25. $12x^2y - 3yz^2$

26. $36a^3b - 4ab^3$

27. $50a^5 - 8a^3b^2$

28. $36x^3y - 225xy^3$

Evaluate the following:

29. $81^2 - 80^2$

30. $102^2 - 100^2$

31. $225^2 - 215^2$

32. $1211^2 - 1210^2$

33. $723^2 - 720^2$

34. $3.8^2 - 3.7^2$

35. $5.24^2 - 4.76^2$

36. $1234^2 - 1235^2$

37. $3.81^2 - 3.8^2$

38. $540^2 - 550^2$

39. $7.68^2 - 2.32^2$

40. $0.003^2 - 0.002^2$

2.10 Quadratic equations

So far, we have met linear equations which have one solution only. Quadratic equations always have an x^2 term, and often an x term and a number term, and generally have two different solutions.

Solution by factors

Consider the equation $a \times b = 0$, where a and b are numbers. The product $a \times b$ can only be zero if either a or b (or both) is equal to zero. Can you think of other possible pairs of numbers which multiply together to give zero?

Example 1

Solve the equation $x^2 + x - 12 = 0$

Factorising, $(x - 3)(x + 4) = 0$

either $\quad x - 3 = 0 \quad$ or $\quad x + 4 = 0$

$\qquad\qquad x = 3 \qquad\qquad\qquad x = -4$

Example 2

Solve the equation $6x^2 + x - 2 = 0$

Factorising, $(2x - 1)(3x + 2) = 0$

either $\quad 2x - 1 = 0 \quad$ or $\quad 3x + 2 = 0$

$\qquad\qquad 2x = 1 \qquad\qquad\qquad 3x = -2$

$\qquad\qquad x = \dfrac{1}{2} \qquad\qquad\qquad x = -\dfrac{2}{3}$

Exercise 28

Solve the following equations:

1. $x^2 + 7x + 12 = 0$

2. $x^2 + 7x + 10 = 0$

3. $x^2 + 2x - 15 = 0$

4. $x^2 + x - 6 = 0$

5. $x^2 - 8x + 12 = 0$

6. $x^2 + 10x + 21 = 0$

7. $x^2 - 5x + 6 = 0$

8. $x^2 - 4x - 5 = 0$

9. $x^2 + 5x - 14 = 0$

10. $2x^2 - 3x - 2 = 0$

11. $3x^2 + 10x - 8 = 0$

12. $2x^2 + 7x - 15 = 0$

13. $6x^2 - 13x + 6 = 0$

14. $4x^2 - 29x + 7 = 0$

15. $10x^2 - x - 3 = 0$

16. $y^2 - 15y + 56 = 0$

17. $12y^2 - 16y + 5 = 0$

18. $y^2 + 2y - 63 = 0$

19. $x^2 + 2x + 1 = 0$

20. $x^2 - 6x + 9 = 0$

21. $x^2 + 10x + 25 = 0$

22. $x^2 - 14x + 49 = 0$

23. $6a^2 - a - 1 = 0$

24. $4a^2 - 3a - 10 = 0$

25. $z^2 - 8z - 65 = 0$

26. $6x^2 + 17x - 3 = 0$

27. $10k^2 + 19k - 2 = 0$

28. $y^2 - 2y + 1 = 0$

29. $36x^2 + x - 2 = 0$

30. $20x^2 - 7x - 3 = 0$

Example 1

Solve the equation $x^2 - 7x = 0$

Factorising, $x(x - 7) = 0$

either $x = 0$ or $x - 7 = 0$

$x = 7$

The solutions are $x = 0$ and $x = 7$.

Example 2

Solve the equation $4x^2 - 9 = 0$

a) Factorising, $(2x - 3)(2x + 3) = 0$

either $2x - 3 = 0$ or $2x + 3 = 0$

$2x = 3$ $2x = -3$

$x = \dfrac{3}{2}$ $x = -\dfrac{3}{2}$

b) Alternative method

$4x^2 - 9 = 0$

$4x^2 = 9$

$x^2 = \dfrac{9}{4}$

$x = +\dfrac{3}{2}$ or $-\dfrac{3}{2}$.

> You must give both the solutions. A common error is to only give the positive square root.

Exercise 29

Solve the following equations:

1. $x^2 - 3x = 0$
2. $x^2 + 7x = 0$
3. $2x^2 - 2x = 0$
4. $3x^2 - x = 0$
5. $x^2 - 16 = 0$
6. $x^2 - 49 = 0$
7. $4x^2 - 1 = 0$
8. $9x^2 - 4 = 0$
9. $6y^2 + 9y = 0$
10. $6a^2 - 9a = 0$
11. $10x^2 - 55x = 0$
12. $16x^2 - 1 = 0$
13. $y^2 - \frac{1}{4} = 0$
14. $56x^2 - 35x = 0$
15. $36x^2 - 3x = 0$
16. $x^2 = 6x$
17. $x^2 = 11x$
18. $2x^2 = 3x$
19. $x^2 = x$
20. $4x = x^2$
21. $3x - x^2 = 0$
22. $4x^2 = 1$
23. $9x^2 = 16$
24. $x^2 = 9$
25. $12x = 5x^2$
26. $1 - 9x^2 = 0$
27. $x^2 = \dfrac{x}{4}$
28. $2x^2 = \dfrac{x}{3}$
29. $4x^2 = \frac{1}{4}$
30. $\dfrac{x}{5} - x^2 = 0$

Solution by formula

The solutions of the quadratic equation $ax^2 + bx + c = 0$ are given by the formula

$$x = \frac{-b \pm \sqrt{(b^2 - 4ac)}}{2a}$$

Use this formula only after trying (and failing) to factorise.

Example

Solve the equation $2x^2 - 3x - 4 = 0$.

In this case $a = 2$, $b = -3$, $c = -4$.

$$x = \frac{-(-3) \pm \sqrt{(-3)^2 - (4 \times 2 \times -4)}}{2 \times 2}$$

$$x = \frac{3 \pm \sqrt{9 + 32}}{4} = \frac{3 \pm \sqrt{41}}{4} = \frac{3 \pm 6.403}{4}$$

either $\quad x = \dfrac{3 + 6.403}{4} \qquad$ or $\qquad x = \dfrac{3 - 6.403}{4} = \dfrac{-3.403}{4}$

$\qquad\qquad = 2.35 \quad$ (2 d.p.) $\qquad\qquad\qquad = -0.85 \quad$ (2 d.p.)

Exercise 30

Solve the following, giving answers to two decimal places where necessary:

1. $2x^2 + 11x + 5 = 0$
2. $3x^2 + 11x + 6 = 0$
3. $6x^2 + 7x + 2 = 0$
4. $3x^2 - 10x + 3 = 0$
5. $5x^2 - 7x + 2 = 0$
6. $6x^2 - 11x + 3 = 0$
7. $2x^2 + 6x + 3 = 0$
8. $x^2 + 4x + 1 = 0$
9. $5x^2 - 5x + 1 = 0$
10. $x^2 - 7x + 2 = 0$
11. $2x^2 + 5x - 1 = 0$
12. $3x^2 + x - 3 = 0$
13. $3x^2 + 8x - 6 = 0$
14. $3x^2 - 7x - 20 = 0$
15. $2x^2 - 7x - 15 = 0$
16. $x^2 - 3x - 2 = 0$
17. $2x^2 + 6x - 1 = 0$
18. $6x^2 - 11x - 7 = 0$
19. $3x^2 + 25x + 8 = 0$
20. $3y^2 - 2y - 5 = 0$
21. $2y^2 - 5y + 1 = 0$
22. $\frac{1}{2}y^2 + 3y + 1 = 0$
23. $2 - x - 6x^2 = 0$
24. $3 + 4x - 2x^2 = 0$
25. $1 - 5x - 2x^2 = 0$
26. $3x^2 - 1 + 4x = 0$
27. $5x - x^2 + 2 = 0$
28. $24x^2 - 22x - 35 = 0$
29. $36x^2 - 17x - 35 = 0$
30. $20x^2 + 17x - 63 = 0$
31. $x^2 + 2.5x - 6 = 0$
32. $0.3y^2 + 0.4y - 1.5 = 0$
33. $10 - x - 3x^2 = 0$
34. $x^2 + 3.3x - 0.7 = 0$
35. $12 - 5x^2 - 11x = 0$
36. $5x - 2x^2 + 187 = 0$

The solution to a problem can involve an equation which does not at first appear to be quadratic. The terms in the equation may need to be rearranged as shown on the next page.

Example

Solve:

$$2x(x-1) = (x+1)^2 - 5$$
$$2x^2 - 2x = x^2 + 2x + 1 - 5$$
$$2x^2 - 2x - x^2 - 2x - 1 + 5 = 0$$
$$x^2 - 4x + 4 = 0$$
$$(x-2)(x-2) = 0$$
$$x = 2$$

In this example the quadratic has a repeated solution of $x = 2$.

Exercise 31

Solve the following, giving answers to two decimal places where necessary:

1. $x^2 = 6 - x$

2. $x(x + 10) = -21$

3. $3x + 2 = 2x^2$

4. $x^2 + 4 = 5x$

5. $6x(x + 1) = 5 - x$

6. $(2x)^2 = x(x - 14) - 5$

7. $(x - 3)^2 = 10$

8. $(x + 1)^2 - 10 = 2x(x - 2)$

9. $(2x - 1)^2 = (x - 1)^2 + 8$

10. $3x(x + 2) - x(x - 2) + 6 = 0$

11. $x = \dfrac{15}{x} - 22$

12. $x + 5 = \dfrac{14}{x}$

13. $4x + \dfrac{7}{x} = 29$

14. $10x = 1 + \dfrac{3}{x}$

15. $2x^2 = 7x$

16. $16 = \dfrac{1}{x^2}$

17. $2x + 2 = \dfrac{7}{x} - 1$

18. $\dfrac{2}{x} + \dfrac{2}{x+1} = 3$

19. $\dfrac{3}{x-1} + \dfrac{3}{x+1} = 4$

20. $\dfrac{2}{x-2} + \dfrac{4}{x+1} = 3$

21. One of the solutions published by Cardan in 1545 for the solution of cubic equations is given below. For an equation in the form $x^3 + px = q$

$$x = \sqrt[3]{\sqrt{\left(\frac{p}{3}\right)^3 + \left(\frac{q}{2}\right)^2} + \frac{q}{2}} - \sqrt[3]{\sqrt{\left(\frac{p}{3}\right)^3 + \left(\frac{q}{2}\right)^2} - \frac{q}{2}}$$

Use the formula to solve the following equations, giving answers to 4 s.f. where necessary.

a) $x^3 + 7x = -8$

b) $x^3 + 6x = 4$

c) $x^3 + 3x = 2$

d) $x^3 + 9x - 2 = 0$

Solution by completing the square

Look at the function $f(x) = x^2 + 6x$

Completing the square, this becomes $f(x) = (x+3)^2 - 9$

This is done as follows:

Halve the 6 to give 3 inside the bracket

Subtract 3^2 from the bracketed expression since expanding the square will give $x^2 + 6x + 9$, which is 9 too many.

Here are some more examples.

a) $x^2 - 12x = (x-6)^2 - 36$

b) $x^2 + 3x = \left(x + \frac{3}{2}\right)^2 - \frac{9}{4}$

c) $x^2 + 6x + 1 = (x+3)^2 - 9 + 1$
$$= (x+3)^2 - 8$$

d) $x^2 - 10x - 17 = (x-5)^2 - 25 - 17$
$$= (x-5)^2 - 42$$

e) $2x^2 - 12x + 7 = 2\left[x^2 - 6x + \frac{7}{2}\right]$
$$= 2\left[(x-3)^2 - 9 + \frac{7}{2}\right]$$
$$= 2\left[(x-3)^2 - \frac{11}{2}\right]$$

Functions and their notation are explained in more detail on page 305.

Example 1

Solve the quadratic equation $x^2 - 6x + 7 = 0$ by completing the square.

$$(x-3)^2 - 9 + 7 = 0$$
$$(x-3)^2 = 2$$

$\therefore \quad x - 3 = +\sqrt{2} \quad$ or $-\sqrt{2}$

$x = 3 + \sqrt{2} \quad$ or $3 - \sqrt{2}$

So, $\quad x = 4.41 \quad$ or 1.59 (2 d.p.)

Example 2

Given $f(x) = x^2 - 8x + 18$, show that $f(x) \geqslant 2$ for all values of x.

Completing the square, $f(x) = (x-4)^2 - 16 + 18$

$$f(x) = (x-4)^2 + 2.$$

Now $(x-4)^2$ is always greater than or equal to zero because it is 'something squared'.

$$\therefore f(x) \geqslant 2$$

Exercise 32

In Questions **1** to **10**, complete the square for each expression by writing each one in the form $(x+a)^2 + b$ where a and b can be positive or negative.

1. $x^2 + 8x$

2. $x^2 - 12x$

3. $x^2 + x$

4. $x^2 + 4x + 1$

5. $x^2 - 6x + 9$

6. $x^2 + 2x - 15$

7. $2x^2 + 16x + 5$

8. $2x^2 - 10x$

9. $6 + 4x - x^2$

10. $3 - 2x - x^2$

11. Solve these equations by completing the square

    a) $x^2 + 4x - 3 = 0$ **b)** $x^2 - 3x - 2 = 0$ **c)** $x^2 + 12x = 1$

12. Try to solve the equation $x^2 + 6x + 10 = 0$, by completing the square. Explain why you can find no solutions.

13. Given $f(x) = x^2 + 6x + 12$, show that $f(x) \geqslant 3$ for all values of x.

14. Given $g(x) = x^2 - 7x + \frac{1}{4}$, show that the least possible value of $g(x)$ is -12.

15. If $f(x) = x^2 + 4x + 7$ find

    a) the smallest possible value of $f(x)$

    b) the value of x for which this smallest value occurs

    c) the greatest possible value of $\dfrac{1}{(x^2 + 4x + 7)}$

2.11 Problems solved by quadratic equations

Example 1

The area of rectangle A is 16 cm^2 greater than the area of rectangle B. Find the height of rectangle A.

Area of rectangle A $= 7(x + 3)$

Area of rectangle B $= (x + 2)(x - 1)$

We are given $(x + 2)(x - 1) + 16 = 7(x + 3)$

7 cm

A $(x + 3)$ cm

B $(x - 1)$ cm

$(x + 2)$ cm

Solve this equation
$$x^2 + 2x - x - 2 + 16 = 7x + 21$$
$$x^2 + x + 14 = 7x + 21$$
$$x^2 - 6x - 7 = 0$$
$$(x - 7)(x + 1) = 0$$
$$x = 7 \ (x \text{ cannot be negative})$$

The height of rectangle A, $x + 3$, is 10 cm.

Example 2

A man bought a certain number of golf balls for \$20. If each ball had cost 20 cents less, he could have bought five more for the same money. How many golf balls did he buy?

Let the number of balls bought be x.

$$\text{Cost of each ball} = \frac{2000}{x} \text{ cents}$$

If five more balls had been bought

$$\text{Cost of each ball now} = \frac{2000}{(x + 5)} \text{ cents}$$

The new price is 20 cents less than the original price.

$$\therefore \quad \frac{2000}{x} - \frac{2000}{(x + 5)} = 20$$

(multiply by x)

$$x \cdot \frac{2000}{x} - x \cdot \frac{2000}{(x + 5)} = 20x$$

$$2000(x + 5) - x \frac{2000}{(x + 5)}(x + 5) = 20x(x + 5) \qquad (\text{multiply by } (x + 5))$$

$$2000x + 10\,000 - 2000x = 20x^2 + 100x$$

$$20x^2 + 100x - 10\,000 = 0$$

$$x^2 + 5x - 500 = 0$$

$$(x - 20)(x + 25) = 0$$

$$x = 20$$
$$\text{or} \quad x = -25$$

We discard $x = -25$ as meaningless.

The number of balls bought $= 20$.

Exercise 33

Solve by forming a quadratic equation:

1. Two numbers, which differ by 3, have a product of 88. Find them.

2. The product of two consecutive odd numbers is 143. Find the numbers.

3. The length of a rectangle exceeds the width by 7 cm. If the area is 60 cm², find the length of the rectangle.

4. The length of a rectangle exceeds the width by 2 cm. If the diagonal is 10 cm long, find the width of the rectangle.

5. The area of the rectangle exceeds the area of the square by 24 m². Find x.

6. The perimeter of a rectangle is 68 cm. If the diagonal is 26 cm, find the dimensions of the rectangle.

7. Sang Jae walks a certain distance due North and then the same distance plus a further 7 km due East. If the final distance from the starting point is 17 km, find the distances he walks North and East.

8. A farmer makes a profit of x cents on each of the $(x + 5)$ eggs her hen lays. If her total profit was 84 cents, find the number of eggs the hen lays.

9. Sirak buys x eggs at $(x - 8)$ cents each and $(x - 2)$ bread rolls at $(x - 3)$ cents each. If the total bill is $1.75, how many eggs does he buy?

10. A number exceeds four times its reciprocal by 3. Find the number.

11. Two numbers differ by 3. The sum of their reciprocals is $\frac{7}{10}$; find the numbers.

12. A cyclist travels 40 km at a speed of x km/h. Find the time taken in terms of x. Find the time taken when his speed is reduced by 2 km/h. If the difference between the times is 1 hour, find the original speed x.

13. An increase of speed of 4 km/h on a journey of 32 km reduces the time taken by 4 hours. Find the original speed.

14. A train normally travels 240 km at a certain speed. One day, due to bad weather, the train's speed is reduced by 20 km/h so that the journey takes two hours longer. Find the normal speed.

Questions 4, 6 and 7 use Pythagoras' theorem. For more information on Pythagoras' theorem see page 141.

If the first odd number is x, what is the next odd number?

15. The speed of a sparrow is x km/h in still air. When the wind is blowing at 1 km/h, the sparrow takes 5 hours to fly 12 kilometres to her nest and 12 kilometres back again. She goes out directly into the wind and returns with the wind behind her. Find her speed in still air.

16. An aircraft flies a certain distance on a bearing of 135° and then twice the distance on a bearing of 225°. Its distance from the starting point is then 350 km. Find the length of the first part of the journey.

A **bearing** is a clockwise angle measured from North. For more information about bearings see page 216.

17. In Figure 1, ABCD is a rectangle with AB = 12 cm and BC = 7 cm. AK = BL = CM = DN = x cm. If the area of KLMN is 54 cm², find x.

18. In Figure 1, AB = 14 cm, BC = 11 cm and AK = BL = CM = DN = x cm. If the area of KLMN is now 97 cm², find x.

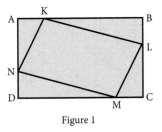

Figure 1

19. The numerator of a fraction is 1 less than the denominator. When both numerator and denominator are increased by 2, the fraction is increased by $\frac{1}{12}$. Find the original fraction.

20. The perimeters of a square and a rectangle are equal. One side of the rectangle is 11 cm and the area of the square is 4 cm² more than the area of the rectangle. Find the side of the square.

2.12 Non-linear simultaneous equations

Sometimes you may be given a pair of simultaneous equations with one linear equation and one quadratic equation. You can solve these by substitution.

Example 1

$y = x + 1$ ... [1]

$y = x^2 + 3x - 2$ ... [2]

Substitute [1] into [2]

$x + 1 = x^2 + 3x - 2$

$0 = x^2 + 2x - 3$

Solve the resulting quadratic equation by factorising

$0 = (x + 3)(x - 1)$

$x = -3$ or $x = 1$

Substitute the x-values into [1]

When $x = -3$, $y = -2$

When $x = 1$, $y = 2$

Example 2

$$2x - y = 3 \qquad \qquad \dots [1]$$
$$y = 2x^2 + 9x - 1 \qquad \qquad \dots [2]$$

Rearrange [1] to make y the subject

$$2x = y + 3$$
$$2x - 3 = y$$

Substitute into [2]

$$2x - 3 = 2x^2 + 9x - 1$$
$$0 = 2x^2 + 7x + 2$$

Solve the resulting quadratic equation using the formula

$$x = \frac{-7 \pm \sqrt{7^2 - 4(2)(2)}}{2(2)} = \frac{-7 \pm \sqrt{33}}{4}$$

either $x = \dfrac{-7 + 5.74456\dots}{4} = -0.31386\dots$

$$\Rightarrow y = -3.6277\dots$$

or $\quad x = \dfrac{-7 - 5.74456\dots}{4} = -3.18614\dots$

$$\Rightarrow y = -9.3722\dots$$

The solutions are $x = -0.31, y = -3.63$ and $x = -3.19, y = -9.37$

> If you have to solve the quadratic equation by using the formula, use the exact x-values when finding y, then round both answers at the end.

Exercise 34

Solve the following pairs of simultaneous equations. Give your answers to two decimal places where necessary.

1. $y = 20 - 2x$
$\quad y = x^2 - 16x + 68$

2. $y = 6x - 8$
$\quad y = x^2 + 2x - 5$

3. $y = 2 - 2x$
$\quad y = x^2 - 4x + 3$

4. $y + 2x = 9$
$\quad y = x^2 - 6x + 12$

5. $y + 10x + 31 = 0$
$\quad y + 6 = x^2$

6. $y + 12x = x^2 + 40$
$\quad y + 8x = 38$

7. $y - 7 = x^2 + 2x$
$\quad y - 9 = 4x$

8. $y - x^2 - 14x = 54$
$\quad 43 = y - 6x$

9. $y + 2x + 7 = 4$
$\quad y - 8 = x^2 + 6x + 2$

10. $2y - 3x = 1$
$\quad y = x^2 + 3x - 7$

11. $3y + 4x = 15$
$\quad y = 2x^2 - 3x + 5$

12. $3y - 2x + 5 = 0$
$\quad y = 7 - 2x - 3x^2$

Revision exercise 2A

1. Solve the equations:

   a) $x + 4 = 3x + 9$

   b) $9 - 3a = 1$

   c) $y^2 + 5y = 0$

   d) $x^2 - 4 = 0$

   e) $3x^2 + 7x - 40 = 0$

Questions 13 and 20 use Pythagoras' theorem. See page 141.

2. Given $a = 3$, $b = 4$ and $c = -2$, evaluate:

   a) $2a^2 - b$

   b) $a(b - c)$

   c) $2b^2 - c^2$

3. Factorise completely:

   a) $4x^2 - y^2$

   b) $2x^2 + 8x + 6$

   c) $6m + 4n - 9km - 6kn$

   d) $2x^2 - 5x - 3$

4. Solve the simultaneous equations:

   a) $3x + 2y = 5$

       $2x - y = 8$

   b) $2m - n = 6$

       $2m + 3n = -6$

   c) $3x - 4y = 19$

       $x + 6y = 10$

   d) $3x - 7y = 11$

       $2x - 3y = 4$

5. Given that $x = 4$, $y = 3$, $z = -2$, evaluate:

   a) $2x(y + z)$ **b)** $(xy)^2 - z^2$

   c) $x^2 + y^2 + z^2$ **d)** $(x + y)(x - z)$

   e) $\sqrt{x(1 - 4z)}$ **f)** $\dfrac{xy}{z}$

6. a) Simplify $3(2x - 5) - 2(2x + 3)$.

   b) Factorise $2a - 3b - 4xa + 6xb$.

   c) Solve the equation $\dfrac{x - 11}{2} - \dfrac{x - 3}{5} = 2$.

d) Remove the brackets and simplify $(x - 2)(x - 3)(x - 4)$.

e) Remove the brackets and simplify $(2x - 3)^3$.

7. Solve the equations:

   a) $5 - 7x = 4 - 6x$

   b) $\dfrac{7}{x} = \dfrac{2}{3}$

   c) $2x^2 - 7x = 0$

   d) $x^2 + 5x + 6 = 0$

   e) $\dfrac{1}{x} + \dfrac{1}{4} = \dfrac{1}{3}$

8. Factorise completely:

   a) $z^3 - 16z$

   b) $x^2y^2 + x^2 + y^2 + 1$

   c) $2x^2 + 11x + 12$

9. Find the value of $\dfrac{2x - 3y}{5x + 2y}$ when $x = 2a$ and $y = -a$.

10. Solve the simultaneous equations:

   a) $7c + 3d = 29$

       $5c - 4d = 33$

   b) $2x - 3y = 7$

       $2y - 3x = -8$

   c) $5x = 3(1 - y)$

       $3x + 2y + 1 = 0$

   d) $5s + 3t = 16$

       $11s + 7t = 34$

   e) $y = x + 4$

       $y = x^2 + 4x + 4$

   f) $2y - 3x - 1 = 0$

       $y = 2x^2 - 4x + 3$

11. Solve the equations:

a) $4(y+1) = \dfrac{3}{1-y}$

b) $4(2x-1) - 3(1-x) = 0$

c) $\dfrac{x+3}{x} = 2$

d) $x^2 = 5x$

12. Solve the following, giving your answers correct to two decimal places.

a) $2x^2 - 3x - 1 = 0$

b) $x^2 - x - 1 = 0$

c) $3x^2 + 2x - 4 = 0$

d) $x+3 = \dfrac{7}{x}$

13. Find x by forming a suitable equation.

a)

b)

14. Given that $m = -2$, $n = 4$, evaluate:

a) $5m + 3n$

b) $5 + 2m - m^2$

c) $m^2 + 2n^2$

d) $(2m + n)(2m - n)$

e) $(n - m)^2$

f) $n - mn - 2m^2$

15. A car travels for x hours at a speed of $(x+2)$ km/h. If the distance travelled is 15 km, write down an equation for x and solve it to find the speed of the car.

16. ABCD is a rectangle, where $AB = x$ cm and BC is 1.5 cm less than AB.

If the area of the rectangle is 52 cm², form an equation in x and solve it to find the dimensions of the rectangle.

17. Solve the equations:

a) $(2x+1)^2 = (x+5)^2$

b) $\dfrac{x+2}{2} - \dfrac{x-1}{3} = \dfrac{x}{4}$

c) $x^2 - 7x + 5 = 0$, giving the answers correct to two decimal places.

18. Solve the equation:

$$\dfrac{x}{x+1} - \dfrac{x+1}{3x-1} = \dfrac{1}{4}$$

19. Given that $a + b = 2$ and that $a^2 + b^2 = 6$, prove that $2ab = -2$.

Find also the value of $(a - b)^2$.

20. The sides of a right-angled triangle have lengths $(x-3)$ cm, $(x+11)$ cm and $2x$ cm, where $2x$ is the hypotenuse. Find x.

21. A jar contains 50 coins, all either 2 cents or 5 cents. The total value of the coins is \$1.87. How many 2 cents coins are there?

22. Pat bought 45 stamps, some for 10c and some for 18c. If he spent \$6.66 altogether, how many 10c stamps did he buy?

23. When each edge of a cube is decreased by 1 cm, its volume is decreased by 91 cm³. Find the length of a side of the original cube.

24. One solution of the equation $2x^2 - 7x + k = 0$ is $x = -\dfrac{1}{2}$. Find the value of k.

Examination-style exercise 2B

1. (a) $\dfrac{2}{3} + \dfrac{5}{6} = \dfrac{x}{2}$.

Find the value of x. [1]

(b) $\dfrac{5}{3} \div \dfrac{3}{y} = \dfrac{40}{9}$.

Find the value of y. [1]

Cambridge IGCSE Mathematics 0580
Paper 2 Q2 November 2006

2. Find the coordinates of the point of intersection of the straight lines

$4x + y = 17$

$3x - 2y = 10$ [3]

3. Solve the equations

(a) $\dfrac{2x}{3} - 9 = 0,$ [2]

(b) $x^2 - 3x - 4 = 0.$ [2]

Cambridge IGCSE Mathematics 0580
Paper 2 Q14 November 2007

4. Solve the simultaneous equations

$0.4x + 2y = 10,$

$0.3x + 5y = 18.$ [3]

Cambridge IGCSE Mathematics 0580
Paper 2 Q12 June 2006

5. $x^2 + 4x - 8$ can be written in the form $(x + p)^2 + q$.

Find the value of p and q. [3]

Cambridge IGCSE Mathematics 0580
Paper 2 Q9 November 2007

6.

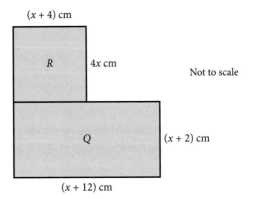

$(x + 4)$ cm

R

$4x$ cm

Not to scale

Q

$(x + 2)$ cm

$(x + 12)$ cm

(a) **i)** Write down an expression for the area of rectangle R. [1]

   ii) Show that the total area of rectangles R and Q is

   $5x^2 + 30x + 24$ square centimetres. [1]

(b) The total area of rectangles R and Q is 64 cm².

   Calculate the value of x correct to 1 decimal place. [4]

Cambridge IGCSE Mathematics 0580
Paper 2 Q20 November 2006

7. (a) **i)** Factorise $x^2 - x - 20$. [2]

   ii) Solve the equation $x^2 - x - 20 = 0$. [1]

(b) Solve the equation $3x^2 - 2x - 2 = 0$.

   Show all your working and give your answers correct to 2 decimal places. [4]

(c) $y = m^2 - 4n^2$.

   i) Factorise $m^2 - 4n^2$. [1]

   ii) Find the value of y when $m = 4.4$ and $n = 2.8$. [1]

   iii) $m = 2x + 3$ and $n = x - 1$.

   Find y in terms of x, in its simplest form. [2]

   iv) Make n the subject of the formula $y = m^2 - 4n^2$. [3]

(d) **i)** $m^4 - 16n^4$ can be written as $(m^2 - kn^2)(m^2 + kn^2)$.

   Write down the value of k. [1]

   ii) Factorise completely $m^4n - 16n^5$. [2]

Cambridge IGCSE Mathematics 0580
Paper 4 Q2 June 2008

8. (a) In triangle ABC, the line BD is perpendicular to AC.

   $AD = (x + 6)$ cm, $DC = (x + 2)$ cm and the height
   $BD = (x + 1)$ cm.

   The area of triangle ABC is 40 cm².

   i) Show that $x^2 + 5x - 36 = 0$. Not to scale [3]

   ii) Solve the equation $x^2 + 5x - 36 = 0$. [2]

   iii) Calculate the length of BC. [2]

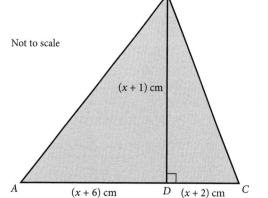

(b) Amira takes 9 hours 25 minutes to complete a long walk.

  i)   Show that the time of 9 hours 25 minutes can be written as $\dfrac{113}{12}$ hours.   [1]

  ii) She walks $(3y+2)$ kilometres at $3\,$km/h and then a
       further $(y+4)$ kilometres at $2\,$km/h.

       Show that the total time taken is $\dfrac{9y+16}{6}$ hours.   [2]

  iii) Solve the equation $\dfrac{9y+16}{6}=\dfrac{113}{12}$.   [2]

  iv) Calculate Amira's average speed, in kilometres per
       hour, for the whole walk.   [3]

Cambridge IGCSE Mathematics 0580
Paper 4 Q6 June 2009

9. **(a)** Remove the brackets and simplify $(x-3)^2(3x+1)$.   [3]

   (b) Hence, or otherwise, simplify fully $(x-3)^2(3x+1)-(x+2)^2$.   [3]

10. The graph shows the curve $y=x^2-x-2$ and the line $2y=x+2$.

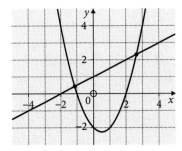

   Find, correct to two decimal places, the coordinates of the points
   of intersection.   [5]

3 Mensuration

Archimedes of Samos (287–212 B.C.) studied at Alexandria as a young man. One of the first to apply scientific thinking to everyday problems, he was a practical man of common sense. He gave proofs for finding the area, the volume and the centre of gravity of circles, spheres, conics and spirals. By drawing polygons with many sides, he arrived at a value of π between $3\frac{10}{71}$ and $3\frac{10}{70}$. He was killed in the siege of Syracuse at the age of 75.

E5.1 Use current units of mass, length, area, volume and capacity in practical situations and express quantities in terms of larger or smaller units.

E5.2 Carry out calculations involving the perimeter and area of a rectangle, triangle, parallelogram and trapezium and compound shapes derived from these.

E5.3 Carry out calculations involving the circumference and area of a circle. Solve problems involving the arc length and sector area as fractions of the circumference and area of a circle.

E5.4 Carry out calculations involving the surface area and volume of a cuboid, prism and cylinder.
Carry out calculations involving the surface area and volume of a sphere, pyramid and cone.

E5.5 Carry out calculations involving the areas and volumes of compound shapes.

3.1 Area

Rectangle	Trapezium	Kite

$$\text{area} = l \times b$$

$$\text{area} = \frac{1}{2}(a+b)h$$

$$\text{area} = \frac{1}{2}a \times b$$
$$= \frac{1}{2} \times (\text{product of diagonals})$$

Exercise 1

For questions **1** to **7**, find the area of each shape. Decide which information to use: you may not need all of it.

1.
2 m
5.1 m

2.
5 cm
7 cm
4 cm
4 cm

3.
12.4 m
10 m
8.2 m

4.
3 cm
6 cm

5.
3 m
7 m
3 m
5 m

6.
0.5 m
130 cm
120 cm

7.

8. Find the area shaded.

9. Find the area shaded.

10. A rectangle has an area of 117 m² and a width of 9 m. Find its length.

11. A trapezium of area 105 cm² has parallel sides of length 5 cm and 9 cm. How far apart are the parallel sides?

12. A kite of area 252 m² has one diagonal of length 9 m. Find the length of the other diagonal.

13. A kite of area 40 m² has one diagonal 2 m longer than the other. Find the lengths of the diagonals.

14. A trapezium of area 140 cm² has parallel sides 10 cm apart and one of these sides is 16 cm long. Find the length of the other parallel side.

15. A floor 5 m by 20 m is covered by square tiles of side 20 cm. How many tiles are needed?

16. On squared paper draw the triangle with vertices at (1, 1), (5, 3), (3, 5). Find the area of the triangle.

17. Draw the quadrilateral with vertices at (1, 1), (6, 2), (5, 5), (3, 6). Find the area of the quadrilateral.

18. A square wall is covered with square tiles. There are 85 tiles altogether along the two diagonals. How many tiles are there on the whole wall?

19. On squared paper draw a 7×7 square. Divide it up into nine smaller squares.

20. A rectangular field, 400 m long, has an area of 6 hectares. Calculate the perimeter of the field [1 hectare = 10 000 m²].

In triangle BCD, $\sin C = \dfrac{h}{a}$

∴ $h = a \sin C$

∴   area of triangle $= \dfrac{1}{2} \times b \times a \sin C$

This formula is useful when *two sides* and the *included* angle are known.

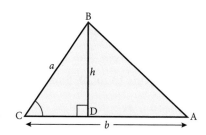

Example

Find the area of the triangle shown.

$$\text{Area} = \frac{1}{2}\, ab \sin C$$

$$= \frac{1}{2} \times 5 \times 7 \times \sin 52°$$

$$= 13.8 \text{ cm}^2 \text{ (1 d.p.)}$$

Triangle

$$\text{area} = \frac{1}{2} \times b \times h$$

Parallelogram

You can find out more about sin θ
in Trigonometry on page 209.

$\text{area} = b \times h$

$\text{area} = ba \sin \theta$

Exercise 2

In questions **1** to **12** find the area of $\triangle ABC$ where $AB = c$, $AC = b$ and $BC = a$.
(Sketch the triangle in each case.) You will need some basic trigonometry (see page 209).

1. $a = 7$ cm, $b = 14$ cm, $\hat{C} = 80°$.

2. $b = 11$ cm, $a = 9$ cm, $\hat{C} = 35°$.

3. $c = 12$ m, $b = 12$ m, $\hat{A} = 67.2°$.

4. $a = 5$ cm, $c = 6$ cm, $\hat{B} = 11.8°$.

5. $b = 4.2$ cm, $a = 10$ cm, $\hat{C} = 120°$.

6. $a = 5$ cm, $c = 8$ cm, $\hat{B} = 142°$.

7. $b = 3.2$ cm, $c = 1.8$ cm, $\hat{B} = 10°$, $\hat{C} = 65°$.

8. $a = 7$ m, $b = 14$ m, $\hat{A} = 32°$, $\hat{B} = 100°$.

9. $a = b = c = 12$ m.

10. $a = c = 8$ m, $\hat{B} = 72°$.

11. $b = c = 10$ cm, $\hat{B} = 32°$.

12. $a = b = c = 0.8$ m.

In questions **13** to **20**, find the area of each shape.

13.

14.

15.

16.

17.

18.

19. Find the area shaded.

20.

21. Find the area of a parallelogram ABCD with AB = 7 m, AD = 20 m and $\widehat{BAD} = 62°$.

22. Find the area of a parallelogram ABCD with AD = 7 m, CD = 11 m and $\widehat{BAD} = 65°$.

23. In the diagram if AE = $\frac{1}{3}$ AB, find the area shaded.

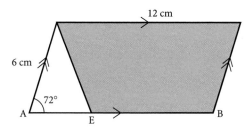

24. The area of an equilateral triangle ABC is 50 cm². Find AB.

25. The area of a triangle ABC is 64 cm². Given AB = 11 cm and BC = 15 cm, find $\widehat{ABC}$.

26. The area of a triangle XYZ is 11m². Given YZ = 7 m and $\widehat{XYZ} = 130°$, find XY.

27. Find the length of a side of an equilateral triangle of area 10.2 m².

28. A rhombus has an area of 40 cm² and adjacent angles of 50° and 130°.
Find the length of a side of the rhombus.

29. A regular hexagon is circumscribed by a circle of radius 3 cm with centre O.

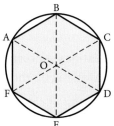

You can find out more about special shapes and their properties in Unit 4.

   a) What is angle EOD?

   b) Find the area of triangle EOD and hence find the area of the hexagon ABCDEF.

30. Hexagonal tiles of side 20 cm are used to tile a room which measures 6.25 m by 4.85 m. Assuming we complete the edges by cutting up tiles, how many tiles are needed?

31. Find the area of a regular pentagon of side 8 cm.

32. The diagram shows a part of the perimeter of a regular polygon with n sides

The centre of the polygon is at O and OA = OB = 1 unit.

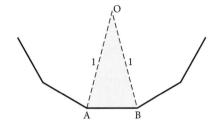

a) What is the angle AOB in terms of n?

b) Work out an expression in terms of n for the area of the polygon.

c) Find the area of polygons where $n = 6$, 10, 300, 1000, 10 000. What do you notice?

33. The area of a regular pentagon is 600 cm².
Calculate the length of one side of the pentagon.

3.2 The circle

For any circle, the ratio $\left(\dfrac{\text{circumference}}{\text{diameter}} \right)$ is equal to π.

The value of π is usually taken to be 3.14, but this is not an exact value. Through the centuries, mathematicians have been trying to obtain a better value for π.

For example, in the third century A.D., the Chinese mathematician Liu Hui obtained the value 3.14159 by considering a regular polygon having 3072 sides! Ludolph van Ceulen (1540–1610) worked even harder to produce a value correct to 35 significant figures. He was so proud of his work that he had this value of π engraved on his tombstone.

Electronic computers are now able to calculate the value of π to many thousands of figures, but its value is still not exact. It was shown in 1761 that π is an *irrational number* which, like $\sqrt{2}$ or $\sqrt{3}$ cannot be expressed exactly as a fraction.

The first fifteen significant figures of π can be remembered from the number of letters in each word of the following sentence.

> *How I need a drink, cherryade of course, after the silly lectures involving Italian kangaroos.*

There remain a lot of unanswered questions concerning π, and many mathematicians today are still working on them.

The following formulae should be memorised.

circumference $= \pi d$

$\qquad = 2\pi r$

area $= \pi r^2$

Exercise 3

For each shape find **a**) the perimeter, **b**) the area. All lengths are in cm.
Use the π button on a calculator or take $\pi = 3.142$. All the arcs are either semi-circles or quarter circles.

1.

10

2.

3

3.

20

4.

7
8

5.

5
3
9

6.

7

7.

10

8.
4
12

9.

7

10.

11.

12.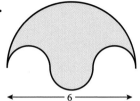

Example 1

A circle has a circumference of 20 m. Find the radius of the circle.

Let the radius of the circle by r m.

$$\text{Circumference} = 2\pi r$$

$\therefore \qquad\qquad 2\pi r = 20$

$\therefore \qquad\qquad r = \dfrac{20}{2\pi}$

$\qquad\qquad\qquad r = 3.18$

The radius of the circle is 3.18 m (3 s.f.).

Example 2

A circle has an area of 45 cm². Find the radius of the circle.

Let the radius of the circle by r cm.

$\qquad \pi r^2 = 45$

$\qquad r^2 = \dfrac{45}{\pi}$

$\qquad r = \sqrt{\left(\dfrac{45}{\pi}\right)} = 3.78 \text{ (3 s.f.)}$

The radius of the circle is 3.78 cm.

Exercise 4

Use the π button on a calculator and give answers to 3 s.f.

1. A circle has an area of 15 cm². Find its radius.
2. A circle has a circumference of 190 m. Find its radius.
3. Find the radius of a circle of area 22 km².
4. Find the radius of a circle of circumference 58.6 cm.
5. A circle has an area of 16 mm². Find its circumference.
6. A circle has a circumference of 2500 km. Find its area.

7. A circle of radius 5 cm is inscribed inside a square as shown. Find the area shaded.

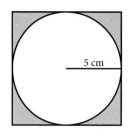

8. A circular pond of radius 6 m is surrounded by a path of width 1 m.

   a) Find the area of the path.

   b) The path is resurfaced with Astroturf which is bought in packs each containing enough to cover an area of 7 m². How many packs are required?

9. Discs of radius 4 cm are cut from a rectangular plastic sheet of length 84 cm and width 24 cm.

   a) How many complete discs can be cut out?
   Find:

   b) the total area of the discs cut

   c) the area of the sheet wasted.

10. The tyre of a car wheel has an outer diameter of 30 cm. How many times will the wheel rotate on a journey of 5 km?

11. A golf ball of diameter 1.68 inches rolls a distance of 4 m in a straight line. How many times does the ball rotate completely? (1 inch = 2.54 cm)

12. 100 yards of cotton is wound without stretching onto a reel of diameter 3 cm. How many times does the reel rotate? (1 yard = 0.914 m. Ignore the thickness of the cotton.)

13. A rectangular metal plate has a length of 65 cm and a width of 35 cm. It is melted down and recast into circular discs of the same thickness. How many complete discs can be formed if

   a) the radius of each disc is 3 cm

   b) the radius of each disc is 10 cm?

14. Calculate the radius of a circle whose area is equal to the sum of the areas of three circles of radii 2 cm, 3 cm and 4 cm respectively.

15. The diameter of a circle is given as 10 cm, correct to the nearest cm. Calculate:

   a) the maximum possible circumference

   b) the minimum possible area of the circle consistent with this data.

16. A square is inscribed in a circle of radius 7 cm. Find:

   a) the area of the square

   b) the area shaded.

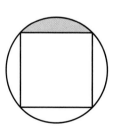

17. An archery target has three concentric regions. The diameters of the regions are in the ratio 1 : 2 : 3. Find the ratio of their areas.

18. The farmer has 100 m of wire fencing. What area can he enclose if he makes a circular pen?

19. The semi-circle and the isosceles triangle have the same base AB and the same area. Find the angle x.

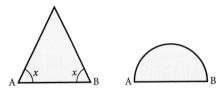

20. Lakmini decided to measure the circumference of the Earth using a very long tape measure. She held the tape measure 1m from the surface of the (perfectly spherical) Earth all the way round. When she had finished her friend said that her measurement gave too large an answer and suggested taking off 6 m. Was her friend correct?
[Take the radius of the Earth to be 6400 km (if you need it).]

21. The large circle has a radius of 10 cm. Find the radius of the largest circle which will fit in the middle.

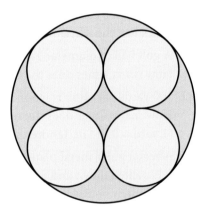

3.3 Arc length and sector area

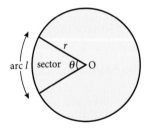

The smaller sector or arc is known as the **minor** sector or arc. The larger sector or arc is known as the **major** sector or arc.

Arc length, $l = \dfrac{\theta}{360} \times 2\pi r$

We take a fraction of the whole circumference depending on the angle at the centre of the circle.

Sector area, $A = \dfrac{\theta}{360} \times \pi r^2$

We take a fraction of the whole area depending on the angle at the centre of the circle.

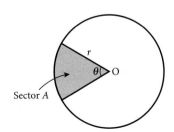

Example 1

Find the length of an arc which subtends
an angle of 140° at the centre of a circle of
radius 12 cm.

$$\text{Arc length} = \frac{140}{360} \times 2 \times \pi \times 12$$

$$= \frac{28}{3}\pi$$

$$= 29.3 \text{ cm (1 d.p.)}$$

Example 2

A sector of a circle of radius 10 cm
has an area of 25 cm². Find the
angle at the centre of the circle.

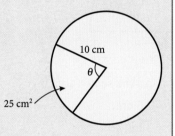

Let the angle at the centre of the
circle be θ.

$$\frac{\theta}{360} \times \pi \times 10^2 = 25$$

$$\therefore \quad \theta = \frac{25 \times 360}{\pi \times 100}$$

$$\theta = 28.6° \text{ (3 s.f.)}$$

The angle at the centre of the circle is 28.6°.

Exercise 5

[Use the π button on a calculator unless told otherwise.]

1. Arc AB subtends an angle θ at the centre of circle radius r.
   Find the arc length and sector area when:
   a) $r = 4$ cm, $\theta = 30°$
   b) $r = 10$ cm, $\theta = 45°$
   c) $r = 2$ cm, $\theta = 235°$.

In questions **2** and **3** find the total area of the shape.

2.

OA = 2 cm, OB = 3 cm, OC = 5 cm, OD = 3 cm.

3.

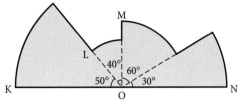

ON = 6 cm, OM = 3 cm, OL = 2 cm, OK = 6 cm.

4. Find the shaded areas.

5. In the diagram the arc length is l and the sector area is A.

a) Find θ, when $r = 5$ cm and $l = 7.5$ cm.

b) Find θ, when $r = 2$ m and $A = 2$ m².

c) Find r, when $\theta = 55°$ and $l = 6$ cm.

6. The length of the minor arc AB of a circle, centre O, is 2π cm and the length of the major arc is 22π cm. Find:

a) the radius of the circle

b) the acute angle AOB.

7. The lengths of the minor and major arcs of a circle are 5.2 cm and 19.8 respectively. Find:

a) the radius of the circle

b) the angle subtended at the centre by the minor arc.

8. A wheel of radius 10 cm is turning at a rate of 5 revolutions per minute. Calculate:

a) the angle through which the wheel turns in 1 second

b) the distance moved by a point on the rim in 2 seconds.

9. The length of an arc of a circle is 12 cm. The corresponding sector area is 108 cm². Find:

a) the radius of the circle

b) the angle subtended at the centre of the circle by the arc.

10. The length of an arc of a circle is 7.5 cm. The corresponding sector area is 37.5 cm².
    Find:
    a) the radius of the circle
    b) the angle subtended at the centre of the circle by the arc.

11. In the diagram the arc length is *l* and the sector area is *A*.
    a) Find *l*, when $\theta = 72°$ and $A = 15$ cm².
    b) Find *l*, when $\theta = 135°$ and $A = 162$ cm².
    c) Find *A*, when $l = 11$ cm and $r = 5.2$ cm.

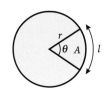

12. A long time ago Dulani found an island shaped like a triangle with three
    straight shores of length 3 km, 4 km and 5 km. He said nobody could come
    within 1 km of his shore. What was the area of his exclusion zone?

3.4 Chord of a circle

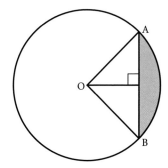

The line AB is a chord. The area of a circle cut off by a chord is
called a *segment*. In the diagram the *minor* segment is shaded and
the *major* segment is unshaded.

a) The line from the centre of a circle to the midpoint of a chord
   bisects the chord at *right angles*.

b) The line from the centre of a circle to the midpoint of a chord
   bisects the angle subtended by the chord at the centre of the circle.

Example

XY is a chord of length 12 cm of a circle of radius 10 cm, centre O.
Calculate:

a) the angle XOY

b) the area of the minor segment cut off by the chord XY.

a) Let the midpoint of XY be M.

$\therefore$ MY = 6 cm

   $\sin\ \text{M}\hat{\text{O}}\text{Y} = \dfrac{6}{10}$

$\therefore$ $\text{M}\hat{\text{O}}\text{Y} = 36.87°$

$\therefore$ $\text{X}\hat{\text{O}}\text{Y} = 2 \times 36.87$

        $= 73.74°$

You can find out more about trigonometry in Unit 6 on page 209.

b)   Area of minor segment = area of sector XOY − area of $\triangle$XOY

   area of sector XOY $= \dfrac{73.74}{360} \times \pi \times 10^2$

        $= 64.32$ cm^2.

   area of $\triangle$XOY $= \dfrac{1}{2} \times 10 \times 10 \times \sin 73.74°$

        $= 48.00$ cm^2

$\therefore$ Area of minor segment = 64.32 − 48.00

        $= 16.3$ cm^2 (3 s.f.)

Exercise 6

Use the π button on a calculator. You will need basic trigonometry (page 209).

1. The chord AB subtends an angle of 130° at the centre O.
   The radius of the circle is 8 cm. Find:

   a) the length of AB

   b) the area of sector OAB

   c) the area of triangle OAB

   d) the area of the minor segment (shown shaded).

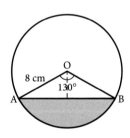

2. Find the shaded area when:

   a) $r = 6$ cm, $\theta = 70°$

   b) $r = 14$ cm, $\theta = 104°$

   c) $r = 5$ cm, $\theta = 80°$

3. Find θ and hence the shaded area when:

   a) AB = 10 cm, $r = 10$ cm

   b) AB = 8 cm, $r = 5$ cm

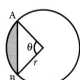

4. How far is a chord of length 8 cm from the centre of a circle of radius 5 cm?

5. How far is a chord of length 9 cm from the centre of a circle of radius 6 cm?

6. The diagram shows the cross-section of a cylindrical pipe with water lying in the bottom.
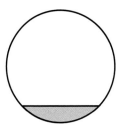

a) If the maximum depth of the water is 2 cm and the radius of the pipe is 7 cm, find the area shaded.

b) What is the *volume* of water in a pipe length of 30 cm?

7. An equilateral triangle is inscribed in a circle of radius 10 cm. Find:
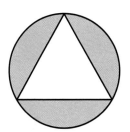

a) the area of the triangle

b) the area shaded.

8. An equilateral triangle is inscribed in a circle of radius 18.8 cm. Find:

a) the area of the triangle

b) the area of the three segments surrounding the triangle.

9. A regular hexagon is circumscribed by a circle of radius 6 cm. Find the area shaded.
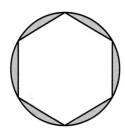

10. A regular octagon is circumscribed by a circle of radius r cm. Find the area enclosed between the circle and the octagon. (Give the answer in terms of r.)

11. Find the radius of the circle:

a) when $\theta = 90°$, $A = 20$ cm²

b) when $\theta = 30°$, $A = 35$ cm²

c) when $\theta = 150°$, $A = 114$ cm²

12. The diagram shows a regular pentagon of side 10 cm with a star inside. Calculate the area of the star.

10 cm

3.5 Volume

Prism

A prism is an object with the same cross-section throughout its length.

Volume of prism = (area of cross-section) × length

$$= A \times l$$

A *cuboid* is a prism whose six faces are all rectangles. A cube is a special case of a cuboid in which all six faces are squares.

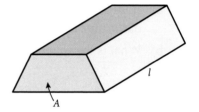

Cylinder

radius = r height = h

A cylinder is a prism whose cross-section is a circle.

Volume of cylinder = (area of cross-section) × length. Volume = $\pi r^2 h$

Example

Calculate the height of a cylinder of volume 500 cm³ and base radius 8 cm.

Let the height of the cylinder be h cm.

$$\pi r^2 h = 500$$
$$3.142 \times 8^2 \times h = 500$$
$$h = \frac{500}{3.142 \times 64}$$
$$h = 2.49 \, (3 \text{ s.f.})$$

The height of the cylinder is 2.49 cm.

Exercise 7

1. Calculate the volume of the prisms. All lengths are in cm.

a)

b)

c)

d)

e)

f)

2. Calculate the volume of the following cylinders:

   a) $r = 4$ cm, $h = 10$ cm

   b) $r = 11$ m, $h = 2$ m

   c) $r = 2.1$ cm, $h = 0.9$ cm

3. Find the height of a cylinder of volume 200 cm^3 and radius 4 cm.

> Remember 1 litre = 1000 cm^3.

4. Find the length of a cylinder of volume 2 litres and radius 10 cm.

5. Find the radius of a cylinder of volume 45 cm^3 and length 4 cm.

6. A prism has volume 100 cm^3 and length 8 cm. If the cross-section is an equilateral triangle, find the length of a side of the triangle.

7. When 3 litres of oil are removed from an upright cylindrical can, the level falls by 10 cm. Find the radius of the can.

8. A solid cylinder of radius 4 cm and length 8 cm is melted down and recast into a solid cube. Find the side of the cube.

9. A solid rectangular block of copper 5 cm by 4 cm by 2 cm is drawn out to make a cylindrical wire of diameter 2 mm. Calculate the length of the wire.

10. Water flows through a circular pipe of internal diameter 3 cm at a speed of 10 cm/s. If the pipe is full, how much water flows from the pipe in one minute? (Answer in litres.)

11. Water flows from a hose-pipe of internal diameter 1 cm at a rate of 5 litres per minute. At what speed is the water flowing through the pipe?

12. A cylindrical metal pipe has external diameter of 6 cm and internal diameter of 4 cm. Calculate the volume of metal in a pipe of length 1m. If 1 cm^3 of the metal has a mass of 8 g, find the mass of the pipe.

13. For two cylinders A and B, the ratio of lengths is 3 : 1 and the ratio of diameters is 1 : 2. Calculate the ratio of their volumes.

14. A machine makes boxes which are either perfect cylinders of diameter and length 4 cm, or perfect cubes of side 5 cm. Which boxes have the greater volume, and by how much? (Take $\pi = 3$)

15. Natalia decided to build a garage and began by calculating the number of bricks required. The garage was to be 6 m by 4 m and 2.5 m in height. Each brick measures 22 cm by 10 cm by 7 cm. Natalia estimated that she would need about 40 000 bricks. Is this a reasonable estimate?

16. A cylindrical can of internal radius 20 cm stands upright on a flat surface. It contains water to a depth of 20 cm. Calculate the rise in the level of the water when a brick of volume 1500 cm³ is immersed in the water.

17. A cylindrical tin of height 15 cm and radius 4 cm is filled with sand from a rectangular box. How many times can the tin be filled if the dimensions of the box are 50 cm by 40 cm by 20 cm?

18. Rain which falls onto a flat rectangular surface of length 6 m and width 4 m is collected in a cylinder of internal radius 20 cm. What is the depth of water in the cylinder after a storm in which 1 cm of rain fell?

Pyramid

Volume $= \frac{1}{3}$ (base area) $\times$ height.

Figure (i)

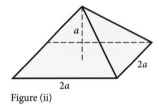

Figure (ii)

Figure (i) shows a cube of side 2*a* broken down into six pyramids of height *a* as shown in Figure (ii).

If the volume of each pyramid is *V*,

then $6V = 2a \times 2a \times 2a$

$V = \frac{1}{6} \times (2a)^2 \times 2a$

so $V = \frac{1}{3} \times (2a)^2 \times a$

$V = \frac{1}{3}$ (base area) $\times$ height

Cone

Volume $= \frac{1}{3}\pi r^2 h$

(note the similarity with the pyramid)

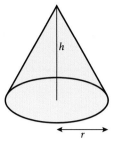

Sphere

Volume $= \frac{4}{3}\pi r^3$

Example 1

A pyramid has a square base of side 5 m and vertical height 4 m. Find its volume.

Volume of pyramid $= \frac{1}{3}(5 \times 5) \times 4$

$= 33\frac{1}{3} \text{ m}^3$

Example 2

Calculate the radius of a sphere of volume 500 cm³.

Let the radius of the sphere be r cm.

$$\frac{4}{3}\pi r^3 = 500$$

$$r^3 = \frac{3 \times 500}{4\pi}$$

$$r = \sqrt[3]{\left(\frac{3 \times 500}{4\pi}\right)} = 4.92 \text{ (3 s.f.)}$$

The radius of the sphere is 4.92 cm.

Exercise 8

Find the volumes of the following objects:

1. cone: height = 5 cm, radius = 2 cm

2. sphere: radius = 5 cm

3. sphere: radius = 10 cm

4. cone: height = 6 cm, radius = 4 cm

5. sphere: diameter = 8 cm

6. cone: height = x cm, radius = $2x$ cm

7. sphere: radius = 0.1 m

8. cone: height = $\dfrac{1}{\pi}$ cm , radius = 3 cm

9. pyramid: rectangular base 7 cm by 8 cm; height = 5 cm

10. pyramid: square base of side 4 m, height = 9 m

11. pyramid: equilateral triangular base of side = 8 cm, height = 10 cm

12. Find the volume of a hemisphere of radius 5 cm.

13. A cone is attached to a hemisphere of radius 4 cm. If the total height of the object is 10 cm, find its volume.

14. A toy consists of a cylinder of diameter 6 cm 'sandwiched' between a hemisphere and a cone of the same diameter. If the cone is of height 8 cm and the cylinder is of height 10 cm, find the total volume of the toy.

15. Find the height of a pyramid of volume $20\,\text{m}^3$ and base area $12\,\text{m}^2$.

16. Find the radius of a sphere of volume $60\,\text{cm}^3$.

17. Find the height of a cone of volume 2.5 litre and radius 10 cm.

18. Six square-based pyramids fit exactly onto the six faces of a cube of side 4 cm. If the volume of the object formed is $256\,\text{cm}^3$, find the height of each of the pyramids.

19. A solid metal cube of side 6 cm is recast into a solid sphere. Find the radius of the sphere.

20. A hollow spherical vessel has internal and external radii of 6 cm and 6.4 cm respectively. Calculate the mass of the vessel if it is made of metal of density 10 g/cm³.

21. Water is flowing into an inverted cone, of diameter and height 30 cm, at a rate of 4 litres per minute. How long, in seconds, will it take to fill the cone?

22. A solid metal sphere is recast into many smaller spheres. Calculate the number of the smaller spheres if the initial and final radii are as follows:

a) initial radius = 10 cm, final radius = 2 cm

b) initial radius = 7 cm, final radius = $\frac{1}{2}$ cm

c) initial radius = 1 m, final radius = $\frac{1}{3}$ cm.

23. A spherical ball is immersed in water contained in a vertical cylinder.

Assuming the water covers the ball, calculate the rise in the water level if:

a) sphere radius = 3 cm, cylinder radius = 10 cm

b) sphere radius = 2 cm, cylinder radius = 5 cm.

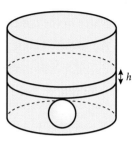

24. A spherical ball is immersed in water contained in a vertical cylinder. The rise in water level is measured in order to calculate the radius of the spherical ball. Calculate the radius of the ball in the following cases:

a) cylinder of radius 10 cm, water level rises 4 cm

b) cylinder of radius 100 cm, water level rises 8 cm.

25. One corner of a solid cube of side 8 cm is removed by cutting through the midpoints of three adjacent sides. Calculate the volume of the piece removed.

26. The cylindrical end of a pencil is sharpened to produce a perfect cone at the end with no overall loss of length. If the diameter of the pencil is 1 cm, and the cone is of length 2 cm, calculate the volume of the shavings.

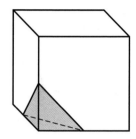

27. Metal spheres of radius 2 cm are packed into a rectangular box of internal dimensions 16 cm × 8 cm × 8 cm. When 16 spheres are packed the box is filled with a preservative liquid. Find the volume of this liquid.

28. The diagram shows the cross-section of an inverted cone of height MC = 12 cm. If AB = 6 cm and XY = 2 cm, use similar triangles to find the length NC.

(You can find out about similar triangles on page 147.)

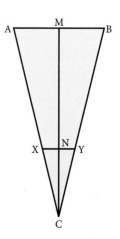

29. An inverted cone of height 10 cm and base radius 6.4 cm contains water to a depth of 5 cm, measured from the vertex. Calculate the volume of water in the cone.

30. An inverted cone of height 15 cm and base radius 4 cm contains water to a depth of 10 cm. Calculate the volume of water in the cone.

31. An inverted cone of height 12 cm and base radius 6 cm contains 20 cm^3 of water. Calculate the depth of water in the cone, measured from the vertex.

32. A frustum is a cone with 'the end chopped off'. A bucket in the shape of a frustum as shown has diameters of 10 cm and 4 cm at its ends and a depth of 3 cm. Calculate the volume of the bucket.

33. Find the volume of a frustum with end diameters of 60 cm and 20 cm and a depth of 40 cm.

34. The diagram shows a sector of a circle of radius 10 cm.

    a) Find, as a multiple of π, the arc length of the sector.

    The straight edges are brought together to make a cone. Calculate:

    b) the radius of the base of the cone

    c) the vertical height of the cone.

35. Calculate the volume of a regular octahedron whose edges are all 10 cm.

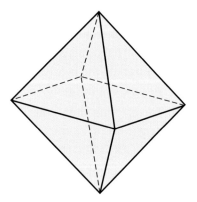

36. A sphere passes through the eight corners of a cube of side 10 cm. Find the volume of the sphere.

37. ind the volume of a regular tetrahedron of side 20 cm.

38. Find the volume of a regular tetrahedron of side 35 cm.

3.6 Surface area

We are concerned here with the surface areas of the *curved* parts of cylinders, spheres and cones. The areas of the plane faces are easier to find.

a) Cylinder
Curved surface area $= 2\pi rh$

b) Sphere
Surface area $= 4\pi r^2$

c) Cone
Curved surface area $= \pi rl$
where l is the slant height.

Example 1

Find the *total* surface area of a solid cone of radius 4 cm and vertical height 3 cm.

Let the slant height of the cone be l cm.

$l^2 = 3^2 + 4^2$ $\quad$ (Pythagoras' theorem)

$l = 5$

Curved surface area $= \pi \times 4 \times 5$
$$= 20\pi \text{ cm}^2$$

Area of end face $= \pi \times 4^2 = 16\pi \text{ cm}^2$

$\therefore$ $\quad$ Total surface area $= 20\pi + 16\pi$
$$= 36\pi \text{ cm}^2$$
$$= 113 \text{ cm}^2 \text{ (3 s.f.)}$$

Example 2

Find the surface area of a prism, whose length is 50 cm and whose cross-section is a regular hexagon with side length 10 cm and area 172 cm².

There is no general formula for the surface area of a prism.

Area of the two hexagons $= 2 \times 172$
$$= 344 \text{ cm}^2$$

Area of the six rectangular faces $= 6 \times 50 \times 10$
$$= 3000 \text{ cm}^2$$

Total area $= 344 + 3000$
$$= 3344 \text{ cm}^2$$

Exercise 9

Use the π button on a calculator unless otherwise instructed.

1. Copy the table and find the quantities marked*. (Leave π in your answers.)

	solid object	radius	vertical height	curved surface area	total surface area
a)	sphere	3 cm		*	
b)	cylinder	4 cm	5 cm		*
c)	cone	6 cm	8 cm	*	
d)	cylinder	0.7 m	1 m		*
e)	sphere	10 m		*	
f)	cone	5 cm	12 cm	*	
g)	cylinder	6 mm	10 mm		*
h)	cone	2.1 cm	4.4 cm	*	
i)	sphere	0.01 m		*	
j)	hemisphere	7 cm		*	*

2. Find the radius of a sphere of surface area 34 cm².

3. Find the slant height of a cone of curved surface area 20 cm² and radius 3 cm.

4. Find the height of a solid cylinder of radius 1 cm and *total* surface area 28 cm².

5. Copy the table and find the quantities marked*. (Take $\pi = 3$)

	object	radius	vertical height	curved surface area	total surface area
a)	cylinder	4 cm	*	72 cm²	
b)	sphere	*		192 cm²	
c)	cone	4 cm	*	60 cm²	
d)	sphere	*		0.48 m²	
e)	cylinder	5 cm	*		330 cm²
f)	cone	6 cm	*		225 cm²
g)	cylinder	2 m	*		108 m²

6. A solid wooden cylinder of height 8 cm and radius 3 cm is cut in two along a vertical axis of symmetry. Calculate the total surface area of the two pieces.

7. A tin of paint covers a surface area of 60 m² and costs $4.50. Find the cost of painting the outside surface of a hemispherical dome of radius 50 m. (Just the curved part.)

8. A solid cylinder of height 10 cm and radius 4 cm is to be plated with material costing $11 per cm². Find the cost of the plating.

9. Find the volume of a sphere of surface area 100 cm².

10. Find the surface area of a sphere of volume 28 cm³.

11. Calculate the total surface area of the combined cone/cylinder/hemisphere.

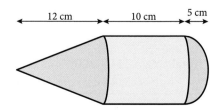

12. A man wants to spray the entire surface of the Earth (including the oceans) with a new weed killer. If it takes him 10 seconds to spray $1\,m^2$, how long will it take to spray the whole world? (Radius of the Earth = 6370 km; ignore leap years)

13. An inverted cone of vertical height 12 cm and base radius 9 cm contains water to a depth of 4 cm. Find the area of the interior surface of the cone not in contact with the water.

14. A circular piece of paper of radius 20 cm is cut in half and each half is made into a hollow cone by joining the straight edges. Find the slant height and base radius of each cone.

15. A golf ball has a diameter of 4.1 cm and the surface has 150 dimples of radius 2 mm. Calculate the total surface area which is exposed to the surroundings. (Assume the 'dimples' are hemispherical.)

16. A cone of radius 3 cm and slant height 6 cm is cut into four identical pieces. Calculate the total surface area of the four pieces.

dimple of radius 2 mm

In questions **17** to **20** find the surface area of each prism.

17.

18.

19.

20.

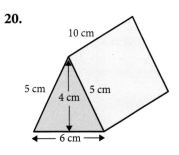

Example

A 1 cm by 1 cm square measures 10 mm by 10 mm. The *area* of the square in mm² is therefore $10 \times 10 = 100 \, \text{mm}^2$.

There are similar area conversions for m² into cm² and km² into m²:

$1 \, \text{m}^2 = 100 \times 100 = 10\,000 \, \text{cm}^2$

$1 \, \text{km}^2 = 1000 \times 1000 = 1\,000\,000 \, \text{m}^2$

A 1 cm by 1 cm by 1 cm cube measures 10 mm by 10 mm by 10 mm. The *volume* of the cube is therefore $10 \times 10 \times 10 = 1000 \, \text{mm}^3$.

Likewise, $1 \, \text{m}^3 = 100 \times 100 \times 100 = 1\,000\,000 \, \text{cm}^3$

1 cm = 10 mm
1 cm = 10 mm
1 cm = 10 mm
1 cm = 10 mm
1 cm = 10 mm

Exercise 10

Copy and complete.

1. $2 \, \text{cm}^2 = \quad \text{mm}^2$
2. $45 \, \text{cm}^2 = \quad \text{mm}^2$
3. $1600 \, \text{mm}^2 = \quad \text{cm}^2$
4. $48 \, \text{mm}^2 = \quad \text{cm}^2$
5. $3 \, \text{m}^2 = \quad \text{cm}^2$
6. $26 \, \text{m}^2 = \quad \text{cm}^2$
7. $8600 \, \text{cm}^2 = \quad \text{m}^2$
8. $760 \, \text{cm}^2 = \quad \text{m}^2$
9. $5 \, \text{km}^2 = \quad \text{m}^2$
10. $4\,500\,000 \, \text{m}^2 = \quad \text{km}^2$
11. $8 \, \text{cm}^3 = \quad \text{mm}^3$
12. $21 \, \text{cm}^3 = \quad \text{mm}^3$
13. $48\,000 \, \text{mm}^3 = \quad \text{cm}^3$
14. $6 \, \text{m}^3 = \quad \text{cm}^3$
15. $28\,000\,000 \, \text{cm}^3 = \quad \text{m}^3$

16. A cuboid measures 3 cm by 2 cm by 4 cm.
    a) Find the volume in mm³.
    b) Find the surface area in mm².

17. A rectangle measures 40 cm by 80 cm. Find the area in m².

18. A sphere has radius 6.2 m.
    a) Find the surface area in cm².
    b) Find the volume in m³.
    c) Find the volume in cm³.

19. A square-based pyramid has base area 300 cm² and height 40 mm.
    Find the volume in mm³.

20. A cylinder has volume 1200 cm³. The length of the cylinder is 42 mm.
    Find the radius of the cylinder in mm.

Revision exercise 3A

1. Find the area of the following shapes:

a)

7 cm
30°
8 cm

b)

7 cm
6 cm
11 cm

c)

6 cm
5 cm
10 cm

d)

4 cm
9 cm

2. a) A circle has radius 9 m. Find its circumference and area.

  b) A circle has circumference 34 cm. Find its diameter.

  c) A circle has area 50 cm². Find its radius.

3. A target consists of concentric circles of radii 3 cm and 9 cm.

  a) Find the area of A, in terms of π.

  b) Find the ratio $\dfrac{\text{area of B}}{\text{area of A}}$.

4. In Figure 1 a circle of radius 4 cm is inscribed in a square. In Figure 2 a square is inscribed in a circle of radius 4 cm.

Calculate the shaded area in each diagram.

 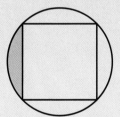

Figure 1   Figure 2

5. Given that OA = 10 cm and $\widehat{AOB} = 70°$ (where O is the centre of the circle), calculate:

  a) the arc length AB

  b) the area of minor sector AOB.

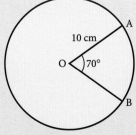

6. The points X and Y lie on the circumference of a circle, of centre O and radius 8 cm, where $\widehat{XOY} = 80°$. Calculate:

  a) the length of the minor arc XY

  b) the length of the chord XY

  c) the area of sector XOY

  d) the area of triangle XOY

  e) the area of the minor segment of the circle cut off by XY.

7. Given that ON = 10 cm and minor arc MN = 18 cm, calculate the angle $\widehat{MON}$ (shown as $x°$).

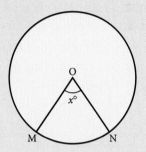

8. A cylinder of radius 8 cm has a volume of 2 litres. Calculate the height of the cylinder.

9. Calculate:

  a) the volume of a sphere of radius 6 cm

  b) the radius of a sphere whose volume is 800 cm³.

10. A sphere of radius 5 cm is melted down and made into a solid cube. Find the length of a side of the cube.

11. The curved surface area of a solid circular cylinder of height 8 cm is 100 cm². Calculate the volume of the cylinder.

12. A cone has base radius 5 cm and vertical height 10 cm, correct to the nearest cm. Calculate the maximum and minimum possible volumes of the cone, consistent with this data.

13. Calculate the radius of a hemispherical solid whose total surface area is 48π cm².

14. Calculate:

   a) the area of an equilateral triangle of side 6 cm

   b) the area of a regular hexagon of side 6 cm

   c) the volume of a regular hexagonal prism of length 10 cm, where the side of the hexagon is 12 cm.

15. Ten spheres of radius 1 cm are immersed in liquid contained in a vertical cylinder of radius 6 cm. Calculate the rise in the level of the liquid in the cylinder.

16. A cube of side 10 cm is melted down and made into ten identical spheres. Calculate the surface area of one of the spheres.

17. The square has sides of length 3 cm and the arcs have centres at the corners. Find the shaded area.

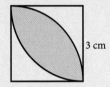

3 cm

18. A copper pipe has external diameter 18 mm and thickness 2 mm. The density of copper is 9 g/cm³ and the price of copper is $150 per tonne. What is the cost of the copper in a length of 5 m of this pipe?

19. Twenty-seven small wooden cubes fit exactly inside a cubical box without a lid. How many of the cubes are touching the sides or the bottom of the box?

20. In the diagram the area of the smaller square is 10 cm². Find the area of the larger square.

21. A piece of wood, to be used for making a ramp, has been cut into the shape of a prism, whose cross-section is a right-angled triangle with side lengths 9 cm, 12 cm and 15 cm. The width of the ramp is 25 cm.

   a) Calculate the volume of the ramp.

   b) Calculate the surface area of the ramp.

9 cm · 15 cm · 12 cm · 25 cm

Examination-style exercise 3B

1. A spacecraft made 58 376 orbits of the Earth and travelled a distance of 2.656×10^9 kilometres.

   (a) Calculate the distance travelled in 1 orbit correct to the nearest kilometre. [2]

   (b) The orbit of the spacecraft is a circle. Calculate the radius of the orbit. [2]

   Cambridge IGCSE Mathematics 0580
   Paper 21 Q14 November 2008

2. A large conference table is made from four rectangular sections and four corner sections.

   Each rectangular section is 4 m long and 1.2 m wide.

   Each corner section is a quarter circle, radius 1.2 m.

   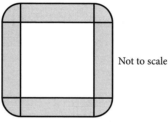

   Not to scale

   Each person sitting at the conference table requires one metre of its outside perimeter.

   Calculate the greatest number of people who can sit around the **outside** of the table.

   Show all your working. [3]

   Cambridge IGCSE Mathematics 0580
   Paper 2 Q11 November 2005

3. In triangle ABC, $AB = 6$ cm, $AC = 8$ cm, and $BC = 12$ cm.
   Angle $ACB = 26.4°$.

   Calculate the area of the triangle ABC. [2]

   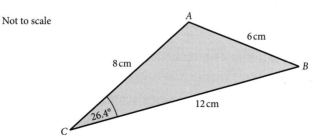

   Not to scale

   Cambridge IGCSE Mathematics 0580
   Paper 2 Q5 June 2006

4.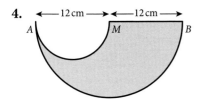

The shape above is made by removing a small semi-circle from a large semi-circle.

$AM = MB = 12$ cm [3]

Calculate the area of the shape.

Cambridge IGCSE Mathematics 0580
Paper 2 Q10 November 2007

5.

Not to scale

The largest possible circle is drawn inside a semi-circle, as shown in the diagram.

The distance AB is 12 centimetres.

(a) Find the shaded area. [4]

(b) Find the perimeter of the shaded area. [2]

Cambridge IGCSE Mathematics 0580
Paper 2 Q23 June 2007

6.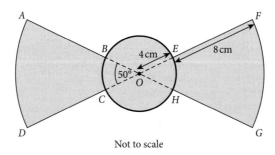

Not to scale

The diagram shows part of a logo that has been designed for an engineering company.

OAD and OFG are sectors, centre O, with radius 12 cm and angle 50°.

B, C, E and H lie on a circle, centre O, and radius 4 cm.

Calculate, correct to 3 significant figures, the area shaded. [4]

7.

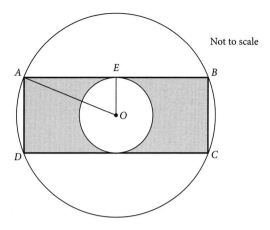

Not to scale

A, B, C and D lie on a circle, centre O, radius 8 cm.

AB and CD are tangents to a circle, centre O, radius 4 cm.

$ABCD$ is a rectangle.

(a) Calculate the distance AE [2]

(b) Calculate the shaded area. [3]

Cambridge IGCSE Mathematics 0580
Paper 2 Q21 November 2005

8.

Not to scale

A solid metal bar is in the shape of a cuboid of length of 250 cm.

The cross-section is a square of side x cm.

The volume of the cuboid is 4840 cm³.

(a) Show that $x = 4.4$. [2]

(b) The mass of 1 cm³ of the metal is 8.8 grams. Calculate the mass of the whole metal bar in kilograms. [2]

(c) A box, in the shape of a cuboid measures 250 cm by 88 cm by h cm.

120 of the metal bars fit exactly in the box.

Calculate the value of h. [2]

(d) One metal bar, of volume 4840 cm³, is melted down to make 4200 identical small spheres.

All the metal is used.

i) Calculate the radius of each sphere. Show that your answer rounds to 0.65 cm, correct to 2 decimal places. [4]

[The volume, V, of a sphere, radius r, is given by $V = \frac{4}{3}\pi r^3$.]

ii) Calculate the surface area of each sphere, using 0.65 cm for the radius. [1]

[The surface area, A, of a sphere, radius r, is given by $A = 4\pi r^2$.]

iii) Calculate the total surface area of all 4200 spheres as a percentage of the surface area of the metal bar. [4]

Cambridge IGCSE Mathematics 0580
Paper 4 Q7 June 2009

9.

Not to scale

A circle, centre O, touches all the sides of the regular octagon *ABCDEFGH* shaded in the diagram.

The sides of the octagon are of length 12 cm.

BA and *GH* are extended to meet at *P*.
HG and *EF* are extended to meet at *Q*.

(a) i) Show that angle *BAH* is 135°. [2]

 ii) Show that angle *APH* is 90°. [1]

(b) Calculate

 i) the length of *PH*, [2]

 ii) the length of *PQ*, [2]

 iii) the area of triangle *APH*, [2]

 iv) the area of the octagon. [3]

(c) Calculate

 i) the radius of the circle, [2]

 ii) the area of the circle as a percentage of the area of the octagon. [3]

Cambridge IGCSE Mathematics 0580
Paper 4 Q5 June 2008

10. Paul and Debbie buy their son a magic set. The box is a prism with a cross-section that is a trapezium, as shown in the diagram.

a) Calculate the area of the cross-section. [2]

b) Calculate the volume of the box. [2]

c) Calculate the surface area of the box. [3]

4 Geometry

Pythagoras (569–500 B.C.) was one of the first of the great mathematical names in Greek antiquity. He settled in southern Italy and formed a mysterious brotherhood with his students who were bound by an oath not to reveal the secrets of numbers and who exercised great influence. They laid the foundations of arithmetic through geometry but failed to resolve the concept of irrational numbers. The work of these and others was brought together by Euclid at Alexandria in a book called 'The Elements', which was still studied in English schools as recently as 1900.

E4.1 Use and interpret the geometrical terms: point, line, parallel, bearing, right angle, acute, obtuse and reflex angles, perpendicular, similarity and congruence. Use and interpret vocabulary of triangles, quadrilaterals, circles, polygons and simple solid figures including nets.

E4.2 Measure and draw lines and angles. Construct a triangle given the three sides using ruler and pair of compasses only.

E4.4 Calculate lengths of similar figures. Use the relationships between areas of similar triangles, with corresponding results for similar figures and extension to volumes and surface areas of similar solids.

E4.5 Use the basic congruence criteria for triangles (SSS, ASA, SAS, RHS).

E4.6 Recognise rotational and line symmetry (including order of rotational symmetry) in two dimensions. Recognise symmetry properties of the prism (including cylinder) and the pyramid (including cone). Use the following symmetry properties of circles:
- equal chords are equidistant from the centre
- the perpendicular bisector of a chord passes through the centre
- tangents from an external point are equal in length.

E4.7 Calculate unknown angles using the following geometrical properties:
- angles at a point
- angles at a point on a straight line and intersecting straight lines
- angles formed within parallel lines
- angle properties of triangles and quadrilaterals
- angle properties of regular polygons
- angle in a semicircle
- angle between tangent and radius of a circle
- angle properties of irregular polygons
- angle at the centre of a circle is twice the angle at the circumference
- angles in the same segment are equal
- angles in opposite segments are supplementary; cyclic quadrilaterals
- alternate segment theorem.

E6.2 Apply Pythagoras' theorem.

4.1 Fundamental results

You should already be familiar with the following results. They are used later in this section and are quoted here for reference.

- The angles on a straight line add up to 180°:

$$\hat{x} + \hat{y} + \hat{z} = 180°$$

- The angles at a point add up to 360°:

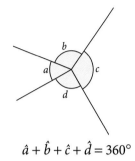

$$\hat{a} + \hat{b} + \hat{c} + \hat{d} = 360°$$

- Vertically opposite angles are equal:

- The angle sum of a triangle is 180°.
- An isosceles triangle has 2 sides and 2 angles the same:

- The angle sum of a quadrilateral is 360°.
- An equilateral triangle has 3 sides and 3 angles the same:

Exercise 1

Find the angles marked with letters. (AB is always a straight line.)

1.

2.

3.

4.

5.

6.

7.

8.

$f = 2e$

9.

10.

11.

12.

$b = 2a$
$c = 4a$
$d = 3a$

13.

14.

15.

16.

17.

18.

19.

20.

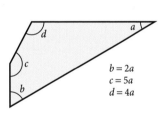

$b = 2a$
$c = 5a$
$d = 4a$

21.

22.

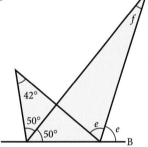

23. Calculate the largest angle of a triangle in which one angle is eight times each of the others.

24. In ΔABC, $\widehat{A}$ is a right angle and D is a point on AC such that BD bisects $\widehat{B}$. If $B\widehat{D}C = 100°$, calculate $\widehat{C}$.

25. WXYZ is a quadrilateral in which $\widehat{W} = 108°$, $\widehat{X} = 88°$, $\widehat{Y} = 57°$ and $W\widehat{X}Z = 31°$. Calculate $W\widehat{Z}X$ and $X\widehat{Z}Y$.

26. In quadrilateral ABCD, AB produced is perpendicular to DC produced. If $\widehat{A} = 44°$ and $\widehat{C} = 148°$, calculate $\widehat{D}$ and $\widehat{B}$.

27. Triangles ABD, CBD and ADC are all isosceles. Find the angle x.

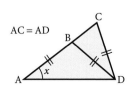

AC = AD

Polygons

i) The exterior angles of a polygon add up to $360°$ ($\hat{a} + \hat{b} + \hat{c} + \hat{d} + \hat{e} = 360°$).

ii) The sum of the interior angles of a polygon is $(n - 2) \times 180°$ where n is the number of sides of the polygon.

This result is investigated in question **3** in the next exercise.

iii) A regular polygon has equal sides and equal angles.

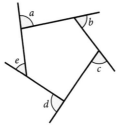

Pentagon = 5 sides
Hexagon = 6 sides
Octagon = 8 sides
Decagon = 10 sides

Example

Find the angles marked with letters.

The sum of the interior angles = $(n - 2) \times 180°$

where n is the number of sides of the polygon.

In this case $n = 6$.

$$\therefore \quad 110 + 120 + 94 + 114 + 2t = 4 \times 180$$
$$438 + 2t = 720$$
$$2t = 282$$
$$t = 141°$$

Exercise 2

1. Find angles a and b for the regular pentagon.

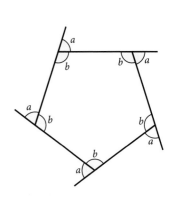

2. Find x and y.

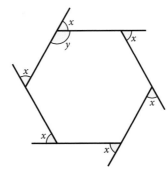

3. Consider the pentagon below which has been divided into three triangles.

$\hat{A} = a + f + g, \hat{B} = b, \hat{C} = c + d, \hat{D} = e + i, \hat{E} = h$

Now $a + b + c = d + e + f = g + h + i = 180°$

$\therefore \quad \hat{A} + \hat{B} + \hat{C} + \hat{D} + \hat{E} = a + b + c + d + e + f + g + h + i$

$\qquad\qquad\qquad = 3 \times 180°$

$\qquad\qquad\qquad = 6 \times 90°$

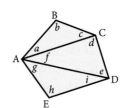

Draw further polygons and make a table of results.

Number of sides n	5	6	7	8 . . .
Sum of interior angles	$3 \times 180°$			

What is the sum of the interior angles for a polygon with n sides?

4. Find a.

5. Find m.

6. Find a.

7. Calculate the number of sides of a regular polygon whose interior angles are each $156°$.

8. Calculate the number of sides of a regular polygon whose interior angles are each $150°$.

9. Calculate the number of sides of a regular polygon whose exterior angles are each $40°$.

10. In a regular polygon each interior angle is $140°$ greater than each exterior angle. Calculate the number of sides of the polygon.

11. In a regular polygon each interior angle is $120°$ greater than each exterior angle. Calculate the number of sides of the polygon.

12. Two sides of a regular pentagon are produced to form angle x. What is x?

Parallel lines

i) $\hat{a} = \hat{c}$ (corresponding angles)

ii) $\hat{c} = \hat{d}$ (alternate angles)

iii) $\hat{b} + \hat{c} = 180°$ (allied angles)

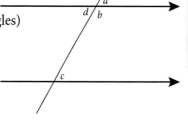

The acute angles (angles less than 90°) are the same and the obtuse angles (angles between 90° and 180°) are the same.

Exercise 3

In questions **1** to **9** find the angles marked with letters.

1.

2.

3.

4.

5.

6.

7.

8.

9.
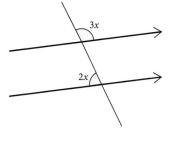

4.2 Pythagoras' theorem

In a right-angled triangle the square on the hypotenuse is equal to the sum of the squares on the other two sides.

$a^2 + b^2 = c^2$

This is the hypotenuse. It is the side opposite the right angle.

Example

Find the side marked d.

$d^2 + 4^2 = 7^2$

$d^2 = 49 - 16$

$d = \sqrt{33} = 5.74$ cm (3 s.f.)

The *converse* is also true:

'If the square on one side of a triangle is equal to the sum of the squares on the other two sides, then the triangle is right-angled'.

Exercise 4

In questions **1** to **10**, find x. All the lengths are in cm.

1.

2.

3.

4.

5.

6.

7.

8.

9.

10.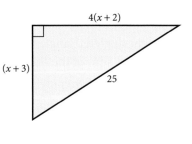

11. Find the length of a diagonal of a rectangle of length 9 cm and width 4 cm.

12. A square has diagonals of length 10 cm. Find the sides of the square.

13. A 4 m ladder rests against a vertical wall with its foot 2 m from the wall. How far up the wall does the ladder reach?

14. A ship sails 20 km due North and then 35 km due East. How far is it from its starting point?

15. Find the length of a diagonal of a rectangular box of length 12 cm, width 5 cm and height 4 cm.

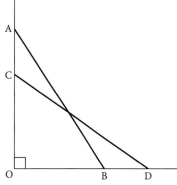

16. Find the length of a diagonal of a rectangular room of length 5 m, width 3 m and height 2.5 m.

17. Find the height of a rectangular box of length 8 cm, width 6 cm where the length of a diagonal is 11 cm.

18. An aircraft flies equal distances South-East and then South-West to finish 120 km due South of its starting-point. How long is each part of its journey?

19. The diagonal of a rectangle exceeds the length by 2 cm. If the width of the rectangle is 10 cm, find the length.

20. A cone has base radius 5 cm and *slant* height 11 cm. Find its vertical height.

21. It is possible to find the sides of a right-angled triangle, with lengths which are whole numbers, by substituting different values of x into the expressions:

    a) $2x^2 + 2x + 1$ **b)** $2x^2 + 2x$ **c)** $2x + 1$

    (**(a)** represents the hypotenuse, **(b)** and **(c)** the other two sides.)

    i) Find the sides of the triangles when $x = 1, 2, 3, 4$ and 5.

    ii) Confirm that $(2x + 1)^2 + (2x^2 + 2x)^2 = (2x^2 + 2x + 1)^2$

22. The diagram represents the starting position (AB) and the finishing position (CD) of a ladder as it slips. The ladder is leaning against a vertical wall.

    Given: AC = x, OC = 4AC, BD = 2AC and OB = 5 m. Form an equation in x, find x and hence find the length of the ladder.

23. A thin wire of length 18 cm is bent into the shape shown. Calculate the length from A to B.

24. An aircraft is vertically above a point which is 10 km West and 15 km North of a control tower. If the aircraft is 4000 m above the ground, how far is it from the control tower?

4.3 Symmetry

Line symmetry

The letter A has one line of symmetry, shown dotted.

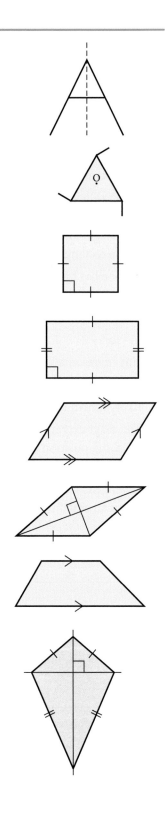

Rotational symmetry

The shape may be turned about O into three identical positions. It has rotational symmetry of order 3.

Quadrilaterals

1. *Square*
   All sides are equal, all angles 90°, opposite sides parallel; diagonals bisect at right angles. Four lines of symmetry. Rotational symmetry of order of 4.

2. *Rectangle*
   Opposite sides parallel and equal, all angles 90°, diagonals bisect each other. Two lines of symmetry. Rotational symmetry of order 2.

3. *Parallelogram*
   Opposite sides parallel and equal, opposite angles equal, diagonals bisect each other (but not equal). No lines of symmetry. Rotational symmetry of order 2.

4. *Rhombus*
   A parallelogram with all sides equal, diagonals bisect each other at right angles and bisect angles. Two lines of symmetry. Rotational symmetry of order 2.

5. *Trapezium*
   One pair of sides is parallel. No line or rotational symmetry.

6. *Kite*
   Two pairs of adjacent sides equal, diagonals meet at right angles bisecting one of them. One line of symmetry. No rotational symmetry.

Exercise 5

1. For each shape state:

   i) the number of lines of symmetry   **ii)** the order of rotational symmetry.

a)

b)

c)

d)

e)

f)

g)

h)

i)

j)

k)

l)

m)

n)

2. Add one line to each of the diagrams below so that the resulting figure has rotational symmetry but not line symmetry.

a)

b)

3. Draw a hexagon with just two lines of symmetry.

4. For each of the following shapes, find:

   a) the number of lines of symmetry

   b) the order of rotational symmetry.

   Square; rectangle; parallelogram; rhombus; trapezium; kite; equilateral triangle; regular hexagon.

In questions **5** to **15**, begin by drawing a diagram.

5. In a rectangle KLMN, $L\hat{N}M = 34°$. Calculate:

   a) $K\hat{L}N$ **b)** $K\hat{M}L$

6. In a trapezium ABCD, $A\hat{B}D = 35°$, $B\hat{A}D = 110°$ and AB is parallel to DC. Calculate:

    a) $A\hat{D}B$ **b)** $B\hat{D}C$

7. In a parallelogram WXYZ, $W\hat{X}Y = 72°$, $Z\hat{W}Y = 80°$. Calculate:

    a) $W\hat{Z}Y$ **b)** $X\hat{W}Z$ **c)** $W\hat{Y}Z$

8. In a kite ABCD, AB = AD; BC = CD; $C\hat{A}D = 40°$ and $C\hat{B}D = 60°$. Calculate:

    a) $B\hat{A}C$ **b)** $B\hat{C}A$ **c)** $A\hat{D}C$

9. In a rhombus ABCD, $A\hat{B}C = 64°$. Calculate:

    a) $B\hat{C}D$ **b)** $A\hat{D}B$ **c)** $B\hat{A}C$

10. In a rectangle WXYZ, M is the midpoint of WX and $Z\hat{M}Y = 70°$. Calculate:

    a) $M\hat{Z}Y$ **b)** $Y\hat{M}X$

11. In a trapezium ABCD, AB is parallel to DC, AB = AD, BD = DC and $B\hat{A}D = 128°$. Find:

    a) $A\hat{B}D$ **b)** $B\hat{D}C$ **c)** $B\hat{C}D$

12. In a parallelogram KLMN, KL = KM and $K\hat{M}L = 64°$. Find:

    a) $M\hat{K}L$ **b)** $K\hat{N}M$ **c)** $L\hat{M}N$

13. In a kite PQRS with PQ = PS and RQ = RS, $Q\hat{R}S = 40°$ and $Q\hat{P}S = 100°$. Find:

    a) $Q\hat{S}R$ **b)** $P\hat{S}Q$ **c)** $P\hat{Q}R$

14. In a rhombus PQRS, $R\hat{P}Q = 54°$. Find:

    a) $P\hat{R}Q$ **b)** $P\hat{S}R$ **c)** $R\hat{Q}S$

15. In a kite PQRS, $R\hat{P}S = 2P\hat{R}S$, PQ = QS = PS and QR = RS. Find:

    a) $Q\hat{P}S$ **b)** $P\hat{R}S$ **c)** $Q\hat{S}R$ **d)** $P\hat{Q}R$

Planes of symmetry

A **plane of symmetry** divides a 3-D shape into two congruent shapes. One shape must be a mirror image of the other shape.

The diagrams show two planes of symmetry of a cube.

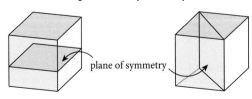

plane of symmetry

Exercise 6

1. How many planes of symmetry does this cuboid have?

2. How many planes of symmetry do these shapes have?

a)

b)

c)

3. a) Draw a diagram of a cube like the one on the previous page and draw a different plane of symmetry.

   b) How many planes of symmetry does a cube have?

4. Draw a pyramid with a square base so that the point of the pyramid is vertically above the centre of the square base. Show any planes of symmetry by shading.

5. The diagrams show the plan view and the side view of an object.

plan view

side view

> The plan view is the view looking down on the object. The side view is the view from one side.

   How many planes of symmetry does this object have?

6. a) How many planes of symmetry does a cylinder have?

   b) Describe the symmetry, if any, of a cone.

4.4 Similarity

Two triangles are similar if they have the same angles. For other shapes, corresponding sides must also be in the same proportion. Thus the two rectangles A and B are *not* similar even though they have the same angles.

Example

In the triangles ABC and XYZ

$\hat{A} = \hat{X}$ and $\hat{B} = \hat{Y}$

so the triangles are similar. ($\hat{C}$ must be equal to $\hat{Z}$.)

We have $\dfrac{BC}{YZ} = \dfrac{AC}{XZ} = \dfrac{AB}{XY}$

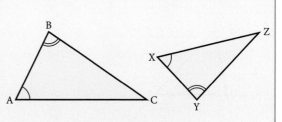

Exercise 7

Find the sides marked with letters in questions **1** to **11**; all lengths are given in centimetres.

1.

2.

3.

4.

5.

6.

7.

8.

9. $\widehat{BAC} = \widehat{DBC}$

10.

11.

12. The photo shows a rectangular picture 16 cm × 8 cm surrounded by a border of width 4 cm. Are the two rectangles similar?

13. The diagonals of a trapezium ABCD intersect at O. AB is parallel to DC, AB = 3 cm and DC = 6 cm. If CO = 4 cm and OB = 3 cm, find AO and DO.

14. A tree of height 4 m casts a shadow of length 6.5 m. Find the height of a house casting a shadow 26 m long.

15. Which of the following *must* be similar to each other?

a) two equilateral triangles   **b)** two rectangles

c) two isosceles triangles   **d)** two squares

e) two regular pentagons   **f)** two kites

g) two rhombuses   **h)** two circles

16. In the diagram $A\hat{B}C = A\hat{D}B = 90°$, AD = p and DC = q.

a) Use similar triangles to show that $x^2 = pz$.

b) Find a similar expression for y^2.

c) Add the expressions for x^2 and y^2 and hence prove Pythagoras' theorem.

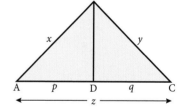

17. In a triangle ABC, a line is drawn parallel to BC to meet AB at D and AC at E. DC and BE meet at X. Prove that:

a) the triangles ADE and ABC are similar

b) the triangles DXE and BXC are similar

c) $\dfrac{AD}{AB} = \dfrac{EX}{XB}$

18. From the rectangle ABCD a square is cut off to leave rectangle BCEF. Rectangle BCEF is similar to ABCD. Find x and hence state the ratio of the sides of rectangle ABCD.

ABCD is called the Golden Rectangle and is an important shape in architecture.

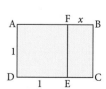

Areas of similar shapes

The two rectangles are similar, the ratio of corresponding sides being k.

area of ABCD $= ab$

area of WXYZ $= ka \times kb = k^2 ab$

$\therefore \quad \dfrac{\text{area WXYZ}}{\text{area ABCD}} = \dfrac{k^2 ab}{ab} = k^2$

This illustrates an important general rule for all similar shapes:

If two figures are similar and the ratio of corresponding sides is k, then the ratio of their areas is k^2.

This result also applies for the surface areas of similar three-dimensional objects.

Note: k is sometimes called the *linear scale factor*.

Example 1

XY is parallel to BC.

$\dfrac{\text{AB}}{\text{AX}} = \dfrac{3}{2}$

If the area of $\triangle$AXY $= 4$ cm², find the area of $\triangle$ABC.

The triangles ABC and AXY are similar.

Ratio of corresponding sides $(k) = \dfrac{3}{2}$

$\therefore \qquad$ Ratio of areas $(k^2) = \dfrac{9}{4}$

$\therefore \quad$ Area of $\triangle$ABC $= \dfrac{9}{4} \times (\text{area of } \triangle\text{AXY})$

$\qquad\qquad\qquad = \dfrac{9}{4} \times (4) = 9$ cm²

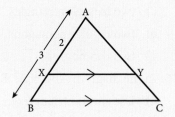

Example 2

Two similar triangles have areas of 18 cm² and 32 cm² respectively.
If the base of the smaller triangle is 6 cm, find the base of the larger triangle.

Ratio of areas $\left(k^2\right) = \dfrac{32}{18} = \dfrac{16}{9}$

$\therefore \quad$ Ratio of corresponding sides $(k) = \sqrt{\left(\dfrac{16}{9}\right)}$

$\qquad\qquad\qquad\qquad\qquad = \dfrac{4}{3}$

$\therefore \qquad$ Base of larger triangle $= 6 \times \dfrac{4}{3} = 8$ cm

Exercise 8

In this exercise a number written inside a figure represents the
area of the shape in cm². Numbers on the outside give linear
dimensions in cm. In questions **1** to **6** find the unknown area *A*.
In each case the shapes are similar.

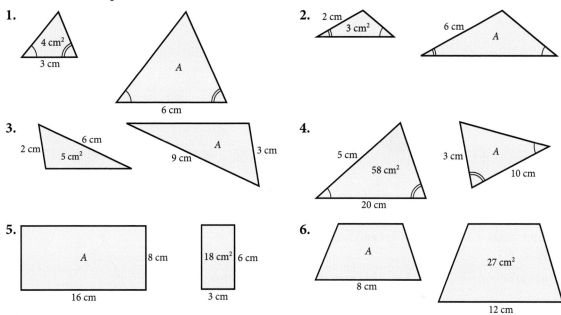

1.
4 cm²
3 cm
A
6 cm

2. 2 cm
3 cm²
6 cm
A

3.
6 cm
2 cm
5 cm²
A
9 cm
3 cm

4.
5 cm
58 cm²
20 cm
3 cm
A
10 cm

5.
A
8 cm
16 cm
18 cm² 6 cm
3 cm

6.
A
8 cm
27 cm²
12 cm

In questions **7** to **12**, find the lengths marked for each pair of similar shapes.

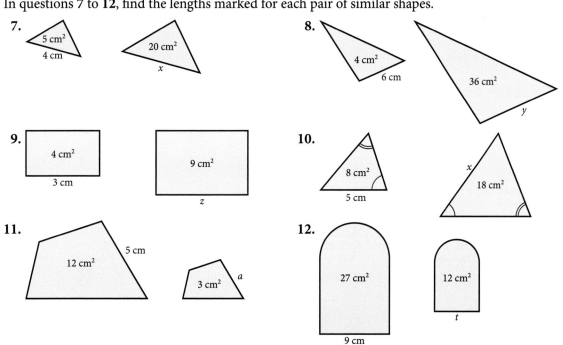

7.
5 cm²
4 cm
20 cm²
x

8.
4 cm²
6 cm
36 cm²
y

9.
4 cm²
3 cm
9 cm²
z

10.
8 cm²
5 cm
x
18 cm²

11.
5 cm
12 cm²
a
3 cm²

12.
27 cm²
9 cm
12 cm²
t

In questions **13** to **16** you have a pair of similar three-dimensional objects. Find the surface area indicated.

13.

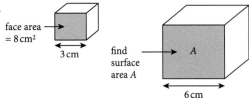

face area = 8 cm²
3 cm
find surface area *A*
6 cm

14.

face area = 3.1 cm²
2 cm
B
find surface area B
6 cm

15.

surface area = 10 cm²
C
find surface area *C*

16. face area = 100 cm²   find face area *D*

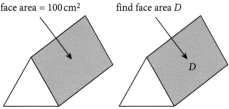

D

The radius of the large sphere is twice the radius of the small sphere.

The length of large solid is 1.5 times the length of the small solid.

17. Given: AD = 3 cm, AB = 5 cm and area of ΔADE = 6 cm².
Find:

a) area of ΔABC   **b)** area of DECB

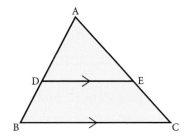

18. Given: XY = 5 cm, MY = 2 cm and area of ΔMYN = 4 cm².
Find:

a) area of ΔXYZ   **b)** area of MNZX

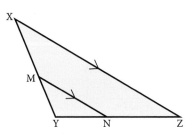

19. Given XY = 2 cm, BC = 3 cm and area of XYCB = 10 cm²,
find the area of ΔAXY.

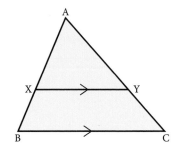

20. Given KP = 3 cm, area of ΔKOP = 2 cm² and area of OPML = 16 cm², find the length of PM.

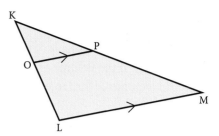

21. The triangles ABC and EBD are similar (AC and DE are *not* parallel).

If AB = 8 cm, BE = 4 cm and the area of ΔDBE = 6 cm², find the area of ΔABC.

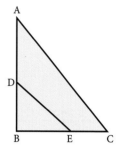

22. Given: AZ = 3 cm, ZC = 2 cm, MC = 5 cm, BM = 3 cm. Find:

a) XY

b) YZ

c) the ratio of areas AXY : AYZ

d) the ratio of areas AXY : ABM

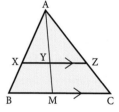

23. A floor is covered by 600 tiles which are 10 cm by 10 cm. How many 20 cm by 20 cm tiles are needed to cover the same floor?

24. A wall is covered by 160 tiles which are 15 cm by 15 cm. How many 10 cm by 10 cm tiles are needed to cover the same wall?

25. When potatoes are peeled do you lose more peel when you use big potatoes or small potatoes?

Volumes of similar objects

When solid objects are similar, one is an accurate enlargement of the other.

If two objects are similar and the ratio of corresponding sides is k, then the ratio of their volumes is k^3.

A line has one dimension, and the scale factor is used once.

An area has two dimensions, and the scale factor is used twice.

A volume has three dimensions, and the scale factor is used three times.

Example 1

Two similar cylinders have heights of 3 cm and 6 cm respectively. If the volume of the smaller cylinder is 30 cm³, find the volume of the larger cylinder.

If linear scale factor $= k$, then ratio of heights $(k) = \dfrac{6}{3} = 2$

$\therefore$ ratio of volume $(k^3) = 2^3$

$= 8$

and volume of larger cylinder $= 8 \times 30$

$= 240 \text{ cm}^3$

Example 2

Two similar spheres made of the same material have masses of 32 kg and 108 kg respectively. If the radius of the larger sphere is 9 cm, find the radius of the smaller sphere.

We may take the ratio of masses to be the same as the ratio of volumes.

ratio of volume $(k^3) = \dfrac{32}{108}$

$= \dfrac{8}{27}$

ratio of corresponding lengths $(k) = \sqrt[3]{\left(\dfrac{8}{27}\right)}$

$= \dfrac{2}{3}$

$\therefore$ Radius of smaller sphere $= \dfrac{2}{3} \times 9$

$= 6 \text{ cm}$

Exercise 9

In this exercise, the objects are similar and a number written inside a figure represents the volume of the object in cm³.

Numbers on the outside give linear dimensions in cm. In questions **1** to **8**, find the unknown volume *V*.

1.

2.

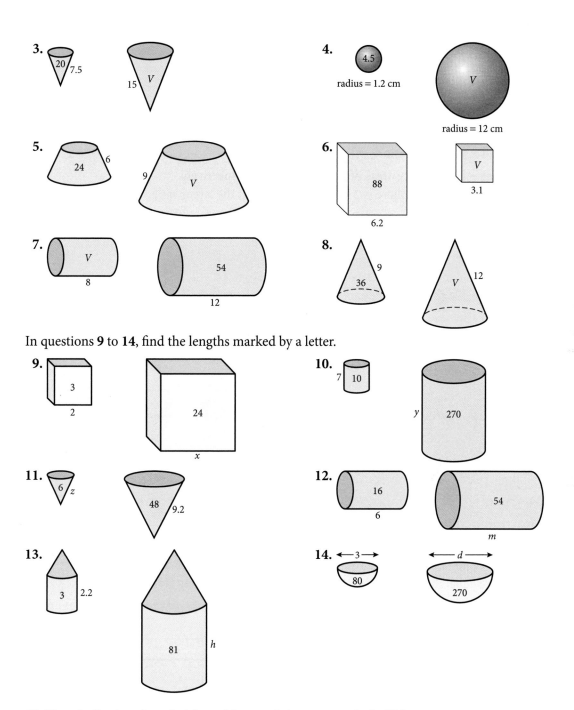

3.

20 7.5

15 *V*

4.

4.5

radius = 1.2 cm

V

radius = 12 cm

5.

24 6

9 *V*

6.

88 6.2

V 3.1

7.

V 8

54 12

8.

9 36

V 12

In questions **9** to **14**, find the lengths marked by a letter.

9.

3 2

24 *x*

10.

7 10

y 270

11.

6 *z*

48 9.2

12.

16 6

54 *m*

13.

3 2.2

81 *h*

14.

←3→ 80

←*d*→ 270

15. Two similar jugs have heights of 4 cm and 6 cm respectively. If the capacity of the smaller jug is 50 cm³, find the capacity of the larger jug.

16. Two similar cylindrical tins have base radii of 6 cm and 8 cm respectively. If the capacity of the larger tin is 252 cm³, find the capacity of the smaller tin.

17. Two solid metal spheres have masses of 5 kg and 135 kg respectively. If the radius of the smaller one is 4 cm, find the radius of the larger one.

18. Two similar cones have surface areas in the ratio 4 : 9. Find the ratio of:

    a) their lengths   b) their volumes.

19. The area of the bases of two similar glasses are in the ratio 4 : 25.
    Find the ratio of their volumes.

20. Two similar solids have volumes V_1 and V_2 and corresponding sides
    of length x_1 and x_2. State the ratio $V_1 : V_2$ in terms of x_1 and x_2.

21. Two solid spheres have surface areas of 5 cm² and 45 cm² respectively
    and the mass of the smaller sphere is 2 kg. Find the mass of the larger sphere.

22. The masses of two similar objects are 24 kg and 81 kg respectively.
    If the surface area of the larger object is 540 cm², find the surface
    area of the smaller object.

23. A cylindrical can has a circumference of 40 cm and a capacity of 4.8 litres.
    Find the capacity of a similar cylinder of circumference 50 cm.

24. A container has a surface area of 5000 cm² and a capacity of 12.8 litres.
    Find the surface area of a similar container which has a capacity of 5.4 litres.

4.5 Congruence

Two plane figures are congruent if one fits exactly on the other.
They must be the same shape and size.

In order to prove that two triangles are congruent, you must prove *one* of the following criteria:

SSS: that all three pairs of corresponding sides are equal.

ASA: that two pairs of corresponding angles are equal, along with one pair of corresponding sides.

SAS: that two pairs of corresponding sides are equal, along with the corresponding *included* angles.

RHS: In the special case of right-angled triangles, you can prove congruence by showing that the hypotenuses are equal in length, along with one pair of corresponding sides.

Example

ABCD is a rectangle. Points E and F are positioned along the diagonal such that AC is perpendicular to both DE and BF.

Prove that triangles DEC and BFA are congruent.

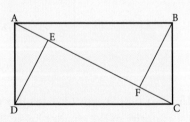

$\hat{DEC} = \hat{BFA}$ (both right-angles)

$DC = AB$ (opposite sides of a rectangle)

$\hat{DCE} = \hat{BAC}$ (alternate angles)

Hence by the criteria **RHS**, it has been proved that triangles DEC and BFA are congruent.

Make sure you give reasons for all of the statements that you make and give a conclusion at the end.

Exercise 10

1. Identify pairs of congruent shapes below.

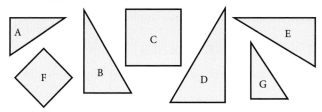

2. Triangle LMN is isosceles with LM = LN; X and Y are points on LM, LN respectively such that LX = LY. Prove that triangles LMY and LNX are congruent.

3. ABCD is a quadrilateral and a line through A parallel to BC meets DC at X. If $\hat{D} = \hat{C}$, prove that $\triangle ADX$ is isosceles.

4. In the diagram, N lies on a side of the square ABCD, AM and LC are perpendicular to DN. Prove that:

a) $\hat{ADN} = \hat{LCD}$ **b)** $AM = LD$

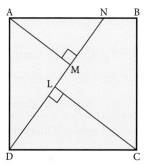

5. Points L and M on the side YZ of a triangle XYZ are drawn so that L is between Y and M. Given that $XY = XZ$ and $\hat{YXL} = \hat{MXZ}$, prove that $YL = MZ$.

6. Squares AMNB and AOPC are drawn on the sides of triangle ABC, so that they lie outside the triangle. Prove that $MC = OB$.

7. In the diagram, $\hat{LMN} = \hat{ONM} = 90°$. P is the midpoint of MN, $MN = 2ML$ and $MN = NO$. Prove that:

a) the triangles MNL and NOP are congruent

b) $\hat{OPN} = \hat{LNO}$

c) $\hat{LQO} = 90°$

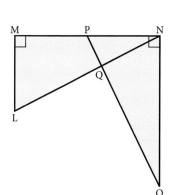

8. PQRS is a parallelogram in which the bisectors of the angles P and Q meet at X. Prove that the angle $\hat{PXQ}$ is a right angle.

4.6 Circle theorems

a) The angle subtended at the centre of a circle is twice the angle subtended at the circumference.

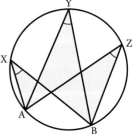

$$A\hat{O}B = 2 \times A\hat{C}B$$

Proof:

Draw the straight line COD.

Let $A\hat{C}O = y$ and $B\hat{C}O = z$.

In triangle AOC,

$$AO = OC \qquad \text{(radii)}$$

$\therefore \quad O\hat{C}A = O\hat{A}C \qquad$ (isosceles triangle)

$\therefore \quad C\hat{O}A = 180 - 2y \quad$ (angle sum of triangle)

$\therefore \quad A\hat{O}D = 2y \qquad$ (angles on a straight line)

Similarly from triangle COB, we find

$$D\hat{O}B = 2z$$

Now $\quad A\hat{C}B = y + z$

and $\quad A\hat{O}B = 2y + 2z$

$\therefore \quad A\hat{O}B = 2 \times A\hat{C}B$ as required.

b) Angles subtended by an arc in the same segment of a circle are equal.

$$A\hat{X}B = A\hat{Y}B = A\hat{Z}B$$

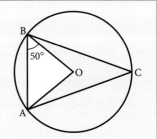

Example 1

Given $A\hat{B}O = 50°$, find $B\hat{C}A$.

Triangle OBA is isosceles (OA = OB).

$\therefore \quad O\hat{A}B = 50°$

$\therefore \quad B\hat{O}A = 80°$ (angle sum of a triangle)

$\therefore \quad B\hat{C}A = 40°$ (angle at the circumference)

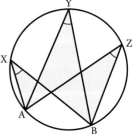

Example 2

Given $B\hat{D}C = 62°$ and $D\hat{C}A = 44°$, find $B\hat{A}C$ and $A\hat{B}D$.

$\qquad B\hat{D}C = B\hat{A}C$ (both subtended by arc BC)

$\therefore \qquad B\hat{A}C = 62°$

$\qquad D\hat{C}A = A\hat{B}D$ (both subtended by arc DA)

$\therefore \qquad A\hat{B}D = 44°$

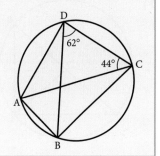

Exercise 11

Find the angles marked with letters. A line passes through the centre
only when point O is shown.

1.

2.

3.

4.

5.

6.

7.

8.

9.

10.

11.

12.

13.

14.

15.

16.

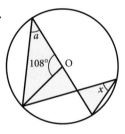

ABCD is a cyclic quadrilateral. The corners touch the circle.

c) The opposite angles in a cyclic quadrilateral add up to $180°$ (the angles are supplementary).

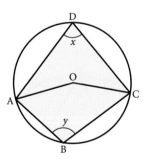

$$\hat{A} + \hat{C} = 180°$$
$$\hat{B} + \hat{D} = 180°$$

Proof:

Draw radii OA and OC.

Let $A\hat{D}C = x$ and $A\hat{B}C = y$.

$\quad A\hat{O}C$ obtuse $= 2x \quad$ (angle at the centre)

$\quad A\hat{O}C$ reflex $= 2y \quad$ (angle at the centre)

$\therefore \quad\quad 2x + 2y = 360° \quad$ (angles at a point)

$\therefore \quad\quad\quad x + y = 180° \quad$ as required

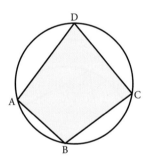

d) The angle in a semicircle is a right angle.

In the diagram, AB is a diameter.

$A\hat{C}B = 90°$.

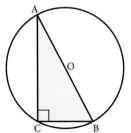

Example 1

Find a and x.

$\qquad a = 180° - 81°$ (opposite angles of a cyclic quadrilateral)

$\therefore \quad a = 99°$

$x + 2x = 180°$ (opposite angles of a cyclic quadrilateral)

$\qquad 3x = 180°$

$\qquad x = 60°$

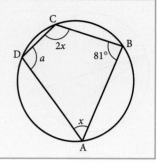

Example 2

Find b.

$\qquad A\widehat{C}B = 90°$ (angle in a semicircle)

$\therefore \qquad b = 180° - (90 + 37)°$

$\qquad\qquad = 53°$

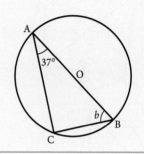

Exercise 12

Find the angles marked with a letter.

1.

2.

3.

4.

5.

6.

7.

8.

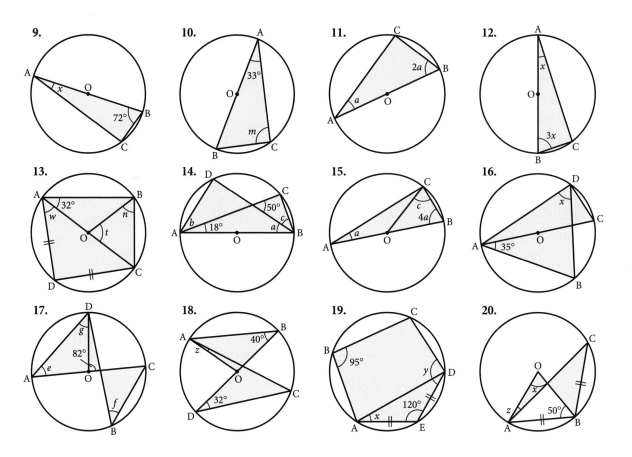

9. *x* 72°

10. 33° *m*

11. 2*a* *a*

12. *x* 3*x*

13. 32° *w* *n* *t*

14. 50° *b* 18° *a* *c*

15. *c* 4*a* *a*

16. *x* 35°

17. *g* 82° *e* *f*

18. 40° *z* 32°

19. 95° *y* 120° *x*

20. *x* *z* 50°

Tangents to circles

a) The angle between a tangent and the radius drawn to the point of contact is 90°.

$\hat{ABO} = 90°$

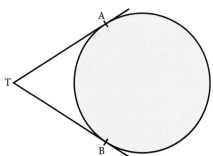

This is a tangent.

b) From any point outside a circle just two tangents to the circle may be drawn and they are of equal length.

TA = TB

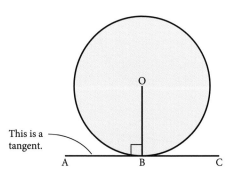

Example

TA and TB are tangents to the circle, centre O.
Given $A\hat{T}B = 50°$, find

a) $A\hat{B}T$

b) $O\hat{B}A$

a) △TBA is isosceles (TA = TB)

∴ $A\hat{B}T = \frac{1}{2}(180 - 50) = 65°$

b) $O\hat{B}T = 90°$ (tangent and radius)

∴ $O\hat{B}A = 90 - 65$

$= 25°$

Exercise 13

For questions **1** to **8**, find the angles marked with a letter.

1.

2.

3.

4.

5.

6.

7.

8.

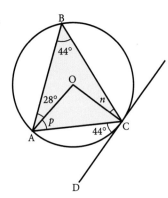

9. Find x, y and z.

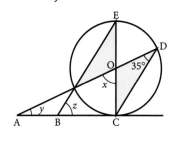

The alternate segment theorem

The angle between a tangent and its chord is equal to the angle in the alternate segment.

$$A\hat{B}C = B\hat{D}C$$

Proof:

EB is a diameter of the circle so $E\hat{C}B = 90°$

$B\hat{E}C + E\hat{B}C = 90°$ (angles in triangle)

AB is a tangent so $A\hat{B}E = 90°$

Thus $A\hat{B}C + E\hat{B}C = 90°$

Hence $A\hat{B}C = B\hat{E}C$

$B\hat{E}C = B\hat{D}C$ (angles in the same segment)

$\therefore A\hat{B}C = B\hat{D}C$ as required.

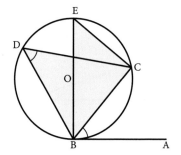

Example

O is the centre of the circle. AB is a tangent to the circle.

$B\hat{O}C = 114°$.

Find the size of $A\hat{B}C$.

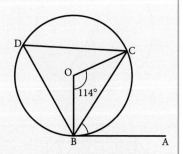

$$B\hat{D}C = \frac{1}{2}B\hat{O}C = 57° \text{ (angle at the centre is twice the angle at the circumference)}$$

$$A\hat{B}C = B\hat{D}C = 57° \text{ (alternate segment theorem)}$$

Hence $A\hat{B}C = 57°$

There might be several ways to work out an unknown angle. Make sure you explain your reasoning carefully.

Exercise 14

For questions **1** to **9**, find the angles marked with a letter.

1.

2.

3.

4.

5.

6.

7.

8.

9.

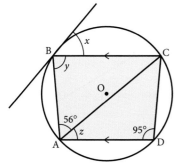

Circle theorems   165

4.7 Constructions

When the word 'construct' is used, the diagram should be drawn using equipment such as a pair of compasses and a ruler.

Example

Draw the triangle ABC full size and measure the angle x.

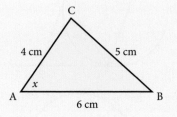

a) Draw a base line AB exactly 6 cm long.

b) Set a pair of compasses to 4 cm and draw an arc centred on A above the base line.

c) Similarly, set a pair of compasses to 5 cm and draw another arc centred on B intersecting the first.

d) Join this crossing point to A and B. The triangle is formed.

e) Measure the angle marked x.
$x = 56°$

Exercise 15

Use a ruler and pair of compasses to make accurate drawings of these triangles and measure the angles marked with x.

1.

2.

3.

4.

5.

6.

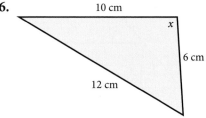

7. Construct a triangle ABC in which AB = 8 cm, AC = 6 cm and BC = 5 cm. Measure the angle AĈB.

8. Construct a triangle PQR in which PQ = 10 cm, PR = 7 cm and RQ = 6 cm. Measure the angle RP̂Q.

9. Construct an equilateral triangle of side 7 cm.

4.8 Nets

If the cube below was made of cardboard, and you cut along some of the edges and laid it out flat, you would have the *net* of the cube.

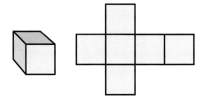

Exercise 16

1. Which of the nets below can be used to make a cube?

a)
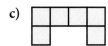

b)

c)

d)

2. The diagram shows the net of a closed rectangular box. All lengths are in cm.

a) Find the lengths *a*, *x*, *y*.

b) Calculate the volume of the box.

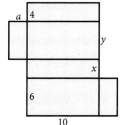

3. The diagram shows the net of a pyramid. The base is shaded. The lengths are in cm.

a) Find the lengths *a*, *b*, *c*, *d*.

b) Find the volume of the pyramid.

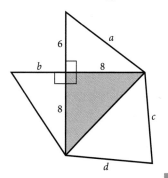

4. The diagram shows the net of a prism.

   a) Find the area of one of the triangular faces (shown shaded).

   b) Find the volume of the prism.

25 mm

14 mm

25 mm

100 mm

5. This is the net of a square-based pyramid. What are the lengths a, b, c, x, y?

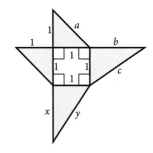

6. Sketch nets for the following:

   a) Closed rectangular box 7 cm × 9 cm × 5 cm.

   b) Closed cylinder: length 10 cm, radius 6 cm.

   c) Prism of length 12 cm, cross-section an equilateral triangle of side 4 cm.

Revision exercise 4A

1. ABCD is a parallelogram and AE bisects angle A. Prove that DE = BC.

2. In a triangle PQR, $P\hat{Q}R = 50°$ and point X lies on PQ such that QX = XR. Calculate $Q\hat{X}R$.

3. a) ABCDEF is a regular hexagon. Calculate $F\hat{D}E$.

   b) ABCDEFGH is a regular eight-sided polygon. Calculate $A\hat{G}H$.

   c) Each interior angle of a regular polygon measures 150°. How many sides has the polygon?

4. In the quadrilateral PQRS, PQ = QS = QR, PS is parallel to QR and $Q\hat{R}S = 70°$. Calculate:

   a) $R\hat{Q}S$

   b) $P\hat{Q}S$

5. Find x.

3 cm

5 cm

6. In the triangle ABC, AB = 7 cm, BC = 8 cm and $A\hat{B}C = 90°$. Point P lies inside the triangle such that BP = PC = 5 cm. Find:

   a) the perpendicular distance from P to BC

   b) the length AP.

7. In triangle PQR the bisector of $P\hat{Q}R$ meets PR at S and the point T lies on PQ such that ST is parallel to RQ.

   a) Prove that QT = TS.

   b) Prove that the triangles PTS and PQR are similar.

   c) Given that PT = 5 cm and TQ = 2 cm, calculate the length of QR.

8. In the quadrilateral ABCD, AB is parallel to DC and $D\hat{A}B = D\hat{B}C$.

   a) Prove that the triangles ABD and DBC are similar.

   b) If AB = 4 cm and DC = 9 cm, calculate the length of BD.

9. A rectangle 11 cm by 6 cm is similar to a rectangle 2 cm by x cm. Find the two possible values of x.

10. In the diagram, triangles ABC and EBD are similar but DE is *not* parallel to AC. Given that AD = 5 cm, DB = 3 cm and BE = 4 cm, calculate the length of BC.

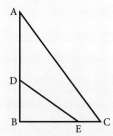

11. The radii of two spheres are in the ratio 2 : 5. The volume of the smaller sphere is 16 cm³. Calculate the volume of the larger sphere.

12. The surface areas of two similar jugs are 50 cm² and 450 cm² respectively.

   a) If the height of the larger jug is 10 cm, find the height of the smaller jug.

   b) If the volume of the smaller jug is 60 cm³, find the volume of the larger jug.

13. A car is an enlargement of a model, the scale factor being 10.

   a) If the windscreen of the model has an area of 100 cm², find the area of the windscreen on the actual car (answer in m²).

   b) If the capacity of the boot of the car is 1 m³, find the capacity of the boot on the model (answer in cm³).

14. Find the angles marked with letters. (O is the centre of the circle.)

15. ABCD is a cyclic quadrilateral in which
AB = BC and $A\hat{B}C = 70°$.

AD produced meets BC produced at the
point P, where $A\hat{P}B = 30°$.

Calculate:

a) $A\hat{D}B$ **b)** $A\hat{B}D$

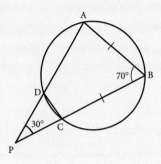

16. Using a ruler and pair of compasses only:

a) Construct the triangle ABC in which
AB = 7 cm, BC = 5 cm and AC = 6 cm.

b) Construct the triangle XYZ in which
XY = 10 cm, YZ = 11 cm and XZ = 9 cm.

Examination-style exercise 4B

1. *ABCDE* is a regular pentagon.

DEF is a straight line.

Calculate

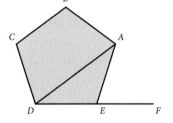

Not to scale

(a) angle *AEF*, [2]

(b) angle *DAE*. [1]

Cambridge IGCSE Mathematics 0580
Paper 2 Q17 November 2005

2. A square *ABCD*, of side 8 cm, has another square, *PQRS*,
drawn inside it.

P, Q, R and *S* are at the midpoints of each side of the
square *ABCD*, as shown in the diagram.

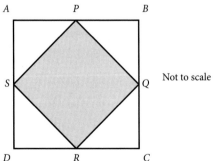

Not to scale

(a) Calculate the length of *PQ*. [2]

(b) Calculate the area of the square *PQRS*. [1]

Cambridge IGCSE Mathematics 0580
Paper 2 Q6 June 2005

3. Two similar vases have heights which are in the ratio $3:2$.

    (a) The volume of the larger vase is 1080 cm³.

        Calculate the volume of the smaller vase.   [2]

    (b) The surface area of the smaller vase is 252 cm².

        Calculate the surface area of the larger vase.   [2]

Cambridge IGCSE Mathematics 0580
Paper 21 Q18 June 2009

4. A company makes two models of television.

    Model A has a rectangular screen that measures 44 cm by 32 cm.

    Model B has a larger screen with these measurements increased in the ratio 5 : 4.

    (a) Work out the measurements of the larger screen.   [2]

    (b) Find the **fraction** $\dfrac{\text{model A screen area}}{\text{model B screen area}}$ in its simplest form.   [1]

Cambridge IGCSE Mathematics 0580
Paper 2 Q14 June 2006

5. A conical beaker has a base radius of 8 cm and a height of 15 cm.

    A conical tank full of acid is a similar shape to the beaker.

    The beaker can be filled with acid from the tank exactly 1728 times.

    Work out the base radius and height of the tank.   [3]

6.

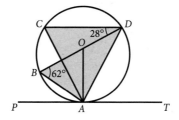

Not to scale

    A, B, C and D lie on a circle, centre O.

    BD is a diameter of the circle and PAT is the tangent to the circle at A.

    Angle $ABD = 62°$ and angle $CDB = 28°$.

    Find

    (a) angle ACD,   [1]

    (b) angle ADB,   [1]

    (c) angle DAT,   [1]

    (d) angle CAO.   [2]

7.

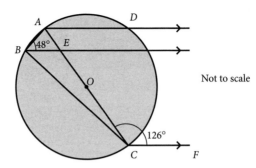

Not to scale

A, B, C and D lie on a circle centre O. AC is a diameter of the circle.

AD, BE and CF are parallel lines. Angle $ABE = 48°$ and angle $ACF = 126°$.

Find

(a) angle DAE, [1]

(b) angle EBC, [1]

(c) angle BAE. [1]

Cambridge IGCSE Mathematics 0580
Paper 2 Q15 November 2005

8. In the diagram, the lines PR and QS intersect at point T.

$PQ = RS$.

PQ is parallel to RS.

Prove that triangles PQT and RST are congruent. [4]

9. $ABCD$ is a cyclic quadrilateral. PQ is a tangent to the circle at A.

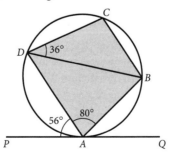

Not to scale

Given that $P\hat{A}D = 56°$, $D\hat{A}B = 80°$ and $C\hat{D}B = 36°$,

prove that AD and CB are parallel. [5]

5 Algebra 2

Girolamo Cardan (1501–1576) was a colourful character who became Professor of Mathematics at Milan. As well as being a distinguished academic, he was an astrologer, a physician, a gambler and a heretic, yet he received a pension from the Pope. His mathematical genius enabled him to open up the general theory of cubic and quartic equations, although a method for solving cubic equations which he claimed as his own was pirated from Niccolo Tartaglia.

E1.6 Order quantities by magnitude and demonstrate familiarity with the symbols $=, \neq, >, <, \geq, \leq$.

E1.7 Understand the meaning of indices (fractional, negative and zero) and use the rules of indices.

E2.1 Construct and rearrange complicated formulae and equations.

E2.3 Manipulate algebraic fractions. Factorise and simplify rational expressions.

E2.4 Use and interpret positive, negative and zero indices. Use and interpret fractional indices. Use the rules of indices.

E2.5 Derive and solve simple linear inequalities.

E2.6 Represent inequalities graphically and use this representation to solve simple linear programming problems.

E2.8 Express direct and inverse proportion in algebraic terms and use this form of expression to find unknown quantities.

5.1 Algebraic fractions

Simplifying fractions

Example

Simplify:
a) $\dfrac{32}{56}$
b) $\dfrac{3a}{5a^2}$
c) $\dfrac{3y + y^2}{6y}$

a) $\dfrac{32}{56} = \dfrac{\cancel{8} \times 4}{\cancel{8} \times 7} = \dfrac{4}{7}$

b) $\dfrac{3a}{5a^2} = \dfrac{3 \times \cancel{a}}{5 \times a \times \cancel{a}} = \dfrac{3}{5a}$

c) $\dfrac{y(3 + y)}{6y} = \dfrac{3 + y}{6}$

Exercise 1

Simplify as far as possible, where you can.

1. $\dfrac{25}{35}$ **2.** $\dfrac{84}{96}$ **3.** $\dfrac{5y^2}{y}$

4. $\dfrac{y}{2y}$ **5.** $\dfrac{8x^2}{2x^2}$ **6.** $\dfrac{2x}{4y}$

7. $\dfrac{6y}{3y}$ **8.** $\dfrac{5ab}{10b}$ **9.** $\dfrac{8ab^2}{12ab}$

10. $\dfrac{7a^2b}{35ab^2}$ **11.** $\dfrac{(2a)^2}{4a}$ **12.** $\dfrac{7yx}{8xy}$

13. $\dfrac{5x + 2x^2}{3x}$ **14.** $\dfrac{9x + 3}{3x}$ **15.** $\dfrac{25 + 7}{25}$

16. $\dfrac{4a + 5a^2}{5a}$ **17.** $\dfrac{3x}{4x - x^2}$ **18.** $\dfrac{5ab}{15a + 10a^2}$

19. $\dfrac{5x + 4}{8x}$ **20.** $\dfrac{12x + 6}{6y}$ **21.** $\dfrac{5x + 10y}{15xy}$

22. $\dfrac{18a - 3ab}{6a^2}$ **23.** $\dfrac{4ab + 8a^2}{2ab}$ **24.** $\dfrac{(2x)^2 - 8x}{4x}$

Example

Simplify:

a) $\dfrac{x^2 + x - 6}{x^2 + 2x - 3} = \dfrac{(x - 2)(x + 3)}{(x + 3)(x - 1)} = \dfrac{x - 2}{x - 1}$

b) $\dfrac{x^2 + 3x - 10}{x^2 - 4} = \dfrac{(x - 2)(x + 5)}{(x - 2)(x + 2)} = \dfrac{x + 5}{x + 2}$

c) $\dfrac{3x^2 - 9x}{x^2 - 4x + 3} = \dfrac{3x(x - 3)}{(x - 1)(x - 3)} = \dfrac{3x}{x - 1}$

Exercise 2

Simplify as far as possible:

1. $\dfrac{x^2 + 2x}{x^2 - 3x}$ **2.** $\dfrac{x^2 - 3x}{x^2 - 2x - 3}$ **3.** $\dfrac{x^2 + 4x}{2x^2 - 10x}$

4. $\dfrac{x^2 + 6x + 5}{x^2 - x - 2}$ **5.** $\dfrac{x^2 - 4x - 21}{x^2 - 5x - 14}$ **6.** $\dfrac{x^2 + 7x + 10}{x^2 - 4}$

7. $\dfrac{x^2 + x - 2}{x^2 - x}$

8. $\dfrac{3x^2 - 6x}{x^2 + 3x - 10}$

9. $\dfrac{6x^2 - 2x}{12x^2 - 4x}$

10. $\dfrac{3x^2 + 15x}{x^2 - 25}$

11. $\dfrac{12x^2 - 20x}{4x^2}$

12. $\dfrac{x^2 + x - 6}{x^2 + 2x - 3}$

Addition and subtraction of algebraic fractions

> ### Example
>
> Write as a single fraction:
>
> **a)** $\dfrac{2}{3} + \dfrac{3}{4}$
>
> **b)** $\dfrac{2}{x} + \dfrac{3}{y}$
>
> Compare these two workings line for line:
>
> **a)** $\dfrac{2}{3} + \dfrac{3}{4}$; the L.C.M. of 3 and 4 is 12.
>
> $$\therefore \quad \dfrac{2}{3} + \dfrac{3}{4} = \dfrac{8}{12} + \dfrac{9}{12}$$
>
> $$= \dfrac{17}{12}$$
>
> **b)** $\dfrac{2}{x} + \dfrac{3}{y}$; the L.C.M. of x and y is xy.
>
> $$\therefore \quad \dfrac{2}{x} + \dfrac{3}{y} = \dfrac{2y}{xy} + \dfrac{3x}{xy}$$
>
> $$= \dfrac{2y + 3x}{xy}$$

Exercise 3

Simplify the following:

1. $\dfrac{2}{5} + \dfrac{1}{5}$

2. $\dfrac{2x}{5} + \dfrac{x}{5}$

3. $\dfrac{2}{x} + \dfrac{1}{x}$

4. $\dfrac{1}{7} + \dfrac{3}{7}$

5. $\dfrac{x}{7} + \dfrac{3x}{7}$

6. $\dfrac{1}{7x} + \dfrac{3}{7x}$

7. $\dfrac{5}{8} + \dfrac{1}{4}$

8. $\dfrac{5x}{8} + \dfrac{x}{4}$

9. $\dfrac{5}{8x} + \dfrac{1}{4x}$

10. $\dfrac{2}{3} + \dfrac{1}{6}$

11. $\dfrac{2x}{3} + \dfrac{x}{6}$

12. $\dfrac{2}{3x} + \dfrac{1}{6x}$

13. $\dfrac{3}{4} + \dfrac{2}{5}$

14. $\dfrac{3x}{4} + \dfrac{2x}{5}$

15. $\dfrac{3}{4x} + \dfrac{2}{5x}$

16. $\dfrac{3}{4} - \dfrac{2}{3}$

17. $\dfrac{3x}{4} - \dfrac{2x}{3}$

18. $\dfrac{3}{4x} - \dfrac{2}{3x}$

19. $\dfrac{x}{2} + \dfrac{x+1}{3}$

20. $\dfrac{x-1}{3} + \dfrac{x+2}{4}$

21. $\dfrac{2x-1}{5} + \dfrac{x+3}{2}$

22. $\dfrac{x+1}{3} - \dfrac{2x+1}{4}$

23. $\dfrac{x-3}{3} - \dfrac{x-2}{5}$

24. $\dfrac{2x+1}{7} - \dfrac{x+2}{2}$

25. $\dfrac{1}{x} + \dfrac{2}{x+1}$

26. $\dfrac{3}{x-2} + \dfrac{4}{x}$

27. $\dfrac{5}{x-2} + \dfrac{3}{x+3}$

28. $\dfrac{7}{x+1} - \dfrac{3}{x+2}$

29. $\dfrac{2}{x+3} - \dfrac{5}{x-1}$

30. $\dfrac{3}{x-2} - \dfrac{4}{x+1}$

5.2 Changing the subject of a formula

The operations involved in solving ordinary linear equations are exactly the same as the operations required in changing the subject of a formula.

Example 1

a) Solve the equation $3x + 1 = 12$.

b) Make x the subject of the formula $Mx + B = A$.

. . . .

a) $3x + 1 = 12$

$\quad 3x = 12 - 1$

$\quad x = \dfrac{12-1}{3} = \dfrac{11}{3}$

b) $Mx + B = A$

$\quad Mx = A - B$

$\quad x = \dfrac{A - B}{M}$

Example 2

a) Solve the equation $3(y - 2) = 5$.

b) Make y the subject of the formula $x(y - a) = e$.

. . . .

a) $3(y - 2) = 5$

$\quad 3y - 6 = 5$

$\quad 3y = 11$

$\quad y = \dfrac{11}{3}$

b) $x(y - a) = e$

$\quad xy - xa = e$

$\quad xy = e + xa$

$\quad y = \dfrac{e + xa}{x}$

Exercise 4

Make x the subject of the following:

1. $2x = 5$	**2.** $7x = 21$	**3.** $Ax = B$
4. $Nx = T$	**5.** $Mx = K$	**6.** $xy = 4$
7. $Bx = C$	**8.** $4x = D$	**9.** $9x = T + N$
10. $Ax = B - R$	**11.** $Cx = R + T$	**12.** $Lx = N - R^2$
13. $R - S^2 = Nx$	**14.** $x + 5 = 7$	**15.** $x + 10 = 3$
16. $x + A = T$	**17.** $x + B = S$	**18.** $N = x + D$
19. $M = x + B$	**20.** $L = x + D^2$	**21.** $N^2 + x = T$
22. $L + x = N + M$	**23.** $Z + x = R - S$	**24.** $x - 5 = 2$
25. $x - R = A$	**26.** $x - A = E$	**27.** $F = x - B$
28. $F^2 = x - B^2$	**29.** $x - D = A + B$	**30.** $x - E = A^2$

Make y the subject of the following:

31. $L = y - B$	**32.** $N = y - T$	**33.** $3y + 1 = 7$
34. $2y - 4 = 5$	**35.** $Ay + C = N$	**36.** $By + D = L$
37. $Dy + E = F$	**38.** $Ny - F = H$	**39.** $Yy - Z = T$
40. $Ry - L = B$	**41.** $Vy + m = Q$	**42.** $ty - m = n + a$
43. $qy + n = s - t$	**44.** $ny - s^2 = t$	**45.** $V^2y + b = c$
46. $r = ny - 6$	**47.** $s = my + d$	**48.** $t = my - b$
49. $j = my + c$	**50.** $2(y + 1) = 6$	**51.** $3(y - 1) = 5$
52. $A(y + B) = C$	**53.** $D(y + E) = F$	**54.** $h(y + n) = a$
55. $b(y - d) = q$	**56.** $n = r(y + t)$	**57.** $t(y - 4) = b$
58. $z = S(y + t)$	**59.** $s = v(y - d)$	**60.** $g = m(y + n)$

Example 1

a) Solve the equation $\dfrac{3a + 1}{2} = 4$.

b) Make a the subject of the formula $\dfrac{na + b}{m} = n$.

a) $\dfrac{3a + 1}{2} = 4$

$3a + 1 = 8$

$3a = 7$

$a = \dfrac{7}{3}$

b) $\dfrac{na + b}{m} = n$

$na + b = mn$

$na = mn - b$

$a = \dfrac{mn - b}{n}$

Exercise 5

Make a the subject.

1. $\dfrac{a}{4} = 3$

2. $\dfrac{a}{5} = 2$

3. $\dfrac{a}{D} = B$

4. $\dfrac{a}{B} = T$

5. $\dfrac{a}{N} = R$

6. $b = \dfrac{a}{m}$

7. $\dfrac{a - 2}{4} = 6$

8. $\dfrac{a - A}{B} = T$

9. $\dfrac{a - D}{N} = A$

10. $\dfrac{a + Q}{N} = B^2$

11. $g = \dfrac{a - r}{e}$

12. $\dfrac{2a + 1}{5} = 2$

13. $\dfrac{Aa + B}{C} = D$

14. $\dfrac{na + m}{p} = q$

15. $\dfrac{ra - t}{S} = v$

16. $\dfrac{za - m}{q} = t$

17. $\dfrac{m + Aa}{b} = c$

18. $A = \dfrac{Ba + D}{E}$

19. $n = \dfrac{ea - f}{h}$

20. $q = \dfrac{ga + b}{r}$

21. $6 - a = 2$

22. $7 - a = 9$

23. $5 = 7 - a$

24. $A - a = B$

25. $C - a = E$

26. $D - a = H$

27. $n - a = m$

28. $t = q - a$

29. $b = s - a$

30. $v = r - a$

31. $t = m - a$

32. $5 - 2a = 1$

33. $T - Xa = B$

34. $M - Na = Q$

35. $V - Ma = T$

36. $L = N - Ra$

37. $r = v^2 - ra$

38. $t^2 = w - na$

39. $n - qa = 2$

40. $\dfrac{3 - 4a}{2} = 1$

41. $\dfrac{5 - 7a}{3} = 2$

42. $\dfrac{B - Aa}{D} = E$

43. $\dfrac{D - Ea}{N} = B$

44. $\dfrac{h - fa}{b} = x$

45. $\dfrac{v^2 - ha}{C} = d$

46. $\dfrac{M(a + B)}{N} = T$

47. $\dfrac{f(Na - e)}{m} = B$

48. $\dfrac{T(M - a)}{E} = F$

49. $\dfrac{y(x - a)}{z} = t$

50. $\dfrac{k^2(m - a)}{x} = x$

Example 1

a) Solve the equation $\dfrac{4}{z} = 7$.

b) Make z the subject of the formula $\dfrac{n}{z} = k$.

• •

a) $\dfrac{4}{z} = 7$

$\quad 4 = 7z$

$\quad \dfrac{4}{7} = z$

b) $\dfrac{n}{z} = k$

$\quad n = kz$

$\quad \dfrac{n}{k} = z$

Example 2

Make t the subject of the formula $\dfrac{x}{t} + m = a$.

$\quad \dfrac{x}{t} = a - m$

$\quad x = (a - m)t$

$\quad \dfrac{x}{(a - m)} = t$

Exercise 6

Make a the subject.

1. $\dfrac{7}{a} = 14$

2. $\dfrac{5}{a} = 3$

3. $\dfrac{B}{a} = C$

4. $\dfrac{T}{a} = X$

5. $\dfrac{M}{a} = B$

6. $m = \dfrac{n}{a}$

7. $t = \dfrac{v}{a}$

8. $\dfrac{n}{a} = \sin 20°$

9. $\dfrac{7}{a} = \cos 30°$

10. $\dfrac{B}{a} = x$

11. $\dfrac{5}{a} = \dfrac{3}{4}$

12. $\dfrac{N}{a} = \dfrac{B}{D}$

13. $\dfrac{H}{a} = \dfrac{N}{M}$

14. $\dfrac{t}{a} = \dfrac{b}{e}$

15. $\dfrac{v}{a} = \dfrac{m}{s}$

16. $\dfrac{t}{b} = \dfrac{m}{a}$

17. $\dfrac{5}{a + 1} = 2$

18. $\dfrac{7}{a - 1} = 3$

19. $\dfrac{B}{a + D} = C$

20. $\dfrac{Q}{a - C} = T$

21. $\dfrac{V}{a - T} = D$

22. $\dfrac{L}{Ma} = B$

23. $\dfrac{N}{Ba} = C$

24. $\dfrac{m}{ca} = d$

25. $t = \dfrac{b}{c - a}$

26. $x = \dfrac{z}{y - a}$

Make x the subject.

27. $\dfrac{2}{x} + 1 = 3$

28. $\dfrac{5}{x} - 2 = 4$

29. $\dfrac{A}{x} + B = C$

30. $\dfrac{V}{x} + G = H$

31. $\dfrac{r}{x} - t = n$

32. $q = \dfrac{b}{x} + d$

33. $t = \dfrac{m}{x} - n$

34. $h = d - \dfrac{b}{x}$

35. $C - \dfrac{d}{x} = e$

36. $r - \dfrac{m}{x} = e^2$

37. $t^2 = b - \dfrac{n}{x}$

38. $\dfrac{d}{x} + b = mn$

39. $\dfrac{M}{x+q} - N = 0$

40. $\dfrac{Y}{x-c} - T = 0$

41. $3M = M + \dfrac{N}{P+x}$

42. $A = \dfrac{B}{c+x} - 5A$

43. $\dfrac{K}{Mx} + B = C$

44. $\dfrac{z}{xy} - z = y$

45. $\dfrac{m^2}{x} - n = -p$

46. $t = w - \dfrac{q}{x}$

Example

Make x the subject of the formulae.

a) $\sqrt{(x^2 + A)} = B$

$\qquad x^2 + A = B^2 \text{ (square both sides)}$

$\qquad\quad x^2 = B^2 - A$

$\qquad\quad\ x = \pm\sqrt{(B^2 - A)}$

b) $(Ax - B)^2 = M$

$\qquad Ax - B = \pm\sqrt{M}\,\text{(square root both sides)}$

$\qquad\quad Ax = B \pm \sqrt{M}$

$\qquad\quad\ x = \dfrac{B \pm \sqrt{M}}{A}$

c) $\sqrt{(R - x)} = T$

$\qquad R - x = T^2$

$\qquad\quad R = T^2 + x$

$\qquad R - T^2 = x$

Exercise 7

Make x the subject.

1. $\sqrt{x} = 2$

2. $\sqrt{(x+1)} = 5$

3. $\sqrt{(x-2)} = 3$

4. $\sqrt{(x+a)} = B$

5. $\sqrt{(x+C)} = D$

6. $\sqrt{(x-E)} = H$

7. $\sqrt{(ax+b)} = c$

8. $\sqrt{(x-m)} = a$

9. $b = \sqrt{(gx - t)}$ **10.** $r = \sqrt{(b - x)}$ **11.** $\sqrt{(d - x)} = t$ **12.** $b = \sqrt{(x - d)}$

13. $c = \sqrt{(n - x)}$ **14.** $f = \sqrt{(b - x)}$ **15.** $g = \sqrt{(c - x)}$ **16.** $\sqrt{(M - Nx)} = P$

17. $\sqrt{(Ax + B)} = \sqrt{D}$ **18.** $\sqrt{(x - D)} = A^2$ **19.** $x^2 = g$ **20.** $x^2 + 1 = 17$

21. $x^2 = B$ **22.** $x^2 + A = B$ **23.** $x^2 - A = M$ **24.** $b = a + x^2$

25. $C - x^2 = m$ **26.** $n = d - x^2$ **27.** $mx^2 = n$ **28.** $b = ax^2$

Make k the subject.

29. $\dfrac{kz}{a} - t$ **30.** $ak^2 - t = m$ **31.** $n = a - k^2$ **32.** $\sqrt{(k^2 - 4)} = 6$

33. $\sqrt{(k^2 - A)} = B$ **34.** $\sqrt{(k^2 + y)} = x$ **35.** $t = \sqrt{(m + k^2)}$ **36.** $2\sqrt{(k + 1)} = 6$

37. $A\sqrt{(k + B)} = M$ **38.** $\sqrt{\left(\dfrac{M}{k}\right)} = N$ **39.** $\sqrt{\left(\dfrac{N}{k}\right)} = B$ **40.** $\sqrt{(a - k)} = b$

41. $\sqrt{(a^2 - k^2)} = t$ **42.** $\sqrt{(m - k^2)} = x$ **43.** $2\pi\sqrt{(k + t)} = 4$ **44.** $A\sqrt{(k + 1)} = B$

45. $\sqrt{(ak^2 - b)} = C$ **46.** $a\sqrt{(k^2 - x)} = b$ **42.** $k^2 + b = x^2$ **48.** $\dfrac{k^2}{a} + b = c$

49. $\sqrt{(c^2 - ak)} = b$ **50.** $\dfrac{m}{k^2} = a + b$

Example

Make x the subject of the formulae.

a)
$Ax - B = Cx + D$
$Ax - Cx = D + B$
$x(A - C) = D + B$ (factorise)
$$x = \frac{D + B}{A - C}$$

b)
$x + a = \dfrac{x + b}{c}$
$c(x + a) = x + b$
$cx + ca = x + b$
$cx - x = b - ca$
$x(c - 1) = b - ca$ (factorise)
$$x = \frac{b - ca}{c - 1}$$

Exercise 8

Make y the subject.

1. $5(y - 1) = 2(y + 3)$ **2.** $7(y - 3) = 4(3 - y)$ **3.** $Ny + B = D - Ny$

4. $My - D = E - 2My$ **5.** $ay + b = 3b + by$ **6.** $my - c = e - ny$

7. $xy + 4 = 7 - ky$ **8.** $Ry + D = Ty + C$ **9.** $ay - x = z + by$

10. $m(y + a) = n(y + b)$

11. $x(y - b) = y + d$

12. $\dfrac{a - y}{a + y} = b$

13. $\dfrac{1 - y}{1 + y} = \dfrac{c}{d}$

14. $\dfrac{M - y}{M + y} = \dfrac{a}{b}$

15. $m(y + n) = n(n - y)$

16. $y + m = \dfrac{2y - 5}{m}$

17. $y - n = \dfrac{y + 2}{n}$

18. $y + b = \dfrac{ay + e}{b}$

19. $\dfrac{ay + x}{x} = 4 - y$

20. $c - dy = e - ay$

21. $y(a - c) = by + d$

22. $y(m + n) = a(y + b)$

23. $t - ay = s - by$

24. $\dfrac{y + x}{y - x} = 3$

25. $\dfrac{v - y}{v + y} = \dfrac{1}{2}$

26. $y(b - a) = a(y + b + c)$

27. $\sqrt{\left(\dfrac{y + x}{y - x} \right)} = 2$

28. $\sqrt{\left(\dfrac{z + y}{z - y} \right)} = \dfrac{1}{3}$

29. $\sqrt{\left[\dfrac{m(y + n)}{y} \right]} = p$

30. $n - y = \dfrac{4y - n}{m}$

Example

Make w the subject of the formula $\sqrt{\left(\dfrac{w}{w + a} \right)} = c.$

Squaring both sides, $\dfrac{w}{w + a} = c^2$

Multiplying by $(w + a)$, $w = c^2(w + a)$

$$w = c^2 w + c^2 a$$

$$w - c^2 w = c^2 a$$

$$w(1 - c^2) = c^2 a$$

$$w = \dfrac{c^2 a}{1 - c^2}$$

Exercise 9

Make the letter in square brackets the subject.

1. $ax + by + c = 0$ $\quad$ [x]

2. $\sqrt{\left\{ a\left(y^2 - b \right) \right\}} = e$ $\quad$ [y]

3. $\dfrac{\sqrt{(k - m)}}{n} = \dfrac{1}{m}$ $\quad$ [k]

4. $a - bz = z + b$ $\quad$ [z]

5. $\dfrac{x + y}{x - y} = 2$ $\quad$ [x]

6. $\sqrt{\left(\dfrac{a}{z} - c \right)} = e$ $\quad$ [z]

7. $lm + mn + a = 0$ $\quad$ [n]

8. $t = 2\pi \sqrt{\left(\dfrac{d}{g} \right)}$ $\quad$ [d]

9. $t = 2\pi \sqrt{\left(\dfrac{d}{g} \right)}$ $\quad$ [g]

10. $\sqrt{(x^2 + a)} = 2x$ $\quad$ [x]

11. $\sqrt{\left\{\dfrac{b\left(m^2+a\right)}{e}\right\}}=t$ $[m]$

12. $\sqrt{\left(\dfrac{x+1}{x}\right)}=a$ $[x]$

13. $a+b-mx=0$ $[m]$

14. $\sqrt{(a^2+b^2)}=x^2$ $[a]$

15. $\dfrac{a}{k}+b=\dfrac{c}{k}$ $[k]$

16. $a-y=\dfrac{b+y}{a}$ $[y]$

17. $G=4\pi\sqrt{(x^2+T^2)}$ $[x]$

18. $M(ax+by+c)=0$ $[y]$

19. $x=\sqrt{\left(\dfrac{y-1}{y+1}\right)}$ $[y]$

20. $a\sqrt{\left(\dfrac{x^2-n}{m}\right)}=\dfrac{a^2}{b}$ $[x]$

21. $\dfrac{M}{N}+E=\dfrac{P}{N}$ $[N]$

22. $\dfrac{Q}{P-x}=R$ $[x]$

23. $\sqrt{(z-ax)}=t$ $[a]$

24. $e+\sqrt{(x+f)}=g$ $[x]$

25. $\dfrac{m\left(ny-e^2\right)}{p}+n=5n$ $[y]$

5.3   Variation

Direct variation

There are several ways of expressing a relationship between two quantities x and y. Here are some examples.

     x varies as y

     x varies directly as y

     x is proportional to y

These three all mean the same and they are written in symbols as follows.

     $x \propto y$

The '$\propto$' sign can always be replaced by '$= k$' where k is a constant:

     $x = ky$

Suppose $x = 3$ when $y = 12$;

then $3 = k \times 12$

and $k = \dfrac{1}{4}$

We can then write $x = \dfrac{1}{4}y$, and this allows us to find the value of x for any value of y and vice versa.

Example 1

y varies as z, and $y = 2$ when $z = 5$; find

a) the value of y when $z = 6$

b) the value of z when $y = 5$

Because $y \propto z$, then $y = kz$ where k is a constant.

$$y = 2 \text{ when } z = 5$$
$$2 = k \times 5$$
$$k = \frac{2}{5}$$

So $\quad y = \frac{2}{5}z$

a) When $z = 6$, $y = \frac{2}{5} \times 6 = 2\frac{2}{5}$

b) When $y = 5$, $5 = \frac{2}{5}z$

$$z = \frac{25}{2} = 12\frac{1}{2}$$

Example 2

The value V of a diamond is proportional to the square of its mass M.

If a diamond with a mass of 10 grams is worth \$200, find:

a) the value of a diamond with a mass of 30 grams

b) the mass of a diamond worth \$5000.

$$V \propto M^2$$

or $\quad V = kM^2$ where k is a constant.

$$V = 200 \text{ when } M = 10$$

$\therefore \quad 200 = k \times 10^2$

$$k = 2$$

So $\quad V = 2M^2$

a) When $M = 30$,
$$V = 2 \times 30^2 = 2 \times 900$$
$$V = \$1800$$

So a diamond with a mass of 30 grams is worth \$1800.

b) When $V = 5000$,
$$5000 = 2 \times M^2$$
$$M^2 = \frac{5000}{2} = 2500$$
$$M = \sqrt{2500} = 50$$

So a diamond of value \$5000 has a mass of 50 grams.

Exercise 10

1. Rewrite the statement connecting each pair of variables using a constant k instead of '$\propto$'.

   a) $S \propto e$ **b)** $v \propto t$ **c)** $x \propto z^2$

   d) $y \propto \sqrt{x}$ **e)** $T \propto \sqrt{L}$ **f)** $C \propto r$

   g) $A \propto r^2$ **h)** $V \propto r^3$

2. y varies as t. If $y = 6$ when $t = 4$, calculate:

   a) the value of y, when $t = 6$ **b)** the value of t, when $y = 4$.

3. z is proportional to m. If $z = 20$ when $m = 4$, calculate:

   a) the value of z, when $m = 7$ **b)** the value of m, when $z = 55$.

4. A varies directly as r^2. If $A = 12$, when $r = 2$, calculate:

   a) the value of A, when $r = 5$ **b)** the value of r, when $A = 48$.

5. Given that $z \propto x$, copy and complete the table.

x	1	3		$5\frac{1}{2}$
z	4		16	

6. Given that $V \propto r^3$, copy and complete the table.

r	1	2		$1\frac{1}{2}$
V	4		256	

7. Given that $w \propto \sqrt{h}$, copy and complete the table.

h	4	9		$2\frac{1}{4}$
w	6		15	

8. s is proportional to $(v-1)^2$. If $s = 8$, when $v = 3$, calculate:

   a) the value of s, when $v = 4$ **b)** the value of v, when $s = 2$.

9. m varies as $(d + 3)$. If $m = 28$ when $d = 1$, calculate:

   a) the value of m, when $d = 3$ **b)** the value of d, when $m = 49$.

10. The pressure of the water P at any point below the surface of the sea varies as the depth of the point below the surface d.
If the pressure is 200 newtons/cm² at a depth of 3 m, calculate the pressure at a depth of 5 m.

11. The distance d through which a stone falls from rest is proportional to the square of the time taken t. If the stone falls 45 m in 3 seconds, how far will it fall in 6 seconds? How long will it take to fall 20 m?

12. The energy E stored in an elastic band varies as the square of the extension x. When the elastic is extended by 3 cm, the energy stored is 243 joules. What is the energy stored when the extension is 5 cm? What is the extension when the stored energy is 36 joules?

13. In the first few days of its life, the length of an earthworm l is thought to be proportional to the square root of the number of hours n which have elapsed since its birth. If a worm is 2 cm long after 1 hour, how long will it be after 4 hours? How long will it take to grow to a length of 14 cm?

14. The number of eggs which a goose lays in a week varies as the cube root of the average number of hours of sleep she has. When she has 8 hours sleep, she lays 4 eggs. How long does she sleep when she lays 5 eggs?

15. The resistance to motion of a car is proportional to the square of the speed of the car. If the resistance is 4000 newtons at a speed of 20 m/s, what is the resistance at a speed of 30 m/s?

At what speed is the resistance 6250 newtons?

16. A road research organisation recently claimed that the damage to road surfaces was proportional to the fourth power of the axle load. The axle load of a 44-tonne HGV is about 15 times that of a car. Calculate the ratio of the damage to road surfaces made by a 44-tonne HGV and a car.

Inverse variation

There are several ways of expressing an inverse relationship between two variables,

> x varies inversely as y

> x is inversely proportional to y.

We write $x \propto \dfrac{1}{y}$ for both statements and proceed using the method outlined in the previous section.

Example

z is inversely proportional to t^2 and $z = 4$ when $t = 1$. Calculate:

a) z when $t = 2$ **b)** t when $z = 16$.

We have $z \propto \dfrac{1}{t^2}$

or $\quad z = k \times \dfrac{1}{t^2}$ (k is a constant)

$z = 4$ when $t = 1$,

$\therefore \quad 4 = k\left(\dfrac{1}{1^2}\right)$

so $\quad k = 4$

$\therefore \quad z = 4 \times \dfrac{1}{t^2}$

. . . .

a) when $t = 2$, $z = 4 \times \dfrac{1}{2^2} = 1$

b) when $z = 16$, $16 = 4 \times \dfrac{1}{t^2}$

$$16t^2 = 4$$

$$t^2 = \dfrac{1}{4}$$

$$t = \pm\dfrac{1}{2}$$

Exercise 11

1. Rewrite the statements connecting the variables using a constant of variation, k.

a) $x \propto \dfrac{1}{y}$ **b)** $s \propto \dfrac{1}{t^2}$ **c)** $t \propto \dfrac{1}{\sqrt{q}}$

d) m varies inversely as w **e)** z is inversely proportional to t^2.

2. b varies inversely as e. If $b = 6$ when $e = 2$, calculate:

    a) the value of b when $e = 12$ **b)** the value of e when $b = 3$.

3. q varies inversely as r. If $q = 5$ when $r = 2$, calculate:

    a) the value of q when $r = 4$ **b)** the value of r when $q = 20$.

4. x is inversely proportional to y^2. If $x = 4$ when $y = 3$, calculate:

    a) the value of x when $y = 1$ **b)** the value of y when $x = 2\frac{1}{4}$.

5. R varies inversely as v^2. If $R = 120$ when $v = 1$, calculate:

    a) the value of R when $v = 10$ **b)** the value of v when $R = 30$.

6. T is inversely proportional to x^2. If $T = 36$ when $x = 2$, calculate:

    a) the value of T when $x = 3$ **b)** the value of x when $T = 1.44$.

7. p is inversely proportional to $\sqrt{y}$. If $p = 1.2$ when $y = 100$, calculate:

    a) the value of p when $y = 4$ **b)** the value of y when $p = 3$.

8. y varies inversely as z. If $y = \frac{1}{8}$ when $z = 4$, calculate:

    a) the value of y when $z = 1$ **b)** the value of z when $y = 10$.

9. Given that $z \propto \frac{1}{y}$, copy and complete the table:

y	2	4		$\frac{1}{4}$
z	8		16	

10. Given that $v \propto \frac{1}{t^2}$, copy and complete the table:

t	2	5		10
v	25		$\frac{1}{4}$	

11. Given that $r \propto \frac{1}{\sqrt{x}}$, copy and complete the table:

x	1	4		
r	12		$\frac{3}{4}$	2

12. e varies inversely as $(y - 2)$. If $e = 12$ when $y = 4$, find

    a) e when $y = 6$ **b)** y when $e = \frac{1}{2}$.

13. M is inversely proportional to the square of l.

    If $M = 9$ when $l = 2$, find:

    a) M when $l = 10$ **b)** l when $M = 1$.

14. Given $z = \dfrac{k}{x^n}$, find k and n, then copy and complete the table.

x	1	2	4
z	100	$12\frac{1}{2}$	$\frac{1}{10}$

15. Given $y = \dfrac{k}{\sqrt[n]{v}}$, find k and n, then copy and complete the table.

v	1	4	36
y	12	6	$\frac{3}{25}$

16. The volume V of a given mass of gas varies inversely as the pressure P. When $V = 2$ m³, $P = 500$ N/m². Find the volume when the pressure is 400 N/m² . Find the pressure when the volume is 5 m³.

17. The number of hours N required to dig a certain hole is inversely proportional to the number of men available x. When 6 men are digging, the hole takes 4 hours. Find the time taken when 8 men are available. If it takes $\frac{1}{2}$ hour to dig the hole, how many men are there?

18. The life expectancy L of a rat varies inversely as the square of the density d of poison distributed around his home. When the density of poison is 1 g/m² the life expectancy is 50 days. How long will he survive if the density of poison is:

a) 5 g/m²? **b)** $\frac{1}{2}$ g/m²?

19. The force of attraction F between two magnets varies inversely as the square of the distance d between them. When the magnets are 2 cm apart, the force of attraction is 18 newtons. How far apart are they if the attractive force is 2 newtons?

5.4 Indices

Rules of indices

1. $a^n \times a^m = a^{n+m}$ e.g. $7^2 \times 7^4 = 7^6$

2. $a^n \div a^m = a^{n-m}$ e.g. $6^6 \div 6^2 = 6^4$

3. $(a^n)^m = a^{nm}$ e.g. $(3^2)^5 = 3^{10}$

Also, $a^{-n} = \dfrac{1}{a^n}$ e.g. $5^{-2} = \dfrac{1}{5^2}$

$a^{\frac{1}{n}}$ means 'the nth root of a' e.g. $9^{\frac{1}{2}} = \sqrt{9}$

$a^{\frac{m}{n}}$ means 'the nth root of a raised to the power m'

e.g. $4^{\frac{3}{2}} = \left(\sqrt{4}\right)^3 = 8$

Example

Simplify:

a) $x^7 \times x^{13}$

b) $x^3 \div x^7$

c) $(x^4)^3$

d) $(3x^2)^3$

e) $(2x^{-1})^2 \div x^{-5}$

f) $3y^2 \times 4y^3$

....

a) $x^7 \times x^{13} = x^{7+13} = x^{20}$

b) $x^3 \div x^7 = x^{3-7} = x^{-4} = \dfrac{1}{x^4}$

c) $(x^4)^3 = x^{12}$

d) $(3x^2)^3 = 3^3 \times (x^2)^3 = 27x^6$

e) $\left(2x^{-1}\right)^2 \div x^{-5} = 4x^{-2} \div x^{-5}$

$\qquad\qquad = 4x^{(-2--5)}$

$\qquad\qquad = 4x^3$

f) $3y^2 \times 4y^3 = 12y^5$

Exercise 12

Express in index form:

1. $3 \times 3 \times 3 \times 3$

2. $4 \times 4 \times 5 \times 5 \times 5$

3. $3 \times 7 \times 7 \times 7$

4. $2 \times 2 \times 2 \times 7$

5. $\dfrac{1}{10 \times 10 \times 10}$

6. $\dfrac{1}{2 \times 2 \times 3 \times 3 \times 3}$

7. $\sqrt{15}$

8. $\sqrt[3]{3}$

9. $\sqrt[5]{10}$

10. $\left(\sqrt{5}\right)^3$

Simplify:

11. $x^3 \times x^4$

12. $y^6 \times y^7$

13. $z^7 \div z^3$

14. $z^{50} \times z^{50}$

15. $m^3 \div m^2$

16. $e^{-3} \times e^{-2}$

17. $y^{-2} \times y^4$

18. $w^4 \div w^{-2}$

19. $y^{\frac{1}{2}} \times y^{\frac{1}{2}}$

20. $(x^2)^5$

21. $x^{-2} \div x^{-2}$

22. $w^{-3} \times w^{-2}$

23. $w^{-7} \times w^2$

24. $x^3 \div x^{-4}$

25. $(a^2)^4$

26. $\left(k^{\frac{1}{2}}\right)^6$

27. $e^{-4} \times e^4$

28. $x^{-1} \times x^{30}$

29. $\left(y^4\right)^{\frac{1}{2}}$

30. $(x^{-3})^{-2}$

31. $z^2 \div z^{-2}$

32. $t^{-3} \div t$

33. $(2x^3)^2$

34. $(4y^5)^2$

35. $2x^2 \times 3x^2$

36. $5y^3 \times 2y^2$

37. $5a^3 \times 3a$

38. $(2a)^3$

39. $3x^3 \div x^3$

40. $8y^3 \div 2y$

41. $10y^2 \div 4y$

42. $8a \times 4a^3$

43. $(2x)^2 \times (3x)^3$

44. $4z^4 \times z^{-7}$

45. $6x^{-2} \div 3x^2$

46. $5y^3 \div 2y^{-2}$

47. $\left(x^2\right)^{\frac{1}{2}} \div \left(x^{\frac{1}{3}}\right)^3$

48. $7w^{-2} \times 3w^{-1}$

49. $(2n)^4 \div 8n^0$

50. $4x^{\frac{3}{2}} \div 2x^{\frac{1}{2}}$

Example

Evaluate:

a) $9^{\frac{1}{2}}$

b) 5^{-1}

c) $4^{-\frac{1}{2}}$

d) $25^{\frac{3}{2}}$

e) $\left(5^{\frac{1}{2}}\right)^3 \times 5^{\frac{1}{2}}$

f) 7^0

a) $9^{\frac{1}{2}} = \sqrt{9} = 3$

b) $5^{-1} = \dfrac{1}{5}$

$a^0 = 1$ for any non-zero value of a.

c) $4^{-\frac{1}{2}} = \dfrac{1}{4^{\frac{1}{2}}} = \dfrac{1}{\sqrt{4}} = \dfrac{1}{2}$

d) $25^{\frac{3}{2}} = \left(\sqrt{25}\right)^3 = 5^3 = 125$

e) $\left(5^{\frac{1}{2}}\right)^3 \times 5^{\frac{1}{2}} = 5^{\frac{3}{2}} \times 5^{\frac{1}{2}} = 5^2$
$= 25$

f) $7^0 = 1 \left[\text{consider } \dfrac{7^3}{7^3} = 7^{3-3} = 7^0 = 1\right]$

Exercise 13

Evaluate the following:

1. $3^2 \times 3$

2. 100^0

3. 3^{-2}

4. $(5^{-1})^{-2}$

5. $4^{\frac{1}{2}}$

6. $16^{\frac{1}{2}}$

7. $81^{\frac{1}{2}}$

8. $8^{\frac{1}{3}}$

9. $9^{\frac{3}{2}}$

10. $27^{\frac{1}{3}}$

11. $9^{-\frac{1}{2}}$

12. $8^{-\frac{1}{3}}$

13. $1^{\frac{5}{2}}$

14. $25^{-\frac{1}{2}}$

15. $1000^{\frac{1}{3}}$

16. $2^{-2} \times 2^5$

17. $2^4 \div 2^{-1}$

18. $8^{\frac{2}{3}}$

19. $27^{-\frac{2}{3}}$

20. $4^{-\frac{3}{2}}$

21. $36^{\frac{1}{2}} \times 27^{\frac{1}{3}}$

22. $10\,000^{\frac{1}{4}}$

23. $100^{\frac{3}{2}}$

24. $\left(100^{\frac{1}{2}}\right)^{-3}$

25. $\left(9^{\frac{1}{2}}\right)^{-2}$

26. $(-16.371)^0$

27. $81^{\frac{1}{4}} \div 16^{\frac{1}{4}}$

28. $\left(5^{-4}\right)^{\frac{1}{2}}$

29. $1000^{-\frac{1}{3}}$

30. $\left(4^{-\frac{1}{2}}\right)^2$

31. $8^{-\frac{2}{3}}$

32. $100^{\frac{5}{2}}$

33. $1^{\frac{4}{3}}$

34. 2^{-5}

35. $\left(0.01\right)^{\frac{1}{2}}$

36. $\left(0.04\right)^{\frac{1}{2}}$

37. $\left(2.25\right)^{\frac{1}{2}}$

38. $(7.63)^0$

39. $3^5 \times 3^{-3}$

40. $\left(3\dfrac{3}{8}\right)^{\frac{1}{3}}$

41. $\left(11\dfrac{1}{9}\right)^{-\frac{1}{2}}$

42. $\left(\dfrac{1}{8}\right)^{-2}$

43. $\left(\dfrac{1}{1000}\right)^{\frac{2}{3}}$

44. $\left(\dfrac{9}{25}\right)^{-\frac{1}{2}}$

45. $\left(10^{-6}\right)^{\frac{1}{3}}$

46. $7^2 \div \left(7^{\frac{1}{2}}\right)^4$

47. $\left(0.0001\right)^{-\frac{1}{2}}$

48. $\dfrac{9^{\frac{1}{2}}}{4^{-\frac{1}{2}}}$

49. $\dfrac{25^{\frac{3}{2}} \times 4^{\frac{1}{2}}}{9^{-\frac{1}{2}}}$

50. $\left(-\dfrac{1}{7}\right)^2 \div \left(-\dfrac{1}{7}\right)^3$

Example

Simplify:

a) $\left(2a\right)^3 \div \left(9a^2\right)^{\frac{1}{2}}$

b) $(3ac^2)^3 \times 2a^{-2}$

c) $(2x)^2 \div 2x^2$

. . . .

a) $\left(2a\right)^3 \div \left(9a^2\right)^{\frac{1}{2}} = 8a^3 \div 3a$

$$= \frac{8}{3}a^2$$

b) $(3ac^2)^3 \times 2a^{-2} = 27a^3c^6 \times 2a^{-2}$

$$= 54ac^6$$

c) $\left(2x\right)^2 \div 2x^2 = 4x^2 \div 2x^2$

$$= 2$$

Exercise 14

Rewrite without brackets:

1. $(5x^2)^2$

2. $(7y^3)^2$

3. $(10ab)^2$

4. $(2xy^2)^2$

5. $\left(4x^2\right)^{\frac{1}{2}}$

6. $(9y)^{-1}$

7. $(x^{-2})^{-1}$

8. $(2x^{-2})^{-1}$

9. $(5x^2\,y)^0$

10. $\left(\dfrac{1}{2}x\right)^{-1}$

11. $(3x)^2 \times (2x)^2$

12. $(5y)^2 \div y$

13. $\left(2x^{\frac{1}{2}}\right)^4$

14. $\left(3y^{\frac{1}{3}}\right)^3$

15. $(5x^0)^2$

16. $[(5x)^0]^2$

17. $(7y^0)^2$

18. $[(7y)^0]^2$

19. $(2x^2y)^3$

20. $(10xy^3)^2$

Simplify the following:

21. $(3x^{-1})^2 \div 6x^{-3}$

22. $\left(4x\right)^{\frac{1}{2}} \div x^{\frac{3}{2}}$

23. $x^2y^2 \times xy^3$

24. $4xy \times 3x^2y$

25. $10x^{-1}\,y^3 \times xy$

26. $\left(3x\right)^2 \times \left(\dfrac{1}{9}x^2\right)^{\frac{1}{2}}$

27. $z^3yx \times x^2yz$

28. $(2x)^{-2} \times 4x^3$

29. $(3y)^{-1} \div (9y^2)^{-1}$

30. $(xy)^0 \times (9x)^{\frac{1}{2}}$

31. $(x^2y)(2xy)(5y^3)$

32. $\left(4x^{\frac{1}{2}}\right) \times \left(8x^{\frac{3}{2}}\right)$

33. $5x^{-3} \div 2x^{-5}$

34. $[(3x^{-1})^{-2}]^{-1}$

35. $(2a)^{-2} \times 8a^4$

36. $(abc^2)^3$

37. Write in the form 2^p (e.g. $4 = 2^2$):

    a) 32   **b)** 128   **c)** 64   **d)** 1

38. Write in the form 3^q:

    a) $\dfrac{1}{27}$ **b)** $\dfrac{1}{81}$ **c)** $\dfrac{1}{3}$ **d)** $9 \times \dfrac{1}{81}$

Evaluate, with $x = 16$ and $y = 8$.

39. $2x^{\frac{1}{2}} \times y^{\frac{1}{3}}$ **40.** $x^{\frac{1}{4}} \times y^{-1}$ **41.** $\left(y^2 \right)^{\frac{1}{6}} \div \left(9x \right)^{\frac{1}{2}}$ **42.** $(x^2y^3)^0$

43. $x + y^{-1}$ **44.** $x^{-\frac{1}{2}} + y^{-1}$ **45.** $y^{\frac{1}{3}} \div x^{\frac{3}{4}}$ **46.** $\left(1000y \right)^{\frac{1}{3}} \times x^{-\frac{5}{2}}$

47. $\left(x^{\frac{1}{4}} + y^{-1} \right) \div x^{\frac{1}{4}}$ **48.** $x^{\frac{1}{2}} - y^{\frac{2}{3}}$ **49.** $\left(x^{\frac{3}{4}}y \right)^{-\frac{1}{3}}$ **50.** $\left(\dfrac{x}{y} \right)^{-2}$

Solve the equations for x.

51. $2^x = 8$ **52.** $3^x = 81$ **53.** $5^x = \dfrac{1}{5}$

54. $10^x = \dfrac{1}{100}$ **55.** $3^{-x} = \dfrac{1}{27}$ **56.** $4^x = 64$

57. $6^{-x} = \dfrac{1}{6}$ **58.** $100\,000^x = 10$ **59.** $12^x = 1$

60. $10^x = 0.0001$ **61.** $2^x + 3^x = 13$ **62.** $\left(\dfrac{1}{2} \right)^x = 32$

63. $5^{2x} = 25$ **64.** $1\,000\,000^{3x} = 10$

65. These two are more difficult. Use a calculator to find solutions correct to three significant figures.

    a) $x^x = 100$ **b)** $x^x = 10\,000$

5.5 Inequalities

$x < 4$ means 'x is *less than* 4'

$y > 7$ means 'y is *greater than* 7'

$z \leqslant 10$ means 'z is *less than or equal to* 10'

$t \geqslant -3$ means 't is *greater than or equal to* -3'

Solving inequalities

We follow the same procedure used for solving equations except that when we multiply or divide by a *negative* number the inequality is *reversed*.

e.g. $4 > -2$

but multiplying by -2,

    $-8 < 4$

Example

Solve the inequalities:

a) $2x - 1 > 5$

$2x > 5 + 1$

$x > \dfrac{6}{2}$

$x > 3$

b) $5 - 3x \leqslant 1$

$5 \leqslant 1 + 3x$

$5 - 1 \leqslant 3x$

$\dfrac{4}{3} \leqslant x$

Exercise 15

Introduce one of the symbols $<$, $>$ or $=$ between each pair of numbers.

1. $-2, 1$

2. $(-2)^2, 1$

3. $\dfrac{1}{4}, \dfrac{1}{5}$

4. $0.2, \dfrac{1}{5}$

5. $10^2, 2^{10}$

6. $\dfrac{1}{4}, 0.4$

7. $40\%, 0.4$

8. $(-1)^2, \left(-\dfrac{1}{2}\right)^2$

9. $5^2, 2^5$

10. $3\dfrac{1}{3}, \sqrt{10}$

11. $\pi^2, 10$

12. $-\dfrac{1}{3}, -\dfrac{1}{2}$

13. $2^{-1}, 3^{-1}$

14. $50\%, \dfrac{1}{5}$

15. $1\%, 100^{-1}$

State whether the following are true or false:

16. $0.7^2 > \dfrac{1}{2}$

17. $10^3 = 30$

18. $\dfrac{1}{8} > 12\%$

19. $(0.1)^3 = 0.0001$

20. $\left(-\dfrac{1}{5}\right)^0 = -1$

21. $\dfrac{1}{5^2} > \dfrac{1}{2^5}$

22. $(0.2)^3 < (0.3)^2$

23. $\dfrac{6}{7} > \dfrac{7}{8}$

24. $0.1^2 > 0.1$

Solve the following inequalities:

25. $x - 3 > 10$

26. $x + 1 < 0$

27. $5 > x - 7$

28. $2x + 1 \leqslant 6$

29. $3x - 4 > 5$

30. $10 \leqslant 2x - 6$

31. $5x < x + 1$

32. $2x \geqslant x - 3$

33. $4 + x < -4$

34. $3x + 1 < 2x + 5$

35. $2(x + 1) > x - 7$

36. $7 < 15 - x$

37. $9 > 12 - x$

38. $4 - 2x \leqslant 2$

39. $3(x - 1) < 2(1 - x)$

40. $7 - 3x < 0$

The number line

The inequality $x < 4$ is represented on the number line as

$x \geqslant -2$ is shown as

In the first case, 4 is *not* included so we have ∘.

In the second case, −2 *is* included so we have •.

$-1 \leqslant x < 3$ is shown as

Exercise 16

For questions **1** to **25**, solve each inequality and show the result on a number line.

In questions **20** to **25**, solve the two inequalities separately.

1. $2x + 1 > 11$

2. $3x - 4 \leqslant 5$

3. $2 < x - 4$

4. $6 \geqslant 10 - x$

5. $8 < 9 - x$

6. $8x - 1 < 5x - 10$

7. $2x > 0$

8. $1 < 3x - 11$

9. $4 - x > 6 - 2x$

10. $\dfrac{x}{3} < -1$

11. $1 < x < 4$

12. $-2 \leqslant x \leqslant 5$

13. $1 \leqslant x < 6$

14. $0 \leqslant 2x < 10$

15. $-3 \leqslant 3x \leqslant 21$

16. $1 < 5x < 10$

17. $\dfrac{x}{4} > 20$

18. $3x - 1 > x + 19$

19. $7(x + 2) < 3x + 4$

20. $1 < 2x + 1 < 9$

21. $10 \leqslant 2x \leqslant x + 9$

22. $x < 3x + 2 < 2x + 6$

23. $10 \leqslant 2x - 1 \leqslant x + 5$

24. $x < 3x - 1 < 2x + 7$

25. $x - 10 < 2(x - 1) < x$

For questions **26** to **35**, find the solutions, subject to the given condition.

26. $3a + 1 < 20$; a is a positive integer

27. $b - 1 \geqslant 6$; b is a prime number less than 20

28. $2e - 3 < 21$; e is a positive even number

29. $1 < z < 50$; z is a square number

30. $0 < 3x < 40$; x is divisible by 5

31. $2x > -10$; x is a negative integer

32. $x + 1 < 2x < x + 13$; x is an integer

33. $x^2 < 100$; x is a positive square number

34. $0 \leqslant 2z - 3 \leqslant z + 8$; z is a prime number

35. $\dfrac{a}{2} + 10 > a$; a is a positive even number

36. State the smallest integer n for which $4n > 19$.

37. Find an integer value of x such that $2x - 7 < 8 < 3x - 11$.

38. Find an integer value of y such that $3y - 4 < 12 < 4y - 5$.

39. Find any value of z such that $9 < z + 5 < 10$.

40. Find any value of p such that $9 < 2p + 1 < 11$.

41. Find a simple fraction q such that $\frac{4}{9} < q < \frac{5}{9}$.

42. Find an integer value of a such that $a - 3 \leqslant 11 \leqslant 2a + 10$.

43. State the largest prime number z for which $3z < 66$.

44. Find a simple fraction r such that $\frac{1}{3} < r < \frac{2}{3}$.

45. Find the largest prime number p such that $p^2 < 400$.

46. Illustrate on a number line the solution set of each pair of simultaneous inequalities:

    a) $x < 6; -3 \leqslant x \leqslant 8$ **b)** $x > -2; -4 < x < 2$

    c) $2x + 1 \leqslant 5; -12 \leqslant 3x - 3$ **d)** $3x - 2 < 19; 2x \geqslant -6$

47. Find the integer n such that $n < \sqrt{300} < n + 1$.

48. A youth club organiser is planning a day trip for the club members. The cost of the trip is $330 and the club has already saved $75. The price of a ticket for the trip is x and there are 21 people going on the trip.

    a) Write down an inequality in terms of x to determine the price of each ticket if the cost of the trip is to be completely funded.

    b) What is the minimum ticket price that the youth club organiser must charge?

49. Chailai has $700 in her bank account. She wants to keep at least $300. She plans to withdraw y per week for the next 12 weeks to pay for entertainment and food.

    a) Write down an inequality in terms of y to determine the amount of money Chailai can withdraw each week.

    b) How much can Chailai withdraw per week?

50. A car hire firm charges $30 per day plus a flat fee of $240 to hire a car. Neema has no more than $470 to pay for the car hire.

    a) Write down an inequality that represents Neema's situation.

    b) Solve the inequality to work out the maximum number of days Neema can hire the car for.

Graphical display

It is useful to represent inequalities on a graph, particularly where two variables are involved.

Drawing accurate graphs is explained in Unit 7.

Example

Draw a sketch graph and leave unshaded the area which represents the set of points that satisfy each of these inequalities:

a) $x > 2$

b) $1 \leqslant y \leqslant 5$

c) $x + y \leqslant 8$

In each graph, the unwanted region is shaded so that the region representing the set of points is left clearly visible.

In (a), the line $x = 2$ is shown as a broken line to indicate that the points on the line are *not* included.

In (b) and (c), the lines $y = 1$, $y = 5$ and $x + y = 8$ are shown as solid lines because points on the line *are* included in the solution set.

An inequality can thus be regarded as a set of points, for example, the unshaded region in Example (c) may be described as

$\{(x, y) : x + y \leqslant 8\}$

i.e. the set of points (x, y) such that $x + y \leqslant 8$.

Exercise 17

In questions **1** to **9** describe the region left unshaded.

1.

2.

3.

4.

5.

6.

7.

8.

9.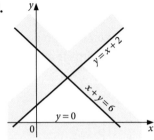

For questions **10** to **27**, draw a sketch graph similar to those above and indicate the set of points which satisfy the inequalities by shading the unwanted regions.

10. $2 \leqslant x \leqslant 7$

11. $0 \leqslant y \leqslant 3\frac{1}{2}$

12. $-2 < x < 2$

13. $x < 6$ and $y \leqslant 4$

14. $0 < x < 5$ and $y < 3$

15. $1 \leqslant x \leqslant 6$ and $2 \leqslant y \leqslant 8$

16. $-3 < x < 0$ and $-4 < y < 2$

17. $y \leqslant x$

18. $x + y < 5$

19. $y > x + 2$ and $y < 7$

20. $x \geqslant 0$ and $y \geqslant 0$ and $x + y \leqslant 7$

21. $x \geqslant 0$ and $x + y < 10$ and $y > x$

22. $8 \geqslant y \geqslant 0$ and $x + y > 3$

23. $x + 2y < 10$ and $x \geqslant 0$ and $y \geqslant 0$

24. $3x + 2y \leqslant 18$ and $x \geqslant 0$ and $y \geqslant 0$

25. $x \geqslant 0$, $y \geqslant x - 2$, $x + y \leqslant 10$

26. $3x + 5y \leqslant 30$ and $y > \dfrac{x}{2}$

27. $y \geqslant \dfrac{x}{2}$, $y \leqslant 2x$ and $x + y \leqslant 8$

5.6 Linear programming

In most linear programming problems, there are two stages:

1. to interpret the information given as a series of simultaneous inequalities and display them graphically.

2. to investigate some characteristic of the points in the unshaded solution set.

Example

A shopkeeper buys two types of cat food for his shop: Bruno at 40c a tin and Blaze at 60c a tin. He has \$15 available and decides to buy at least 30 tins altogether. He also decides that at least one third of the tins should be Blaze. He buys x tins of Bruno and y tins of Blaze.

a) Write down three inequalities which correspond to the above conditions.

b) Illustrate these inequalities on a graph.

c) He makes a profit of 10c a tin on Bruno and a profit of 20c a tin on Blaze. Assuming he can sell all his stock, find how many tins of each type he should buy to maximise his profit and find that profit.

a) Cost $40x + 60y \leqslant 1500$ $2x + 3y \leqslant 75$ ... [line A on graph]

Total number $x + y \geqslant 30$ ... [line B on graph]

At least one third Blaze: This means that the ratio of Blaze to Bruno should be at least 1:2, i.e. $\dfrac{y}{x} \geqslant \dfrac{1}{2}$ or $2y \geqslant x$ ... [line C on graph]

b) The graph below shows these three equations.

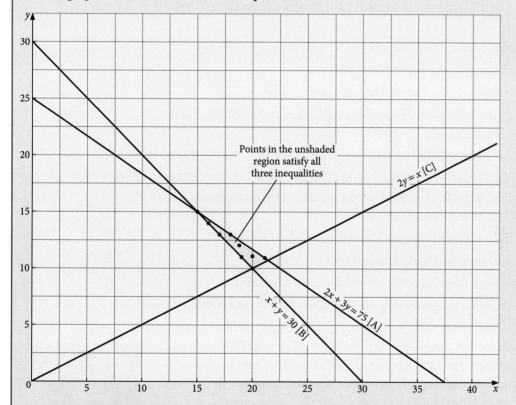

c) The table below shows the points on the graph in the unshaded region together with the corresponding figure for the profit.

The points marked * will clearly not provide a maximum profit.

x	15	16	17*	18	19	19*	20*	20*	21
y	15	14	13	13	12	11	11	10	11
profit	150	160		180	190				210
	+300	+280		+260	+240				+220
	450c	440c		440c	430c				430c

Conclusion: he should buy 15 tins of Bruno and 15 tins of Blaze. His maximised profit is then 450c.

Exercise 18

For questions **1** to **3**, draw an accurate graph to represent the inequalities listed, using shading to show the unwanted regions.

1. $x + y \leqslant 11; y \geqslant 3; y \leqslant x$

   Find the point having whole number coordinates and satisfying these inequalities which gives:

   a) the maximum value of $x + 4y$

   b) the minimum value of $3x + y$

2. $3x + 2y > 24; x + y < 12; y < \frac{1}{2}x; y > 1$

   Find the point having whole number coordinates and satisfying these inequalities which gives:

   a) the maximum value of $2x + 3y$

   b) the minimum value of $x + y$

3. $3x + 2y \leqslant 60; x + 2y \leqslant 30; x \geqslant 10; y \geqslant 0$

   Find the point having whole number coordinates and satisfying these inequalities which gives:

   a) the maximum value of $2x + y$ b) the maximum value of xy

4. Kojo is given $1.20 to buy some peaches and apples. Peaches cost 20c each, apples 10c each. He is told to buy at least 6 individual fruits, but he must not buy more apples than peaches.

   Let x be the number of peaches Kojo buys.

   Let y be the number of apples Kojo buys.

   a) Write down three inequalities which must be satisfied.

   b) Draw a linear programming graph and use it to list the combinations of fruit that are open to Kojo.

5. Ulla is told to buy some melons and oranges. Melons are 50c each and oranges 25c each, and she has $2 to spend. She must not buy more than 2 melons and she must buy at least 4 oranges. She is also told to buy at least 6 fruits altogether.

   Let x be the number of melons.

   Let y be the number of oranges.

   a) Write down four inequalities which must be satisfied.

   b) Draw a graph and use it to list the combinations of fruit that are open to Ulla.

6. A chef is going to make some fruit cakes and sponge cakes. He has plenty of all ingredients except for flour and sugar. He has only 2000 g of flour and 1200 g of sugar.

A fruit cake uses 500 g of flour and 100 g of sugar.

A sponge cake uses 200 g of flour and 200 g of sugar.

He wishes to make *more than* 4 cakes altogether.

Let the number of fruit cakes be x.

Let the number of sponge cakes be y.

a) Write down three inequalities which must be satisfied.

b) Draw a graph and use it to list the possible combinations of fruit cakes and sponge cakes which he can make.

7. Kwame has a spare time job spraying cars and vans. Vans take 2 hours each and cars take 1 hour each. He has 14 hours available per week. He has an agreement with one firm to do 2 of their vans every week. Apart from that he has no fixed work.

Kwame's permission to use his back garden contains the clause that he must do at least twice as many cars as vans.

Let x be the number of vans sprayed each week.

Let y be the number of cars sprayed each week.

a) Write down three inequalities which must be satisfied.

b) Draw a graph and use it to list the possible combinations of vehicles which Kwame can spray each week.

8. The manager of a football team has $100 000 to spend on buying new players. He can buy defenders at $6000 each or forwards at $8000 each. There must be at least 6 of each sort. To cover for injuries he must buy at least 13 players altogether. Let x represent the number of defenders he buys and y the number of forwards.

a) In what ways can he buy players?

b) If the wages are $10 000 per week for each defender and $20 000 per week for each forward, what is the combination of players which has the lowest wage bill?

9. A tennis-playing golfer has €15 to spend on golf balls (x) costing €1 each and tennis balls (y) costing 60c each. He must buy at least 16 altogether and he must buy *more* golf balls than tennis balls.

a) What is the greatest number of balls he can buy?

b) After using them, he can sell golf balls for 10c each and tennis balls for 20c each. What is his maximum possible income from sales?

10. A travel agent has to fly 1000 people and 35 000 kg of baggage from Hong Kong to Shanghai. Two types of aircraft are available: A which takes 100 people and 2000 kg of baggage, or B which takes 60 people and 3000 kg of baggage. He can use no more than 16 aircraft altogether. Write down three inequalities which must be satisfied if he uses x of A and y of B.

a) What is the smallest number of aircraft he could use?

b) If the hire charge for each aircraft A is $10 000 and for each aircraft B is $12 000, find the cheapest option available to him.

c) If the hire charges are altered so that each A costs $10 000 and each B costs $20 000, find the cheapest option now available to him.

11. A farmer has to transport 20 people and 32 sheep to a market. He can use either Fiats (x) which take 2 people and 1 sheep, or Rolls Royces (y) which take 2 people and 4 sheep.

He must not use more than 15 cars altogether.

a) What is the lowest total numbers of cars he could use?

b) If it costs $10 to hire each Fiat and $30 for each Rolls Royce, what is the *cheapest* solution?

12. Ahmed wishes to buy up to 20 notebooks for his shop. He can buy either type A for $1.50 each or type B for $3 each. He has a total of $45 he can spend. He must have at least 6 of each type in stock.

a) If he buys x of type A and y of type B, write down four inequalities which must be satisfied and represent the information on a graph.

b) If he makes a profit of 40c on each of type A and $1 on each of type B, how many of each should he buy for maximum profit?

c) If the profit is 80c on each of type A and $1 on each of type B, how many of each should he buy now?

13. A farmer needs to buy up to 25 cows for a new herd. He can buy either brown cows (x) at $50 each or black cows ($y$) at $80 each and he can spend a total of no more than $1600. He must have at least 9 of each type.

On selling the cows he makes a profit of $50 on each brown cow and $60 on each black cow. How many of each sort should he buy for maximum profit?

14. The manager of a car park allows 10 m² of parking space for each car and 30 m² for each lorry. The total space available is 300 m². He decides that the maximum number of vehicles at any time must not exceed 20 and he also insists that there must be at least as many cars as lorries. If the number of cars is x and the number of lorries is y, write down three inequalities which must be satisfied.

a) If the parking charge is $1 for a car and $5 for a lorry, find how many vehicles of each kind he should admit to maximise his income.

b) If the charges are changed to $2 for a car and $3 for a lorry, find how many of each kind he would be advised to admit.

Revision exercise 5A

1. Express the following as single fractions:

a) $\dfrac{x}{4} + \dfrac{x}{5}$ **b)** $\dfrac{1}{2x} + \dfrac{2}{3x}$

c) $\dfrac{x+2}{2} + \dfrac{x-4}{3}$ **d)** $\dfrac{7}{x-1} - \dfrac{2}{x+3}$

2. a) Factorise $x^2 - 4$

b) Simpliy $\dfrac{3x-6}{x^2-4}$

3. Given that $s - 3t = rt$, express:

a) s in terms of r and t

b) r in terms of s and t

c) t in terms of s and r.

4. a) Given that $x - z = 5y$, express z in terms of x and y.

b) Given that $mk + 3m = 11$, express m in terms of k.

c) For the formula $T = C\sqrt{z}$, express z in terms of T and C.

5. It is given that $y = \dfrac{k}{x}$ and that $1 \leqslant x \leqslant 10$.

a) If the smallest possible value of y is 5, find the value of the constant k.

b) Find the largest possible value of y.

6. Given that y varies as x^2 and that $y = 36$ when $x = 3$, find:

a) the value of y when $x = 2$

b) the value of x when $y = 64$.

7. a) Evaluate:

i) $9^{\frac{1}{2}}$ **ii)** $8^{\frac{2}{3}}$ **iii)** $16^{-\frac{1}{2}}$

b) Find x, given that

i) $3^x = 81$ **ii)** $7^x = 1$.

8. List the integer values of x which satisfy.

a) $2x - 1 < 20 < 3x - 5$

b) $5 < 3x + 1 < 17$.

9. Given that $t = k\sqrt{(x+5)}$, express x in terms of t and k.

10. Given that $z = \dfrac{3y+2}{y-1}$, express y in terms of z.

11. Given that $y = \dfrac{k}{k+w}$

a) Find the value of y when $k = \frac{1}{2}$ and $w = \frac{1}{3}$

b) Express w in terms of y and k.

12. On a suitable sketch graph, identify clearly the region A defined by $x \geqslant 0$, $x + y \leqslant 8$ and $y \geqslant x$.

13. Without using a calculator, calculate the value of:

a) $9^{-\frac{1}{2}} + \left(\dfrac{1}{8}\right)^{\frac{1}{3}} + (-3)^0$

b) $(1000)^{-\frac{1}{3}} - (0.1)^2$

14. It is given that $10^x = 3$ and $10^y = 7$. What is the value of 10^{x+y}?

15. Make x the subject of the following formulae:

a) $x + a = \dfrac{2x-5}{a}$

b) $cz + ax + b = 0$

c) $a = \sqrt{\left(\dfrac{x+1}{x-1}\right)}$

16. Write the following as single fractions:

a) $\dfrac{3}{x} + \dfrac{1}{2x}$

b) $\dfrac{3}{a-2} + \dfrac{1}{a^2-4}$

c) $\dfrac{3}{x(x+1)} - \dfrac{2}{x(x-2)}$

17. p varies jointly as the square of t and inversely as s. Given that $p = 5$ when $t = 1$ and $s = 2$, find a formula for p in terms of t and s.

18. A positive integer r is such that $pr^2 = 168$, where p lies between 3 and 5. List the possible values of r.

19. The shaded region A is formed by the lines $y = 2$, $y = 3x$ and $x + y = 6$. Write down the three inequalities which define A.

20. The shaded region B is formed by the lines $x = 0$, $y = x - 2$ and $x + y = 7$.

Write down the four inequalities which define B.

21. In the diagram, the solution set $-1 \leqslant x < 2$ is shown on a number line.

Illustrate, on similar diagrams, the solution set of the following pairs of simultaneous inequalities.

a) $x > 2$, $x \leqslant 7$

b) $4 + x \geqslant 2$, $x + 4 < 10$

c) $2x + 1 \geqslant 3$, $x - 3 \leqslant 3$.

22. In a laboratory we start with 2 cells in a dish. The number of cells in the dish doubles every 30 minutes.

a) How many cells are in the dish after four hours?

b) After what time are there 2^{13} cells in the dish?

c) After $10\frac{1}{2}$ hours there are 2^{22} cells in the dish and an experimental fluid is added which eliminates half of the cells. How many cells are left?

Examination-style exercise 5B

1. Write as a fraction in its simplest form $\dfrac{x-3}{4} + \dfrac{4}{x-3}$. [3]

Cambridge IGCSE Mathematics 0580
Paper 2 Q10 June 2007

2. Write as a single fraction in its simplest form $\dfrac{4}{2x+3} - \dfrac{2}{x-3}$. [3]

Cambridge IGCSE Mathematics 0580
Paper 21 Q11 November 2008

3. $(0.8)^{\frac{1}{2}}$, $\quad 0.8$, $\quad \sqrt{0.8}$, $\quad (0.8)^{-1}$, $\quad (0.8)^{2}$.

From the numbers above, write down

(a) the smallest, [1]

(b) the largest. [1]

Cambridge IGCSE Mathematics 0580
Paper 2 Q6 November 2005

4. Simplify $\left(27x^3\right)^{\frac{2}{3}}$. [2]

Cambridge IGCSE Mathematics 0580
Paper 21 Q8 June 2008

5. Find the value of n in each of the following statements.
   (a) $32^n = 1$ [1]
   (b) $32^n = 2$ [1]
   (c) $32^n = 8$ [1]

Cambridge IGCSE Mathematics 0580
Paper 2 Q7 November 2006

6. (a) Simplify $\left(27x^6\right)^{\frac{1}{3}}$. [2]

   (b) $\left(512\right)^{-\frac{2}{3}} = 2^p$. Find p. [2]

Cambridge IGCSE Mathematics 0580
Paper 2 Q21 November 2007

7. Write $\dfrac{1}{c} + \dfrac{1}{d} - \dfrac{c-d}{cd}$ as a single fraction in its simplest form. [3]

Cambridge IGCSE Mathematics 0580
Paper 21 Q10 June 2009

8. Solve the inequality $\dfrac{3x-4}{7} < \dfrac{x+3}{4}$. [3]

9. Rearrange the formula to make b the subject: $a = \sqrt{\dfrac{b}{4}} - 2$. [3]

10. (a) Factorise $cp^3 + dp^3$. [1]

   (b) Make p the subject of the formula $cp^3 + dp^3 - a^2 = b^3$. [2]

11. The quantity p varies inversely as the square of $(q+2)$.
   $p = 5$ when $q = 3$.
   Find p when $q = 8$. [3]

Cambridge IGCSE Mathematics 0580
Paper 21 Q13 November 2008

12. A spray can is used to paint a wall.

The thickness of the paint on the wall is t. The distance of the spray can from the wall is d.

t is inversely proportional to the square of d.

$t = 0.2$ when $d = 8$. [3]

Find t when $d = 10$.

Cambridge IGCSE Mathematics 0580
Paper 21 Q13 June 2009

13. The length, y, of a solid is inversely proportional to the square of its height, x.

  (a) Write down a general equation for x and y.

      Show that when $x = 5$ and $y = 4.8$ the equation becomes $x^2y = 120$. [2]

  (b) Find y when $x = 2$. [1]

  (c) Find x when $y = 10$. [2]

  (d) Find x when $y = x$. [2]

  (e) Describe exactly what happens to y when x is doubled. [2]

  (f) Describe exactly what happens to x when y is decreased by 36%. [2]

  (g) Make x the subject of the formula $x^2y = 120$. [2]

Cambridge IGCSE Mathematics 0580
Paper 4 Q5 June 2006

14. **Answer the whole of this question on a sheet of graph paper.**

Tiago does some work during the school holidays.

In one week he spends x hours cleaning cars and y hours repairing cycles.

The time he spends repairing cycles is at least equal to the time he spends cleaning cars.

This can be written as $y \geqslant x$.

He spends no more than 12 hours working.

He spends at least 4 hours cleaning cars.

  (a) Write down two more inequalities in x and/or y to show this information. [3]

  (b) Draw x and y axes from 0 to 12, using a scale of 1 cm to represent 1 unit on each axis. [1]

  (c) Draw three lines to show the three inequalities. Shade the **unwanted** regions. [5]

  (d) Tiago receives \$3 each hour for cleaning cars and \$1.50 each hour for repairing cycles.

     i) What is the least amount he could receive? [2]

     ii) What is the largest amount he could receive? [2]

Cambridge IGCSE Mathematics 0580
Paper 4 Q9 November 2006

15. (a) The surface area, A, of a cylinder, radius r and height h, is given by the formula

$A = 2\pi rh + 2\pi r^2$.

    i) Calculate the surface area of a cylinder of radius 5 cm and height 9 cm. [2]

    ii) Make h the subject of the formula. [2]

    iii) A cylinder has a radius of 6 cm and a surface area of 377 cm². Calculate the height of this cylinder. [2]

    iv) A cylinder has a surface area of 1200 cm² and its radius and height are equal. Calculate the radius. [3]

(b) i) On Monday a shop receives $60.30 by selling bottles of water at 45 cents each. How many bottles are sold? [1]

    ii) On Tuesday the shop receives x **cents** by selling bottles of water at 45 cents each. In terms of x, how many bottles are sold? [1]

    iii) On Wednesday the shop receives $(x - 75)$ **cents** by selling bottles of water at 48 cents each. In terms of x, how many bottles are sold? [1]

    iv) The number of bottles sold on Tuesday was 7 more than the number of bottles sold on Wednesday.

    Write down an equation in x and solve your equation. [4]

Cambridge IGCSE Mathematics 0580
Paper 4 Q8 November 2006

6 Trigonometry

Leonard Euler (1707–1783) was born near Basel in Switzerland but moved to St Petersburg in Russia and later to Berlin. He had an amazing facility for figures but delighted in speculating in the realms of pure intellect. In trigonometry he introduced the use of small letters for the sides and capitals for the angles of a triangle. He also wrote r, R and s for the radius of the inscribed and of the circumscribed circles and the semi-perimeter, giving the beautiful formula $4rRs = abc$.

E4.3 Read and make scale drawings.

E6.1 Interpret and use three-figure bearings.

E6.2 Apply Pythagoras' theorem and the sine, cosine and tangent ratios for acute angles to the calculation of a side or of an angle of a right-angled triangle. Solve trigonometrical problems in two dimensions involving angles of elevation and depression.

E6.3 Recognise, sketch and interpret graphs of simple trigonometric functions. Graph and know the properties of trigonometric functions. Solve simple trigonometric equations for values between 0° and 360°.

E6.4 Solve problems using the sine and cosine rules for any triangle and the formula area of triangle = ½ ab sin C.

E6.5 Solve simple trigonometrical problems in three dimensions including angle between a line and a plane.

6.1 Right-angled triangles

The side opposite the right angle is called the hypotenuse (we will use H). It is the longest side.

The side opposite the marked angle of 35° is called the opposite (we will use O).

The other side is called the adjacent (we will use A).

Consider two triangles, one of which is an enlargement of the other.

It is clear that the *ratio* $\dfrac{O}{H}$ will be the same in both triangles.

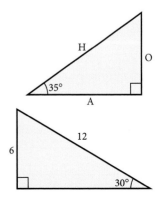

Sine, cosine and tangent

Three important functions are defined as follows:

$$\sin x = \frac{O}{H}$$

$$\cos x = \frac{A}{H}$$

$$\tan x = \frac{O}{A}$$

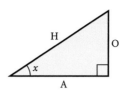

It is important to get the letters in the right order. Some people find a simple sentence helpful when the first letters of each word describe sine, cosine or tangent and Hypotenuse, Opposite and Adjacent. An example is:

Silly Old Harry Caught A Herring Trawling Off Afghanistan.

e.g.   SOH : $\sin = \dfrac{O}{H}$

For any angle x the values for $\sin x$, $\cos x$ and $\tan x$ can be found using a calculator.

> An alternative way of remembering the order of the letters is to use the mnemonic **SOHCAHTOA.**

Exercise 1

1. Draw a circle of radius 10 cm and construct a tangent to touch the circle at T.

   Draw OA, OB and OC where $A\hat{O}T = 20°$

   $$B\hat{O}T = 40°$$

   $$C\hat{O}T = 50°$$

   Measure the length AT and compare it with the value for $\tan 20°$ given on a calculator or in tables. Repeat for BT, CT and for other angles of your own choice.

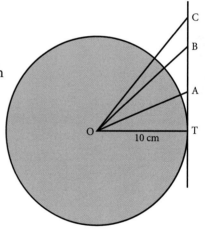

Finding the length of a side

Example 1

Find the side marked x.

a) Label the sides of the triangle H, O, A (in brackets).

b) In this example, we know nothing about H so we need the function involving O and A.

$$\tan 25.4° = \frac{O}{A} = \frac{x}{10}$$

---

c) Solve for *x*.

$x = 10 \times \tan 25.4° = 4.748$

$x = 4.75\,\text{cm}$ (to 3 s.f.)

Example 2

Find the side marked *z*.

a) Label H, O, A.

b) $\sin 31.3° = \dfrac{O}{H} = \dfrac{7.4}{z}$

c) Multiply by *z*.

$z \times (\sin 31.3°) = 7.4$

$z = \dfrac{7.4}{\sin 31.3}$

d) On a calculator, press the keys as follows:

$\boxed{7.4}\;\boxed{\div}\;\boxed{\sin}\;\boxed{31.3}\;\boxed{=}$

$z = 14.2\,\text{cm}$ (to 3 s.f.)

On some calculators you press

$\boxed{7.4}\;\boxed{\div}\;\boxed{31.3}\;\boxed{\sin}\;\boxed{=}$

Exercise 2

In questions **1** to **22** all lengths are in centimetres. Find the sides marked with letters. Give your answers to three significant figures.

1.

2.

3.

4.

5.

6.

7.

8.

9.

10.

11.

12.

13.

14.

15.

16.

17.

18.

19.

20.

21.

22.

In questions **23** to **34**, the triangle has a right angle at the middle letter.

23. In $\triangle ABC$, $\widehat{C} = 40°$, $BC = 4$ cm. Find AB.

24. In $\triangle DEF$, $\widehat{F} = 35.3°$, $DF = 7$ cm. Find ED.

25. In $\triangle GHI$, $\widehat{I} = 70°$, $GI = 12$ m. Find HI.

26. In $\triangle JKL$, $\widehat{L} = 55°$, $KL = 8.21$ m. Find JK.

27. In $\triangle MNO$, $\widehat{M} = 42.6°$, $MO = 14$ cm. Find ON.

28. In $\triangle$PQR, $\hat{P} = 28°$, PQ = 5.071 m. Find PR.

29. In $\triangle$STU, $\hat{S} = 39°$, TU = 6 cm. Find SU.

30. In $\triangle$VWX, $\hat{X} = 17°$, WV = 30.7 m. Find WX.

31. In $\triangle$ABC, $\hat{A} = 14.3°$, BC = 14 m. Find AC.

32. In $\triangle$KLM, $\hat{K} = 72.8°$, KL = 5.04 cm. Find LM.

33. In $\triangle$PQR, $\hat{R} = 31.7°$, QR = 0.81 cm. Find PR.

34. In $\triangle$XYZ, $\hat{X} = 81.07°$, YZ = 52.6 m. Find XY.

Example

Find the length marked x.

a) Find BD from triangle BDC.

$$\tan 32° = \frac{BD}{10}$$

$$BD = 10 \times \tan 32°$$

$\qquad\qquad\qquad\qquad$ ...[1]

b) Now find x from triangle ABD.

$$\sin 38° = \frac{x}{BD}$$

$\therefore\qquad x = BD \times \sin 38°$

$\qquad x = 10 \times \tan 32° \times \sin 38°$ (from [1])

$\qquad x = 3.85$ cm (to 3 s.f.)

Notice that BD was *not* calculated in [1].

It is better to do all the multiplications at one time.

Exercise 3

In questions **1** to **10**, find each side marked with a letter.
All lengths are in centimetres.

1.

2.

3.

4.

5.

6.

7.

8.

9.

10.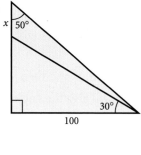

11. $\widehat{BAD} = \widehat{ACD} = 90°$

$\widehat{CAD} = 35°$

$\widehat{BDA} = 41°$

$AD = 20$ cm

Calculate:

a) AB

b) DC

c) BD

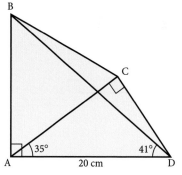

12. $\widehat{ABD} = \widehat{ADC} = 90°$

$\widehat{CAD} = 31°$

$\widehat{BDA} = 43°$

$AD = 10$ cm

Calculate:

a) AB

b) CD

c) DB

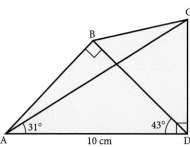

Finding an unknown angle

Example

Find the angle marked m.

a) Label the sides of the triangle H, O, A in relation to angle m.

b) In this example, we do not know 'O' so we need the cosine.

$$\cos m = \left(\frac{A}{H}\right) = \frac{4}{5}$$

c) Change $\frac{4}{5}$ to a decimal: $\frac{4}{5} = 0.8$

d) $\cos m = 0.8$

Press $\boxed{\text{Shift}}$ and then $\boxed{\cos}$ $\boxed{\text{Ans}}$

This will give the angle as $36.86989765°$.

We require the angle to one place of decimals so $m = 36.9°$.

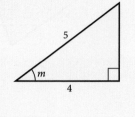

Note

On some calculators press $\boxed{\text{Inv}}$ $\boxed{\cos}$

Exercise 4

In questions **1** to **15**, find the angle marked with a letter. All lengths are in cm.

1.

2.

3.

4.

5.

6.

7.

8.

9.

10.

11.

12.

13.

14.

15.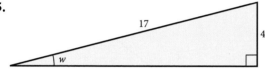

In questions **16** to **20**, the triangle has a right angle at the middle letter.

16. In $\triangle ABC$, BC = 4, AC = 7. Find $\hat{A}$.

17. In $\triangle DEF$, EF = 5, DF = 10. Find $\hat{F}$.

18. In $\triangle GHI$, GH = 9, HI = 10. Find $\hat{I}$.

19. In $\triangle JKL$, JL = 5, KL = 3. Find $\hat{J}$.

20. In $\triangle MNO$, MN = 4, NO = 5. Find $\hat{M}$.

In questions **21** to **26**, find the angle x.

21.

22.

23.

24.

25.

26.

Bearings

A bearing is an angle measured clockwise from North.

It is given using three digits.

In the diagram:

the bearing of B from A is 052°

the bearing of A from B is 232°.

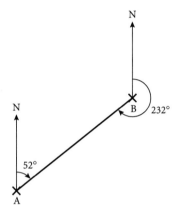

Example

A ship sails 22 km from A on a bearing of 042°, and a further 30 km on a bearing of 090° to arrive at B. What is the distance and bearing of B from A?

a) Draw a clear diagram and label extra points as shown.

b) Find DE and AD.

i) $\sin 42° = \dfrac{DE}{22}$

∴ $DE = 22 \times \sin 42° = 14.72$ km

ii) $\cos 42° = \dfrac{AD}{22}$

∴ $AD = 22 \times \cos 42° = 16.35$ km

c) Using triangle ABF,

$$AB^2 = AF^2 + BF^2 \quad \text{(Pythagoras' theorem)}$$

and $\quad AF = DE + EB$

$\quad\quad AF = 14.72 + 30 = 44.72 \text{ km}$

and $\quad BF = AD = 16.35 \text{ km}$

$\therefore \quad\quad AB^2 = 44.72^2 + 16.35^2$

$\quad\quad\quad = 2267.2$

$\quad\quad AB = 47.6 \text{ km (to 3 s.f.)}$

d) The bearing of B from A is given by the angle $D\hat{A}B$.

But $D\hat{A}B = A\hat{B}F$.

$$\tan ABF = \frac{AF}{BF} = \frac{44.72}{16.35}$$

$\quad\quad\quad = 2.7352$

$\therefore \quad\quad A\hat{B}F = 69.9°$

B is 47.6 km from A on a bearing of 069.9°.

Exercise 5

In this exercise, start by drawing a clear diagram.

1. A ladder of length 6 m leans against a vertical wall so that the base of the ladder is 2 m from the wall. Calculate the angle between the ladder and the wall.

2. A ladder of length 8 m rests against a wall so that the angle between the ladder and the wall is 31°. How far is the base of the ladder from the wall?

3. A ship sails 35 km on a bearing of 042°.
   a) How far north has it travelled?
   b) How far east has it travelled?

4. A ship sails 200 km on a bearing of 243.7°.
   a) How far south has it travelled?
   b) How far west has it travelled?

5. Find TR if PR = 10 m and QT = 7 m.

6. Find d.

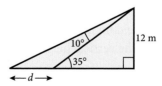

7. An aircraft flies 400 km from a point O on a bearing of 025°
   and then 700 km on a bearing of 080° to arrive at B.

   a) How far north of O is B?

   b) How far east of O is B?

   c) Find the distance and bearing of B from O.

8. An aircraft flies 500 km on a bearing of 100° and then 600 km on a
   bearing of 160°.

   Find the distance and bearing of the finishing point from the starting point.

For questions **9** to **12**, plot the points for each question on a sketch graph
with x- and y-axes drawn to the same scale.

9. For the points A(5, 0) and B(7, 3), calculate the angle between AB
   and the x-axis.

10. For the points C(0, 2) and D(5, 9), calculate the angle between CD
    and the y-axis.

11. For the points A(3, 0), B(5, 2) and C(7, −2), calculate the angle BAC.

12. For the points P(2, 5), Q(5, 1) and R(0, −3), calculate the angle PQR.

13. From the top of a tower of height 75 m, a man sees two goats,
    both due west of him. If the angles of depression of the two
    goats are 10° and 17°, calculate the distance between them.

14. An isosceles triangle has sides of length 8 cm, 8 cm and 5 cm.
    Find the angle between the two equal sides.

15. The angles of an isosceles triangle are 66°, 66° and 48°. If the
    shortest side of the triangle is 8.4 cm, find the length of one of the
    two equal sides.

16. A chord of length 12 cm subtends an angle of 78.2° at the centre
    of a circle. Find the radius of the circle.

17. Find the acute angle between the diagonals of a rectangle whose
    sides are 5 cm and 7 cm.

18. A kite flying at a height of 55 m is attached to a string which makes
    an angle of 55° with the horizontal. What is the length of the string?

19. A boy is flying a kite from a string of length 150 m. If the
    string is taut and makes an angle of 67° with the horizontal,
    what is the height of the kite?

20. A rocket flies 10 km vertically, then 20 km at an angle of
    15° to the vertical and finally 60 km at an angle of 26° to the
    vertical. Calculate the vertical height of the rocket at the end
    of the third stage.

21. Find x, given AD = BC = 6 m.

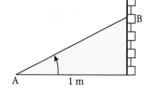

22. Find x.

23. Ants can hear each other up to a range of 2 m. An ant at A, 1 m from a wall sees her friend at B about to be eaten by a spider. If the angle of elevation of B from A is 62°, will the spider have a meal or not? (Assume B escapes if he hears A calling.)

24. A hedgehog wishes to cross a road without being run over. He observes the angle of elevation of a lamp post on the other side of the road to be 27° from the edge of the road and 15° from a point 10 m back from the road. How wide is the road? If he can run at 1 m/s, how long will he take to cross?

If cars are travelling at 20 m/s, how far apart must they be if he is to survive?

25. From a point 10 m from a vertical wall, the angles of elevation of the bottom and the top of a statue of Sir Isaac Newton, set in the wall, are 40° and 52°. Calculate the height of the statue.

6.2 Scale drawing

On a scale drawing you must always state the scale you use.

Exercise 6

Make a scale drawing and then answer the questions.

1. A field has four sides as shown in the diagram.

How long is the side x in metres?

2. Two ships leave a port at the same time. The first ship sails at 38 knots on a bearing of 042° and the second ship sails at 25 knots on a bearing of 315°. How far apart are the ships two hours later? [1 knot is a speed of 1 nautical mile per hour.]

3. Two radar stations A and B are 80 km apart and B is due east of A. One aircraft is on a bearing of 030° from A and 346° from B. A second aircraft is on a bearing of 325° from A and 293° from B. How far apart are the two aircraft?

4. A ship sails 95 km on a bearing of 140°, then a further 102 km on a bearing of 260° and then returns directly to its starting point. Find the length and bearing of the return journey.

5. A control tower observes the flight of an aircraft.

At 09:23 the aircraft is 580 km away on a bearing of 043°.
At 09:25 the aircraft is 360 km away on a bearing of 016°.
What is the speed and the course of the aircraft?
[Use a scale of 1 cm to 50 km.]

6. Make a scale drawing of the diagram and find the length of CD in km.

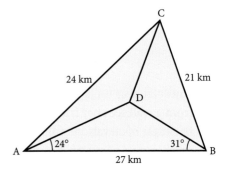

6.3 Three-dimensional problems

Always draw a large, clear diagram. It is often helpful to redraw the triangle which contains the length or angle to be found.

Example

A rectangular box with top WXYZ and base ABCD has AB = 6 cm, BC = 8 cm and WA = 3 cm.

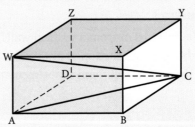

Calculate:

a) the length of AC

b) the angle between WC and AC.

. . . .

a) Redraw triangle ABC.

$$AC^2 = 6^2 + 8^2 = 100$$

$$AC = 10 \text{ cm}$$

b) Redraw triangle WAC.

Let $\ W\hat{C}A = \theta$

$$\tan\theta = \frac{3}{10}$$

$$\theta = 16.7°$$

The angle between WC and AC is 16.7°.

Exercise 7

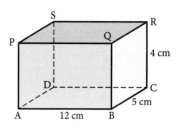

1. In the rectangular box shown, find:

   a) AC

   b) AR

   c) the angle between AC and AR.

2. A vertical pole BP stands at one corner of a horizontal
rectangular field as shown.

If AB = 10 m, AD = 5 m and the angle of elevation of P from A
is 22°, calculate:

   a) the height of the pole

   b) the angle of elevation of P from C

   c) the length of a diagonal of the rectangle ABCD

   d) the angle of elevation of P from D.

3. In the cube shown, find:

   a) BD

   b) AS

   c) BS

   d) the angle SBD

   e) the angle ASB

4. In the square-based pyramid, V is vertically above the middle
of the base, AB = 10 cm and VC = 20 cm. Find:

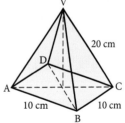

   a) AC

   b) the height of the pyramid

   c) the angle between VC and the base ABCD

   d) the angle AVB

   e) the angle AVC

5. In the wedge shown, PQRS is perpendicular to ABRQ; PQRS
and ABRQ are rectangles with AB = QR = 6 m, BR = 4 m,
RS = 2 m. Find:

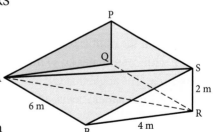

   a) BS   **b)** AS

   c) angle BSR   **d)** angle ASR

   e) angle PAS

6. The edges of a box are 4 cm, 6 cm and 8 cm. Find the length
of a diagonal and the angle it makes with the diagonal on the
largest face.

7. In the diagram A, B and O are points in a horizontal plane and P is vertically above O, where OP = h m.

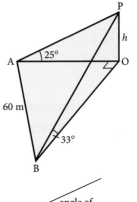

A is due West of O, B is due South of O and AB = 60 m. The angle of elevation of P from A is 25° and the angle of elevation of P from B is 33°.

   a) Find the length AO in terms of h.

   b) Find the length BO in terms of h.

   c) Find the value of h.

8. The angle of elevation of the top of a tower is 38° from a point A due south of it. The angle of elevation of the top of the tower from another point B, due east of the tower is 29°. Find the height of the tower if the distance AB is 50 m.

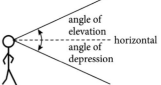

9. An observer at the top of a tower of height 15 m sees a man due west of him at an angle of depression 31°. He sees another man due south at an angle of depression 17°. Find the distance between the men.

10. The angle of elevation of the top of a tower is 27° from a point A due east of it. The angle of elevation of the top of the tower is 11° from another point B due south of the tower. Find the height of the tower if the distance AB is 40 m.

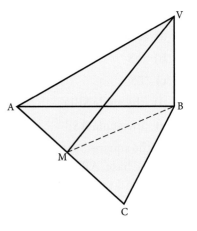

11. The figure shows a triangular pyramid on a horizontal base ABC, V is vertically above B where VB = 10 cm, $A\hat{B}C = 90°$ and AB = BC =15 cm. Point M is the midpoint of AC. Calculate the size of angle VMB.

6.4 Sine, cosine and tangent for any angle

So far we have used sine, cosine and tangent only in right-angled triangles. For angles greater than 90°, we will see that there is a close connection between trigonometric ratios and circles.

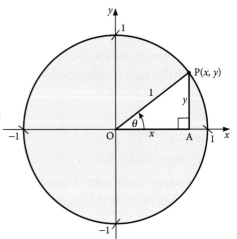

The circle on the right is of radius 1 unit with centre (0, 0). A point P with coordinates (x, y) moves round the circumference of the circle. The angle that OP makes with the positive x-axis as it turns in an anticlockwise direction is θ.

In triangle OAP, $\cos \theta = \dfrac{x}{1}$ and $\sin \theta = \dfrac{y}{1}$

The x-coordinate of P is $\cos\theta$.

The y-coordinate of P is $\sin\theta$.

This idea is used to define the cosine and the sine of any angle, including angles greater than 90°. Here is an angle that is greater than 90°.

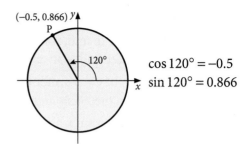

$\cos 120° = -0.5$
$\sin 120° = 0.866$

A graphics calculator can be used to show the graph of $y = \sin x$ for any range of angles.
The graphs below show:

- $y = \sin x$ for x from 0° to 180°. The sine curve above the x-axis has reflective symmetry about $x = 90°$.

- $y = \cos x$ for x from 0° to 180°. The cosine curve has rotational symmetry about $x = 90°$.

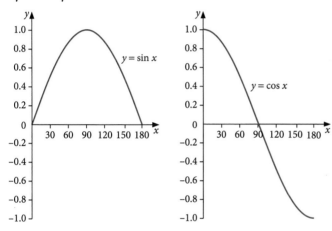

Note:

$\sin 150° = \sin 30°$	and	$\cos 150° = -\cos 30°$

$\sin 150° = \sin 30°$ and $\cos 150° = -\cos 30°$

$\sin 110° = \sin 70°$ $\cos 110° = -\cos 70°$

$\sin 163° = \sin 17°$ $\cos 163° = -\cos 17°$

or $\sin x = \sin(180° - x)$ or $\cos x = -\cos(180° - x)$

These two results are particularly important for use with obtuse angles ($90° < x < 180°$) in Sections 6.5 and 6.6 when applying the sine rule formula or the cosine rule formula.

The graph of $y = \tan x$ is different to those for sine and cosine. Looking at the unit circle at the bottom of page 222, you can see that $\tan\theta = \dfrac{x}{y}$ and when $\theta = 90°$ the y-coordinate is zero. This means that when you try to calculate $\tan\theta$ for $\theta = 90°$ you divide by zero. Hence $\tan\theta$ is *undefined* when $\theta = 90°$. This is shown on the graph as a vertical dotted line through 90°. This line is called an **asymptote**.

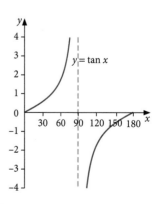

Exercise 8

1. **a)** Use a calculator to find, correct to 2 decimal places where necessary, the cosine of all angles $0°$, $30°$, $60°$, ..., $360°$.

   b) Draw a graph of $y = \cos x$ for $0° \leqslant x \leqslant 360°$. Use a scale of 1 cm to $30°$ on the x-axis and 5 cm to 1 unit on the y-axis.

2. Draw the graph of $y = \sin x$ using the same angles and scales as in question **1**.

3. Draw the graph of $y = \tan x$ for $0° \leqslant x \leqslant 360°$. Choose the angles you use to calculate the tangent and your scales carefully. Check your graph using a graphical calculator if possible.

In questions **4** to **12** do not use a calculator. Use the symmetries of the graphs $y = \sin x$, $y = \cos x$ and $y = \tan x$.

4. If $\sin 18° = 0.309$, give another angle whose sine is 0.309.

5. If $\sin 27° = 0.454$, give another angle whose sine is 0.454.

6. If $\sin 230° = -0.766$, give another angle whose sine is -0.766.

7. Give another angle which has the same sine as:

   a) $40°$ **b)** $130°$ **c)** $300°$

8. If $\cos 70° = 0.342$, give another angle whose cosine is 0.342.

9. If $\cos 105° = -0.259$, give another angle whose cosine is -0.259.

10. If $\cos 20° = 0.940$, give two angles whose cosine is -0.940.

11. If $\tan 36° = 0.727$, give another angle whose tangent is 0.727.

12. If $\tan 112° = -2.475$, give another angle whose tangent is -2.475.

13. Solve the following equations. Give your answers in the interval $0° \leqslant x \leqslant 360°$.

   a) $\sin x = \dfrac{\sqrt{3}}{2}$ **b)** $\cos x = 0.9$ **c)** $\tan x = 0.5$

   d) $\cos x = -\dfrac{\sqrt{2}}{2}$ **e)** $\sin x = -0.75$ **f)** $\tan x = -6$

14. Solve the following equations. Give your answers in the interval $0° \leqslant x \leqslant 360°$.

   a) $2 \sin x = 1$ **b)** $3 \cos x = 2$ **c)** $2 \tan x = 7$

   d) $1 + 3 \sin x = 0$ **e)** $5 \cos x + 4 = 0$ **f)** $4 + 3 \tan x = 0$

   g) $\sin(x + 30°) = \dfrac{1}{\sqrt{2}}$ **h)** $\tan(x - 45°) = 1$

15. Find *two* solutions of the equation $\cos^2 x = \dfrac{1}{4}$ for x between $0°$ and $180°$.

6.5 The sine rule

The sine rule enables us to calculate sides and angles in some triangles where there is not a right angle.

In $\triangle ABC$, we use the convention that
a is the side opposite $\hat{A}$

b is the side opposite $\hat{B}$, etc.

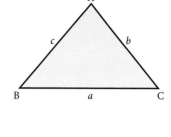

Either
$$\frac{a}{\sin A} = \frac{b}{\sin B} = \frac{c}{\sin C} \qquad \ldots[1]$$

or
$$\frac{\sin A}{a} = \frac{\sin B}{b} = \frac{\sin C}{c} \qquad \ldots[2]$$

Use [1] when finding a *side*, and [2] when finding an *angle*.

Example 1

Find c.

$$\frac{c}{\sin C} = \frac{b}{\sin B}$$

$$\frac{c}{\sin 50°} = \frac{7}{\sin 60°}$$

$$c = \frac{7 \times \sin 50°}{\sin 60°} = 6.19 \text{ cm} \text{ (to 3 s.f.)}$$

Although we cannot have an angle of more than 90° in a right-angled triangle, it is still useful to define sine, cosine and tangent for these angles. For an obtuse angle x, we have $\sin x = \sin(180 - x)$.

Examples

$\sin 130° = \sin 50°$
$\sin 170° = \sin 10°$
$\sin 116° = \sin 64°$

Most people simply use a calculator when finding the sine of an obtuse angle.

Example 2

Find $\hat{B}$.

$$\frac{\sin B}{b} = \frac{\sin A}{a}$$

$$\frac{\sin B}{6} = \frac{\sin 120°}{15} \quad (\sin 120° = \sin 60°)$$

$$\sin B = \frac{6 \times \sin 60°}{15}$$

$$\sin B = 0.346$$

$$\hat{B} = 20.3°$$

Exercise 9

For questions **1** to **6**, find each side marked with a letter.
Give answers correct to 3 significant figures.

1.

2.

3.

4.

5.

6.

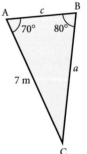

7. In $\triangle ABC$, $\hat{A} = 61°$, $\hat{B} = 47°$, $AC = 7.2$ cm. Find BC.

8. In $\triangle XYZ$, $\hat{Z} = 32°$, $\hat{Y} = 78°$, $XY = 54$ cm. Find XZ.

9. In $\triangle PQR$, $\hat{Q} = 100°$, $\hat{R} = 21°$, $PQ = 3.1$ cm. Find PR.

10. In $\triangle LMN$, $\hat{L} = 21°$, $\hat{N} = 30°$, $MN = 7$ cm. Find LN.

In questions **11** to **18**, find each angle marked *. All lengths are in centimetres.

11.

12.

13.

14.

15.

16.

17.

18.

19. In $\triangle ABC$, $\widehat{A} = 62°$, $BC = 8$, $AB = 7$. Find $\widehat{C}$.

20. In $\triangle XYZ$, $\widehat{Y} = 97.3°$, $XZ = 22$, $XY = 14$. Find $\widehat{Z}$.

21. In $\triangle DEF$, $\widehat{D} = 58°$, $EF = 7.2$, $DE = 5.4$. Find $\widehat{F}$.

22. In $\triangle LMN$, $\widehat{M} = 127.1°$, $LN = 11.2$, $LM = 7.3$. Find $\widehat{L}$.

6.6 The cosine rule

We use the cosine rule when we have either

a) two sides and the included angle or   **b)** all three sides.

There are two forms.

1. To find the length of a side.

$$a^2 = b^2 + c^2 - (2bc \cos A)$$

or $b^2 = c^2 + a^2 - (2ac \cos B)$

or $c^2 = a^2 + b^2 - (2ab \cos C)$

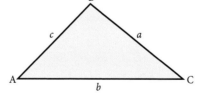

2. To find an angle when given all three sides.

$$\cos A = \frac{b^2 + c^2 - a^2}{2bc}$$

or $$\cos B = \frac{a^2 + c^2 - b^2}{2ac}$$

or $$\cos C = \frac{a^2 + b^2 - c^2}{2ab}$$

For an obtuse angle x we have $\cos x = -\cos(180 - x)$.

Examples $\cos 120° = -\cos 60°$

$\cos 142° = -\cos 38°$

Example 1

Find b.

$$b^2 = a^2 + c^2 - (2ac \cos B)$$

$$b^2 = 8^2 + 5^2 - (2 \times 8 \times 5 \times \cos 112°)$$

$$b^2 = 64 + 25 - [80 \times (-0.3746)]$$

$$b^2 = 64 + 25 + 29.968$$

(Notice the change of sign for the obtuse angle.)

$$b = \sqrt{118.968} = 10.9 \text{ cm (to 3 s.f.)}$$

Example 2

Find angle C.

$$\cos C = \frac{a^2 + b^2 - c^2}{2ab}$$

$$\cos C = \frac{5^2 + 6^2 - 7^2}{2 \times 5 \times 6} = \frac{12}{60} = 0.200$$

$$\hat{C} = 78.5°$$

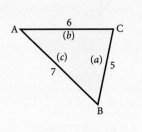

Exercise 10

Find the sides marked *. All lengths are in centimetres.

1.

2.

3.

4.

5.

6.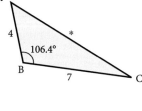

7. In $\triangle ABC$, $AB = 4$ cm, $AC = 7$ cm, $\hat{A} = 57°$. Find BC.

8. In $\triangle XYZ$, $XY = 3$ cm, $YZ = 3$ cm, $\hat{Y} = 90°$. Find XZ.

9. In $\triangle LMN$, $LM = 5.3$ cm, $MN = 7.9$ cm, $\hat{M} = 127°$. Find LN.

10. In $\triangle PQR$, $\hat{Q} = 117°$, $PQ = 80$ cm, $QR = 100$ cm. Find PR.

In questions **11** to **16**, find each angle marked *.

11.

12.

13.

14.

15.

16.
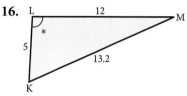

17. In $\triangle ABC$, $a = 4.3$ cm, $b = 7.2$ cm, $c = 9$ cm. Find $\hat{C}$.

18. In $\triangle DEF$, $d = 30$ cm, $e = 50$ cm, $f = 70$ cm. Find $\hat{E}$.

19. In $\triangle PQR$, $p = 8$ cm, $q = 14$ cm, $r = 7$ cm. Find $\hat{Q}$.

20. In $\triangle LMN$, $l = 7$ cm, $m = 5$ cm, $n = 4$ cm. Find $\hat{N}$.

21. In $\triangle XYZ$, $x = 5.3$ cm, $y = 6.7$ cm, $z = 6.14$ cm. Find $\hat{Z}$.

22. In $\triangle ABC$, $a = 4.1$ cm, $c = 6.3$ cm, $\hat{B} = 112.2°$. Find b.

23. In $\triangle PQR$, $r = 0.72$ cm, $p = 1.14$ cm, $\hat{Q} = 94.6°$. Find q.

24. In $\triangle LMN$, $n = 7.206$ cm, $l = 6.3$ cm, $\hat{L} = 51.2°$, $\hat{N} = 63°$. Find m.

Example

A ship sails from a port P a distance of 7 km on a bearing of 306° and then a further 11 km on a bearing of 070° to arrive at X. Calculate the distance from P to X.

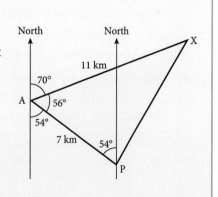

$PX^2 = 7^2 + 11^2 - (2 \times 7 \times 11 \times \cos 56°)$

$\qquad = 49 + 121 - (86.12)$

$PX^2 = 83.88$

$\quad PX = 9.16$ km (to 3 s.f.)

The distance from P to X is 9.16 km.

Exercise 11

Start each question by drawing a large, clear diagram.

1. In triangle PQR, $\hat{Q} = 72°$, $\hat{R} = 32°$ and PR = 12 cm. Find PQ.

2. In triangle LMN, $\hat{M} = 84°$, LM = 7 m and MN = 9 m. Find LN.

3. A destroyer D and a cruiser C leave port P at the same time. The destroyer sails 25 km on a bearing of 040° and the cruiser sails 30 km on a bearing of 320°. How far apart are the ships?

4. Two honeybees A and B leave the hive H at the same time; A flies 27 m due South and B flies 9 m on a bearing of 111°. How far apart are they?

5. Find all the angles of a triangle in which the sides are in the ratio $5:6:8$.

6. A golfer hits his ball B a distance of 170 m towards a hole H which measures 195 m from the tee T to the green. If his shot is directed 10° away from the true line to the hole, find the distance between his ball and the hole.

7. From A, B lies 11 km away on a bearing of 041° and C lies 8 km away on a bearing of 341°. Find:

   a) the distance between B and C

   b) the bearing of B from C.

8. From a lighthouse L an aircraft carrier A is 15 km away on a bearing of 112° and a submarine S is 26 km away on a bearing of 200°. Find:

   a) the distance between A and S

   b) the bearing of A from S.

9. If the line BCD is horizontal find:

   a) AE

   b) EÂC

   c) the angle of elevation of E from A.

10. An aircraft flies from its base 200 km on a bearing of 162°, then 350 km on a bearing of 260°, and then returns directly to base. Calculate the length and bearing of the return journey.

11. Town Y is 9 km due North of town Z. Town X is 8 km from Y, 5 km from Z and somewhere to the west of the line YZ.

    a) Draw triangle XYZ and find angle YZX.

    b) During an earthquake, town X moves due South until it is due West of Z. Find how far it has moved.

12. Calculate WX, given YZ = 15 m.

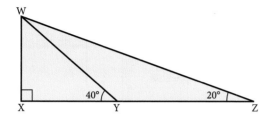

13. A golfer hits her ball a distance of 127 m so that it finishes 31 m from the hole. If the straight line distance to the hole is 150 m, calculate the angle between the line of her shot and the direct line to the hole.

Revision exercise 6A

1. Calculate the side or angle marked with a letter.

a)

b)

c)

d)

2. Given that x is an acute angle and that

$$3 \tan x - 2 = 4 \cos 35.3°$$

calculate:

a) $\tan x$

b) the value of x in degrees correct to 1 d.p.

3. Solve the following equations. Give your answers in the interval $0° \leqslant x \leqslant 360°$.

a) $\sin x = 0.75$ **b)** $\cos x = -0.2$

c) $\tan x = -2$ **d)** $5 \sin x + 3 = 0$

e) $6 \cos x - 5 = 0$ **f)** $\tan(x + 20°) = 1.5$

4. In the triangle XYZ, XY = 14 cm, XZ = 17 cm and angle YXZ = 25°. A is the foot of the perpendicular from Y to XZ.

Calculate:

a) the length XA   **b)** the length YA

c) the angle $Z\hat{Y}A$

5. Calculate the length of AB.

6. a) A lies on a bearing of 040° from B. Calculate the bearing of B from A.

b) The bearing of X from Y is 115°. Calculate the bearing of Y from X.

7. Given BD = 1 m, calculate the length AC.

8. In the triangle PQR, angle PQR = 90° and angle RPQ = 31°. The length of PQ is 11 cm.

Calculate:

a) the length of QR

b) the length of PR

c) the length of the perpendicular from Q to PR.

9. $\hat{BAD} = \hat{DCA} = 90°$, $\hat{CAD} = 32.4°$, $\hat{BDA} = 41°$ and AD = 100 cm.

Calculate:

a) the length of AB

b) the length of DC

c) the length of BD.

10. An observer at the top of a tower of height 20 m sees a man due East of him at an angle of depression of 27°. He sees another man due South of him at an angle of depression of 30°. Find the distance between the men on the ground.

11. The figure shows a cube of side 10 cm.

Calculate:

a) the length of AC

b) the angle $Y\hat{A}C$

c) the angle $Z\hat{B}D$.

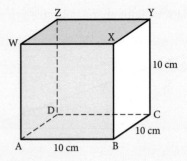

12. The diagram shows a rectangular block. AY = 12 cm, AB = 8 cm, BC = 6 cm.

Calculate:

a) the length YC

b) the angle $Y\hat{A}Z$.

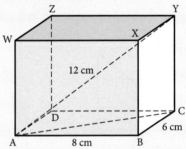

13. VABCD is a pyramid in which the base ABCD is a square of side 8 cm; V is vertically above the centre of the square and VA = VB = VC = VD = 10 cm.

Calculate:

a) the length AC

b) the height of V above the base

c) the angle $V\hat{C}A$.

Questions **14** to **19** may be answered either by scale drawing or by using the sine and cosine rules.

14. Two lighthouses A and B are 25 km apart and A is due West of B. A submarine S is on a bearing of 137° from A and on a bearing of 170° from B. Find the distance of S from A and the distance of S from B.

15. In triangle PQR, PQ = 7 cm, PR = 8 cm and QR = 9 cm. Find angle $Q\hat{P}R$.

16. In triangle XYZ, XY = 8 m, $\hat{X} = 57°$ and $\hat{Z} = 50°$. Find the lengths YZ and XZ.

17. In triangle ABC, $\hat{A} = 22°$ and $\hat{C} = 44°$.

Find the ratio $\dfrac{BC}{AB}$.

18. Given cos $A\hat{C}B = 0.6$, AC = 4 cm, BC = 5 cm and CD = 7 cm, find the length of AB and AD.

19. Find the smallest angle in a triangle whose sides are of length $3x$, $4x$ and $6x$.

20. In the cuboid shown, find:

a) WY

b) DY

c) WD

d) the angle $W\hat{D}Y$

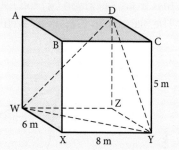

Examination-style exercise 6B

1.

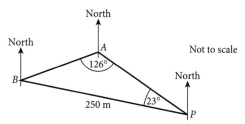

A shop has a wheelchair ramp to its entrance from the pavement.
The ramp is 3.17 metres long and is inclined at 5° to the horizontal.
Calculate the height, h metres, of the entrance above the pavement.
Show all your working. [2]

Cambridge IGCSE Mathematics 0580
Paper 2 Q2 June 2005

2.

The diagram shows three straight horizontal roads in a town, connecting points P, A, and B.

PB = 250 m, angle APB = 23° and angle BAP = 126°.

(a) Calculate the length of the road AB. [3]

(b) The bearing of A from P is 303°.

Find the bearing of

i) *B* from *P*, [1]

ii) *A* from *B*. [2]

Cambridge IGCSE Mathematics 0580
Paper 4 Q4 June 2009

3. A plane flies from Auckland (*A*) to Gisborne (*G*) on a bearing of 115°. The plane then flies on to Wellington (*W*). Angle $AGW = 63°$.

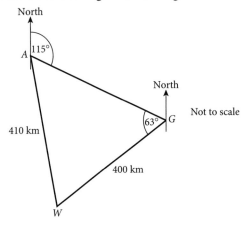

(a) Calculate the bearing of Wellington from Gisborne. [2]

(b) The distance from Wellington to Gisborne is 400 kilometres.

The distance from Auckland to Wellington is 410 kilometres.

Calculate the bearing of Wellington from Auckland. [4]

Cambridge IGCSE Mathematics 0580
Paper 2 Q20 June 2005

4.

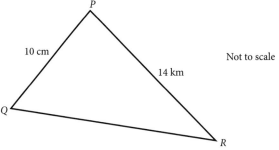

In triangle *PQR*, angle *QPR* is acute, *PQ* = 10 cm and *PR* = 14 cm.

(a) The area of triangle *PQR* is 48 cm².

Calculate angle *QPR* and show that it rounds to 43.3°, correct to 1 decimal place.

You must show all your working. [3]

(b) Calculate the length of the side *QR*. [4]

Cambridge IGCSE Mathematics 0580
Paper 4 Q3 June 2009

5.

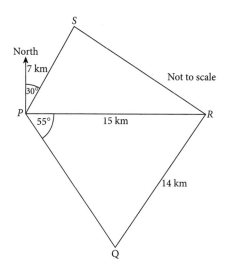

North
7 km
30°
P
55°
15 km
R
Not to scale
S
14 km
Q

The quadrilateral *PQRS* shows the boundary of a forest. A straight
15 kilometre road goes due East from *P* to *R*.

(a) The bearing of *S* from *P* is 030° and *PS* = 7 km.

   i)   Write down the size of angle *SPR*.   [1]

   ii) Calculate the length of *RS*.   [4]

(b) Angle *RPQ* = 55° and *QR* = 14 km.

   i)   Write down the bearing of *Q* from *P*.   [1]

   ii) Calculate the acute angle *PQR*.   [3]

   iii) Calculate the length of *PQ*.   [3]

(c) Calculate the area of the forest, correct to the nearest square kilometre.   [4]

Cambridge IGCSE Mathematics 0580
Paper 4 Q3 November 2005

6. $\sin x° = -\frac{1}{2}$ and $0 \le x \le 360°$.

Find the two values of *x*.   [2]

7.

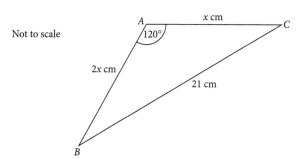

Not to scale

A
120°
x cm
C
2*x* cm
21 cm
B

In triangle ABC, $AB = 2x$ cm, $AC = x$ cm, $BC = 21$ cm and angle $BAC = 120°$.

Calculate the value of x. [3]

Cambridge IGCSE Mathematics 0580
Paper 21 Q11 June 2008

8.

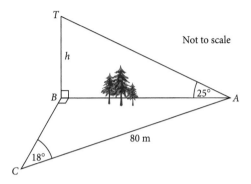

Not to scale

Mahmoud is working out the height, h metres, of a tower BT which stands on level ground.

He measures the angle TAB as $25°$.

He cannot measure the distance AB and so he walks 80 m from A to C, where angle $ACB = 18°$ and angle $ABC = 90°$.

Calculate

(a) the distance AB, [2]

(b) the height of the tower, BT. [2]

Cambridge IGCSE Mathematics 0580
Paper 21 Q15 June 2009

9.

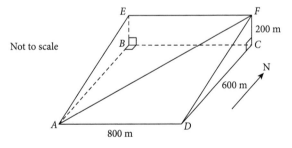

Not to scale

$ABCD$, $BEFC$ and $AEFD$ are all rectangles.

$ABCD$ is horizontal, $BEFC$ is vertical and $AEFD$ represents a hillside.

AF is a path on the hillside.

$AD = 800$ m, $DC = 600$ m and $CF = 200$ m.

(a) Calculate the angle that the path AF makes with $ABCD$. [5]

(b) In the diagram D is due south of C.

Jasmine walks down the path from F to A in bad weather.
She cannot see the path ahead.

The compass bearing she must use is the bearing of A from C.
Calculate this bearing. [3]

Cambridge IGCSE Mathematics 0580
Paper 21 Q21 June 2008

10.

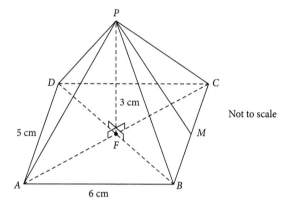

The diagram shows a pyramid on a rectangular base $ABCD$,
with $AB = 6$ cm and $AD = 5$ cm.

The diagonals AC and BD intersect at F.

The vertical height $FP = 3$ cm.

(a) How many planes of symmetry does the pyramid have? [1]

(b) Calculate the volume of the pyramid.

[The volume of a pyramid is $\frac{1}{3} \times$ area of base $\times$ height.] [2]

(c) The midpoint of BC is M.

Calculate the angle between PM and the base. [2]

(d) Calculate the angle between PB and the base. [4]

(e) Calculate the length of PB. [2]

Cambridge IGCSE Mathematics 0580
Paper 4 Q6 November 2005

11. Sketch the graph of $y = \cos x$ for $0° \leqslant x \leqslant 360°$. [2]

Hence solve the equation

$$3 \cos x + 1 = 0$$

for $0° \leqslant x \leqslant 360°$. Give your answers to one decimal place. [3]

7 Graphs

René Descartes (1596–1650) was one of the greatest philosophers of his time. Strangely his restless mind only found peace and quiet as a soldier and he apparently discovered the idea of 'cartesian' geometry in a dream before the battle of Prague. The word 'cartesian' is derived from his name and his work formed the link between geometry and algebra which inevitably led to the discovery of calculus. He finally settled in Holland for ten years, but later moved to Sweden where he soon died of pneumonia.

E2.10	Interpret and use graphs in practical situations including travel graphs and conversion graphs. Draw graphs from given data. Apply the idea of rate of change to simple kinematics involving distance–time and speed–time graphs, acceleration and deceleration. Calculate distance travelled as area under a speed–time graph.
E2.11	Construct tables of values and draw graphs for functions of the form ax^n (and simple sums of these) and for functions of the form $ab^x + c$. Solve associated equations approximately, including finding and interpreting roots by graphical methods. Draw and interpret graphs representing exponential growth and decay problems. Recognise, sketch and interpret graphs of functions.
E2.12	Estimate gradients of curves by drawing tangents.
E2.13	Understand the idea of a derived function. Use the derivatives of functions of the form ax^n, and simple sums of not more than three of these. Apply differentiation to gradients and turning points (stationary points). Discriminate between maxima and minima by any method.
E3.1	Demonstrate familiarity with Cartesian coordinates in two dimensions.
E3.2	Find the gradient of a straight line. Calculate the gradient of a straight line from the coordinates of two points on it.
E3.3	Calculate the length and the coordinates of the midpoint of a straight line from the coordinates of its end points.
E3.4	Interpret and obtain the equation of a straight-line graph.
E3.5	Determine the equation of a straight line parallel to a given line.
E3.6	Find the gradient of parallel and perpendicular lines.
E6.2	Know that the perpendicular distance from a point to a line is the shortest distance to the line.

7.1 Drawing accurate graphs

Example

Draw the graph of $y = 2x - 3$ for values of x from -2 to $+4$.

a) The coordinates of points on the line are calculated in a table.

x	-2	-1	0	1	2	3	4
$2x$	-4	-2	0	2	4	6	8
-3	-3	-3	-3	-3	-3	-3	-3
y	-7	-5	-3	-1	1	3	5

b) Draw and label axes using suitable scales.

c) Plot the points and draw a pencil line through them. Label the line with its equation.

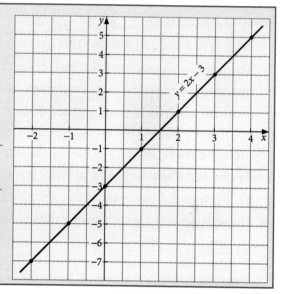

Exercise 1

Draw the following graphs, using a scale of 2 cm to 1 unit on the x-axis and 1 cm to 1 unit on the y-axis.

1. $y = 2x + 1$ for $-3 \leqslant x \leqslant 3$

2. $y = 3x - 4$ for $-3 \leqslant x \leqslant 3$

3. $y = 2x - 1$ for $-3 \leqslant x \leqslant 3$

4. $y = 8 - x$ for $-2 \leqslant x \leqslant 4$

5. $y = 10 - 2x$ for $-2 \leqslant x \leqslant 4$

6. $y = \dfrac{x + 5}{2}$ for $-3 \leqslant x \leqslant 3$

7. $y = 3(x - 2)$ for $-3 \leqslant x \leqslant 3$

8. $y = \dfrac{1}{2}x + 4$ for $-3 \leqslant x \leqslant 3$

9. $v = 2t - 3$ for $-2 \leqslant t \leqslant 4$

10. $z = 12 - 3t$ for $-2 \leqslant t \leqslant 4$

In each question from **11** to **16**, draw the graphs on the same page and hence find the coordinates of the vertices of the polygon formed. Give the answers as accurately as your graph will allow.

11. a) $y = x$ b) $y = 8 - 4x$ c) $y = 4x$
    Take $-1 \leqslant x \leqslant 3$ and $-4 \leqslant y \leqslant 14$.

12. a) $y = 2x + 1$ b) $y = 4x - 8$ c) $y = 1$
    Take $0 \leqslant x \leqslant 5$ and $-8 \leqslant y \leqslant 12$.

13. a) $y = 3x$ b) $y = 5 - x$ c) $y = x - 4$
    Take $-2 \leqslant x \leqslant 5$ and $-9 \leqslant y \leqslant 8$.

14. a) $y = -x$ b) $y = 3x + 6$ c) $y = 8$ d) $x = 3\dfrac{1}{2}$
    Take $-2 \leqslant x \leqslant 5$ and $-6 \leqslant y \leqslant 10$.

15. a) $y = \frac{1}{2}(x-8)$ b) $2x + y = 6$ c) $y = 4(x+1)$

     Take $-3 \leqslant x \leqslant 4$ and $-7 \leqslant y \leqslant 7$.

16. a) $y = 2x + 7$ b) $3x + y = 10$ c) $y = x$ d) $2y + x = 4$

     Take $-2 \leqslant x \leqslant 4$ and $0 \leqslant y \leqslant 13$.

17. The equation connecting the annual distance travelled M km, of a certain car and the annual running cost, C is $C = \frac{M}{20} + 200$.

Draw the graph for $0 \leqslant M \leqslant 10\,000$ using scales of 1 cm for 1000 km for M and 2 cm for $100 for C.

From the graph find:

a) the cost when the annual distance travelled is 7200 km,

b) the annual distance travelled corresponding to a cost of $320.

18. The equation relating the cooking time t hours and the mass m kg

for a cake is $t = \dfrac{3m + 1}{4}$.

Draw the graph for $0 \leqslant m \leqslant 5$. From the graph find:

a) the mass of a cake requiring a cooking time of 2.8 hours,

b) the cooking time for a cake with a mass of 4.1 kg.

19. Some drivers try to estimate their annual cost of repairs $c in relation to their average speed of driving s km/h using the equation $c = 6s + 50$. Draw the graph for $0 \leqslant s \leqslant 160$. From the graph find:

a) the estimated repair bill for a man who drives at an average speed of 65 km/h

b) the average speed at which a motorist drives if his annual repair bill is $300

c) the annual saving for a man who, on returning from a holiday, reduces his average speed of driving from 100 km/h to 65 km/h.

20. The value of a car v is related to the number of km n which it has travelled by the equation

$v = 4500 - \dfrac{n}{20}$.

Draw the graph for $0 \leqslant n \leqslant 90\,000$. From the graph find:

a) the value of a car which has travelled 3700 km

b) the number of km travelled by a car valued at $3200.

7.2 Gradients

The gradient of a straight line is a measure of how steep it is.

Example 1

Find the gradient of the line joining the points A(1, 2) and B(6, 5).

$$\text{gradient of AB} = \frac{BC}{AC} = \frac{3}{5}$$

It is possible to use the formula

$$\text{gradient} = \frac{\text{difference in } y\text{-coordinates}}{\text{difference in } x\text{-coordinates}}$$

Example 2

Find the gradient of the line joining the points D(1, 5) and E(5, 2).

$$\text{gradient of DE} = \frac{5-2}{1-5} = \frac{3}{-4} = -\frac{3}{4}$$

Note:

a) Lines which slope upward to the right have a *positive* gradient.

b) Lines which slope downward to the right have a *negative* gradient.

Example 3

a) Find the length of the line segment drawn from P(2, 1) to Q(6, 4).

b) Find the coordinates of the midpoint of the line segment PQ.

· ·

a) Draw triangle PQR. PR = 4 units and QR = 3 units.

By Pythagoras' theorem $PQ^2 = 4^2 + 3^2 = 25$

$$PQ = 5 \text{ units}$$

b) Add the x-coordinates of P and Q and then divide by 2.
Add the y-coordinates of P and Q and then divide by 2.

The midpoint has coordinates $\left[\dfrac{(2+6)}{2}, \dfrac{(1+4)}{2}\right]$

i.e. $\left(4, 2\frac{1}{2}\right)$

Exercise 2

Calculate the gradient of the line joining the following pairs of points.

1. (3, 1), (5, 4)
2. (1, 1), (3, 5)
3. (3, 0), (4, 3)

4. (−1, 3), (1, 6)
5. (−2, −1), (0, 0)
6. (7, 5), (1, 6)

7. (2, −3), (1, 4)
8. (0, −2), (−2, 0)
9. $\left(\frac{1}{2}, 1\right), \left(\frac{3}{4}, 2\right)$

10. $\left(-\frac{1}{2}, 1\right), (0, -1)$
11. (3.1, 2), (3.2, 2.5)
12. (−7, 10), (0, 0)

13. $\left(\frac{1}{3}, 1\right), \left(\frac{1}{2}, 2\right)$
14. (3, 4), (−2, 4)
15. (2, 5), (1.3, 5)

16. (2, 3), (2, 7)
17. (−1, 4), (−1, 7.2)
18. (2.3, − 2.2), (1.8, 1.8)

19. (0.75, 0), (0.375, −2)
20. (17.6, 1), (1.4, 1)
21. (a, b), (c, d)

22. (m, n), (a, − b)
23. (2a, f), (a, −f)
24. (2k, − k), (k, 3k)

25. (m, 3n), (−3m, 3n)
26. $\left(\frac{c}{2}, -d\right), \left(\frac{c}{4}, \frac{d}{2}\right)$

In questions **27** and **28**, find the gradient of each straight line.

27.

28.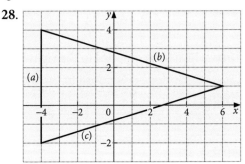

29. Find the value of a if the line joining the points (3a, 4) and (a, −3) has a gradient of 1.

30. a) Write down the gradient of the line joining the points (2m, n) and (3, −4).

  b) Find the value of n if the line is parallel to the x-axis.

  c) Find the value of m if the line is parallel to the y-axis.

31. a) Draw a pair of x- and y-axes and plot the points A(1, 2) and B(7, 6).

  b) Find the length of the line segment AB. Give your answer correct to one decimal place.

  c) Find the coordinates of the midpoint of AB.

32. a) On a graph plot the points P(1, 4), Q(4, 8), R(5, 1).

  b) Determine whether or not the triangle PQR is isosceles.

  c) Find the coordinates of the midpoint of PR.

7.3 The form $y = mx + c$

When the equation of a straight line is written in the form $y = mx + c$, the gradient of the line is m and the intercept on the y-axis is c.

Example 1

Draw the line $y = 2x + 3$ on a *sketch* graph.

The word 'sketch' implies that we do not plot a series of points but simply show the position and slope of the line.

The line $y = 2x + 3$ has a gradient of 2 and cuts the y-axis at (0, 3).

Example 2

Draw the line $x + 2y - 6 = 0$ on a sketch graph.

a) Rearrange the equation to make y the subject.

$$x + 2y - 6 = 0$$
$$2y = -x + 6$$
$$y = -\frac{1}{2}x + 3$$

b) The line has a gradient of $-\frac{1}{2}$ and cuts the y-axis at (0, 3).

Exercise 3

In questions **1** to **20**, find the gradient of the line and the intercept on the y-axis. Hence draw a small sketch graph of each line.

1. $y = x + 3$
2. $y = x - 2$
3. $y = 2x + 1$
4. $y = 2x - 5$

5. $y = 3x + 4$
6. $y = \frac{1}{2}x + 6$
7. $y = 3x - 2$
8. $y = 2x$

9. $y = \frac{1}{4}x - 4$
10. $y = -x + 3$
11. $y = 6 - 2x$
12. $y = 2 - x$

13. $y + 2x = 3$
14. $3x + y + 4 = 0$
15. $2y - x = 6$
16. $3y + x - 9 = 0$

17. $4x - y = 5$
18. $3x - 2y = 8$
19. $10x - y = 0$
20. $y - 4 = 0$

Finding the equation of a line

Example

Find the equation of the straight line which passes through (1, 3) and (3, 7).

a) Let the equation of the line take the form $y = mx + c$.

The gradient $m = \dfrac{7-3}{3-1} = 2$

so we may write the equation as

$y = 2x + c$ ... [1]

b) Since the line passes through (1, 3), substitute 3 for y and 1 for x in [1].

∴ $3 = 2 \times 1 + c$

     $1 = c$

The equation of the line is $y = 2x + 1$.

Exercise 4

In questions **1** to **11** find the equation of the line which:

1. Passes through (0, 7) at a gradient of 3
2. Passes through (0, −9) at a gradient of 2
3. Passes through (0, 5) at a gradient of −1
4. Passes through (2, 3) at a gradient of 2
5. Passes through (2, 11) at a gradient of 3
6. Passes through (4, 3) at a gradient of −1
7. Passes through (6, 0) at a gradient of $\frac{1}{2}$
8. Passes through (2, 1) and (4, 5)
9. Passes through (5, 4) and (6, 7)
10. Passes through (0, 5) and (3, 2)
11. Passes through (3, −3) and (9, −1)

Exercise 5

1. Find the equations of the lines A and B.

2. Find the equations of the lines C and D.

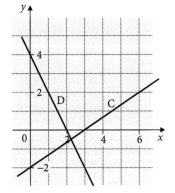

3. Look at the graph.

a) Find the equation of the line which is parallel to line A and which passes through the point (0, 5).

b) Find the equation of the line which is parallel to line B and which passes through the point (0, 3).

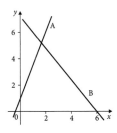

4. Look at the graphs in Question **1**.

   a) Find the equation of the line which is parallel to line A and which passes through the point $(0, 1)$.

   b) Find the equation of the line which is parallel to line B and which passes through the point $(0, -2)$.

Example

Find the gradient of lines A and B.

Gradient of line A: $m_1 = 2$

Gradient of line B: $m_2 = -\dfrac{1}{2}$

Lines A and B are *perpendicular* to each other. Notice that the product of their gradients $m_1 \times m_2 = -1$.

This is true for all pairs of perpendicular lines and hence we can find the gradient of one when we know the other.

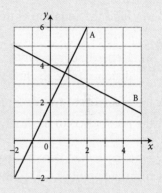

Find the equation of the line perpendicular to $y = 3x - 5$ which passes through $(2, 2)$.

Gradient of perpendicular line: $m_2 = -1 \div 3 = -\dfrac{1}{3}$

so we may write the equation as $y = -\dfrac{1}{3}x + c$

Substitute for y and x: $2 = -\dfrac{1}{3} \times 2 + c$

$$2 = -\dfrac{2}{3} + c$$

$$c = \dfrac{8}{3}$$

The equation of the line is $y = -\dfrac{1}{3}x + \dfrac{8}{3}$

Exercise 6

Find the equation of the line which:

1. passes through $(3, 4)$ and is perpendicular to $y = x + 2$

2. passes through $(2, -1)$ and is perpendicular to $y = -\dfrac{1}{2}x + 1$

3. passes through $(-1, 6)$ and is perpendicular to $y = 4x - 3$

4. passes through $(5, 0)$ and is perpendicular to $y = -\dfrac{1}{6}x + 4$

5. passes through $(7, 2)$ and is perpendicular to $y = 5x - 2$.

6. passes through $(-1, 0)$ and is perpendicular to the line through $(3, 1)$ and $(5, 7)$.

7. **a)** Find the equation of the line which is perpendicular to the line $y = 2x + 1$ and passes through $(3, 3)$.

   b) Find the exact coordinates of the point of intersection of the line you found in part **a)** and the line $y = 2x + 1$.

   c) Hence find, correct to two decimal places, the distance from the point $(3, 3)$ to the point you found in part **b)**.

   > This distance is the **perpendicular** distance from the point $(3, 3)$ to the line $y = 2x + 1$. This is the **shortest** distance from the point to the line.

8. **a)** Find the equation of the line which is perpendicular to the line $y = 0.5x + 3$ and passes through $(1, -1)$.

   b) Hence find, correct to two decimal places, the shortest distance from the line $y = 0.5x + 3$ to the point $(1, -1)$.

9. Find, correct to two decimal places, the shortest distance from the point $(2, 3)$ to the line $y = -\frac{1}{3}x + 4$.

10. Find, correct to two decimal places, the shortest distance from the point $(4, -1)$ to the line $y = -5x - 3$.

7.4 Plotting curves

Example

Draw the graph of the function $y = 2x^2 + x - 6$, for $-3 \leqslant x \leqslant 3$.

a)

x	-3	-2	-1	0	1	2	3
$2x^2$	18	8	2	0	2	8	18
x	-3	-2	-1	0	1	2	3
-6	-6	-6	-6	-6	-6	-6	-6
y	9	0	-5	-6	-3	4	15

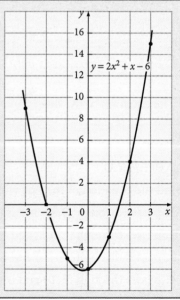

b) Draw and label axes using suitable scales.

c) Plot the points and draw a smooth curve through them with a pencil.

d) Check any points which interrupt the smoothness of the curve.

e) Label the curve with its equation.

Sometimes the function notation f(x) is used. f(x) means 'a function of x'. If, for example, f(x) = $x^2 + 2x$ then the graph of $y = $ f(x) is simply the graph of $y = x^2 + 2x$.

> Functions are explained in greater detail on page 305.

To find the value of y when $x = 1$ we obtain,

$f(1) = 1^2 + 2 \times 1 = 3$, so $y = 3$

Similarly,

$f(2) = 2^2 + 2 \times 2 = 8$

$f(3) = 3^2 + 2 \times 3 = 15$, and so on.

An alternative way of writing
$f(x) = x^2 + 2x$ is f: $x \rightarrow x^2 + 2x$

Exercise 7

Draw the graphs of the following functions using a scale of 2 cm
for 1 unit on the x-axis and 1 cm for 1 unit on the y-axis.

1. $y = x^2 + 2x$, for $-3 \leqslant x \leqslant 3$
2. $y = x^2 + 4x$, for $-3 \leqslant x \leqslant 3$
3. $y = x^2 - 3x$, for $-3 \leqslant x \leqslant 3$
4. $y = x^2 + 2$, for $-3 \leqslant x \leqslant 3$
5. $y = x^2 - 7$, for $-3 \leqslant x \leqslant 3$
6. $y = x^2 + x - 2$, for $-3 \leqslant x \leqslant 3$
7. $y = x^2 + 3x - 9$, for $-4 \leqslant x \leqslant 3$
8. $y = x^2 - 3x - 4$, for $-2 \leqslant x \leqslant 4$
9. $y = x^2 - 5x + 7$, for $0 \leqslant x \leqslant 6$
10. $y = 2x^2 - 6x$, for $-1 \leqslant x \leqslant 5$
11. $y = 2x^2 + 3x - 6$, for $-4 \leqslant x \leqslant 2$
12. $y = 3x^2 - 6x + 5$, for $-1 \leqslant x \leqslant 3$
13. $y = 2 + x - x^2$, for $-3 \leqslant x \leqslant 3$
14. $f(x) = 1 - 3x - x^2$, for $-5 \leqslant x \leqslant 2$
15. $f(x) = 3 + 3x - x^2$, for $-2 \leqslant x \leqslant 5$
16. $f(x) = 7 - 3x - 2x^2$, for $-3 \leqslant x \leqslant 3$
17. $f(x) = 6 + x - 2x^2$, for $-3 \leqslant x \leqslant 3$
18. f: $x \rightarrow 8 + 2x - 3x^2$, for $-2 \leqslant x \leqslant 3$
19. f: $x \rightarrow x(x - 4)$, for $-1 \leqslant x \leqslant 6$
20. f: $x \rightarrow (x + 1)(2x - 5)$, for $-3 \leqslant x \leqslant 3$.

Example
Draw the graph of $y = \dfrac{12}{x} + x - 6$, for $1 \leqslant x \leqslant 8$.

Use the graph to find approximate values for:

a) the minimum value of $\dfrac{12}{x} + x - 6$

b) the value of $\dfrac{12}{x} + x - 6$ when $x = 2.25$

c) the gradient of the tangent to the curve drawn at the point where $x = 5$.

Here is the table of values:

x	1	2	3	4	5	6	7	8	1.5
$\dfrac{12}{x}$	12	6	4	3	2.4	2	1.71	1.5	8
x	1	2	3	4	5	6	7	8	1.5
-6	-6	-6	-6	-6	-6	-6	-6	-6	-6
y	7	2	1	1	1.4	2	2.71	3.5	3.5

Notice that an 'extra' value of y has been
calculated at $x = 1.5$ because of the large
difference between the y-values at $x = 1$ and $x = 2$.

a) From the graph, the minimum value of
$\dfrac{12}{x} + x - 6$ (i.e. y) is approximately 0.9.

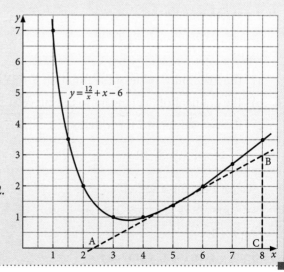

b) At $x = 2.25$, y is approximately 1.6.

c) The tangent AB is drawn to touch the curve at $x = 5$

The gradient of AB $= \dfrac{BC}{AC}$

gradient $= \dfrac{3}{8 - 2.4} = \dfrac{3}{5.6} \approx 0.54$

> The gradient is the 'rate of change of y with respect to x'. On a velocity–time graph the gradient is the *acceleration* at that point.

It is difficult to obtain an accurate value for the gradient of a tangent so the above result is more realistically 'approximately 0.5'.

Exercise 8

Draw the following curves. The scales given are for one unit of x and y.

1. $y = x^2$, for $0 \leqslant x \leqslant 6$.

(Scales: 2 cm for x, $\dfrac{1}{2}$ cm for y)

Find:

a) the gradient of the tangent to the curve at $x = 2$

b) the gradient of the tangent to the curve at $x = 4$

c) the y-value at $x = 3.25$.

2. $y = x^2 - 3x$, for $-2 \leqslant x \leqslant 5$.

(Scales: 2 cm for x, 1 cm for y)

Find:

a) the gradient of the tangent to the curve at $x = 3$

b) the gradient of the tangent to the curve at $x = -1$

c) the value of x where the gradient of the curve is zero.

3. $y = 5 + 3x - x^2$, for $-2 \leqslant x \leqslant 5$.

(Scales: 2 cm for x, 1 cm for y)

Find:

a) the maximum value of the function $5 + 3x - x^2$

b) the gradient of the tangent to the curve at $x = 2.5$

c) the two values of x for which $y = 2$.

4. $y = \dfrac{12}{x}$, for $1 \leqslant x \leqslant 10$.

(Scales: 1 cm for x and y)

5. $y = \dfrac{9}{x}$, for $1 \leqslant x \leqslant 10$.

(Scales: 1 cm for x and y)

6. $y = \dfrac{12}{x + 1}$, for $0 \leqslant x \leqslant 8$.)

(Scales: 2 cm for x, 1 cm for y

7. $y = \dfrac{8}{x - 4}$, for $-4 \leqslant x \leqslant 3.5$.

(Scales: 2 cm for x, 1 cm for y)

8. $y = \dfrac{15}{3 - x}$, for $-4 \leqslant x \leqslant 2$.

(Scales: 2 cm for x, 1 cm for y)

9. $y = \dfrac{x}{x + 4}$, for $-3.5 \leqslant x \leqslant 4$.

(Scales: 2 cm for x and y)

10. $y = \dfrac{3x}{5 - x}$, for $-3 \leqslant x \leqslant 4$.

(Scales: 2 cm for x, 1 cm for y)

11. $y = \dfrac{x + 8}{x + 1}$, for $0 \leqslant x \leqslant 8$.

(Scales: 2 cm for x and y)

12. $y = \dfrac{x - 3}{x + 2}$, for $-1 \leqslant x \leqslant 6$.

(Scales: 2 cm for x and y)

13. $y = \dfrac{10}{x} + x$, for $1 \leqslant x \leqslant 7$.

(Scales: 2 cm for x, 1 cm for y)

14. $y = \dfrac{12}{x} - x$, for $1 \leqslant x \leqslant 7$.

(Scales: 2 cm for x, 1 cm for y)

15. $y = \dfrac{15}{x} + x - 7$, for $1 \leqslant x \leqslant 7$.

(Scales: 1 cm for x and y)

Find:

a) the minimum value of y

b) the y-value when $x = 5.5$.

16. $y = x^3 - 2x^2$, for $0 \leqslant x \leqslant 4$.

(Scales: 2 cm for x, $\frac{1}{2}$ cm for y)

Find:

a) the y-value at $x = 2.5$,

b) the x-value at $y = 15$.

17. $y = \frac{1}{10}\left(x^3 + 2x + 20\right)$, for $-3 \leqslant x \leqslant 3$.

(Scales: 2 cm for x and y)

Find:

a) the x-value where $x^3 + 2x + 20 = 0$

b) the gradient of the tangent to the curve at $x = 2$.

18. Copy and complete the table for the function $y = 7 - 5x - 2x^2$, giving values of y correct to one decimal place.

x	−4	−3.5	−3	−2.5	−2	−1.5
7	7	7		7		7
$-5x$	20	17.5		12.5		7.5
$-2x^2$	−32	−24.5		−12.5		−4.5
y	−5	0		7		10

x	−1	−0.5	0	0.5	1	1.5	2
7		7		7		7	
$-5x$		2.5		−2.5		−7.5	
$-2x^2$		−0.5		−0.5		−4.5	
y		9		4		−5	

Draw the graph, using a scale of 2 cm for x and 1 cm for y. Find:

a) the gradient of the tangent to the curve at $x = -2.5$

b) the maximum value of y

c) the value of x at which this maximum value occurs.

19. Draw the graph of $y = \dfrac{x}{x^2 + 1}$, for $-6 \leqslant x \leqslant 6$.

(Scales: 1 cm for x, 10 cm for y)

20. Draw the graph of $E = \dfrac{5000}{x} + 3x$ for

$10 \leqslant x \leqslant 80$. (Scales: 1 cm to 5 units for x and 1 cm to 25 units for E)
From the graph find:

a) the minimum value of E

b) the value of x corresponding to this minimum value

c) the range of values of x for which E is less than 275.

Exercise 9

1. In a scientific experiment, the number of bacteria in a colony can be modelled using the function $y = 4 \times 2^{x-1}$ where x is the number of minutes.

a) How many bacteria were there at the start of the experiment?

b) Draw the graph for $0 \leqslant x \leqslant 8$.

c) At what time were there 100 bacteria in the colony?

2. The number of atoms of a particular chemical element is modelled by the following function: $y = 600 \times 3^{-x}$ where x is the number of hours.

a) How many atoms of the element were there at the start?

b) Draw a graph for $0 \leqslant x \leqslant 4$.

c) At what time were there 150 atoms?

3. Draw the graph of the function $f(x) = 3 \times 2^x + 1$ for $x = 0, 1, 2, 3, 4$.
(Scales: 2 cm per unit for x, 5 units per cm for y)

4. Draw the graph of $y = 2 \times 3^{-x} + 5$ for $x = 0, 1, 2, 3, 4, 5$.
(Scales: 2 cm per unit for x, 2 units per cm for y)

5. A new drug is designed to kill dangerous bacteria. When treated with the drug, the number of bacteria at time t hours is modelled using the function $f(t) = 1000 - 4 \times 2^t$.

a) State the number of bacteria at the start.

b) Draw the graph of the function for $0 \leqslant t \leqslant 7$.

c) Use your graph to estimate the time when there are 800 bacteria.

d) Estimate the number of bacteria after 3.5 hours.

e) Explain why the function is not valid for $t = 9$ hours.

Sketch graphs

You need to recognise and be able to sketch the graphs of:

$y = \dfrac{a}{x}$

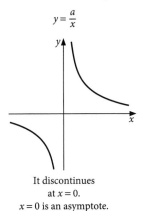

It discontinues
at $x = 0$.
$x = 0$ is an asymptote.

$y = \dfrac{a}{x^2}$

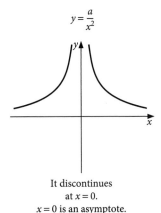

It discontinues
at $x = 0$.
$x = 0$ is an asymptote.

$y = a^x$

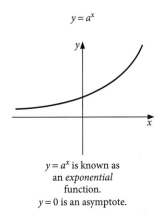

$y = a^x$ is known as
an *exponential*
function.
$y = 0$ is an asymptote.

Exercise 10

1. A rectangle has a perimeter of 14 cm and length x cm. Show that
   the width of the rectangle is $(7 - x)$ cm and hence that the area A
   of the rectangle is given by the formula $A = x(7 - x)$. Draw
   the graph, plotting x on the horizontal axis with a scale of
   2 cm to 1 unit, and A on the vertical axis with a scale of 1 cm
   to 1 unit.
   Take x from 0 to 7. From the graph find:
   a) the area of the rectangle when $x = 2.25$ cm
   b) the dimensions of the rectangle when its area is 9 cm²
   c) the maximum area of the rectangle
   d) the length and width of the rectangle corresponding to the
      maximum area
   e) what shape of rectangle has the largest area.

2. A farmer has 60 m of wire fencing which he uses to make a
   rectangular pen for his sheep. He uses a stone wall as one side of
   the pen so the wire is used for only 3 sides of the pen.

   If the width of the pen is x m, what is the length (in terms of x)?
   What is the area A of the pen?

Draw a graph with area A on the vertical axis and the width x on the horizontal axis. Take values of x from 0 to 30.

What dimensions should the pen have if the farmer wants to enclose the largest possible area?

3. A ball is thrown in the air so that t seconds after it is thrown, its height h metres above its starting point is given by the function $h = 25t - 5t^2$. Draw the graph of the function for $0 \leqslant t \leqslant 6$, plotting t on the horizontal axis with a scale of 2 cm to 1 second, and h on the vertical axis with a scale of 2 cm for 10 metres. Use the graph to find:

   a) the time when the ball is at its greatest height

   b) the greatest height reached by the ball

   c) the interval of time during which the ball is at a height of more than 30 m.

4. The velocity v m/s of a rocket t seconds after launching is given by the equation $v = 54t - 2t^3$. Draw a graph, plotting t on the horizontal axis with a scale of 2 cm to 1 second, and v on the vertical axis with a scale of 1 cm for 10 m/s. Take values of t from 0 to 5.

   Use the graph to find:

   a) the maximum velocity reached

   b) the time taken to accelerate to a velocity of 70 m/s

   c) the interval of time during which the rocket is travelling at more than 100 m/s.

5. Draw the graph of $y = 2^x$, for $-4 \leqslant x \leqslant 4$.
   (Scales: 2 cm for x, 1 cm for y)

6. Draw the graph of $y = 3^x$, for $-3 \leqslant x \leqslant 3$.
   (Scales: 2 cm for x, $\frac{1}{2}$ cm for y)
   Find the gradient of the tangent to the curve at $x = 1$.

7. Consider the equation $y = \dfrac{1}{x}$.

   When $x = \dfrac{1}{2}$, $y = \dfrac{1}{\frac{1}{2}} = 2$.

   When $x = \dfrac{1}{100}$, $y = \dfrac{1}{\frac{1}{100}} = 100$.

As the denominator of the fraction $\frac{1}{x}$ gets smaller, the answer gets larger. An 'infinitely small' denominator gives an 'infinitely large' answer.

We write $\frac{1}{0} \to \infty$. '$\frac{1}{0}$ tends to an infinitely large number.'

Draw the graph of $y = \frac{1}{x}$ for $x = -4, -3, -2, -1, -0.5, -0.25, 0.5, 1, 2, 3, 4$
(Scales: 2 cm for x and y)

8. Draw the graph of $y = x + \frac{1}{x}$ for $x = -4, -3, -2, -1, -0.5, -0.25, 0.25,$
   0.5, 1, 2, 3, 4 (Scales: 2 cm for x and y)

9. Draw the graph of $y = x + \frac{1}{x^2}$ for $x = -4, -3, -2, -1, -0.5, -0.25, 0.25,$
   0.5, 1, 2, 3, 4 (Scales: 2 cm for x, 1 cm for y)

10. This sketch shows a water tank with a square base. It is 1.5 m high, and the length of the base is x metres.

    a) Explain why the volume of the tank is given by the formula $V = 1.5x^2$.

    1.5 m

    x m

    b) Complete the table to show the volume for various values of x.

x	0.1	0.2	0.3	0.4	0.5	0.6	0.7	0.8
V	0.02	0.06	0.14	0.24		0.54	0.74	0.96

x	0.9	1.0	1.1	1.2	1.3	1.4	1.5
V	1.2		1.82		2.54		3.38

    c) Draw the graph of $V = 1.5x^2$ for values of x from 0 to 1.5.

    d) What value of x will give a volume of 3 m³?

    e) A guest house needs a tank with a volume at least 2 m³. To fit the tank into the loft, it must not be more than 1.3 m wide. Write down the range of values for x which will satisfy these conditions.

7.5 Interpreting graphs

Exercise 11

1. The graph shows how to convert miles into kilometres.

   a) Use the graph to find approximately how many kilometres are the same as:

       i)   25 miles   **ii)**   15 miles

       iii) 45 miles   **iv)**   5 miles

   b) Use the graph to find approximately how many miles are the same as:

       i)   64 km   **ii)**   56 km

       iii) 16 km   **iv)**   32 km

2. The graph shows how to convert pounds into euros.

   a) Use the graph to find approximately how many euros are the same as:

       i)   £20   **ii)**   £80   **iii)**   £50

   b) Use the graph to find approximately how many pounds are the same as:

       i)   €56   **ii)**   €84   **iii)**   €140

   c) Tim spends €154 on clothes in Paris. How many pounds has he spent?

3. A company hires out vans at a basic charge of $35 plus a charge of 20c per km travelled. Copy and complete the table where x is the number of km travelled and C is the total cost in dollars.

x	0	50	100	150	200	250	300
C	35			65			95

   Draw a graph of C against x, using scales of 2 cm for 50 km on the x-axis and 1 cm for $10 on the C-axis.

   a) Use the graph to find the number of miles travelled when the total cost was $71.

   b) What is the formula connecting C and x?

4. A car travels along a motorway and the amount of petrol in its tank is monitored as shown on the graph on the next page.

   a) How much petrol was bought at the first stop?

   b) What was the petrol consumption in km per litre:

       i)   before the first stop   **ii)**   between the two stops?

   c) What was the average petrol consumption over the 200 km?

After it leaves the second service station the car is stuck in slow traffic for the next 20 km. Its petrol consumption is reduced to 4 km per litre. After that, the road clears and the car travels a further 75 km during which time the consumption is 7.5 km/litre. Draw the graph above and extend it to show the next 95 km.

How much petrol is in the tank at the end of the journey?

5. A firm makes a profit of P thousand dollars from producing x thousand tiles.

Corresponding values of P and x are given below

x	0	0.5	1.0	1.5	2.0	2.5	3.0
P	−1.0	0.75	2.0	2.75	3.0	2.75	2.0

Using a scale of 4 cm to one unit on each axis, draw the graph of P against x. [Plot x on the horizontal axis.] Use your graph to find:

a) the number of tiles the firm should produce in order to make the maximum profit

b) the minimum number of tiles that should be produced to cover the cost of production

c) the range of values of x for which the profit is more than $2850.

6. A small firm increases its monthly expenditure on advertising and records its monthly income from sales.

Month	1	2	3	4	5	6	7
Expenditure ($)	100	200	300	400	500	600	700
Income ($)	280	450	560	630	680	720	740

Draw a graph to display expenditure against income.

a) Is it wise to spend $100 per month on advertising?

b) Is it wise to spend $700 per month?

c) What is the most sensible level of expenditure on advertising?

7.6 Graphical solution of equations

Accurately drawn graphs enable us to find approximate solutions to a wide range of equations, many of which are impossible to solve exactly by 'conventional' methods.

Example 1

Draw the graph of the function

$$y = 2x^2 - x - 3$$

for $-2 \leqslant x \leqslant 3$. Use the graph to find approximate solutions to the following equations.

a) $2x^2 - x - 3 = 6$ **b)** $2x^2 - x = x + 5$

The table of values for $y = 2x^2 - x - 3$ is found. Note the 'extra' value at $x = \frac{1}{2}$.

x	-2	-1	0	1	2	3	$\frac{1}{2}$
$2x^2$	8	2	0	2	8	18	$\frac{1}{2}$
$-x$	2	1	0	-1	-2	-3	$-\frac{1}{2}$
-3	-3	-3	-3	-3	-3	-3	-3
y	7	0	-3	-2	3	12	-3

The graph drawn from this table is opposite.

a) To solve the equation $2x^2 - x - 3 = 6$, the line $y = 6$ is drawn. At the points of intersection (A and B), y simultaneously equals both 6 and $(2x^2 - x - 3)$. So we may write

$$2x^2 - x - 3 = 6$$

The solutions are the x-values of the points A and B.

i.e. $x = -1.9$ and $x = 2.4$ approx.

b) To solve the equation $2x^2 - x = x + 5$, we rearrange the equation to obtain the function $(2x^2 - x - 3)$ on the left-hand side. In this case, subtract 3 from both sides.

$$2x^2 - x - 3 = x + 5 - 3$$
$$2x^2 - x - 3 = x + 2$$

If we now draw the line $y = x + 2$, the solutions of the equation are given by the x-values of C and D, the points of intersection.

i.e. $x = -1.2$ and $x = 2.2$ approx.

It is important to rearrange the equation to be solved so that the function already plotted is on one side.

Example 2

Assuming that the graph of $y = x^2 - 3x + 1$ has been drawn, find the equation of the line which should be drawn to solve the equation:

$$x^2 - 4x + 3 = 0$$

Rearrange $x^2 - 4x + 3 = 0$ in order to obtain $(x^2 - 3x + 1)$ on the left-hand side.

$$x^2 - 4x + 3 = 0$$

add x $x^2 - 3x + 3 = x$

subtract 2 $x^2 - 3x + 1 = x - 2$

Therefore draw the line $y = x - 2$ to solve the equation.

Exercise 12

1. In the diagram, the graphs of $y = x^2 - 2x - 3$, $y = -2$ and $y = x$ have been drawn. Use the graphs to find approximate solutions to the following equations:

   a) $x^2 - 2x - 3 = -2$

   b) $x^2 - 2x - 3 = x$

   c) $x^2 - 2x - 3 = 0$

   d) $x - 2x - 1 = 0$

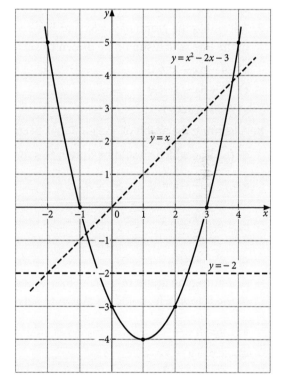

In questions **2** to **4**, use a scale of 2 cm to 1 unit for x and 1 cm to 1 unit for y.

2. Draw the graphs of the functions $y = x^2 - 2x$ and $y = x + 1$ for $-1 \leqslant x \leqslant 4$.
   Hence find approximate solutions of the equation $x^2 - 2x = x + 1$.

3. Draw the graphs of the functions $y = x^2 - 3x + 5$ and $y = x + 3$ for $-1 \leqslant x \leqslant 5$.
   Hence find approximate solutions of the equation $x^2 - 3x + 5 = x + 3$.

4. Draw the graphs of the functions $y = 6x - x^2$ and $y = 2x + 1$ for $0 \leqslant x \leqslant 5$.
Hence find approximate solutions of the equation $6x - x^2 = 2x + 1$.

In questions **5** to **9**, do *not* draw any graphs.

5. Assuming the graph of $y = x^2 - 5x$ has been drawn, find the equation
of the line which should be drawn to solve the equations:

a) $x^2 - 5x = 3$ b) $x^2 - 5x = -2$

c) $x^2 - 5x = x + 4$ d) $x^2 - 6x = 0$

e) $x^2 - 5x - 6 = 0$

6. Assuming the graph of $y = x^2 + x + 1$ has been drawn, find the equation
of the line which should be drawn to solve the equations:

a) $x^2 + x + 1 = 6$ b) $x^2 + x + 1 = 0$

c) $x^2 + x - 3 = 0$ d) $x^2 - x + 1 = 0$

e) $x^2 - x - 3 = 0$

7. Assuming the graph of $y = 6x - x^2$ has been drawn, find the equation
of the line which should be drawn to solve the equations:

a) $4 + 6x - x^2 = 0$ b) $4x - x^2 = 0$

c) $2 + 5x - x^2 = 0$ d) $x^2 - 6x = 3$

e) $x^2 - 6x = -2$

8. Assuming the graph of $y = x + \dfrac{4}{x}$ has been drawn, find the equation
of the line which should be drawn to solve the equations:

a) $x + \dfrac{4}{x} - 5 = 0$ b) $\dfrac{4}{x} - x = 0$

c) $x + \dfrac{4}{x} = 0.2$ d) $2x + \dfrac{4}{x} - 3 = 0$

e) $x^2 + 4 = 3x$

9. Assuming the graph of $y = x^2 - 8x - 7$ has been drawn, find the equation
of the line which should be drawn to solve the equations:

a) $x = 8 + \dfrac{7}{x}$ b) $2x^2 = 16x + 9$

c) $x^2 = 7$ d) $x = \dfrac{4}{x - 8}$

e) $2x - 5 = \dfrac{14}{x}$.

For questions **10** to **14**, use scales of 2 cm to 1 unit for x and 1 cm to 1 unit for y.

10. Draw the graph of $y = x^2 - 2x + 2$ for $-2 \leqslant x \leqslant 4$. By drawing other graphs,
solve the equations:

a) $x^2 - 2x + 2 = 8$ b) $x^2 - 2x + 2 = 5 - x$

c) $x^2 - 2x - 5 = 0$

11. Draw the graph of $y = x^2 - 7x$ for $0 \leqslant x \leqslant 7$. Draw suitable straight lines to solve the equations:

a) $x^2 - 7x + 9 = 0$ **b)** $x^2 - 5x + 1 = 0$

12. Draw the graph of $y = x^2 + 4x + 5$ for $-6 \leqslant x \leqslant 1$. Draw suitable straight lines to find approximate solutions of the equations:

a) $x^2 + 3x - 1 = 0$ **b)** $x^2 + 5x + 2 = 0$

13. Draw the graph of $y = 2x^2 + 3x - 9$ for $-3 \leqslant x \leqslant 2$. Draw suitable straight lines to find approximate solutions of the equations:

a) $2x^3 + 3x - 4 = 0$ **b)** $2x^2 + 2x - 9 = 1$

14. Draw the graph of $y = 2 + 3x - 2x^2$ for $-2 \leqslant x \leqslant 4$.

a) Draw suitable straight lines to find approximate solutions of the equations:

    i) $2 + 4x - 2x^2 = 0$ **ii)** $2x^2 - 3x - 2 = 0$

b) Find the range of values of x for which $2 + 3x - 2x^2 \geqslant -5$.

15. Draw the graph of $y = \dfrac{18}{x}$ for $1 \leqslant x \leqslant 10$, using scales of 1 cm to one unit on both axes. Use the graph to solve approximately:

a) $\dfrac{18}{x} = x + 2$ **b)** $\dfrac{18}{x} + x = 10$

c) $x^2 = 18$

16. Draw the graph of $y = \dfrac{1}{2}x^2 - 6$ for $-4 \leqslant x \leqslant 4$, taking 2 cm to 1 unit on each axis.

a) Use your graph to solve approximately the equation $\dfrac{1}{2}x^2 - 6 = 1$.

b) Using tables or a calculator confirm that your solutions are approximately $\pm\sqrt{14}$ and explain why this is so.

c) Use your graph to find the square roots of 8.

17. Draw the graph of $y = 6 - 2x - \dfrac{1}{2}x^3$ for $x = \pm2, \pm1\frac{1}{2}, \pm1, \pm\frac{1}{2}, 0$.

Take 4 cm to 1 unit for x and 1 cm to 1 unit for y.
Use your graph to find approximate solutions of the equations:

a) $\dfrac{1}{2}x^3 + 2x - 6 = 0$ **b)** $x - \dfrac{1}{2}x^3 = 0$

Using tables confirm that two of the solutions to the equation in part **b)** are $\pm\sqrt{2}$ and explain why this is so.

18. Draw the graph of $y = x + \dfrac{12}{x} - 5$ for $x = 1, 1\frac{1}{2}, 2, 3, 4, 5, 6, 7, 8$, taking 2 cm to 1 unit on each axis.

a) From your graph find the range of values of x for which $x + \dfrac{12}{x} \leqslant 9$.

b) Find an approximate solution of the equation $2x - \dfrac{12}{x} - 12 = 0$.

19. Draw the graph of $y = 2^x$ for $-4 \leqslant x \leqslant 4$, taking 2 cm to one unit for x and 1 cm to one unit for y. Find approximate solutions to the equations:

a) $2^x = 6$
b) $2^x = 3x$
c) $x2^x = 1$

d) Find also the approximate value of $2^{2.5}$.

20. Draw the graph of $y = \dfrac{1}{x}$ for $-4 \leqslant x \leqslant 4$
taking 2 cm to one unit on each axis. Find approximate solutions to the equations:

a) $\dfrac{1}{x} = x + 1$

b) $2x^2 - x - 1 = 0$

7.7 Distance–time graphs

When a distance–time graph is drawn the *gradient* of the graph gives the *speed* of the object.

From O to A : constant speed

      A to B : speed goes down to zero

      B to C : at rest

      C to D : accelerates

      D to E : constant speed (not as fast as O to A)

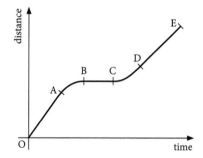

Exercise 13

1. The graph shows the journeys made by a van and a car starting at Baden, travelling to St Gallen and returning to Baden.

a) For how long was the van stationary during the journey?

b) At what time did the car first overtake the van?

c) At what speed was the van travelling between 09:30 and 10:00?

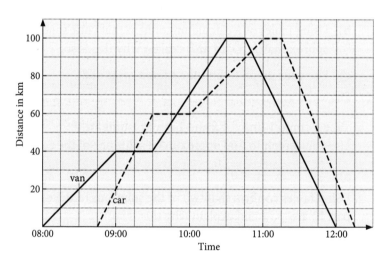

d) What was the greatest speed attained by the car during the entire journey?

e) What was the average speed of the car over its entire journey?

2. The graph shows the journeys of a bus and a car along the same road The bus goes from Sofia to Rila and back to Sofia. The car goes from Rila to Sofia and back to Rila.

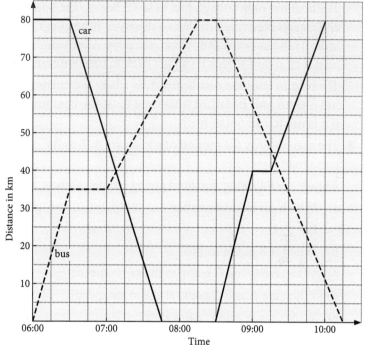

a) When did the bus and the car meet for the second time?

b) At what speed did the car travel from Rila to Sofia?

c) What was the average speed of the bus over its entire journey?

d) Approximately how far apart were the bus and the car at 09:45?

e) What was the greatest speed attained by the car during its entire journey?

In questions **3, 4, 5** draw a travel graph to illustrate the journey described. Draw axes with similar scales to question **2**.

3. Mrs Chuong leaves home at 08:00 and drives at a speed of 50 km/h. After $\frac{1}{2}$ hour she reduces her speed to 40 km/h and continues at this speed until 09:30. She stops from 09:30 until 10:00 and then returns home at a speed of 60 km/h.

Use the graph to find the approximate time at which she arrives home.

4. Kemen leaves home at 09:00 and drives at a speed of 20 km/h. After $\frac{3}{4}$ hour he increases his speed to 45 km/h and continues at this speed until 10:45. He stops from 10:45 until 11:30 and then returns home at a speed of 50 km/h.

Draw a graph and use it to find the approximate time at which he arrives home.

5. At 10:00 Akram leaves home and cycles to his grandparents' house which is 70 km away. He cycles at a speed of 20 km/h until 11:15, at which time he stops for $\frac{1}{2}$ hour. He then completes the journey at a speed of 30 km/h. At 11:45 Akram's sister, Hameeda, leaves home and drives her car at 60 km/h. Hameeda also goes to her grandparents' house and uses the same road as Akram.

At approximately what time does Hameeda overtake Akram?

6. A boat can travel at a speed of 20 km/h in still water. The current in a river flows at 5 km/h so that downstream the boat travels at 25 km/h and upstream it travels at only 15 km/h.

The boat has only enough fuel to last 3 hours. The boat leaves its base and travels downstream. Draw a distance–time graph and draw lines to indicate the outward and return journeys. After what time must the boat turn round so that it can get back to base without running out of fuel?

7. The boat in question **6** sails in a river where the current is 10 km/h and it has fuel for four hours. At what time must the boat turn round this time if it is not to run out of fuel?

8. The graph shows the motion of three cars A, B and C along the same road.

   Answer the following questions giving estimates where necessary.

   a) Which car is in front after

   i) 10 s   ii) 20 s?

   b) When is B in the front?

   c) When are B and C going at the same speed?

   d) When are A and C going at the same speed?

   e) Which car is going fastest after 5 s?

   f) Which car starts slowly and then goes faster and faster?

9. Three girls Hanna, Fateema and Carine took part in an egg and spoon race. Describe what happened, giving as many details as possible.

7.8 Speed–time graphs

The diagram is the speed–time graph of the first 30 seconds of a car journey. Two quantities are obtained from such graphs:

a) acceleration = gradient of speed–time graph

b) distance travelled = area under graph.

In this example,

a) The gradient of line OA $= \frac{20}{10} = 2$

∴ The acceleration in the first 10 seconds is 2 m/s².

b) The distance travelled in the first 30 seconds is given by the area of OAD plus the area of ABCD.

Distance $= \left(\frac{1}{2} \times 10 \times 20\right) + \left(20 \times 20\right)$

$= 500$ m

Exercise 14

On the graphs in this exercise speeds are in m/s and all times are in seconds.

1. Find:

a) the acceleration when $t = 4$

b) the total distance travelled

c) the average speed for the whole journey.

2. Find:

a) the total distance travelled

b) the average speed for the whole journey

c) the distance travelled in the first 10 seconds

d) the acceleration when $t = 20$.

3. Find:

a) the total distance travelled

b) the distance travelled in the first 40 seconds

c) the acceleration when $t = 15$.

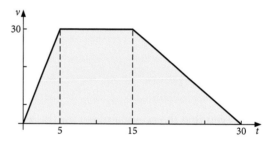

4. Find:

a) V if the total distance travelled is 900 m

b) the distance travelled in the first 60 seconds.

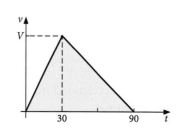

5. Find:

  a) T if the initial acceleration is 2 m/s²

  b) the total distance travelled

  c) the average speed for the whole journey.

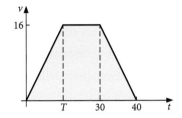

6. Given that the total distance travelled = 810 m, find:

  a) the value of V

  b) the rate of change of the speed when $t = 30$

  c) the time taken to travel the first 420 m of the journey.

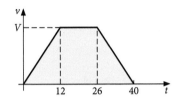

7. Given that the total distance travelled is 1.5 km, find:

  a) the value of V

  b) the rate of deceleration after 10 seconds.

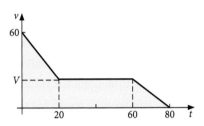

8. Given that the total distance travelled is 1.4 km, and the acceleration is 4 m/s² for the first T seconds, find:

  a) the value of V **b)** the value of T.

9. Given that the average speed for the whole journey is 37.5 m/s and that the deceleration between T and $2T$ is 2.5 m/s², find:

  a) the value of V **b)** the value of T.

10. Given that the total distance travelled is 4 km and that the initial deceleration is 4 m/s², find:

  a) the value of V **b)** the value of T.

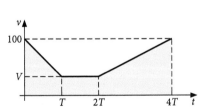

Exercise 15

Sketch a speed–time graph for each question.

All accelerations are taken to be uniform.

  1. A car accelerated from 0 to 50 m/s in 9 s. How far did it travel in this time?

2. A motorcycle accelerated from 10 m/s to 30 m/s in 6 s. How far did it travel in this time?

3. A train slowed down from 50 km/h to 10 km/h in 2 minutes. How far did it travel in this time?

4. When taking off, an aircraft accelerates from 0 to 100 m/s in a distance of 500 m. How long did it take to travel this distance?

5. An earthworm accelerates from a speed of 0.01 m/s to 0.02 m/s over a distance of 0.9 m. How long did it take?

6. A car travelling at 60 km/h is stopped in 6 seconds. How far does it travel in this time?

7. A car accelerates from 15 km/h to 60 km/h in 3 seconds. How far does it travel in this time?

8. At lift-off a rocket accelerates from 0 to 1000 km/h in just 10 s. How far does it travel in this time?

9. A coach accelerated from 0 to 60 km/h in 30 s. How many metres did it travel in this time?

10. Hamad was driving a car at 30 m/s when he saw an obstacle 45 m in front of him. It took a reaction time of 0.3 seconds before he could press the brakes and a further 2.5 seconds to stop the car. Did he hit the obstacle?

11. An aircraft is cruising at a speed of 200 m/s. When it lands it must be travelling at a speed of 50 m/s. In the air it can slow down at a rate of 0.2 m/s². On the ground it slows down at a rate of 2 m/s². Draw a velocity–time graph for the aircraft as it reduces its speed from 200 m/s to 50 m/s and then to 0 m/s. How far does it travel in this time?

12. The speed of a train is measured at regular intervals of time from $t = 0$ to $t = 60$ s, as shown below.

t s	0	10	20	30	40	50	60
v m/s	0	10	16	19.7	22.2	23.8	24.7

Draw a speed–time graph to illustrate the motion. Plot t on the horizontal axis with a scale of 1 cm to 5 s and plot v on the vertical axis with a scale of 2 cm to 5 m/s.

Use the graph to estimate:

a) the acceleration at $t = 10$

b) the distance travelled by the train from $t = 30$ to $t = 60$.

[An approximate value for the area under a curve can be found by splitting the area into several trapeziums.]

13. The speed of a car is measured at regular intervals of time from t = 0 to t = 60 s, as shown below.

t s	0	10	20	30	40	50	60
v m/s	0	1.3	3.2	6	10.1	16.5	30

Draw a speed–time graph using the same scales as in question **11**.

Use the graph to estimate:

a) the acceleration at t = 30

b) the distance travelled by the car from t = 20 to t = 50.

7.9 Differentiation

Completing the square

In Chapter 2, the method of completing the square was used to solve quadratic equations. Completing the square can also be used to find the coordinates of the minimum or maximum point on the graph of a quadratic function. This point is called the **turning point**.

When the quadratic function is written in the form $f(x) = (x - a)^2 + b$, the coordinates of the turning point on the graph are (a, b).

Example

$f(x) = x^2 - 4x + 1$

Find the coordinates of the turning point on the graph of $y = f(x)$.

$$f(x) = (x - 2)^2 - 2^2 + 1$$
$$f(x) = (x - 2)^2 - 3$$

Hence the coordinates of the turning point are $(2, -3)$.

Exercise 16

Find the coordinates of the turning points on the graphs of these quadratic functions.

1. $y = x^2 - 6x + 2$

2. $y = x^2 + 4x - 3$

3. $y = x^2 + 5x - 2$

4. $y = x^2 - 7x + 5$

5. $f(x) = 6 - 4x - x^2$

6. $y = 4 - 3x - x^2$

7. $f(x) = 2x^2 - 6x + 5$

8. $f(x) = 3x^2 + 6x - 4$

9. $f(x) = 4 - 3x - 2x^2$

10. $f(x) = 7 - 5x - 4x^2$

Derivative functions

Completing the square to find the coordinates of the turning point is only possible if the function is quadratic.

In order to find the turning points on the graphs of other functions, for example a cubic function, a different method is required.

The gradient of a curve at a particular point can be found by drawing a tangent to the curve at that point and finding the gradient of the tangent.

For example, the gradient of the curve $y = x^2 - 4x + 1$ at the point where $x = 3$ is 2.

It is possible to make a table for the values of the gradient at various points on the curve and hence plot the **gradient function**.

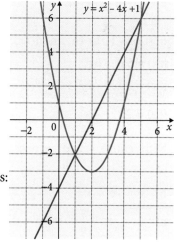

x	-1	0	1	2	3	4
Gradient	-6	-4	-2	0	2	4

Plotting the graph of the gradient function, it is clear that it is a straight line.

The gradient function is called the **derivative function** and, if $y = f(x)$, it is denoted using the notation $\dfrac{dy}{dx}$ (the derivative of y with respect to x, or 'dy by dx'),

or using the notation $f'(x)$ ('f dash of x').

In this case, $\dfrac{dy}{dx} = 2x - 4$, as can be seen from the graph.

The rule for finding the derivative function for integer powers of x is:

$y = x^n \rightarrow \dfrac{dy}{dx} = nx^{n-1}$ ('Multiply by the power and reduce it by one.')

In the case of $y = x^2 - 4x + 1$,

$$\frac{dy}{dx} = 2 \times x^{2-1} - 1 \times 4x^{1-1} + 0 \times 1 = 2x - 4$$

The process of finding the derivative function is called **differentiation**.

> Notice that the constant term in y disappears since the power of x is zero and zero multiplied by anything is zero.

Example

Find the derivative functions in each case:

a) $y = x^4 - 3x^2 + 2$ **b)** $f(x) = 5x^3 - 2x^2 + 6x$

....

a) $\dfrac{dy}{dx} = 4 \times x^{4-1} - 2 \times 3x^{2-1} + 0$

           $= 4x^3 - 6x$

> In part **a**, use the $\dfrac{dy}{dx}$ notation and in part **b** use the f′(x) notation.

b) $f'(x) = 3 \times 5x^{3-1} - 2 \times 2x^{2-1} + 1 \times 6x^{1-1}$

           $= 15x^2 - 4x + 6$

Exercise 17

In questions **1** to **10**, find $\dfrac{dy}{dx}$.

1. $y = 3x^2$

2. $y = 2x^3 - 4x$

3. $y = 6x^4$

4. $y = 2x^5 - 4x^2 + 5$

5. $y = 4x^4 - 3x^3 + 5x^2$

6. $y = 5 - 3x^2 - 3x^4$

7. $y = x^7 + x^6 + x^5$

8. $y = \dfrac{1}{2}x^3 + \dfrac{2}{3}x^2$

9. $y = \dfrac{1}{5}x^4 + \dfrac{3}{4}x^3 - \dfrac{2}{5}x^2$

10. $y = \dfrac{1}{16}x^4 - \dfrac{1}{3}x^3 + \dfrac{17}{25}$

In questions **11** to **16**, find f′(x).

11. $f(x) = 5x^3 - 6x^2$

12. $f(x) = 6x^5 - 4x^4 + 3$

13. $f(x) = 20x^2 - 5x^5 + 2x$

14. $f(x) = 7x^8 - 13x$

15. $f(x) = \dfrac{1}{8}x^7 - \dfrac{1}{6}x^5$

16. $f(x) = \dfrac{8}{9}x^5 + \dfrac{1}{15}x^3 + \dfrac{1}{8}$

17. Differentiate y with respect to x.

     a) $y = 14x^5 - 16x^4 - 13x$

     b) $y = 8x^9 - 5x^2 - 18$

     c) $y = \dfrac{1}{14}x^7 - \dfrac{5}{6}x^6 + \dfrac{1}{4}x^3$

> 'Differentiate y with respect to x' just means 'find the derivative function'.

Finding gradients

To find the gradient of a curve at a particular point, substitute the given x-value into the derivative function.

Example

$f(x) = 6x^2 - 3x^3 - 5x$

Find the gradient of the curve $y = f(x)$ when $x = 6$.

$$f'(x) = 12x - 9x^2 - 5$$

When $x = 6$, $f'(x) = 12 \times 6 - 9 \times 6^2 - 5 = -257$

Exercise 18

1. $f(x) = 2x^2 - 3x^3$

   Find the gradient of the curve $y = f(x)$ when

   a) $x = 1$ **b)** $x = 4$ **c)** $x = -5$

2. $f(x) = 4x^3 - 5x$

   Find the gradient of the curve $y = f(x)$ when

   a) $x = 2$ **b)** $x = -6$ **c)** $x = 0.5$

3. $f(x) = 6x^2 + 8x^3 - 7x$

   Find the gradient of the curve $y = f(x)$ when

   a) $x = 3$ **b)** $x = -4$ **c)** $x = \frac{2}{3}$

4. The curve $y = x^2 - 4x + 3$ has a gradient of -1 at the point where $x = a$.
   Find the value of a.

5. The curve $y = 3x^2 - 2x + 7$ has a gradient of -20 at the point where $x = b$.
   Find the value of b.

6. Find the coordinates of the point on the curve $y = 7 - 3x - 2x^2$ where the gradient is 5.

7. The curve $y = x^3 + 2x^2 - 3x$ has a gradient of 4 at points A and B.
   Find the x-coordinates of A and B.

8. The curve $y = \frac{1}{3}x^3 + \frac{1}{2}x^2 - 5x$ has a gradient of -3 at points P and Q.
   Find the coordinates of P and Q.

9. The curve $y = \frac{1}{2}x^4 - 4x^2 - 3x$ has a gradient of -3 at three points.
   Find the coordinates of these points.

10. Find the coordinates of the points on the curve $y = x^3 - 5x^2 - 8x$ where the gradient is zero.

Turning points

A **turning point** (or **stationary point**) is a point on a graph where the gradient is zero. On the cubic graph on the right, there are two turning points.

Above, completing the square was used to find the turning point on a quadratic graph but for other graphs this does not work.

Turning points for other graphs (and for quadratic graphs) can be found by setting the derivative function equal to zero and solving the resulting equation.

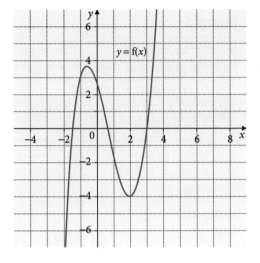

Turning points are often referred to as 'local maximums' or 'local minimums'.

Example

$f(x) = 3x^3 - 2x^2$

Find the coordinates of the turning points on the curve $y = f(x)$.

$$f'(x) = 9x^2 - 4x$$

Set $f'(x) = 0$: $9x^2 - 4x = 0$

$$x(9x - 4) = 0$$

Hence $x = 0$ or $x = \dfrac{4}{9}$

When $x = 0$, $y = 0$ so one turning point is at $(0, 0)$.

When $x = \dfrac{4}{9}$, $y = -\dfrac{32}{243}$ so the other turning point is at $\left(\dfrac{4}{9}, -\dfrac{32}{243}\right)$.

Unless the graph of $y = f(x)$ is given, it may not be possible to determine whether a turning point is a maximum point or a minimum point.

There are two ways to find this out:

Method 1

Investigate just to the left and just to the right of the turning point.

Take the turning point in the example above when $x = 0$:

$f'(0) = 0$ so look at $f'(-0.1)$ and $f'(0.1)$:

$$f'(-0.1) = 0.49$$

$$f'(0.1) = -0.31$$

Since the gradient just to the left is positive and the gradient just to the right is negative, the curve turns from positive to negative when $x = 0$ so the point $(0, 0)$ is a **maximum** point.

Method 2

Find the **second derivative** and substitute the coordinates of the turning point in.

The *sign* of the second derivative determines whether the point is a maximum or minimum.

Take the turning point in the example above when $x = \frac{4}{9}$:

The second derivative is found by differentiating $f'(x)$ again so $f''(x) = 18x - 4$.

$$f''\left(\frac{4}{9}\right) = 4$$

> $f''(x)$ is one possible notation for the second derivative.
> $\dfrac{d^2 y}{dx^2}$ can also be used.

If the second derivative is *positive*, the turning point is a **minimum** point.
If the second derivative is *negative*, the turning point is a **maximum**.

Exercise 19

1. Use differentiation to find the coordinates of the turning point of the graph of $y = f(x)$ when
   a) $f(x) = x^2 - 3x - 5$
   b) $f(x) = 4x^2 - 7x$
   c) $f(x) = 2 - 3x - 2x^2$

2. Determine the nature of the turning points in question **1**.

3. $f(x) = 5x^2 - 7x + 6$
   a) Find the coordinates of the turning point on the graph of $y = f(x)$.
   b) Show that the turning point is a minimum point.

4. $f(x) = 2x^3 - 2x^2 - 3$
   a) Find the exact coordinates of the turning points on the graph of $y = f(x)$.
   b) Determine the nature of the turning points.

5. $f(x) = 2x^3 - 6x - 5$
   a) Find the exact coordinates of the turning points on the graph of $y = f(x)$.
   b) Determine the nature of the turning points.

6. $f(x) = 3 + 12x - x^3$
   a) Find the exact coordinates of the turning points on the graph of $y = f(x)$.
   b) Determine the nature of the turning points.

7. $f(x) = 4 - 2x - x^3$
   Show that the graph of $y = f(x)$ has no turning points.

   > Turning points occur when $f'(x) = 0$.
   > Show that the quadratic equation $f'(x) = 0$ has no solutions.

8. $f(x) = kx + x^2 - x^3$
   The graph of $y = f(x)$ has no turning points. Find the range of values of k.

   > Find the value(s) of k such that $f'(x) = 0$ has no solutions.

Revision exercise 7A

1. Find the equation of the straight line satisfied by the following points:

a)

x	2	7	10
y	−5	0	3

b)

x	1	2	3
y	7	9	11

c)

x	1	2	3
y	8	6	4

d)

x	3	4	5
y	2	$2\frac{1}{2}$	3

2. Find the gradient of the line joining each pair of points.

a) $(3, 3)(5, 7)$

b) $(3, -1)(7, 3)$

c) $(-1, 4)(1, -3)$

d) $(2, 4)(-3, 4)$

e) $(0.5, -3)(0.4, -4)$

3. Find the gradient and the intercept on the y-axis for the following lines. Draw a *sketch* graph of each line.

a) $y = 2x - 7$

b) $y = 5 - 4x$

c) $2y = x + 8$

d) $2y = 10 - x$

e) $y + 2x = 12$

f) $2x + 3y = 24$

4. In the diagram, the equations of the lines are $y = 3x$, $y = 6$, $y = 10 - x$ and $y = \frac{1}{2}x - 3$.

Find the equation corresponding to each line.

5. In the diagram, the equations of the lines are $2y = x - 8$, $2y + x = 8$, $4y = 3x - 16$ and $4y + 3x = 16$.

Find the equation corresponding to each line.

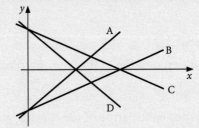

6. Find the equations of the lines which pass through the following pairs of points:

a) $(2, 1)(4, 5)$ b) $(0, 4)(-1, 1)$

c) $(2, 8)(-2, 12)$ d) $(0, 7)(-3, 7)$

7. The sketch represents a section of the curve $y = x^2 - 2x - 8$.

Calculate:

a) the coordinates of A and of B

b) the gradient of the line AB

c) the equation of the straight line AB.

8. Find the area of the triangle formed by the intersection of the lines $y = x$, $x + y = 10$ and $x = 0$.

9. Find, correct to two decimal places, the shortest distance from the point $(-1, 2)$ to the line $y = 2x - 3$.

10. Draw the graph of $y = 7 - 3x - 2x^2$ for $-4 \leqslant x \leqslant 2$.

    Find the gradient of the tangent to the curve at the point where the curve cuts the y-axis.

11. Draw the graph of $y = \dfrac{4000}{x} + 3x$ for $10 \leqslant x \leqslant 80$. Find the minimum value of y.

12. Draw the graph of $y = \dfrac{1}{x} + 2^x$ for

    $x = \dfrac{1}{4}, \dfrac{1}{2}, \dfrac{3}{4}, 1, 1\dfrac{1}{2}, 2, 3.$

13. Assuming that the graph of $y = 4 - x^2$ has been drawn, find the equation of the straight line which should be drawn in order to solve the following equations:

    a) $4 - 3x - x^2 = 0$

    b) $\dfrac{1}{2}(4 - x^2) = 0$

    c) $x^2 - x + 7 = 0$

    d) $\dfrac{4}{x} - x = 5$

14. Draw the graph of $y = 5 - x^2$ for $-3 \leqslant x \leqslant 3$, taking 2 cm to one unit for x and 1 cm to one unit for y.

    Use the graph to find:

    a) approximate solutions to the equation $4 - x - x^2 = 0$

    b) the square roots of 5

    c) the square roots of 7.

15. Draw the graph of $y = \dfrac{5}{x} + 2x - 3$, for $\dfrac{1}{2} \leq x \leq 7$, taking 2 cm to one unit for x and 1 cm to one unit for y. Use the graph to find:

    a) approximate solutions to the equation $2x^2 - 10x + 7 = 0$

    b) the range of values of x for which $\dfrac{5}{x} + 2x - 3 < 6.$

    c) the minimum value of y.

16. Draw the graph of $y = 4^x$ for $-2 \leqslant x \leqslant 2$. Use the graph to find:

    a) the approximate value of $4^{1.6}$,

    b) the approximate value of $4^{-\frac{1}{3}}$,

    c) the gradient of the curve at $x = 0$

    d) an approximate solution to the equation $4^x = 10$.

17. a) Draw the graph of the function $f(x) = 4 \times 2^{x-1} - 3$ for $x = 0, 1, 2, 3, 4$.

    (Scales: 2 cm per unit for x, 5 units per cm for y)

    b) Use your graph to estimate the value of x when $y = 11$.

18. The diagram is the speed–time graph of a bus. Calculate:

    a) the acceleration during the first 50 seconds

    b) the total distance travelled

    c) how long it takes before it is moving at 12 m/s for the first time.

19. The diagram is the speed–time graph of a car. Given that the total distance travelled is 2.4 km, calculate:

    a) the value of the maximum speed V

b) the distance travelled in the first 30 seconds of the motion.

20. $y = 3x^4 - 6x^2 + 7$

Find $\dfrac{dy}{dx}$.

21. $f(x) = \dfrac{1}{4}x^6 - \dfrac{2}{5}x^3 + \dfrac{7}{8}x^2$

a) Find $f'(x)$.

b) Find the gradient of the curve $y = f(x)$ when $x = 2$.

22. The curve $y = x^3 - 6x^2 - 7x$ has two turning points.

Find, correct to two decimal places, the x-coordinates of the turning points and determine their nature.

Examination-style exercise 7B

1.

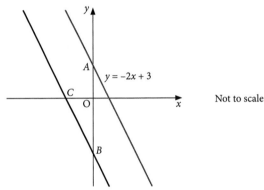

The distance AB is 8 units.

(a) Write down the equation of the line through B which is parallel to $y = -2x + 3$.   [1]

(b) Find the coordinates of the point C where this line crosses the x-axis.   [2]

2. The equation of a straight line can be written in the form $3x + 2y - 8 = 0$.

(a) Rearrange this equation to make y the subject.   [2]

(b) Write down the gradient of the line.   [1]

(c) Write down the coordinates of the point where the line crosses the y-axis.   [1]

Cambridge IGCSE Mathematics 0580
Paper 2 Q18 June 2007

3. A straight line passes through two points with coordinates (6, 8) and (0, 5).

Work out the equation of the line. [3]

Cambridge IGCSE Mathematics 0580
Paper 21 Q9 June 2008

4. In an experiment, the number of bacteria, N, after x days, is $N = 1000 \times 1.4^x$.

(a) Copy and complete the table.

x	0	1	2	3	4
N					

[2]

(b) Draw a graph to show this information. [2]

(c) How many days does it take for the number of bacteria to reach 3000?

Give your answer correct to 1 decimal place. [1]

Cambridge IGCSE Mathematics 0580
aper 21 Q16 November 2008

5.

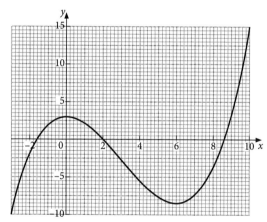

The diagram shows the accurate graph of $y = f(x)$.

(a) Use the graph to find

   i) f(0), [1]

   ii) f(8). [1]

(b) Use the graph to solve

   i) $f(x) = 0$, [2]

   ii) $f(x) = 5$. [1]

(c) k is an integer for which the equation $f(x) = k$ has exactly two solutions.

   Use the graph to find the two values of k. [2]

(d) Write down the range of values of x for which the graph of $y = f(x)$ has a negative gradient. [2]

(e) The equation $f(x) + x - 1 = 0$ can be solved by drawing a line on the grid.

 i) Write down the equation of this line. [1]

 ii) How many solutions are there for $f(x) + x - 1 = 0$? [1]

Cambridge IGCSE Mathematics 0580
Paper 4 Q4 June 2007

6. Answer the whole of this question on a sheet of graph paper.

The table shows some of the values of the function $f(x) = x^2 - \dfrac{1}{x}, x \neq 0$.

x	-3	-2	-1	-0.5	-0.2	0.2	0.5	1	2	3
y	9.3	4.5	2.0	2.3	p	-5.0	-1.8	q	3.5	r

(a) Find the values of p, q and r correct to 1 decimal place. [3]

(b) Using a scale of 2 cm to represent 1 unit on the x-axis and 1 cm to represent 1 unit on the y-axis, draw an x-axis for $-3 \leqslant x \leqslant 3$ and a y-axis for $-6 \leqslant y \leqslant 10$.

Draw the graph of $y = f(x)$ for $-3 \leqslant x \leqslant -0.2$ and $0.2 \leqslant x \leqslant 3$. [6]

(c) i) By drawing a suitable straight line, find the three values of x where $f(x) = -3x$. [3]

 ii) $x^2 - \dfrac{1}{x} = -3x$ can be written as $x^3 + ax^2 + b = 0$.

 Find the values of a and b. [2]

(d) Draw a tangent to the graph of $y = f(x)$ at the point where $x = -2$.

Use it to estimate the gradient of $y = f(x)$ when $x = -2$. [3]

Cambridge IGCSE Mathematics 0580
Paper 4 Q3 November 2008

7.

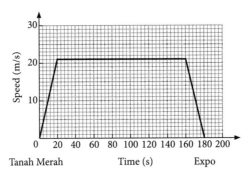

The graph shows the train journey between Tanah Merah and Expo in Singapore. Work out

(a) the acceleration of the train when it leaves Tanah Merah, [2]

(b) the distance between Tanah Merah and Expo, [3]

(c) the average speed of the train for the journey. [1]

Cambridge IGCSE Mathematics 0580
Paper 21 Q18 November 2008

8. (a) A train completed a journey of 850 kilometres with an average speed of 80 kilometres per hour.

Calculate, giving **exact** answers, the time taken for this journey in

   i) hours, [2]

   ii) hours, minutes and seconds. [1]

(b) Another train took 10 hours 48 minutes to complete the same 850 km journey.

   i) It departed at 19:20.

      At what time, on the next day, did this train complete the journey? [1]

   ii) Calculate the average speed, in kilometres per hour, for the journey. [2]

(c)

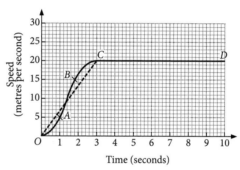

The **solid** line *OABCD* on the grid shows the first 10 seconds of a car journey.

   i) Describe briefly what happens to the **speed** of the car between *B* and *C*. [1]

   ii) Describe briefly what happens to the **acceleration** of the car between *B* and *C*. [1]

   iii) Calculate the acceleration between *A* and *B*. [2]

   iv) Using the **broken** straight line *OC*, estimate the total distance travelled by the car in the whole 10 seconds. [3]

   v) Explain briefly why, in this case, using the broken line makes the answer to **part (iv)** a good estimate of the distance travelled. [1]

   vi) Calculate the average speed of the car during the 10 seconds.

Give your answer in kilometres per hour. [2]

Cambridge IGCSE Mathematics 0580
Paper 4 Q1 June 2006

9. **Answer the whole of this question on one sheet of graph paper.**

$$f(x) = 1 - \frac{1}{x^2}, \; x \neq 0.$$

(a)

x	−3	−2	−1	−0.5	−0.4	−0.3	0.3	0.4	0.5	1	2	3
$f(x)$	p	0.75	0	−3	−5.25	q	q	−5.25	−3	0	0.75	p

Find the values p and q. [2]

(b) i) Draw an x-axis for $-3 \leqslant x \leqslant 3$ using 2 cm to represent 1 unit
and a y-axis for $-11 \leqslant y \leqslant 2$ using 1 cm to represent 1 unit. [1]

   ii) Draw the graph of $y = f(x)$ for $-3 \leqslant x \leqslant -0.3$ and for $0.3 \leqslant x \leqslant 3$. [5]

(c) Write down an integer k such that $f(x) = k$ has no solutions. [1]

(d) **On the same grid**, draw the graph of $y = 2x - 5$ for $-3 \leqslant x \leqslant 3$. [2]

(e) i) Use your graphs to find solutions of the equation $1 - \frac{1}{x^2} = 2x - 5$. [3]

   ii) Rearrange $1 - \frac{1}{x^2} = 2x - 5$ into the form $ax^3 + bx^2 + c = 0$,
   where a, b and c are integers. [2]

(f) i) Draw a tangent to the graph of $y = f(x)$ which is
parallel to the line $y = 2x - 5$. [1]

   ii) Write down the equation of this tangent. [2]

Cambridge IGCSE Mathematics 0580
Paper 4 Q5 November 2005

10. (a) Find the equation of the straight line through point $(6, 5)$
that is perpendicular to the line $y = \frac{1}{2}x + 1$. [3]

   (b) Hence find, correct to three decimal places, the shortest
   distance from the point $(6, 5)$ to the line $y = \frac{1}{2}x + 1$. [4]

11. The diagram shows the graph of $y = f(x)$ where $f(x) = x^3 - 2x^2 - 4x$.

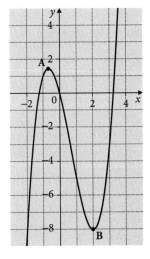

(a) Find $f'(x)$. [3]

(b) Find the exact coordinates of the points marked A and B. [4]

(c) Show mathematically that point A is a maximum point. [2]

12. A curve C has equation $y = 2x^3 - 4x^2 + 5x$.

(a) Find $\dfrac{dy}{dx}$. [3]

(b) Find the value of the gradient of the curve at the point where $x = 0.5$. [2]

(c) Explain, with a reason, whether curve C has any turning points. [2]

8 Sets, Vectors, Functions and Transformations

Bertrand Russell (1872–1970) tried to reduce all mathematics to formal logic. He showed that the idea of a set of all sets which are not members of themselves leads to contradictions. He wrote to Gottlieb Frege just as he was putting the finishing touches to a book that represented his life's work, pointing out that Frege's work was invalidated.

E1.2 Use language, notation and Venn diagrams to describe sets and represent relationships between sets.
Definition of sets e.g. $A = \{x: x \text{ is a natural number}\}$, $B = \{(x, y): y = mx + c\}$, $C = \{x: a \leqslant x \leqslant b\}$, $D = \{a, b, c, \ldots\}$

E2.9 Use function notation, e.g. $f(x) = 3x - 5$, f: $x \rightarrow 3x - 5$, to describe simple functions. Find inverse functions $f^{-1}(x)$. Form composite functions as defined by $gf(x) = g(f(x))$.

E7.1 Describe a translation by using a vector represented by e.g. $\begin{pmatrix} x \\ y \end{pmatrix}$, $\overrightarrow{AB}$ or **a**. Add and subtract vectors. Multiply a vector by a scalar.

E7.2 Reflect simple plane figures. Rotate simple plane figures through multiples of 90°. Construct given translations and enlargements of simple plane figures. Recognise and describe reflections, rotations, translations and enlargements.

E7.3 Calculate the magnitude of a vector $\begin{pmatrix} x \\ y \end{pmatrix}$ as $\sqrt{x^2 + y^2}$. Represent vectors by directed line segments. Use the sum and difference of two vectors to express given vectors in terms of two coplanar vectors. Use position vectors.

8.1 Sets

1. ∩ 'intersection'
   $A \cap B$ is shaded.

2. ∪ 'union'
   $A \cup B$ is shaded.

3. ⊂ 'is a **proper** subset of'

A ⊂ B means A lies inside B but cannot be equal to B

[B ⊄ A means 'B is *not* a **proper** subset of A']

[A ⊆ B means 'is a subset of' and A *can* equal B.]

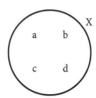

4. ∈ 'is a member of'

'belongs to'

b ∈ X

[e ∉ X means 'e is not a member of set X']

5. ε 'universal set'

The universal set is the set of all things that you are considering at the time.

ε = {a, b, c, d, e}

6. A′ 'complement of'

'not in A'

A′ is shaded

(A ∪ A′ = ε)

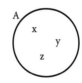

7. n(A) 'the number of elements in set A'

n(A) = 3

8. A = {x: x is an integer, 2 ≤ x ≤ 9}

A is the ⌈set of⌉ elements x ⌈such that⌉ x is an integer and 2 ≤ x ≤ 9.

The set A is {2, 3, 4, 5, 6, 7, 8, 9}.

9. ∅ or {} 'empty set'

(Note: ∅ ⊂ A for any set A)

Exercise 1

1. In the Venn diagram,

ε = {people in a hotel}

T = {people who like toast}

E = {people who like eggs}

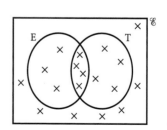

a) How many people like toast?

b) How many people like eggs but not toast?

c) How many people like toast and eggs?

d) How many people are in the hotel?

e) How many people like neither toast nor eggs?

2. In the Venn diagram,

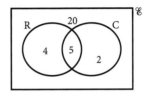

ε = {boys in Year 10}

R = {members of the rugby team}

C = {members of the cricket team}

a) How many are in the rugby team?

b) How many are in both teams?

c) How many are in the rugby team but not in the cricket team?

d) How many are in neither team?

e) How many are there in Year 10?

3. In the Venn diagram,

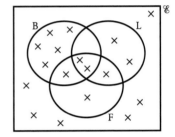

ε = {cars in a street}

B = {blue cars}

L = {cars with left-hand drive}

F = {cars with four doors}

a) How many cars are blue?

b) How many blue cars have four doors?

c) How many cars with left-hand drive have four doors?

d) How many blue cars have left-hand drive?

e) How many cars are in the street?

f) How many blue cars with left-hand drive do not have four doors?

4. In the Venn diagram,

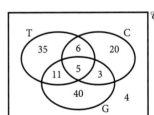

ε = {houses in the street}

C = {houses with central heating}

T = {houses with a colour T.V.}

G = {houses with a garden}

a) How many houses have gardens?

b) How many houses have a colour T.V. and central heating?

c) How many houses have a colour T.V. and central heating and a garden?

d) How many houses have a garden but not a T.V. or central heating?

e) How many houses have a T.V. and a garden but not central heating?

f) How many houses are there in the street?

5. In the Venn diagram,

ε = {children in a mixed school}

G = {girls in the school}

S = {children who can swim}

L = {children who are left-handed}

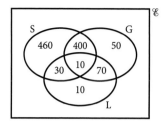

a) How many left-handed children are there?

b) How many girls cannot swim?

c) How many boys can swim?

d) How many girls are left-handed?

e) How many boys are left-handed?

f) How many left-handed girls can swim?

g) How many boys are there in the school?

Example

ε = {1, 2, 3, …, 12}, A = {2, 3, 4, 5, 6} and B = {2, 4, 6, 8, 10}.

a) $A \cup B$ = {2, 3, 4, 5, 6, 8, 10}

b) $A \cap B$ = {2, 4, 6}

c) A' = {1, 7, 8, 9, 10, 11, 12}

d) $n(A \cup B) = 7$

e) $B' \cap A$ = {3, 5}

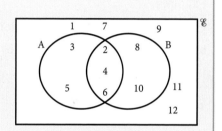

Exercise 2

In this exercise, be careful to use set notation only when the answer *is* a set.

1. If M = {1, 2, 3, 4, 5, 6, 7, 8}, N = {5, 7, 9, 11, 13}, find:

a) $M \cap N$ **b)** $M \cup N$ **c)** $n(N)$ **d)** $n(M \cup N)$

State whether true or false:

e) $5 \in M$ **f)** $7 \in (M \cup N)$ **g)** $N \subset M$ **h)** $\{5, 6, 7\} \subset M$

2. If A = {2, 3, 5, 7}, B = {1, 2, 3,…, 9}, find:

a) $A \cap B$ **b)** $A \cup B$ **c)** $n(A \cap B)$ **d)** $\{1, 4\} \cap A$

State whether true or false:

e) $A \in B$ **f)** $A \subset B$ **g)** $9 \subset B$ **h)** $3 \in (A \cap B)$

3. If X = {1, 2, 3, …, 10}, Y = {2, 4, 6, …, 20} and Z = {$x : x$ is an integer, $15 \le x \le 25$}, find:

a) $X \cap Y$ **b)** $Y \cap Z$ **c)** $X \cap Z$

d) $n(X \cup Y)$ **e)** $n(Z)$ **f)** $n(X \cup Z)$

State whether true or false:

g) $5 \in Y$ **h)** $20 \in X$ **i)** $n(X \cap Y) = 5$ **j)** $\{15, 20, 25\} \subset Z.$

4. If D = {1, 3, 5}, E = {3, 4, 5}, F = {1, 5, 10}, find:

a) $D \cup E$ b) $D \cap F$ c) $n(E \cap F)$

d) $(D \cup E) \cap F$ e) $(D \cap E) \cup F$ f) $n(D \cup F)$

State whether true or false:

g) $D \subset (E \cup F)$ h) $3 \in (E \cap F)$ i) $4 \notin (D \cap E)$

5. Find:

a) $n(E)$ b) $n(F)$ c) $E \cap F$

d) $E \cup F$ e) $n(E \cup F)$ f) $n(E \cap F)$

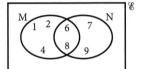

6. Find:

a) $n(M \cap N)$ b) $n(N)$ c) $M \cup N$

d) $M' \cap N$ e) $N' \cap M$ f) $(M \cap N)'$

g) $M \cup N'$ h) $N \cup M'$ i) $M' \cup N'$

Example

On a Venn diagram, shade the regions:

a) $A \cap C$ b) $(B \cap C) \cap A'$

where A, B, C are intersecting sets.

· ·

a) $A \cap C$

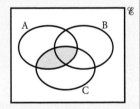

b) $(B \cap C) \cap A'$
   [find $(B \cap C)$ first]

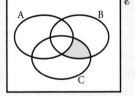

Exercise 3

1. Draw six diagrams similar to Figure 1 and shade the following sets:

a) $A \cap B$ b) $A \cup B$ c) A'

d) $A' \cap B$ e) $B' \cap A$ f) $(B \cup A)'$

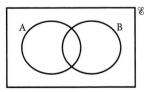

Figure 1

2. Draw four diagrams similar to Figure 2 and shade the following sets:

a) $A \cap B$ b) $A \cup B$ c) $B' \cap A$ d) $(B \cup A)'$

Figure 2

3. Draw four diagrams similar to Figure 3 and shade the following sets:

a) $A \cup B$ b) $A \cap B$ c) $A \cap B'$ d) $(B \cup A)'$

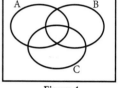

Figure 3

4. Draw eleven diagrams similar to Figure 4 and shade the following sets:

a) $A \cap B$ b) $A \cup C$ c) $A \cap (B \cap C)$
d) $(A \cup B) \cap C$ e) $B \cap (A \cup C)$ f) $A \cap B'$
g) $A \cap (B \cup C)'$ h) $(B \cup C) \cap A$ i) $C' \cap (A \cap B)$
j) $(A \cup C) \cup B'$ k) $(A \cup C) \cap (B \cap C)$

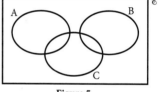

Figure 4

5. Draw nine diagrams similar to Figure 5 and shade the following sets:

a) $(A \cup B) \cap C$ b) $(A \cap B) \cup C$ c) $(A \cup B) \cup C$
d) $A \cap (B \cup C)$ e) $A' \cap C$ f) $C' \cap (A \cup B)$
g) $(A \cap B) \cap C$ h) $(A \cap C) \cup (B \cap C)$ i) $(A \cup B \cup C)'$

Figure 5

6. Copy each diagram and shade the region indicated.

a)

$X' \cap Y$

b)

$E \cup F$

c)

$A \cap B$

d)

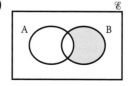

$(M \cap N)'$

7. Describe the shaded region.

a)

b)

c)

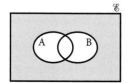

d)

Sets   285

8.2 Logical problems

Example 1

In a form of 30 girls, 18 play netball and 14 play hockey, whilst 5 play neither. Find the number who play both netball and hockey.

Let $\varepsilon = \{\text{girls in the form}\}$

$N = \{\text{girls who play netball}\}$

$H = \{\text{girls who play hockey}\}$

and $x = $ the number of girls who play both netball and hockey

The number of girls in each portion of the universal set is shown in the Venn diagram.

Since

$$n(\varepsilon) = 30$$

$$18 - x + x + 14 - x + 5 = 30$$

$$37 - x = 30$$

$$x = 7$$

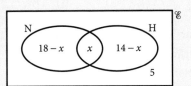

∴ Seven girls play both netball and hockey.

Example 2

If $A = \{\text{sheep}\}$

$B = \{\text{horses}\}$

$C = \{\text{'intelligent' animals}\}$

$D = \{\text{animals which make good pets}\}$

a) Express the following sentences in set language:

i) No sheep are 'intelligent' animals.

ii) All horses make good pets.

iii) Some sheep make good pets.

b) Interpret the following statements:

i) $B \subseteq C$

ii) $B \cup C = D$

---

a) i) $A \cap C = \varnothing$

ii) $B \subseteq D$

iii) $A \cap D \neq \varnothing$

b) i) All horses are intelligent animals.

ii) Animals which make good pets are either horses or 'intelligent' animals (or both).

Exercise 4

1. In the Venn diagram $n(A) = 10$, $n(B) = 13$, $n(A \cap B) = x$ and $n(A \cup B) = 18$.

   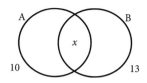

   a) Write in terms of x the number of elements in A but not in B.

   b) Write in terms of x the number of elements in B but not in A.

   c) Add together the number of elements in the three parts of the diagram to obtain the equation $10 - x + x + 13 - x = 18$.

   d) Hence find the number of elements in both A and B.

2. In the Venn diagram $n(A) = 21$, $n(B) = 17$, $n(A \cap B) = x$ and $n(A \cup B) = 29$.

   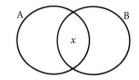

   a) Write down in terms of x the number of elements in each part of the diagram.

   b) Form an equation and hence find x.

3. The sets M and N intersect such that $n(M) = 31$, $n(N) = 18$ and $n(M \cup N) = 35$. How many elements are in both M and N?

4. The sets P and Q intersect such that $n(P) = 11$, $n(Q) = 29$ and $n(P \cup Q) = 37$. How many elements are in both P and Q?

5. The sets A and B intersect such that $n(A \cap B) = 7$, $n(A) = 20$ and $n(B) = 23$. Find $n(A \cup B)$.

6. Twenty boys all play either football or basketball (or both). If thirteen play football and ten play basketball, how many play both sports?

7. Of the 53 staff at a school, 36 drink tea, 18 drink coffee and 10 drink neither tea nor coffee. How many drink both tea and coffee?

8. Of the 32 students in a class, 18 play golf, 16 play the piano and 7 play both. How many play neither?

9. Of the students in a class, 15 can spell 'parallel', 14 can spell 'Pythagoras', 5 can spell both words and 4 can spell neither. How many students are there in the class?

10. In a school, students must take at least one of these subjects: Maths, Physics or Chemistry. In a group of 50 students, 7 take all three subjects, 9 take Physics and Chemistry only, 8 take Maths and Physics only and 5 take Maths and Chemistry only. Of these 50 students, x take Maths only, x take Physics only and $x + 3$ take Chemistry only. Draw a Venn diagram, find x, and hence find the number taking Maths.

11. All of 60 different vitamin pills contain at least one of the vitamins A, B and C. Twelve have A only, 7 have B only, and 11 have C only. If 6 have all three vitamins and there are x having A and B only, B and C only and A and C only, how many pills contain vitamin A?

12. The IGCSE results of the 30 members of a rugby squad were as follows: All 30 players passed at least two subjects, 18 players passed at least three subjects, and 3 players passed four subjects or more. Calculate:

a) how many passed exactly two subjects,

b) what fraction of the squad passed exactly three subjects.

13. In a group of 59 people, some are wearing hats, gloves or scarves (or a combination of these), 4 are wearing all three, 7 are wearing just a hat and gloves, 3 are wearing just gloves and a scarf and 9 are wearing just a hat and scarf. The number wearing only a hat or only gloves is x, and the number wearing only a scarf or none of the three items is $(x-2)$. Find x and hence the number of people wearing a hat.

14. In a street of 150 houses, three different newspapers are delivered: T, G and M. Of these, 40 receive T, 35 receive G, and 60 receive M; 7 receive T and G, 10 receive G and M and 4 receive T and M; 34 receive no paper at all. How many receive all three?

Note: If '7 receive T and G', this information does not mean 7 receive T and G *only*.

15. If S = {Serbian men}, G = {good footballers}, express the following statements in words:

a) $G \subseteq S$

b) $G \cap S = \varnothing$

c) $G \cap S \neq \varnothing$

(Ignore the truth or otherwise of the statements.)

16. Given that ε = {students in a school}, B = {boys}, H = {hockey players}, F = {football players}, express the following in words:

a) $F \subseteq B$　　　　**b)** $H \subseteq B'$　　　　**c)** $F \cap H \neq \varnothing$

d) $B \cap H = \varnothing$

Express in set notation:

e) No boys play football.

f) All students play either football or hockey.

17. If ε = {living creatures}, S = {spiders}, F = {animals that fly}, T = {animals which taste nice}, express in set notation:

a) No spiders taste nice.

b) All animals that fly taste nice.

c) Some spiders can fly.

Express in words:

d) $S \cup F \cup T = \varepsilon$ **e)** $T \subseteq S$

18. ε = {tigers}, T = {tigers who like lions}, X = {tigers who like elephants}, H = {tigers in hospital}.

Express in words:

a) $T \subseteq X$ **b)** $T \cup X = H$ **c)** $H \cap X = \varnothing$

Express in set notation:

d) All tigers in hospital like lions.

e) Some tigers like both lions and elephants.

19. ε = {school teachers}, P = {teachers called Peter}, B = {good bridge players}, W = {women teachers}.

Express in words:

a) $P \cap B = \varnothing$ **b)** $P \cup B \cup W = \varepsilon$ **c)** $P \cap W \neq \varnothing$

Express in set notation:

d) Women teachers cannot play bridge well.

e) All good bridge players are women called Peter.

8.3 Vectors

A vector quantity has both magnitude and direction. Problems involving forces, velocities and displacements are often made easier when vectors are used.

Addition of vectors

Vectors **a** and **b** represented by the line segments can be added using the parallelogram rule or the 'nose-to-tail' method.

The 'tail' of vector **b** is joined to the 'nose' of vector **a**.

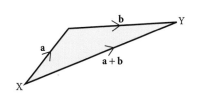

Alternatively the tail of **a** can be joined to the 'nose' of vector **b**.

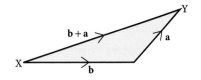

In both cases the vector $\overrightarrow{XY}$ has the same length and direction and therefore

a + b = b + a

Multiplication by a scalar

A scalar quantity has a magnitude but no direction (e.g. mass, volume, temperature). Ordinary numbers are scalars.

When vector **x** is multiplied by 2, the result is 2**x**.

When **x** is multiplied by −3 the result is −3**x**.

Note:

1. The negative sign reverses the direction of the vector.

2. The result of **a − b** is **a + −b**.

i.e. Subtracting **b** is equivalent to adding the negative of **b**.

Example
The diagram shows vectors **a** and **b**.

Find $\overrightarrow{OP}$ and $\overrightarrow{OQ}$ such that

$\overrightarrow{OP} = 3\mathbf{a} + \mathbf{b}$

$\overrightarrow{OQ} = -2\mathbf{a} - 3\mathbf{a}$

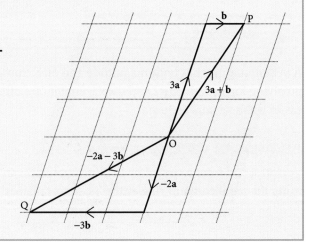

Exercise 5

In questions **1** to **26**, use the diagram below to describe the vectors
given in terms of **c** and **d** where $\mathbf{c} = \overrightarrow{QN}$ and $\mathbf{d} = \overrightarrow{QR}$.

e.g. $\overrightarrow{QS} = 2\mathbf{d}$, $\overrightarrow{TD} = \mathbf{c} + \mathbf{d}$

1. $\overrightarrow{AB}$	2. $\overrightarrow{SG}$	3. $\overrightarrow{VK}$
4. $\overrightarrow{KH}$	5. $\overrightarrow{OT}$	6. $\overrightarrow{WJ}$
7. $\overrightarrow{FH}$	8. $\overrightarrow{FT}$	9. $\overrightarrow{KV}$
10. $\overrightarrow{NQ}$	11. $\overrightarrow{OM}$	12. $\overrightarrow{SD}$
13. $\overrightarrow{PI}$	14. $\overrightarrow{YG}$	15. $\overrightarrow{OI}$
16. $\overrightarrow{RE}$	17. $\overrightarrow{XM}$	18. $\overrightarrow{ZH}$
19. $\overrightarrow{MR}$	20. $\overrightarrow{KA}$	21. $\overrightarrow{RZ}$
22. $\overrightarrow{CR}$	23. $\overrightarrow{NV}$	24. $\overrightarrow{EV}$
25. $\overrightarrow{JS}$	26. $\overrightarrow{LE}$	

In questions **27** to **38**, use the same diagram to find vectors for the
following in terms of the capital letters, starting from Q each time.

e.g. $3\mathbf{d} = \overrightarrow{QT}$, $\mathbf{c} + \mathbf{d} = \overrightarrow{QA}$.

27. $2\mathbf{c}$	28. $4\mathbf{d}$	29. $2\mathbf{c} + \mathbf{d}$	30. $2\mathbf{d} + \mathbf{c}$
31. $3\mathbf{d} + 2\mathbf{c}$	32. $2\mathbf{c} - \mathbf{d}$	33. $-\mathbf{c} + 2\mathbf{d}$	34. $\mathbf{c} - 2\mathbf{d}$
35. $2\mathbf{c} + 4\mathbf{d}$	36. $-\mathbf{c}$	37. $-\mathbf{c} - \mathbf{d}$	38. $2\mathbf{c} - 2\mathbf{d}$

In questions **39** to **43**, write each vector in terms of **a** and/or **b**.

39. a) $\overrightarrow{BA}$ **b)** $\overrightarrow{AC}$
    c) $\overrightarrow{DB}$ **d)** $\overrightarrow{AD}$

40. a) $\overrightarrow{ZX}$ **b)** $\overrightarrow{YW}$
    c) $\overrightarrow{XY}$ **d)** $\overrightarrow{XZ}$

41. a) $\overrightarrow{MK}$ **b)** $\overrightarrow{NL}$
    c) $\overrightarrow{NK}$ **d)** $\overrightarrow{KN}$

42. a) $\overrightarrow{FE}$ **b)** $\overrightarrow{BC}$
    c) $\overrightarrow{FC}$ **d)** $\overrightarrow{DA}$

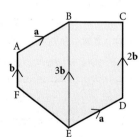

In questions **43** to **45**, write each vector in terms of **a**, **b** and **c**.

43. a) $\overrightarrow{FC}$ **b)** $\overrightarrow{GB}$ **c)** $\overrightarrow{AB}$

    d) $\overrightarrow{HE}$ **e)** $\overrightarrow{CA}$

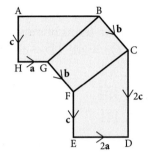

44. a) $\overrightarrow{OF}$ **b)** $\overrightarrow{OC}$ **c)** $\overrightarrow{BC}$

    d) $\overrightarrow{EB}$ **e)** $\overrightarrow{FB}$

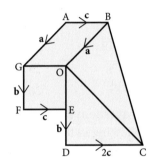

45. a) $\overrightarrow{GD}$ **b)** $\overrightarrow{GE}$ **c)** $\overrightarrow{AD}$

    d) $\overrightarrow{AF}$ **e)** $\overrightarrow{FE}$

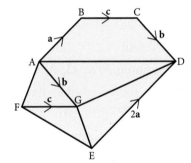

Example

Using Figure 1, express each of the following vectors in terms of **a** and/or **b**.

a) $\overrightarrow{AP}$ **b)** $\overrightarrow{AB}$

c) $\overrightarrow{OQ}$ **d)** $\overrightarrow{PO}$

e) $\overrightarrow{PQ}$ **f)** $\overrightarrow{PN}$

g) $\overrightarrow{ON}$ **h)** $\overrightarrow{AN}$

i) $\overrightarrow{BP}$ **j)** $\overrightarrow{QA}$

OA = AP

BQ = 3OB

N is the midpoint of PQ

$\overrightarrow{OA}$ = **a**, $\overrightarrow{OB}$ = **b**

Figure 1

a) $\overrightarrow{AP}$ = **a**

b) $\overrightarrow{AB}$ = −**a** + **b**

c) $\overrightarrow{OQ}$ = 4**b**

d) $\overrightarrow{PO}$ = −2**a**

e) $\overrightarrow{PQ}$ = $\overrightarrow{PO}$ + $\overrightarrow{OQ}$

  = − 2**a** + 4**b**

f) $\overrightarrow{PN}$ = $\frac{1}{2}\overrightarrow{PQ}$

  = −**a** + 2**b**

g) $\overrightarrow{ON}$ = $\overrightarrow{OP}$ + $\overrightarrow{PN}$

  = 2**a** + (−**a** + 2**b**)

  = **a** + 2**b**

h) $\overrightarrow{AN}$ = $\overrightarrow{AP}$ + $\overrightarrow{PN}$

  = **a** + (−**a** + 2**b**)

  = 2**b**

i) $\overrightarrow{BP}$ = $\overrightarrow{BO}$ + $\overrightarrow{OP}$

  = −**b** + 2**a**

j) $\overrightarrow{QA}$ = $\overrightarrow{QO}$ + $\overrightarrow{OA}$

  = − 4**b** + **a**

Exercise 6

In questions **1** to **6**, $\overrightarrow{OA}$ = **a** and $\overrightarrow{OB}$ = **b**. Copy each diagram and use the information given to express the following vectors in terms of **a** and/or **b**.

a) $\overrightarrow{AP}$ b) $\overrightarrow{AB}$ c) $\overrightarrow{OQ}$ d) $\overrightarrow{PO}$ e) $\overrightarrow{PQ}$

f) $\overrightarrow{PN}$ g) $\overrightarrow{ON}$ h) $\overrightarrow{AN}$ i) $\overrightarrow{BP}$ j) $\overrightarrow{QA}$

1. A, B and N are midpoints of OP, OQ and PQ respectively.

2. A and N are midpoints of OP and PQ and BQ = 2OB.

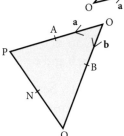

3. AP = 2OA, BQ = OB, PN = NQ.

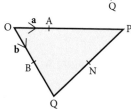

4. OA = 2AP, BQ = 3OB, PN = 2NQ.

5. $AP = 5OA$, $OB = 2BQ$, $NP = 2QN$.

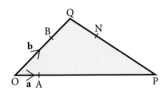

6. $OA = \frac{1}{5}OP$, $OQ = 3OB$, N is $\frac{1}{4}$ of the way along PQ.

7. In $\triangle XYZ$, the midpoint of YZ is M.
If $\overrightarrow{XY} = \mathbf{s}$ and $\overrightarrow{ZX} = \mathbf{t}$,
find $\overrightarrow{XM}$ in terms of $\mathbf{s}$ and $\mathbf{t}$.

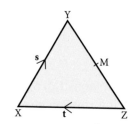

8. In $\triangle AOB$, $AM:MB = 2:1$. If $\overrightarrow{OA} = \mathbf{a}$ and $\overrightarrow{OB} = \mathbf{b}$,
find $\overrightarrow{OM}$ in term of $\mathbf{a}$ and $\mathbf{b}$.

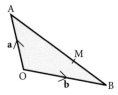

9. O is any point in the plane of the square ABCD. The vectors
$\overrightarrow{OA}$, $\overrightarrow{OB}$ and $\overrightarrow{OC}$ are $\mathbf{a}$, $\mathbf{b}$ and $\mathbf{c}$ respectively. Find the vector
$\overrightarrow{OD}$ in terms of $\mathbf{a}$, $\mathbf{b}$ and $\mathbf{c}$.

10. ABCDEF is a regular hexagon with $\overrightarrow{AB}$ representing the vector $\mathbf{m}$, $\overrightarrow{AF}$
representing the vector $\mathbf{n}$. Find the vector representing $\overrightarrow{AD}$.

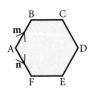

11. ABCDEF is a regular hexagon with centre O.
$\overrightarrow{FA} = \mathbf{a}$ and $\overrightarrow{FB} = \mathbf{b}$.

Express the following vectors in terms of $\mathbf{a}$ and/or $\mathbf{b}$.

a) $\overrightarrow{AB}$ b) $\overrightarrow{FO}$ c) $\overrightarrow{FC}$

d) $\overrightarrow{BC}$ e) $\overrightarrow{AO}$ f) $\overrightarrow{FD}$

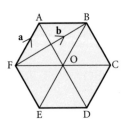

12. In the diagram, M is the midpoint of CD, BP : PM = 2 : 1, $\overrightarrow{AB} = \mathbf{x}$, $\overrightarrow{AC} = \mathbf{y}$ and $\overrightarrow{AD} = \mathbf{z}$.

Express the following vectors in terms of **x**, **y** and **z**.

a) $\overrightarrow{DC}$ b) $\overrightarrow{DM}$ c) $\overrightarrow{AM}$

d) $\overrightarrow{BM}$ e) $\overrightarrow{BP}$ f) $\overrightarrow{AP}$

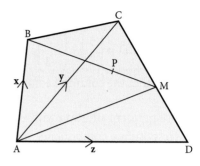

8.4 Column vectors

The vector $\overrightarrow{AB}$ may be written as a *column vector*.

$$AB = \begin{pmatrix} 5 \\ 3 \end{pmatrix}.$$

The top number is the horizontal component of $\overrightarrow{AB}$ (i.e. 5) and the bottom number is the vertical component (i.e. 3).

Similarly $\overrightarrow{CD} = \begin{pmatrix} 4 \\ -2 \end{pmatrix}$

$$\overrightarrow{EF} = \begin{pmatrix} 0 \\ 6 \end{pmatrix}$$

Addition of vectors

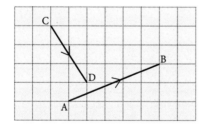

Figure 1

Suppose we wish to add vectors $\overrightarrow{AB}$ and $\overrightarrow{CD}$ in Figure 1.

First move $\overrightarrow{CD}$ so that $\overrightarrow{AB}$ and $\overrightarrow{CD}$ join 'nose to tail' as in Figure 2. Remember that changing the *position* of a vector does not change the vector. A vector is described by its length and direction.

The broken line shows the result of adding $\overrightarrow{AB}$ and $\overrightarrow{CD}$.

Figure 2

In column vectors,

$$\vec{AB} + \vec{CD} = \begin{pmatrix} 5 \\ 2 \end{pmatrix} + \begin{pmatrix} 2 \\ -3 \end{pmatrix}$$

We see that the column vector for the broken line is $\begin{pmatrix} 7 \\ -1 \end{pmatrix}$.

So we perform addition with vectors by adding together the corresponding components of the vectors.

Subtraction of vectors

Figure 3 shows $\vec{AB} - \vec{CD}$.

To subtract vector $\vec{CD}$ from $\vec{AB}$ we *add* the *negative* of $\vec{CD}$ to $\vec{AB}$.

So $\vec{AB} - \vec{CD} = \vec{AB} + \left(-\vec{CD} \right)$

In column vectors,

$$\vec{AB} + \left(-\vec{CD} \right) = \begin{pmatrix} 5 \\ 2 \end{pmatrix} + \begin{pmatrix} -2 \\ 3 \end{pmatrix} = \begin{pmatrix} 3 \\ 5 \end{pmatrix}$$

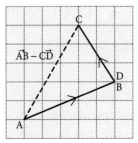

Figure 3

Multiplication by a scalar

If $\mathbf{a} = \begin{pmatrix} 3 \\ -4 \end{pmatrix}$ then $2\mathbf{a} = 2\begin{pmatrix} 3 \\ -4 \end{pmatrix} = \begin{pmatrix} 6 \\ -8 \end{pmatrix}$.

Each component is multiplied by the number 2.

Parallel vectors

Vectors are parallel if they have the same direction. Both components of one vector must be in the same ratio to the corresponding components of the parallel vector.

e.g. $\begin{pmatrix} 3 \\ -5 \end{pmatrix}$ is parallel to $\begin{pmatrix} 6 \\ -10 \end{pmatrix}$,

because $\begin{pmatrix} 6 \\ -10 \end{pmatrix}$ may be written $2\begin{pmatrix} 3 \\ -5 \end{pmatrix}$.

In general the vector $k\begin{pmatrix} a \\ b \end{pmatrix}$ is parallel to $\begin{pmatrix} a \\ b \end{pmatrix}$.

Exercise 7

Questions **1** to **36** refer to the following vectors.

$$\mathbf{a} = \begin{pmatrix} 3 \\ 4 \end{pmatrix} \qquad \mathbf{b} = \begin{pmatrix} 1 \\ 4 \end{pmatrix} \qquad \mathbf{c} = \begin{pmatrix} 4 \\ -3 \end{pmatrix} \qquad \mathbf{d} = \begin{pmatrix} -1 \\ 1 \end{pmatrix}$$

$$\mathbf{e} = \begin{pmatrix} 5 \\ 12 \end{pmatrix} \qquad \mathbf{f} = \begin{pmatrix} 3 \\ -2 \end{pmatrix} \qquad \mathbf{g} = \begin{pmatrix} -4 \\ -2 \end{pmatrix} \qquad \mathbf{h} = \begin{pmatrix} -12 \\ 5 \end{pmatrix}$$

Draw and label the following vectors on graph paper (take 1 cm to 1 unit).

1. **c**
2. **f**
3. **2b**
4. **−a**

5. **−g**
6. **3a**
7. $\frac{1}{2}$**e**
8. **5d**

9. $-\frac{1}{2}$**h**
10. $\frac{3}{2}$**g**
11. $\frac{1}{5}$**h**
12. **−3b**

Find the following vectors in component form.

13. **b + h**
14. **f + g**
15. **e − b**

16. **a − d**
17. **g − h**
18. **2a + 3c**

19. **3f + 2d**
20. **4g − 2b**
21. **5a** $+\frac{1}{2}$**g**

22. **a + b + c**
23. **3f − a + c**
24. **c + 2d + 3e**

In each of the following, find **x** in component form.

25. **x + b = e**
26. **x + d = a**
27. **c + x = f**

28. **x − g = h**
29. **2x + b = g**
30. **2x − 3d = g**

31. **2b = d − x**
32. **f − g = e − x**
33. **2x + b = x + e**

34. **3x − b = x + h**
35. **a + b + x = b + a**
36. **2x + e = 0** (zero vector)

37. **a)** Draw and label each of the following vectors on graph paper.

$$\mathbf{l} = \begin{pmatrix} -3 \\ -3 \end{pmatrix}; \mathbf{m} = \begin{pmatrix} 2 \\ 0 \end{pmatrix}; \mathbf{n} = \begin{pmatrix} 3 \\ 2 \end{pmatrix}; \mathbf{p} = \begin{pmatrix} 1 \\ -2 \end{pmatrix}; \mathbf{q} = \begin{pmatrix} 3 \\ 0 \end{pmatrix};$$

$$\mathbf{r} = \begin{pmatrix} 6 \\ 4 \end{pmatrix}; \mathbf{s} = \begin{pmatrix} 2 \\ 2 \end{pmatrix}; \mathbf{t} = \begin{pmatrix} 2 \\ -4 \end{pmatrix}; \mathbf{u} = \begin{pmatrix} -1 \\ -3 \end{pmatrix}; \mathbf{v} = \begin{pmatrix} 0 \\ 3 \end{pmatrix}$$

b) Find four pairs of parallel vectors amongst the ten vectors.

38. State whether 'true' or 'false'.

a) $\begin{pmatrix} 3 \\ -1 \end{pmatrix}$ is parallel to $\begin{pmatrix} 9 \\ -3 \end{pmatrix}$

b) $\begin{pmatrix} -2 \\ 0 \end{pmatrix}$ is parallel to $\begin{pmatrix} 4 \\ 0 \end{pmatrix}$

c) $\begin{pmatrix} -1 \\ 1 \end{pmatrix}$ is parallel to $\begin{pmatrix} 1 \\ -1 \end{pmatrix}$

d) $\begin{pmatrix} 5 \\ -15 \end{pmatrix} = 5\begin{pmatrix} 1 \\ -3 \end{pmatrix}$

e) $\begin{pmatrix} 4 \\ 0 \end{pmatrix}$ is parallel to $\begin{pmatrix} 0 \\ 6 \end{pmatrix}$

f) $\begin{pmatrix} 3 \\ -1 \end{pmatrix} + \begin{pmatrix} -4 \\ -2 \end{pmatrix} = \begin{pmatrix} -1 \\ 1 \end{pmatrix}$

39. **a)** Draw a diagram to illustrate the vector addition $\overrightarrow{AB} + \overrightarrow{CD}$.

b) Draw a diagram to illustrate $\overrightarrow{AB} - \overrightarrow{CD}$.

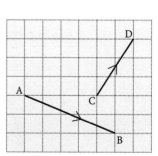

40. Draw separate diagrams to illustrate the following.

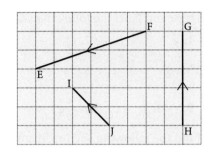

a) $\overrightarrow{FE} + \overrightarrow{JI}$

b) $\overrightarrow{HG} + \overrightarrow{FE}$

c) $\overrightarrow{JI} - \overrightarrow{FE}$

d) $\overrightarrow{HG} + \overrightarrow{JI}$

Exercise 8

1. If D has coordinates (7, 2) and E has coordinates (9, 0), find the column vector for $\overrightarrow{DE}$.

2. Find the column vector $\overrightarrow{XY}$ where X and Y have coordinates (−1, 4) and (5, 2) respectively.

3. In the diagram $\overrightarrow{AB}$ represents the vector $\begin{pmatrix} 5 \\ 2 \end{pmatrix}$ and $\overrightarrow{BC}$ represents the vector $\begin{pmatrix} 0 \\ 3 \end{pmatrix}$.

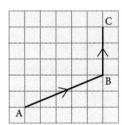

a) Copy the diagram and mark point D such that ABCD is a parallelogram.

b) Write $\overrightarrow{AD}$ and $\overrightarrow{CA}$ as column vectors.

4. a) On squared paper draw $\overrightarrow{AB} = \begin{pmatrix} 3 \\ -2 \end{pmatrix}$ and $\overrightarrow{BC} = \begin{pmatrix} 4 \\ 2 \end{pmatrix}$ and mark point D such that ABCD is a parallelogram.

b) Write $\overrightarrow{AD}$ and $\overrightarrow{CA}$ as column vectors.

5. Copy the diagram in which $\overrightarrow{OA} = \begin{pmatrix} 5 \\ 2 \end{pmatrix}$ and $\overrightarrow{OB} = \begin{pmatrix} 2 \\ 5 \end{pmatrix}$.

M is the midpoint of AB. Express the following as column vectors:

a) $\overrightarrow{BA}$ b) $\overrightarrow{BM}$ c) $\overrightarrow{OM}$ (use $\overrightarrow{OM} = \overrightarrow{OB} + \overrightarrow{BM}$)

Hence write down the coordinates of M.

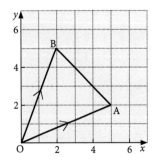

6. On a graph with origin at O, draw $\overrightarrow{OA} = \begin{pmatrix} 5 \\ -1 \end{pmatrix}$ and

$\overrightarrow{OB} = \begin{pmatrix} 6 \\ -7 \end{pmatrix}$. Given that M is the midpoint of AB express

the following as column vectors:

a) $\overrightarrow{BA}$ b) $\overrightarrow{BM}$ c) $\overrightarrow{OM}$

Hence write down the coordinates of M.

7. On a graph with origin at O, draw $\overrightarrow{OA} = \begin{pmatrix} -2 \\ 5 \end{pmatrix}$,

$\overrightarrow{OB} = \begin{pmatrix} 4 \\ 2 \end{pmatrix}$ and $\overrightarrow{OC} = \begin{pmatrix} -2 \\ -4 \end{pmatrix}$.

a) Given that M divides AB such that AM:MB = 2:1, express
    the following as column vectors:

   i) $\overrightarrow{BA}$ ii) $\overrightarrow{BM}$ iii) $\overrightarrow{OM}$

b) Given that N divides AC such that AN:NC = 1:2, express
    the following as column vectors:

   i) $\overrightarrow{AC}$ ii) $\overrightarrow{AN}$ iii) $\overrightarrow{ON}$

8. In square ABCD, side AB has column vector $\begin{pmatrix} 2 \\ 1 \end{pmatrix}$. Find two
possible column vectors for $\overrightarrow{BC}$.

9. Rectangle KLMN has an area of 10 square units and $\overrightarrow{KL}$ has

column vector $\begin{pmatrix} 5 \\ 0 \end{pmatrix}$. Find two possible column vectors for $\overrightarrow{LM}$.

10. In the diagram, ABCD is a trapezium in which $\overrightarrow{DC} = 2\overrightarrow{AB}$.
If $\overrightarrow{AB} = \mathbf{p}$ and $\overrightarrow{AD} = \mathbf{q}$ express in terms of $\mathbf{p}$ and $\mathbf{q}$:

a) $\overrightarrow{BD}$ b) $\overrightarrow{AC}$ c) $\overrightarrow{BC}$

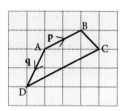

11. Find the image of the vector $\begin{pmatrix} 1 \\ 3 \end{pmatrix}$ after reflection in the
following lines:

a) $y = 0$ b) $x = 0$ c) $y = x$ d) $y = -x$

Modulus of a vector

The modulus of a vector **a** is written |**a**| and represents the length
(or magnitude) of the vector.

In the diagram, $\mathbf{a} = \begin{pmatrix} 5 \\ 3 \end{pmatrix}$.

By Pythagoras' theorem, $|\mathbf{a}| = \sqrt{(5^2 + 3^2)}$

$$|\mathbf{a}| = \sqrt{34} \text{ units}$$

In general if $\mathbf{x} = \begin{pmatrix} m \\ n \end{pmatrix}, |\mathbf{x}| = \sqrt{(m^2 + n^2)}$

Exercise 9

Questions **1** to **12** refer to the following vectors:

$$\mathbf{a} = \begin{pmatrix} 3 \\ 4 \end{pmatrix} \qquad \mathbf{b} = \begin{pmatrix} 4 \\ 1 \end{pmatrix} \qquad \mathbf{c} = \begin{pmatrix} 5 \\ 12 \end{pmatrix} \qquad \mathbf{d} = \begin{pmatrix} -3 \\ 0 \end{pmatrix}$$

$$\mathbf{e} = \begin{pmatrix} -4 \\ -3 \end{pmatrix} \qquad \mathbf{f} = \begin{pmatrix} -3 \\ 6 \end{pmatrix}$$

Find the following, leaving the answer in square root form where necessary.

1. $|\mathbf{a}|$
2. $|\mathbf{b}|$
3. $|\mathbf{c}|$
4. $|\mathbf{d}|$
5. $|\mathbf{e}|$
6. $|\mathbf{f}|$
7. $|\mathbf{a} + \mathbf{b}|$
8. $|\mathbf{c} - \mathbf{d}|$
9. $|2\mathbf{e}|$
10. $|\mathbf{f} + 2\mathbf{b}|$

11. **a)** Find $|\mathbf{a} + \mathbf{c}|$. **b)** Is $|\mathbf{a} + \mathbf{c}|$ equal to $|\mathbf{a}| + |\mathbf{c}|$?

12. **a)** Find $|\mathbf{c} + \mathbf{d}|$. **b)** Is $|\mathbf{c} + \mathbf{d}|$ equal to $|\mathbf{c}| + |\mathbf{d}|$?

13. If $\overrightarrow{AB} = \begin{pmatrix} 3 \\ -1 \end{pmatrix}$ and $\overrightarrow{BC} = \begin{pmatrix} 2 \\ 3 \end{pmatrix}$, find $|\overrightarrow{AC}|$.

14. If $\overrightarrow{PQ} = \begin{pmatrix} 5 \\ -2 \end{pmatrix}$ and $\overrightarrow{QR} = \begin{pmatrix} 0 \\ 1 \end{pmatrix}$, find $|\overrightarrow{PR}|$.

15. If $\overrightarrow{WX} = \begin{pmatrix} 1 \\ 3 \end{pmatrix}$, $\overrightarrow{XY} = \begin{pmatrix} -2 \\ 1 \end{pmatrix}$ and $\overrightarrow{YZ} = \begin{pmatrix} 2 \\ -1 \end{pmatrix}$, find $|\overrightarrow{WZ}|$.

16. Given that $\overrightarrow{OP} = \begin{pmatrix} 0 \\ 5 \end{pmatrix}$ and $\overrightarrow{OQ} = \begin{pmatrix} n \\ 3 \end{pmatrix}$, find:

   a) $|\overrightarrow{OP}|$ **b)** a value for n if $|\overrightarrow{OP}| = |\overrightarrow{OQ}|$

17. Given that $\overrightarrow{OA} = \begin{pmatrix} 5 \\ 12 \end{pmatrix}$ and $\overrightarrow{OB} = \begin{pmatrix} 0 \\ m \end{pmatrix}$, find:

   a) $|\overrightarrow{OA}|$ **b)** a value for m if $|\overrightarrow{OA}| = |\overrightarrow{OB}|$

18. Given that $\overrightarrow{LM} = \begin{pmatrix} -3 \\ 4 \end{pmatrix}$ and $\overrightarrow{MN} = \begin{pmatrix} -15 \\ p \end{pmatrix}$, find:

   a) $|\overrightarrow{LM}|$ **b)** a value for p if $|\overrightarrow{MN}| = 3|\overrightarrow{LM}|$

19. **a** and **b** are two vectors and $|\mathbf{a}| = 3$.

   Find the value of $|\mathbf{a} + \mathbf{b}|$ when:

   a) $\mathbf{b} = 2\mathbf{a}$

   b) $\mathbf{b} = -3\mathbf{a}$

   c) **b** is perpendicular to **a** and $|\mathbf{b}| = 4$

20. **r** and **s** are two vectors and $|\mathbf{r}| = 5$.

Find the value of $|\mathbf{r} + \mathbf{s}|$ when:

a) $\mathbf{s} = 5\mathbf{r}$

b) $\mathbf{s} = -2\mathbf{r}$

c) **r** is perpendicular to **s** and $|\mathbf{s}| = 5$

d) **s** is perpendicular to $(\mathbf{r} + \mathbf{s})$ and $|\mathbf{s}| = 3$

8.5 Vector geometry

Example

In the diagram, $\overrightarrow{OD} = 2\overrightarrow{OA}$, $\overrightarrow{OE} = 4\overrightarrow{OB}$, $\overrightarrow{OA} = \mathbf{a}$ and $\overrightarrow{OB} = \mathbf{b}$.

a) Express $\overrightarrow{OD}$ and $\overrightarrow{OE}$ in terms of **a** and **b** respectively.

b) Express $\overrightarrow{BA}$ in terms of **a** and **b**.

c) Express $\overrightarrow{ED}$ in terms of **a** and **b**.

d) Given that $\overrightarrow{BC} = 3\overrightarrow{BA}$, express $\overrightarrow{OC}$ in terms of **a** and **b**.

e) Express $\overrightarrow{EC}$ in terms of **a** and **b**.

f) Hence show that the points E, D and C lie on a straight line.

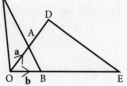

....

a) $\overrightarrow{OD} = 2\mathbf{a}$

   $\overrightarrow{OE} = 4\mathbf{b}$

b) $\overrightarrow{BA} = -\mathbf{b} + \mathbf{a}$

c) $\overrightarrow{ED} = -4\mathbf{b} + 2\mathbf{a}$

d) $\overrightarrow{OC} = \overrightarrow{OB} + \overrightarrow{BC}$

   $\overrightarrow{OC} = \mathbf{b} + 3(-\mathbf{b} + \mathbf{a})$

   $\overrightarrow{OC} = -2\mathbf{b} + 3\mathbf{a}$

e) $\overrightarrow{EC} = \overrightarrow{EO} + \overrightarrow{OC}$

   $\overrightarrow{EC} = -4\mathbf{b} + (-2\mathbf{b} + 3\mathbf{a})$

   $\overrightarrow{EC} = -6\mathbf{b} + 3\mathbf{a}$

> $\overrightarrow{OD}, \overrightarrow{OC}$ and $\overrightarrow{OB}$ are called **position vectors**. The position vector $\overrightarrow{OB}$ gives the position of B relative to the origin, O.

f) Using the results for $\overrightarrow{ED}$ and $\overrightarrow{EC}$, we see that $\overrightarrow{EC} = \frac{3}{2}\overrightarrow{ED}$.

Since $\overrightarrow{EC}$ and $\overrightarrow{ED}$ are parallel vectors which both pass through the point E, the points E, D and C must lie on a straight line.

Exercise 10

1. $\overrightarrow{OD} = 2\overrightarrow{OA}$,

   $\overrightarrow{OE} = 3\overrightarrow{OB}$,

   $\overrightarrow{OA} = \mathbf{a}$ and

   $\overrightarrow{OB} = \mathbf{b}$.

   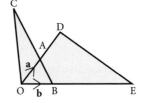

   a) Express $\overrightarrow{OD}$ and $\overrightarrow{OE}$ in terms of $\mathbf{a}$ and $\mathbf{b}$ respectively.

   b) Express $\overrightarrow{BA}$ in terms of $\mathbf{a}$ and $\mathbf{b}$.

   c) Express $\overrightarrow{ED}$ in terms of $\mathbf{a}$ and $\mathbf{b}$.

   d) Given that $\overrightarrow{BC} = 4\overrightarrow{BA}$, express $\overrightarrow{OC}$ in terms of $\mathbf{a}$ and $\mathbf{b}$.

   e) Express $\overrightarrow{EC}$ in terms of $\mathbf{a}$ and $\mathbf{b}$.

   f) Use the results for $\overrightarrow{ED}$ and $\overrightarrow{EC}$ to show that points E, D and C lie on a straight line.

2. $\overrightarrow{OY} = 2\overrightarrow{OB}$,

   $\overrightarrow{OX} = \frac{5}{2}\overrightarrow{OA}$,

   $\overrightarrow{OA} = \mathbf{a}$ and

   $\overrightarrow{OB} = \mathbf{b}$.

   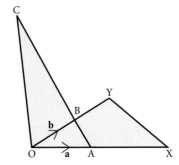

   a) Express $\overrightarrow{OY}$ and $\overrightarrow{OX}$ in terms of $\mathbf{b}$ and $\mathbf{a}$ respectively.

   b) Express $\overrightarrow{AB}$ in terms of $\mathbf{a}$ and $\mathbf{b}$.

   c) Express $\overrightarrow{XY}$ in terms of $\mathbf{a}$ and $\mathbf{b}$.

   d) Given that $\overrightarrow{AC} = 6\overrightarrow{AB}$, express $\overrightarrow{OC}$ in terms of $\mathbf{a}$ and $\mathbf{b}$.

   e) Express $\overrightarrow{XC}$ in terms of $\mathbf{a}$ and $\mathbf{b}$.

   f) Use the results for $\overrightarrow{XY}$ and $\overrightarrow{XC}$ to show that points X, Y and C lie on a straight line.

3. $\overrightarrow{OA} = \mathbf{a}$,

   $\overrightarrow{OB} = \mathbf{b}$,

   $\overrightarrow{AQ} = \frac{1}{2}\mathbf{b}$,

   $\overrightarrow{BR} = \mathbf{b}$ and

   $\overrightarrow{AP} = 2\overrightarrow{BA}$.

   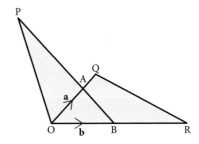

   a) Express $\overrightarrow{BA}$ and $\overrightarrow{BP}$ in terms of $\mathbf{a}$ and $\mathbf{b}$.

   b) Express $\overrightarrow{RQ}$ in terms of $\mathbf{a}$ and $\mathbf{b}$.

   c) Express $\overrightarrow{QA}$ and $\overrightarrow{QP}$ in terms of $\mathbf{a}$ and $\mathbf{b}$.

   d) Using the vectors for $\overrightarrow{RQ}$ and $\overrightarrow{QP}$, show that R, Q and P lie on a straight line.

4. In the diagram, $\overrightarrow{OA}$ and $\overrightarrow{OB}$, M is the midpoint of OA and P lies on AB such that $\overrightarrow{AP} = \frac{2}{3}\overrightarrow{AB}$.

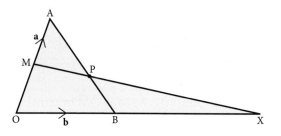

a) Express $\overrightarrow{AB}$ and $\overrightarrow{AP}$ in terms of **a** and **b**.

b) Express $\overrightarrow{MA}$ and $\overrightarrow{MP}$ in terms of **a** and **b**.

c) If X lies on OB produced such that OB = BX, express $\overrightarrow{MX}$ in terms of **a** and **b**.

d) Show that MPX is a straight line.

5. $\overrightarrow{OP} = \mathbf{a}$,

$\overrightarrow{OA} = 3\mathbf{a}$,

$\overrightarrow{OB} = \mathbf{b}$ and

M is the midpoint of AB.

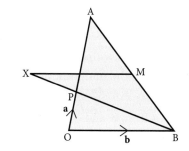

a) Express $\overrightarrow{BP}$ and $\overrightarrow{AB}$ in terms of **a** and **b**.

b) Express $\overrightarrow{MB}$ in terms of **a** and **b**.

c) If X lies on BP produced so that $\overrightarrow{BX} = k\overrightarrow{BP}$, express $\overrightarrow{MX}$ in terms of **a**, **b** and k.

d) Find the value of k if MX is parallel to BO.

6. AC is parallel to OB,

$\overrightarrow{AX} = \frac{1}{4}\overrightarrow{AB}$,

$\overrightarrow{OA} = \mathbf{a}$,

$\overrightarrow{OB} = \mathbf{b}$ and

$\overrightarrow{AC} = m\mathbf{b}$.

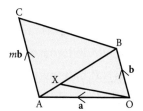

a) Express $\overrightarrow{AB}$ in terms of **a** and **b**.

b) Express $\overrightarrow{AX}$ in terms of **a** and **b**.

c) Express $\overrightarrow{BC}$ in terms of **a**, **b** and m.

d) Given that OX is parallel to BC, find the value of m.

7. CY is parallel to OD,

$\overrightarrow{CX} = \frac{1}{5}\overrightarrow{CD}$,

$\overrightarrow{OC} = \mathbf{c}$,

$\overrightarrow{OD} = \mathbf{d}$ and

$\overrightarrow{CY} = n\mathbf{d}$.

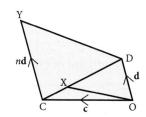

a) Express $\overrightarrow{CD}$ in terms of **c** and **d**.

b) Express $\overrightarrow{CX}$ in terms of **c** and **d**.

c) Express $\overrightarrow{OX}$ in terms of **c** and **d**.

d) Express $\overrightarrow{DY}$ in terms of **c**, **d** and n.

e) Given that OX is parallel to DY, find the value of n.

8. M is the midpoint of AB,

   N is the midpoint of OB,

   $\overrightarrow{OA} = \mathbf{a}$ and

   $\overrightarrow{OB} = \mathbf{b}.$

   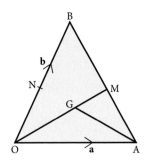

   a) Express $\overrightarrow{AB}$, $\overrightarrow{AM}$ and $\overrightarrow{OM}$ in terms of $\mathbf{a}$ and $\mathbf{b}$.

   b) Given that G lies on OM such that $OG : GM = 2 : 1$, express $\overrightarrow{OG}$ in terms of $\mathbf{a}$ and $\mathbf{b}$.

   c) Express $\overrightarrow{AG}$ in terms of $\mathbf{a}$ and $\mathbf{b}$.

   d) Express $\overrightarrow{AN}$ in terms of $\mathbf{a}$ and $\mathbf{b}$.

   e) Show that $\overrightarrow{AG} = m\overrightarrow{AN}$ and find the value of m.

9. M is the midpoint of AC and N is the midpoint of OB,

   $\overrightarrow{OA} = \mathbf{a},$

   $\overrightarrow{OB} = \mathbf{b}$ and

   $\overrightarrow{OC} = \mathbf{c}.$

   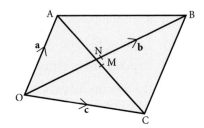

   a) Express $\overrightarrow{AB}$ in terms of $\mathbf{a}$ and $\mathbf{b}$.

   b) Express $\overrightarrow{ON}$ in terms of $\mathbf{b}$.

   c) Express $\overrightarrow{AC}$ in terms of $\mathbf{a}$ and $\mathbf{c}$.

   d) Express $\overrightarrow{AM}$ in terms of $\mathbf{a}$ and $\mathbf{c}$.

   e) Express $\overrightarrow{OM}$ in terms of $\mathbf{a}$ and $\mathbf{c}$.

   f) Express $\overrightarrow{NM}$ in terms of $\mathbf{a}$, $\mathbf{b}$ and $\mathbf{c}$.

   g) If N and M coincide, write down an equation connecting $\mathbf{a}$, $\mathbf{b}$ and $\mathbf{c}$.

10. $\overrightarrow{OA} = \mathbf{a}$ and

    $\overrightarrow{OB} = \mathbf{b}.$

    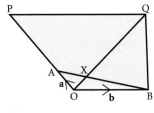

    a) Express $\overrightarrow{BA}$ in terms of $\mathbf{a}$ and $\mathbf{b}$.

    b) Given that $\overrightarrow{BX} = m\overrightarrow{BA}$, show that $\overrightarrow{OX} = m\mathbf{a} + (1 - m)\mathbf{b}$.

    c) Given that $OP = 4\mathbf{a}$ and $\overrightarrow{PQ} = 2\mathbf{b}$, express $\overrightarrow{OQ}$ in terms of $\mathbf{a}$ and $\mathbf{b}$.

    d) Given that $\overrightarrow{OX} = n\overrightarrow{OQ}$ use the results for $\overrightarrow{OX}$ and $\overrightarrow{OQ}$ to find the values of m and n.

11. X is the midpoint of OD, Y lies on CD such that

    $\overrightarrow{CY} = \frac{1}{4}\overrightarrow{CD},$

    $\overrightarrow{OC} = \mathbf{c}$ and

    $\overrightarrow{OD} = \mathbf{d}.$

    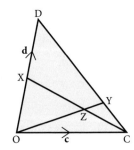

    a) Express $\overrightarrow{CD}$, $\overrightarrow{CY}$ and $\overrightarrow{OY}$ in terms of $\mathbf{c}$ and $\mathbf{d}$.

    b) Express $\overrightarrow{CX}$ in terms of $\mathbf{c}$ and $\mathbf{d}$.

    c) Given that $\overrightarrow{CZ} = h\overrightarrow{CX}$, express $\overrightarrow{OZ}$ in terms of $\mathbf{c}$, $\mathbf{d}$ and h.

    d) If $\overrightarrow{OZ} = k\overrightarrow{OY}$, form an equation and hence find the values of h and k.

8.6 Functions

The idea of a function is used in almost every branch of mathematics.

The two common notations used are:

a) $f(x) = x + 4$ **b)** $f : x \mapsto x^2 + 4$

We may interpret b) as follows: 'function f such that x is mapped onto $x^2 + 4$'.

Example

If $f(x) = 3x - 1$ and $g(x) = 1 - x^2$ find:

a) $f(2)$ **b)** $f(-2)$ **c)** $g(0)$ **d)** $g(3)$ **e)** x if $f(x) = 1$

....

a) $f(2) = 5$ **b)** $f(-2) = -7$ **c)** $g(0) = 1$ **d)** $g(3) = -8$ **e)** If $\quad f(x) = 1$

$$\text{Then} \quad 3x - 1 = 1$$
$$3x = 2$$
$$x = \frac{2}{3}$$

Flow diagrams

The function f in the example consisted of two simpler functions as illustrated by a flow diagram.

$$x \longrightarrow \boxed{\text{multiply by 3}} \xrightarrow{3x} \boxed{\text{subtract 1}} \xrightarrow{3x - 1}$$

It is obviously important to 'multiply by 3' and 'subtract 1' in the correct order.

Example

Draw flow diagrams for the functions:

a) $f : x \mapsto (2x + 5)^2$,   **b)** $g(x) = \dfrac{5 - 7x}{3}$

....

a) $x \rightarrow \boxed{\text{multiply by 2}} \xrightarrow{2x} \boxed{\text{add 5}} \xrightarrow{2x + 5} \boxed{\text{square}} \xrightarrow{(2x + 5)^2}$

b) $x \rightarrow \boxed{\text{multiply by (-7)}} \xrightarrow{-7x} \boxed{\text{add 5}} \xrightarrow{5 - 7x} \boxed{\text{divide by 3}} \xrightarrow{\frac{5 - 7x}{3}}$

Exercise 11

1. Given the functions $h : x \mapsto x^2 + 1$ and $g : x \mapsto 10x + 1$. Find:

     a) $h(2), h(-3), h(0)$ **b)** $g(2), g(10), g(-3)$

In questions **2** to **15**, draw a flow diagram for each function.

   2. $f : x \mapsto 5x + 4$ **3.** $f : x \mapsto 3(x - 4)$ **4.** $f : x \mapsto (2x + 7)^2$

   5. $f : x \mapsto \left(\dfrac{9 + 5x}{4} \right)$ **6.** $f : x \mapsto \dfrac{4 - 3x}{5}$ **7.** $f : x \mapsto 2x^2 + 1$

8. $f: x \mapsto \dfrac{3x^2}{2} + 5$ **9.** $f: x \mapsto \sqrt{(4x - 5)}$ **10.** $f: x \mapsto 4\sqrt{(x^2 + 10)}$

11. $f: x \mapsto (7 - 3x)^2$ **12.** $f: x \mapsto 4(3x + 1)^2 + 5$ **13.** $f: x \mapsto 5 - x^2$

14. $f: x \mapsto \dfrac{10\sqrt{(x^2 + 1)} + 6}{4}$ **15.** $f: x \mapsto \left(\dfrac{x^3}{4} + 1\right)^2 - 6$

For questions **16**, **17** and **18**, the functions f, g and h are defined as follows:

$f: x \mapsto 1 - 2x$

$g: x \mapsto \dfrac{x^3}{10}$

$h: x \mapsto \dfrac{12}{x}$

16. Find:

    a) $f(5), f(-5), f\left(\frac{1}{4}\right)$ **b)** $g(2), g(-3), g\left(\frac{1}{2}\right)$ **c)** $h(3), h(10), h\left(\frac{1}{3}\right)$

17. Find:

    a) x if $f(x) = 1$ **b)** x if $f(x) = -11$ **c)** x if $h(x) = 1$

18. Find:

    a) y if $g(y) = 100$ **b)** z if $h(z) = 24$ **c)** w if $g(w) = 0.8$

For questions **19** and **20**, the functions k, l and m are defined as follows:

$k: x \mapsto \dfrac{2x^2}{3}$

$l: x \mapsto \sqrt{(y - 1)(y - 2)}$

$m: x \mapsto 10 - x^2$

19. Find:

    a) $k(3), k(6), k(-3)$ **b)** $l(2), l(0), l(4)$ **c)** $m(4), m(-2), m\left(\frac{1}{2}\right)$

20. Find:

    a) x if $k(x) = 6$ **b)** x if $m(x) = 1$ **c)** y if $k(y) = 2\dfrac{2}{3}$

    d) p if $m(p) = -26$

21. $f(x)$ is defined as the product of the digits of x,

    e.g. $f(12) = 1 \times 2 = 2$

    a) Find: **i)** $f(25)$ **ii)** $f(713)$

    b) If x is an integer with three digits, find:

        i) x such that $f(x) = 1$

        ii) the largest x such that $f(x) = 4$

        iii) the largest x such that $f(x) = 0$

        iv) the smallest x such that $f(x) = 2$

22. $g(x)$ is defined as the sum of the prime factors of x,
e.g. $g(12) = 2 + 3 = 5$. Find:

a) $g(10)$ b) $g(21)$ c) $g(36)$

d) $g(99)$ e) $g(100)$ f) $g(1000)$

23. $h(x)$ is defined as the number of letters in the English word
describing the number x, e.g.
$h(1) = 3$. Find:

a) $h(2)$ b) $h(11)$ c) $h(18)$

d) the largest value of x for which $h(x) = 3$

24. If $f: x \mapsto$ next prime number greater than x, find:

a) $f(7)$ b) $f(14)$ c) $f[f(3)]$

25. If $g: x \to 2^x + 1$, find:

a) $g(2)$ b) $g(4)$ c) $g(-1)$

d) the value of x if $g(x) = 9$

26. The function f is defined as f: $x \to ax + b$ where a and b are constants.
If $f(1) = 8$ and $f(4) = 17$, find the values of a and b.

27. The function g is defined as $g(x) = ax^2 + b$ where a and b are constants.
If $g(2) = 3$ and $g(-3) = 13$, find the values of a and b.

28. Functions h and k are defined as follows:
$h: x \mapsto x^2 + 1$, $k: x \mapsto ax + b$, where a and b are constants.
If $h(0) = k(0)$ and $k(2) = 15$, find the values of a and b.

Composite functions

The function $f(x) = 3x + 2$ is itself a composite function, consisting of
two simpler functions: 'multiply by 3' and 'add 2'.

If $f(x) = 3x + 2$ and $g(x) = x^2$ then $f[g(x)]$ is a composite function
where g is performed first and then f is performed on the result of g.
$f[g(x)]$ is usually abbreviated to fg(x).

The function fg may be found using a flow diagram.

Thus

$$x \xrightarrow{} \boxed{\text{square}} \xrightarrow{x^2} \boxed{\text{multiply by 3}} \xrightarrow{3x^2} \boxed{\text{add 2}} \xrightarrow{3x^2 + 2}$$
$$ g f$$

$fg(x) = 3x^2 + 2$

Inverse functions

If a function f maps a number n onto m, then the inverse function f^{-1}
maps m onto n. The inverse of a given function is found using a flow diagram.

Example

Method 1

Find the inverse of f where $f: x \to \dfrac{5x-2}{3}$.

a) Draw a flow diagram for f.

$$x \to \boxed{\text{multiply by 5}} \xrightarrow{5x} \boxed{\text{subtract 2}} \xrightarrow{5x-2} \boxed{\text{divide by 3}} \to \frac{5x-2}{3}$$

b) Draw a new flow diagram with each operation replaced by its inverse. Start with x on the right.

$$\frac{3x+2}{5} \leftarrow \boxed{\text{divide by 5}} \xleftarrow{3x+2} \boxed{\text{add 2}} \xleftarrow{3x} \boxed{\text{multiply by 3}} \leftarrow x$$

Thus the inverse of f is given by

$$f^{-1}: x \mapsto \frac{3x+2}{5} \text{ or } f^{-1}(x) = \frac{3x+2}{5}$$

Method 2

Again find the inverse of f where $f: x \to \dfrac{5x-2}{3}$.

Let $y = \dfrac{5x-2}{3}$

Rearrange this equation to make x the subject:

$$3y = 5x - 2$$
$$3y + 2 = 5x$$
$$x = \frac{3y+2}{5}$$

For an inverse function we interchange x and y.

So the inverse function is $\dfrac{3x+2}{5}$.

Many people prefer this algebraic method. You should use the method which you find easier.

Exercise 12

For questions **1** and **2**, the functions f, g and h are as follows:

$f: x \mapsto 4x$

$g: x \mapsto x + 5$

$h: x \mapsto x^2$

1. Find the following in the form '$x \mapsto \ldots$'

a) fg	**b)** gf	**c)** hf	**d)** fh
e) gh	**f)** fgh	**g)** hfg	

2. Find:

    a) x if $hg(x) = h(x)$ **b)** x if $fh(x) = gh(x)$

For questions **3, 4** and **5**, the functions f, g and h are as follows:

    $f : x \mapsto 2x$

    $g : x \mapsto x - 3$

    $h : x \mapsto x^2$

3. Find the following in the form '$x \mapsto \dots$'

    a) fg   **b)** gf   **c)** gh

    d) hf   **e)** ghf   **f)** hgf

4. Evaluate:

    a) fg(4)   **b)** gf(7)   **c)** gh(−3)

    d) fgf(2)   **e)** ggg(10)   **f)** hfh(−2)

5. Find:

    a) x if $f(x) = g(x)$ **b)** x if $hg(x) = gh(x)$

    c) x if $gf(x) = 0$ **d)** x if $fg(x) = 4$

For questions **6, 7** and **8**, the functions l, m and n are as follows:

    $l : x \mapsto 2x + 1$

    $m : x \mapsto 3x - 1$

    $n : x \mapsto x^2$

6. Find the following in the form '$x \mapsto \dots$'

    a) lm   **b)** ml   **c)** ln

    d) nm   **e)** lnm   **f)** mln

7. Find:

    a) lm(2)   **b)** nl(1)   **c)** mn(−2)

    d) mm (2)   **e)** nln(2)   **f)** llm(0)

8. Find:

    a) x if $l(x) = m(x)$

    b) two values of x if $nl(x) = nm(x)$

    c) x if $ln(x) = mn(x)$

In questions **9** to **22**, find the inverse of each function in the form '$x \mapsto \dots$'

9. $f : x \mapsto 5x - 2$ **10.** $f : x \mapsto 5(x - 2)$ **11.** $f : x \mapsto 3(2x + 4)$

12. $g : x \mapsto \dfrac{2x + 1}{3}$ **13.** $f : x \mapsto \dfrac{3(x - 1)}{4}$ **14.** $g : x \mapsto 2(3x + 4) - 6$

15. $h : x \mapsto \dfrac{1}{2}(4 + 5x) + 10$ **16.** $k : x \mapsto -7x + 3$ **17.** $j : x \mapsto \dfrac{12 - 5x}{3}$

18. $l: x \mapsto \dfrac{4-x}{3} + 2$

19. $m: x \mapsto \dfrac{\left[\dfrac{(2x-1)}{4}\right] - 3}{5}$

20. $f: x \mapsto \dfrac{3(10-2x)}{7}$

21. $g: x \mapsto \left[\dfrac{\dfrac{x}{4} + 6}{5}\right] + 7$

22. A calculator has the following function buttons:

$$x \mapsto x^2; \ x \mapsto \sqrt{x}; \ x \mapsto \dfrac{1}{x}; \ x \mapsto \log x;$$

$$x \mapsto \ln x; \ x \mapsto \sin x; \ x \mapsto \cos x; \ x \mapsto \tan x; \ x \mapsto x!$$

$x!$ is 'x factorial'
$4! = 4 \times 3 \times 2 \times 1$
$3! = 3 \times 2 \times 1$ etc

Find which button was used for the following input/outputs:

a) $1\,000\,000 \to 1000$

b) $1000 \to 3$

c) $3 \to 6$

d) $0.2 \to 0.04$

e) $10 \to 0.1$

f) $45 \to 1$

g) $0.5 \to 2$

h) $64 \to 8$

i) $60 \to 0.5$

j) $1 \to 0$

k) $135 \to -1$

l) $10 \to 3\,628\,800$

m) $0 \to 1$

n) $30 \to 0.5$

o) $90 \to 0$

p) $0.4 \to 2.5$

q) $4 \to 24$

r) $1\,000\,000 \to 6$

8.7 Simple transformations

Reflection

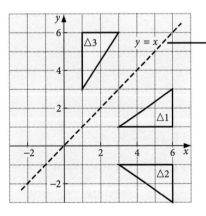

You must describe a mirror line fully.

$\Delta 2$ is the image of $\Delta 1$ after reflection in the x-axis.

$\Delta 3$ is the image of $\Delta 1$ after reflection in the line $y = x$.

Exercise 13

In questions **1** to **6** draw the object and its image after reflection in the broken line.

1.

2.

3.

4.

5.

6.

In questions **7, 8, 9** draw the image of the given shape after reflection in line M₁ and then reflect this new shape in line M₂.

7.

8.

9.

Exercise 14

For each question draw x- and y-axes with values from -8 to 8.

1. a) Draw the triangle ABC at A(6, 8), B(2, 8), C(2, 6). Draw the lines $y = 2$ and $y = x$.

b) Draw the image of $\triangle$ABC after reflection in:

   i) the y-axis. Label it $\triangle 1$.

   ii) the line $y = 2$. Label it $\triangle 2$.

   iii) the line $y = x$. Label it $\triangle 3$.

c) Write down the coordinates of the image of point A in each case.

2. a) Draw the triangle DEF at D(-6, 8), E(-2, 8), F(-2, 6).

   Draw the lines $x = 1$, $y = x$, $y = -x$.

b) Draw the image of $\triangle$DEF after reflection in:

   i) the line $x = 1$. Label it $\triangle 1$.

   ii) the line $y = x$. Label it $\triangle 2$.

   iii) the line $y = -x$. Label it $\triangle 3$.

c) Write down the coordinates of the image of point D in each case.

3. a) Draw the triangle ABC at A(5, 1), B(8, 1), C(8, 3). Draw the lines $x + y = 4$, $y = x - 3$, $x = 2$.

b) Draw the image of $\triangle$ABC after reflection in:

   i) the line $x + y = 4$. Label it $\triangle 1$.

   ii) the line $y = x - 3$. Label it $\triangle 2$.

   iii) the line $x = 2$. Label it $\triangle 3$.

c) Write down the coordinates of the image of point A in each case.

4. a) Draw and label the following triangles:

   $\triangle 1$: (3, 3), (3, 6), (1, 6)

   $\triangle 2$: (3, -1), (3, -4), (1, -4)

   $\triangle 3$: (3, 3), (6, 3), (6, 1)

   $\triangle 4$: (-6, -1), (-6, -3), (-3, -3)

   $\triangle 5$: (-6, 5), (-6, 7), (-3, 7)

b) Find the equation of the mirror line for the reflection:

   i) $\triangle 1$ onto $\triangle 2$

   ii) $\triangle 1$ onto $\triangle 3$

   iii) $\triangle 1$ onto $\triangle 4$

   iv) $\triangle 4$ onto $\triangle 5$

5. **a)** Draw Δ1 at (3, 1), (7, 1), (7, 3).

   b) Reflect Δ1 in the line $y = x$ onto Δ2.

   c) Reflect Δ2 in the x-axis onto Δ3.

   d) Reflect Δ3 in the line $y = -x$ onto Δ4.

   e) Reflect Δ4 in the line $x = 2$ onto Δ5.

   f) Write down the coordinates of Δ5.

6. **a)** Draw Δ1 at (2, 6), (2, 8), (6, 6).

   b) Reflect Δ1 in the line $x + y = 6$ onto Δ2.

   c) Reflect Δ2 in the line $x = 3$ onto Δ3.

   d) Reflect Δ3 in the line $x + y = 6$ onto Δ4.

   e) Reflect Δ4 in the line $y = x - 8$ onto Δ5.

   f) Write down the coordinates of Δ5.

Rotation

Example

The letter L has been rotated through 90° clockwise about the centre O. The angle, direction, and centre are needed to fully describe a rotation.

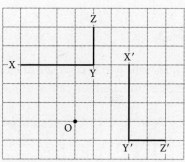

We say that the object *maps* onto the image. Here,

    X maps onto X′

    Y maps onto Y′

    Z maps onto Z′

In this work, a clockwise rotation is *negative* and an anticlockwise rotation is *positive*: in this example, the letter L has been rotated through −90°. The angle, the direction, and the centre of rotation can be found using tracing paper and a sharp pencil placed where you think the centre of rotation is.

For more accurate work, draw the perpendicular bisector of the line joining two corresponding points, e.g. Y and Y′. Repeat for another pair of corresponding points. The centre of rotation is at the intersection of the two perpendicular bisectors.

Exercise 15

In questions **1** to **4** draw the object and its image under the rotation given.
Take O as the centre of rotation in each case.

1.

90° clockwise

2.

90° anticlockwise

3.

180°

4.

90° clockwise

In questions **5** to **8**, copy the diagram on squared paper and find the angle, the direction, and the centre of the rotation.

5.

6.

7.

8.

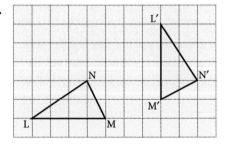

Exercise 16

For all questions draw *x*- and *y*-axes for values from −8 to + 8.

1. a) Draw the object triangle ABC at A(1, 3), B(1, 6), C(3, 6), rotate ABC through 90° clockwise about (0, 0), mark A′B′C′.

b) Draw the object triangle DEF at D(3, 3), E(6, 3), F(6, 1), rotate DEF through 90° clockwise about (0, 0), mark D′E′F′.

c) Draw the object triangle PQR at P(−4, 7), Q(−4, 5), R(− 1, 5), rotate PQR through 90° anticlockwise about (0, 0), mark P′Q′R′.

2. a) Draw Δ1 at (1, 4), (1, 7), (3, 7).

b) Draw the images of Δ1 under the following rotations:

  i) 90° clockwise, centre (0, 0). Label it Δ2.

  ii) 180°, centre (0, 0). Label it Δ3.

  iii) 90° anticlockwise, centre (0, 0). Label it Δ4.

3. a) Draw triangle PQR at P(1, 2), Q(3, 5), R(6, 2).

b) Find the image of PQR under the following rotations:

  i) 90° anticlockwise, centre (0, 0); label the image P′Q′R′

  ii) 90° clockwise, centre (−2, 2); label the image P″Q″R″

  iii) 180°, centre (1, 0); label the image P*Q*R*.

c) Write down the coordinates of P′, P″, P*.

4. a) Draw Δ1 at (1, 2), (1, 6), (3, 5).

b) Rotate Δ1 90° clockwise, centre (1, 2) onto Δ2.

c) Rotate Δ2 180°, centre (2, −1) onto Δ3.

d) Rotate Δ3 90° clockwise, centre (2, 3) onto Δ4.

e) Write down the coordinates of Δ4.

5. a) Draw and label the following triangles:

  Δ1: (3, 1), (6, 1), (6, 3)

  Δ2: (−1, 3), (−1, 6), (−3, 6)

  Δ3: (1, 1), (−2, 1), (−2, −1)

  Δ4: (3, −1), (3, −4), (5, −4)

  Δ5: (4, 4), (1, 4), (1, 2)

b) Describe fully the following rotations:

  i) Δ1 onto Δ2

  ii) Δ1 onto Δ3

  iii) Δ1 onto Δ4

  iv) Δ1 onto Δ5

  v) Δ5 onto Δ4

  vi) Δ3 onto Δ2

6. a) Draw Δ1 at (4, 7), (8, 5), (8, 7).

b) Rotate Δ1 90° clockwise, centre (4, 3) onto Δ2.

c) Rotate Δ2 180°, centre (5, −1) onto Δ3.

d) Rotate Δ3 90° anticlockwise, centre (0, −8) onto Δ4.

e) Describe fully the following rotations:

    i) Δ4 onto Δ1

    ii) Δ4 onto Δ2

Translation

The triangle ΔABC below has been transformed onto the triangle A′B′C′ by a *translation*.

Here the translation is 7 squares to the right and 2 squares up the page. The translation can be described by a column vector.

In this case the translation is $\begin{pmatrix} 7 \\ 2 \end{pmatrix}$.

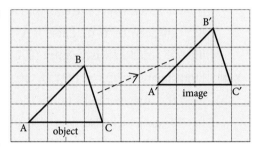

Exercise 17

1. Make a copy of the diagram below and write down the column vector for each of the following translations:

a) D onto A   **b)** B onto F

c) E onto A   **d)** A onto C

e) E onto C   **f)** C onto B

g) F onto E   **h)** B onto C.

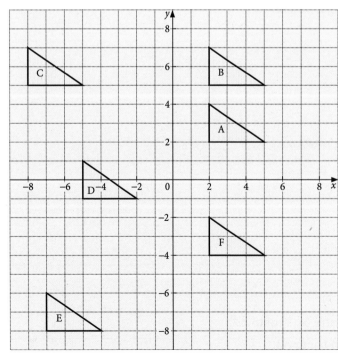

For questions **2** to **11** draw x- and y-axes with values from -8 to 8.
Draw object triangle ABC at A$(-4, -1)$, B$(-4, 1)$, C$(-1, -1)$ and shade it.

Draw the image of ABC under the translations described by the vectors below. For each question, write down the new coordinates of point C.

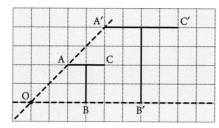

2. $\begin{pmatrix} 6 \\ 3 \end{pmatrix}$

3. $\begin{pmatrix} 6 \\ 7 \end{pmatrix}$

4. $\begin{pmatrix} 9 \\ -4 \end{pmatrix}$

5. $\begin{pmatrix} 1 \\ 7 \end{pmatrix}$

6. $\begin{pmatrix} 5 \\ -6 \end{pmatrix}$

7. $\begin{pmatrix} -2 \\ 5 \end{pmatrix}$

8. $\begin{pmatrix} -2 \\ -4 \end{pmatrix}$

9. $\begin{pmatrix} 0 \\ -7 \end{pmatrix}$

10. $\begin{pmatrix} 3 \\ 1 \end{pmatrix}$ followed by $\begin{pmatrix} 3 \\ 2 \end{pmatrix}$ **11.** $\begin{pmatrix} -2 \\ 0 \end{pmatrix}$ followed by $\begin{pmatrix} 0 \\ 3 \end{pmatrix}$ followed by $\begin{pmatrix} 1 \\ -1 \end{pmatrix}$

Enlargement

In the diagram below, the letter T has been enlarged by a scale factor of 2 using the point O as the centre of the enlargement.

Notice that   OA$'$ = 2 × OA
OB$'$ = 2 × OB

The scale factor and the centre of enlargement are both required to describe an enlargement.

Example 1

Draw the image of triangle ABC under an enlargement scale factor of $\frac{1}{2}$ using O as centre of enlargement.

a) Draw lines through OA, OB and OC.

b) Mark A$'$ so that OA$' = \frac{1}{2}$OA

Mark B$'$ so that OB$' = \frac{1}{2}$OB

Mark C$'$ so that OC$' = \frac{1}{2}$OC.

c) Join A$'$B$'$C$'$ as shown.

Remember always to measure the lengths from O, not from A, B or C.

Example 2

P′Q′R′ is the image of PQR after enlargement with scale factor −2 and centre O. Notice that P′ and P are on opposite sides of point O. Similarly Q′ and Q, R′ and R.

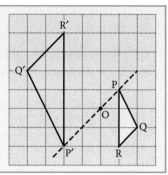

Exercise 18

In questions **1** to **6** copy the diagram and draw an enlargement using the centre O and the scale factor given.

1. Scale factor 2

2. Scale factor 3

3. Scale factor 3

4. Scale factor −2

5. Scale factor −3

6. Scale factor $1\frac{1}{2}$

Answer questions **7** to **19** on graph paper taking x and y from 0 to 15. The vertices of the object are given in coordinate form.

In questions **7** to **10**, enlarge the object with the centre of enlargement and scale factor indicated.

	Object	Centre	Scale factor
7.	(2, 4)(4, 2)(5, 5)	(0, 0)	+ 2
8.	(2, 4)(4, 2)(5, 5)	(1, 2)	+ 2
9.	(1, 1)(4, 2)(2, 3)	(1, 1)	+ 3
10.	(4, 4)(7, 6)(9, 3)	(7, 4)	+ 2

In questions **11** to **14** plot the object and image and find the centre of enlargement and the scale factor.

11. Object A(2, 1), B(5, 1), C(3, 3)
Image A′(2, 1), B′(11, 1), C′(5, 7)

12. Object A(2, 5), B(9, 3), C(5, 9)
Image A′$\left(6\frac{1}{2}, 7\right)$, B′(10, 6), C′(8, 9)

13. Object A(2, 2), B(4, 4), C(2, 6)
Image A′(11, 8), B′(7, 4), C′(11, 0)

14. Object A(0, 6), B(4, 6), C(3, 0)
Image A′(12, 6), B′(8, 6), C′(9, 12)

In questions **15** to **19** enlarge the object using the centre of enlargement and scale factor indicated.

	Object	*Centre*	*Scale factor*
15.	(1, 2), (13, 2), (1, 10)	(0, 0)	$+\frac{1}{2}$
16.	(5, 10), (5, 7), (11, 7)	(2, 1)	$+\frac{1}{3}$
17.	(7, 3), (9, 3), (7, 8)	(5, 5)	-1
18.	(1, 1), (3, 1), (3, 2)	(4, 3)	-2
19.	(9, 2), (14, 2), (14, 6)	(7, 4)	$-\frac{1}{2}$

The next exercise contains questions involving the four basic transformations: reflection, rotation, translation, enlargement.

Exercise 19

1. a) Copy the diagram below.

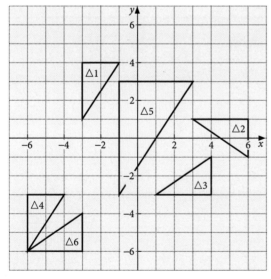

b) Describe fully the following transformations:

  i) Δ1 → Δ2   **ii)** Δ1 → Δ3

  iii) Δ4 → Δ1   **iv)** Δ1 → Δ5

  v) Δ3 → Δ6   **vi)** Δ6 → Δ4

2. Plot and label the following triangles:

Δ1: $(-5, -5), (-1, -5), (-1, -3)$ Δ2: $(1, 7), (1, 3), (3, 3)$

Δ3: $(3, -3), (7, -3), (7, -1)$ Δ4: $(-5, -5), (-5, -1), (-3, -1)$

Δ5: $(1, -6), (3, -6), (3, -5)$ Δ6: $(-3, 3), (-3, 7), (-5, 7)$

Describe fully the following transformations:

a) Δ1 → Δ2   **b)** Δ1 → Δ3

c) Δ1 → Δ4   **d)** Δ1 → Δ5

e) Δ1 → Δ6   **f)** Δ5 → Δ3

g) Δ2 → Δ3

3. Plot and label the following triangles:

Δ1: $(-3, -6), (-3, -2), (-5, -2)$ Δ2: $(-5, -1), (-5, -7), (-8, -1)$

Δ3: $(-2, -1), (2, -1), (2, 1)$ Δ4: $(6, 3), (2, 3), (2, 5)$

Δ5: $(8, 4), (8, 8), (6, 8)$ Δ6: $(-3, 1), (-3, 3), (-4, 3)$

Describe fully the following transformations:

a) Δ1 → Δ2   **b)** Δ1 → Δ3

c) Δ1 → Δ4   **d)** Δ1 → Δ5

e) Δ1 → Δ6   **f)** Δ3 → Δ5

g) Δ6 → Δ2

8.8 Combined transformations

It is convenient to denote transformations by a symbol.

Let **A** denote 'reflection in line $x = 3$' and

B denote 'translation $\begin{pmatrix} 2 \\ 1 \end{pmatrix}$'.

Perform **A** on Δ1.

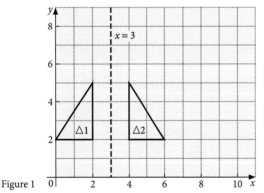

Figure 1

Δ2 is the image of Δ1 under the reflection in $x = 3$

     i.e. $\mathbf{A}(Δ1) = Δ2$

$A(\Delta 1)$ means 'perform the transformation A on triangle $\Delta 1$'
Perform B on $\Delta 2$.

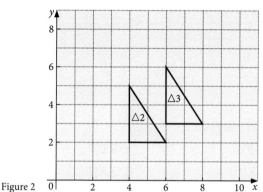

Figure 2

From Figure 2 we can see that

$$B(\Delta 2) = \Delta 3$$

The effect of going from $\Delta 1$ to $\Delta 3$ may be written

$$BA(\Delta 1) = \Delta 3$$

It is very important to notice that $BA(\Delta 1)$ means do A first and then B.

Repeated transformations

$XX(P)$ means 'perform transformation X on P and then perform X on the image'.

It may be written $X^2(P)$

Similarly $TTT(P) = T^3(P)$.

Inverse transformations

If translation T has vector $\begin{pmatrix} 3 \\ -2 \end{pmatrix}$, the translation which has the

opposite effect has vector $\begin{pmatrix} -3 \\ 2 \end{pmatrix}$. This is written T^{-1}.

If rotation R denotes $90°$ clockwise rotation about $(0, 0)$, then R^{-1} denotes $90°$ *anti*clockwise rotation about $(0, 0)$.

The *inverse* of a transformation is the transformation which takes the *image* back to the object.

Note:

For all reflections, the inverse is the same reflection.

e.g. if X is reflection in $x = 0$, then X^{-1} is also reflection in $x = 0$.
The symbol T^{-3} means $(T^{-1})^3$ i.e. perform T^{-1} three times.

Exercise 20

Draw x- and y-axes with values from -8 to $+8$ and plot the point P(3, 2).

R denotes 90° clockwise rotation about (0, 0);

X denotes reflection in $x = 0$.

H denotes 180° rotation about (0, 0);

T denotes translation $\begin{pmatrix} 3 \\ 2 \end{pmatrix}$.

For each question, write down the coordinates of the final image of P.

1. R(P)	**2.** TR(P)	**3.** T(P)	**4.** RT(P)
5. TH(P)	**6.** XT(P)	**7.** HX(P)	**8.** XX(P)
9. R^{-1} (P)	**10.** T^{-1} (P)	**11.** X^3 (P)	**12.** T^{-2} (P)
13. R^2(P)	**14.** $T^{-1} R^2$ (P)	**15.** THX(P)	**16.** R^3 (P)
17. TX^{-1}(P)	**18.** T^3X(P)	**19.** T^2H^{-1}(P)	**20.** XTH(P)

Exercise 21

In this exercise, transformations **A**, **B**, ..., **H**, are as follows:

A denotes reflection in $x = 2$

B denotes 180° rotation, centre (1, 1)

C denotes translation $\begin{pmatrix} -6 \\ 2 \end{pmatrix}$

D denotes reflection in $y = x$

E denotes reflection in $y = 0$

F denotes translation $\begin{pmatrix} 4 \\ 3 \end{pmatrix}$

G denotes 90° rotation clockwise, centre (0, 0)

H denotes enlargement, scale factor $+\frac{1}{2}$, centre (0, 0)

Draw x- and y-axes with values from -8 to $+8$.

1. Draw triangle LMN at L(2, 2), M(6, 2), N(6, 4).

Find the image of LMN under the following combinations of transformations. Write down the coordinates of the image of point L in each case:

a) CA(LMN)   b) ED(LMN)   c) DB(LMN)

d) BE(LMN)   e) EB(LMN)

2. Draw triangle PQR at P(2, 2), Q(6, 2), R(6, 4). Find the image of PQR under the following combinations of transformations. Write down the coordinates of the image of point P in each case:

a) **AF**(PQR) b) **CG**(PQR)

c) **AG**(PQR) d) **HE**(PQR)

3. Draw triangle XYZ at X(−2, 4), Y(−2, 1), Z(−4, 1). Find the image of XYZ under the following combinations of transformations and state the equivalent single transformation in each case:

a) **G^{2}E**(XYZ) b) **CB**(XYZ) c) **DA**(XYZ)

4. Draw triangle OPQ at O(0, 0), P(0, 2), Q(3, 2).

Find the image of OPQ under the following combinations of transformations and state the equivalent single transformation in each case:

a) **DE**(OPQ) b) **FC**(OPQ)

c) **DEC**(OPQ) d) **DFE**(OPQ)

5. Draw triangle RST at R(−4, −1), S$\left(-2\frac{1}{2}, -2\right)$, T(−4, −4). Find the image of RST under the following combinations of transformations and state the equivalent single transformation in each case:

a) **EAG**(RST) b) **FH**(RST) c) **GF**(RST)

6. Write down the inverses of the transformations **A, B, …, H**.

7. Draw triangle JKL at J(−2, 2), K(−2, 5), L(−4, 5). Find the image of JKL under the following transformations. Write down the coordinates of the image of point J in each case:

a) **C^{-1}** b) **F^{-1}** c) **G^{-1}**

d) **D^{-1}** e) **A^{-1}**

8. Draw triangle PQR at P(−2, 4), Q(−2, 1), R(−4, 1). Find the image of PQR under the following combinations of transformations. Write down the coordinates of the image of point P in each case:

a) **DF^{-1}**(PQR) b) **EC^{-1}**(PQR) c) **D^{2}F**(PQR)

d) **GA**(PQR) e) **C^{-1}G^{-1}**(PQR)

9. Draw triangle LMN at L(−2, 4), M(−4, 1), N(−2, 1). Find the image of LMN under the following combinations of transformations. Write down the coordinates of the image of point L in each case:

a) **HE**(LMN) b) **EAG^{-1}**(LMN)

c) **EDA**(LMN) d) **BG^{2}E**(LMN)

10. Draw triangle XYZ at X(1, 2), Y(1, 6), Z(3, 6).

    a) Find the image of XYZ under each of the transformations **BC** and **CB**.

    b) Describe fully the single transformation equivalent to **BC**.

    c) Describe fully the transformation **M** such that **MCB = BC**.

Revision exercise 8A

1. Given that $\varepsilon = \{1, 2, 3, 4, 5, 6, 7, 8\}$,

A = $\{1, 3, 5\}$, B = $\{5, 6, 7\}$, list the members of the sets:

    a) $A \cap B$ **b)** $A \cup B$ **c)** A'

    d) $A' \cap B'$ **e)** $A \cup B'$

2. The sets P and Q are such that
$n(P \cup Q) = 50$, $n(P \cap Q) = 9$ and $n(P) = 27$.
Find the value of $n(Q)$.

3. Draw three diagrams similar to Figure 1, and shade the following

    a) $Q \cap R'$ **b)** $(P \cup Q) \cap R$

    c) $(P \cap Q) \cap R'$

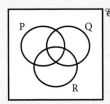

Figure 1

4. Describe the shaded regions in Figures 2 and 3.

    a)

Figure 2

    b)

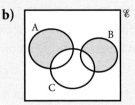

Figure 3

5. Given that $\varepsilon = \{$people on a train$\}$,
M = $\{$males$\}$, T = $\{$people over 25 years old$\}$
and S = $\{$snooker players$\}$,

    a) express in set notation:

        i) all the snooker players are over 25

        ii) some snooker players are women

    b) express in words: $T \cap M' = \varnothing$

6. The figures in the diagram indicate the number of elements in each subset of ε.

    a) Find $n(P \cap R)$.

    b) Find $n(Q \cup R)'$.

    c) Find $n(P' \cap Q')$.

7. In $\triangle$OPR, the midpoint of PR is M.

If $\overrightarrow{OP} = \mathbf{p}$ and $\overrightarrow{OR} = \mathbf{r}$, find in terms of $\mathbf{p}$ and $\mathbf{r}$:

    a) $\overrightarrow{PR}$ **b)** $\overrightarrow{PM}$ **c)** $\overrightarrow{OM}$

8. If $\mathbf{a} = \begin{pmatrix} 1 \\ 4 \end{pmatrix}$ and $\mathbf{b} = \begin{pmatrix} -3 \\ 4 \end{pmatrix}$, find:

   a) $|\mathbf{b}|$ b) $|\mathbf{a}+\mathbf{b}|$ c) $|2\mathbf{a}-\mathbf{b}|$

9. If $4\begin{pmatrix} 1 \\ 3 \end{pmatrix} + 2\begin{pmatrix} 1 \\ m \end{pmatrix} = 3\begin{pmatrix} n \\ -6 \end{pmatrix}$ find the values of m and n.

10. The points O, A and B have coordinates $(0, 0)$, $(5, 0)$ and $(-1, 4)$ respectively. Write as column vectors.

   a) $\overrightarrow{OB}$ b) $\overrightarrow{OA} + \overrightarrow{OB}$

   c) $\overrightarrow{OA} - \overrightarrow{OB}$

   d) $\overrightarrow{OM}$ where M is the midpoint of AB.

11. In the parallelogram OABC, M is the midpoint of AB and N is the midpoint of BC.

   If $\overrightarrow{OA} = \mathbf{a}$ and $\overrightarrow{OC} = \mathbf{c}$, express in terms of $\mathbf{a}$ and $\mathbf{c}$:

   a) $\overrightarrow{CA}$ b) $\overrightarrow{ON}$ c) $\overrightarrow{NM}$

   Describe the relationship between CA and NM.

12. The vectors $\mathbf{a}$, $\mathbf{b}$, $\mathbf{c}$ are given by:

   $\mathbf{a} = \begin{pmatrix} 1 \\ 5 \end{pmatrix}, \mathbf{b} = \begin{pmatrix} -2 \\ 1 \end{pmatrix}, \mathbf{c} = \begin{pmatrix} -1 \\ 17 \end{pmatrix}$

   Find numbers m and n so that $m\mathbf{a} + n\mathbf{b} = \mathbf{c}$.

13. Given that $\overrightarrow{OP} = \begin{pmatrix} 3 \\ 2 \end{pmatrix}$, $\overrightarrow{OQ} = \begin{pmatrix} 0 \\ 4 \end{pmatrix}$ and that M is the midpoint of PQ, express as column vectors:

   a) $\overrightarrow{PQ}$ b) $\overrightarrow{PM}$ c) $\overrightarrow{OM}$

14. Given $f : x \mapsto 2x - 3$ and $g : x \mapsto x^2 - 1$, find:

   a) $f(-1)$ b) $g(-1)$

   c) $fg(-1)$ d) $gf(3)$

   Write the function ff in the form 'ff : $x \mapsto$ ...'

15. If $f : x \mapsto 3x + 4$ and $h : x \mapsto \dfrac{x-2}{5}$ express f^{-1} and h^{-1} in the form '$x \mapsto$ ...' .

   Find:

   a) $f^{-1}(13)$ b) the value of z if $f(z) = 20$

16. Given that $f(x) = x - 5$, find:

   a) the value of s such that $f(s) = -2$

   b) the values of t such that $t \times f(t) = 0$

17. Find the coordinates of the image of $(1, 4)$ under:

   a) a clockwise rotation of $90°$ about $(0, 0)$

   b) a reflection in the line $y = x$

   c) a translation which maps $(5, 3)$ onto $(1, 1)$

18. Draw x- and y-axes with values from -8 to $+8$. Draw triangle $A(1, -1)$, $B(3, -1)$, $C(1, -4)$. Find the image of ABC under the following enlargements:

   a) scale factor 2, centre $(5, -1)$

   b) scale factor 2, centre $(0, 0)$

   c) scale factor $\dfrac{1}{2}$, centre $(1, 3)$

   d) scale factor $-\dfrac{1}{2}$, centre $(3, 1)$

   e) scale factor -2, centre $(0, 0)$

19. Using the diagram, describe the transformations for the following:

   a) $T_1 \rightarrow T_6$ b) $T_4 \rightarrow T_5$

   c) $T_8 \rightarrow T_2$ d) $T_4 \rightarrow T_1$

   e) $T_8 \rightarrow T_4$ f) $T_6 \rightarrow T_8$

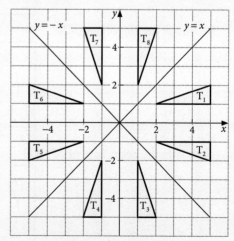

20. Describe the single transformation which maps:

a) $\triangle ABC$ onto $\triangle DEF$

b) $\triangle ABC$ onto $\triangle PQR$

c) $\triangle ABC$ onto $\triangle XYZ$

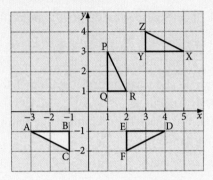

21. M is a reflection in the line $x + y = 0$. **R** is an anticlockwise rotation of $90°$ about $(0, 0)$. **T** is a translation which maps $(-1, -1)$ onto $(2, 0)$. Find the image of the point $(3, 1)$ under:

a) **M**   b) **R**   c) **T**

d) **MR**   e) **RT**   f) **TMR**

22. A is a rotation of $180°$ about $(0, 0)$. **B** is a reflection in the line $x = 3$. **C** is a translation which maps $(3, -1)$ onto $(-2, -1)$. Find the image of the point $(1, -2)$ under:

a) **A**   b) **A²**   c) **BC**

d) **C⁻¹**   e) **ABC**   f) **C⁻¹B⁻¹A⁻¹**

Examination-style exercise 8B

1. (a) Shade the region $A \cap B$.

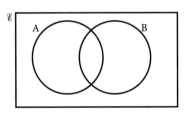

[1]

(b) Shade the region $(A \cup B)'$.

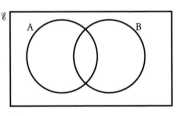

[1]

(c) Shade the complement of set B.

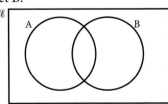

[1]

Cambridge IGCSE Mathematics 0580
Paper 2 Q11 November 2006

2. $\varepsilon = \{1, 3, 5, 7, 9, 10, 12, 14, 16\}$

$A = \{1, 5, 9, 12, 14\}$ $B = \{1, 3, 9, 16\}$

$C = \{1, 5, 9, 16\}$

(a) Draw a Venn diagram to show this information.   [2]

(b) Write down the value of $n(B' \cap C)$.   [1]

3. A and B are sets.

Write the following sets in their simplest form.

(a) $A \cap A'$.   [1]

(b) $A \cup A'$.   [1]

(c) $(A \cap B) \cup (A \cap B)'$.   [1]

Cambridge IGCSE Mathematics 0580
Paper 2 Q12 November 2007

4.

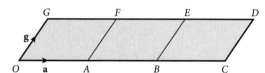

The diagram is made from three identical parallelograms.

O is the origin. $\overrightarrow{OA} = \mathbf{a}$ and $\overrightarrow{OG} = \mathbf{g}$.

Write down in terms of $\mathbf{a}$ and $\mathbf{g}$

(a) $\overrightarrow{GB}$,   [1]

(b) the position vector of the centre of the parallelogram $BCDE$.   [1]

Cambridge IGCSE Mathematics 0580
Paper 21 Q8 June 2009

5.

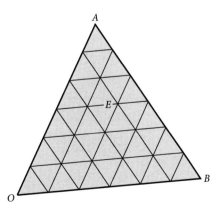

O is the origin, $\overrightarrow{OA} = \mathbf{a}$, and $\overrightarrow{OB} = \mathbf{b}$.

(a) C has position vector $\dfrac{1}{3}\mathbf{a} + \dfrac{2}{3}\mathbf{b}$.

Mark the point C on the diagram. [1]

(b) Write down, in terms of **a** and **b**, the position vector of the point *E*. [1]

(c) Find, in terms of **a** and **b**, the vector $\overrightarrow{EB}$. [2]

Cambridge IGCSE Mathematics 0580
Paper 2 Q15 November 2007

6.

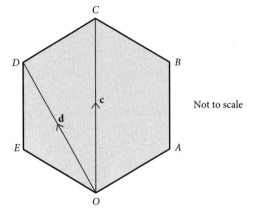

Not to scale

OABCDE is a regular hexagon.

With *O* as origin the position vector of *C* is **c** and the position vector of *D* is **d**.

(a) Find, in terms of **c** and **d**,

    i) $\overrightarrow{DC}$, [1]

    ii) $\overrightarrow{OE}$, [2]

    iii) the position vector of *B*. [2]

(b) The sides of the hexagon are each of length 8 cm.

    Calculate

    i) the size of angle *ABC*,

    ii) the area of triangle *ABC*,

    iii) the length of the straight line *AC*,

    iv) the area of the hexagon.

Cambridge IGCSE Mathematics 0580
Paper 4 Q5 June 2005

7. $f(x) = x^3 - 3x^2 + 6x - 4$ and $g(x) = 2x - 1$.

Find:

(a) $f(-1)$, [1]

(b) $gf(x)$, [2]

(c) $g^{-1}(x)$. [2]

Cambridge IGCSE Mathematics 0580
Paper 21 Q18 June 2008

8. $f : x \mapsto 5 - 3x$.

    (a) Find $f(-1)$.   [1]

    (b) Find $f^{-1}(x)$.   [2]

    (c) Find $ff^{-1}(8)$.   [1]

Cambridge IGCSE Mathematics 0580
Paper 2 Q15 November 2006

9. $f(x) = \sin x°$, $g(x) = 3x + 6$.

Find

    (a) $f(30)$,   [1]

    (b) $fg(58)$,   [2]

    (c) $g^{-1}(f(x))$.   [2]

10. $f(x) = 2x - 1$, $g(x) = \dfrac{3}{x} + 1$, $h(x) = 2^x$.

    (a) Find the value of $fg(6)$.   [1]

    (b) Write, as **single fraction**, $gf(x)$ in terms of x.   [3]

    (c) Find $g^{-1}(x)$.   [3]

    (d) Find $hh(3)$.   [2]

    (e) Find x when $h(x) = g\left(-\dfrac{24}{7}\right)$ [2]

Cambridge IGCSE Mathematics 0580
Paper 4 Q8 November 2007

11. Answer the whole of this question on one sheet of graph paper.

    (a) Draw and label x- and y-axes from -8 to $+8$, using a scale of 1 cm to 1 unit on each axis.   [1]

    (b) Draw and label triangle ABC with $A(2, 2)$, $B(5, 2)$ and $C(5, 4)$.   [1]

    (c) On your grid:

        i) translate **triangle ABC** by the vector $\begin{pmatrix} 3 \\ -9 \end{pmatrix}$ and label this image $A_1B_1C_1$;   [2]

        ii) reflect **triangle ABC** in the line $x = -1$ and label this image $A_2B_2C_2$;   [2]

        iii) rotate **triangle ABC** by $180°$ about $(0, 0)$ and label this image $A_3B_3C_3$.   [2]

Cambridge IGCSE Mathematics 0580
Paper 4 Q2 November 2005

12. **Answer the whole of this question on a sheet of graph paper.**

   (a) Draw a label x- and y-axes from −6 to 6, using a scale of 1 cm to 1 unit. [1]

   (b) Draw triangle ABC with $A(2, 1)$, $B(3, 3)$ and $C(5, 1)$. [1]

   (c) Draw the reflection of triangle ABC in the line $y = x$. Label this $A_1B_1C_1$. [2]

   (d) Rotate **triangle $A_1B_1C_1$** about $(0, 0)$ through 90° anticlockwise. Label this $A_2B_2C_2$. [2]

   (e) Describe fully the single transformation which maps triangle ABC onto triangle $A_2B_2C_2$. [2]

Cambridge IGCSE Mathematics 0580
Paper 4 Q2 June 2007

9 Statistics

Florence Nightingale (1820–1910), was a famous nurse during the Crimean War, which took place between 1853 and 1856. She is generally considered to have founded the modern nursing profession, by establishing her own nursing school at St Thomas' Hospital in London in 1860. She was also a gifted mathematician, and used statistical diagrams to illustrate the conditions that existed in the hospitals where she worked. Although she did not invent the pie chart, she popularised its use, along with other diagrams such as the rose diagram, which is like a circular histogram. In 1859, she was elected the first female member of the Royal Statistical Society.

E9.1 Collect, classify and tabulate statistical data.

E9.2 Read, interpret and draw inferences from tables and statistical diagrams.
Compare sets of data using tables, graphs and statistical measures.
Appreciate restrictions on drawing conclusions from given data.

E9.3 Construct and interpret bar charts, pie charts, pictograms, stem-and-leaf diagrams, simple frequency distributions, histograms with equal and unequal intervals and scatter diagrams.

E9.4 Calculate the mean, median, mode and range for individual and discrete data and distinguish between the purposes for which they are used.

E9.5 Calculate an estimate of the mean for grouped and continuous data.
Identify the modal class from a grouped frequency distribution.

E9.6 Construct and use cumulative frequency diagrams.
Estimate and interpret the median, percentiles, quartiles and interquartile range.
Construct and interpret box-and-whisker plots.

E9.7 Understand what is meant by positive, negative and zero correlation with reference to a scatter diagram.

E9.8 Draw, interpret and use lines of best fit by eye.

9.1 Data display

Bar chart

The length of each bar represents the quantity in question. The width of each bar has no significance. In this bar chart, the number of the cars of each colour in a car park is shown. The bars can be joined together or separated.

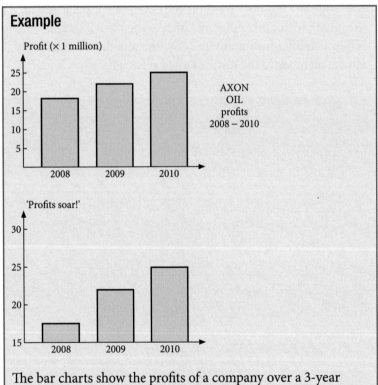

Example

AXON OIL profits 2008 – 2010

The bar charts show the profits of a company over a 3-year period. The second graph has been drawn to give the impression that the profits have increased dramatically over the last three years. How has this been done?

Pie chart

The information is displayed using sectors of a circle.

This pie chart shows the same information as the bar chart on the previous page.

The angles of the sectors are calculated as follows:

Total number of cars = 10 + 14 + 20 + 10 + 6 = 60

Angle representing green cars $= \dfrac{10}{60} \times 360° = 60°$

Angle representing blue cars $= \dfrac{14}{60} \times 360°$, etc.

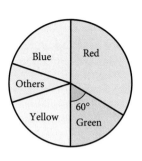

Exercise 1

1. The bar chart shows the number of children playing various games on a given day.

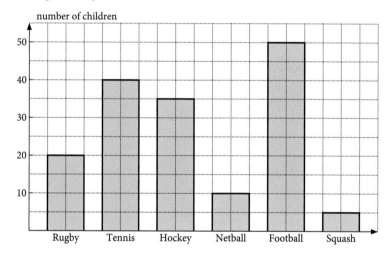

a) Which game had the least number of players?

b) What was the total number of children playing all the games?

c) How many more footballers were there than tennis players?

2. The table shows the number of cars of different makes in a car park. Illustrate this data on a bar chart.

Make	Skoda	Renault	Saab	Kia	Subaru	Lexus
Number	14	23	37	5	42	18

3. The pie chart illustrates the values of various goods sold by a certain shop. If the total value of the sales was $24 000, find the sales value of:

a) toys

b) grass seed

c) records

d) food.

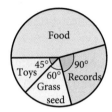

4. The table shows the colours of a random selection of sweets. Calculate the angles on a pie chart corresponding to each colour.

Colour	red	green	blue	yellow	pink
Number	5	7	11	4	9

5. A quantity of scrambled eggs is made using the following recipe:

Ingredient	eggs	milk	butter	cheese	salt/pepper
Mass	450 g	20 g	39 g	90 g	1 g

Calculate the angles on a pie chart corresponding to each ingredient.

6. Calculate the angles on a pie chart corresponding to quantities A, B, C, D and E given in the tables.

a)
Quantity	A	B	C	D	E
Number	3	5	3	7	0

b)
Quantity	A	B	C	D	E
Mass	10 g	15 g	34 g	8 g	5 g

c)
Quantity	A	B	C	D	E
Length	7	11	9	14	11

7. A firm making artificial sand sold its products in four countries:

  5% were sold in Spain

  15% were sold in France

  15% were sold in Germany

  65% were sold in the U.K.

What would be the angles on a pie chart drawn to represent this information?

8. The weights of A, B, C are in the ratio $2:3:4$. Calculate the angles representing A, B and C on a pie chart.

9. The cooking times for meals L, M and N are in the ratio $3:7:x$. On a pie chart, the angle corresponding to L is $60°$. Find x.

10. The results of an opinion poll of 2000 people are represented on a pie chart. The angle corresponding to 'don't know' is $18°$. How many people in the sample did not know?

11. The pie chart illustrates the sales of various makes of petrol.

a) What percentage of sales does 'Esso' have?

b) If 'Jet' accounts for $12\frac{1}{2}\%$ of total sales, calculate the angles x and y.

12.

	% of total spent
Press	51
Television	40
Posters	
Cinema	
Radio	3
Total	100

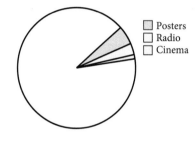

□ Posters
□ Radio
□ Cinema

In Spain money was spent on advertisements in the press, television, posters, etc. The incomplete table and pie chart show the way this was divided between the media.

a) Calculate the angle of the sector representing television, and complete the pie chart.

b) The angle of the sector representing posters is $18°$. Calculate the percentage spent on posters, and hence complete the table.

13. The diagram illustrates the production of apples in two countries.

U.K.
470
thousand
tonnes

FRANCE
950
thousand
tonnes

In what way could the pictorial display be regarded as misleading?

14. The graph shows the performance of a company in the year in which a new manager was appointed.

In what way is the graph misleading?

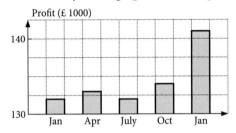

Stem-and-leaf diagrams

Data can be displayed in groups using a stem-and-leaf diagram.

Here are the ages of 20 people who attended a concert.

$$25 \quad 65 \quad 43 \quad 16 \quad 28 \quad 32 \quad 57 \quad 21 \quad 17 \quad 61$$

$$21 \quad 43 \quad 36 \quad 21 \quad 14 \quad 35 \quad 22 \quad 44 \quad 52 \quad 47$$

We start by choosing a sensible way to group the data. Here we can use the tens digit of the ages, giving us the groups 10–19, 20–29, 30–39, 40–49, 50–59, 60–69.

We then use the tens digit as the 'stem' and the units digit as the 'leaf'.

First we complete the diagram using the data in the order it appears in the list.

The last digit of the data will always form the leaf; all other digits will form the stem.

Then we make a second diagram, putting the data in numerical order. You also need to include a key, containing a sample piece of data, so that people know how to interpret your diagram.

Stem	Leaf
1	6 7 4
2	5 8 1 1 1 2
3	2 6 5
4	3 3 4 7
5	7 2
6	5 1

Stem	Leaf
1	4 6 7
2	1 1 1 2 5 8
3	2 5 6
4	3 3 4 7
5	2 7
6	1 5

Key

1 | 4 means 14

From this diagram, it is easy to find the mode, the median and the range of the data.

Back-to-back stem plots

Two sets of data can be compared using a back-to-back stem plot.

10 students who received coaching and 10 students who did not receive coaching all took part in a mathematics competition. Their scores are shown in this back-to-back stem plot.

Key (Coached)	Coached		Not coached	Key (Not coached)
9 | 1 means 19		0	4 8	1 | 5 means 15
	9 5 4	1	0 2 5 9	
	7 6 0	2	4 8	
	6 5 4 1	3	2 4	

Because the two sets of data share the same stem, we can clearly see that, on average, the students who were coached performed better in the competition.

Exercise 2

1. The marks scored by 25 students in a history test are as follows.

62 45 53 76 60 45 33 64 53 36

71 42 26 48 62 66 29 37 21 74

48 56 52 68 62

a) Draw a stem-and-leaf diagram to display this data.

b) What was the median score for the students?

c) Write down the range of the scores.

2. Here is a stem-and-leaf diagram showing the times taken by a group of amateur athletes to run 100 metres, measured to the nearest tenth of a second.

Stem	Leaf	Key
12	9	13 | 5 means 13.5 seconds
13	0 1 5 8	
14	1 6 8	
15	2 2 6 7	

a) How many athletes' scores were recorded?

b) What was the median time taken?

c) What was the range of the times recorded?

d) What was the modal time?

3. A group containing girls and boys measured their handspans in centimetres. Here are the results.

Girls   17.4 19.4 18.8 16.7 16.1 21.0 19.3 16.5 20.8 18.5

Boys   17.7 21.0 21.9 18.2 23.1 22.2 18.8 22.7 17.5 19.3

a) Copy and complete the following back-to-back stem plot to display this data.

	Girls		Boys	
Key (Girls)		16		Key (Boys)
4 | 17 means		17		19 | 3 means
17.4 cm		18		19.3 cm
		19		
		20		
		21		
		22		
		23		

b) What are the median handspans for both girls and boys?

c) What are the ranges of the handspans for girls and boys?

4. The lengths, to the nearest minute, of 10 horror films and 10 action films are collected.

Horror 99 90 94 85 105 92 88 95 89 100

Action 110 88 99 90 119 100 121 106 93 110

a) Display this data in a back-to-back stem plot.

b) What is the median length of each type of film?

c) Based on this sample, which type of film is, on average, longer?

Frequency polygons

A frequency polygon can be drawn by joining the midpoints of the tops of the bars on a frequency chart.

Frequency polygons are used mainly to compare data.

- Here is a frequency chart showing the heights (or lengths) of the babies treated at a hospital one day.

- Here is the corresponding frequency polygon, drawn by joining the mid-points of the tops of the bars.

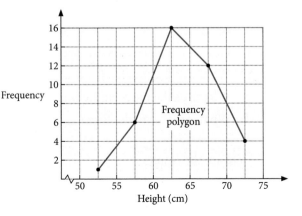

It is not necessary to draw the bars if you require only the frequency polygon.

The diagram on the right shows the frequency polygons for the exam results of 34 students in two subjects, Maths and French.

Two main differences are apparent:

a) The marks obtained in the Maths exam were significantly lower for most students.

b) The marks obtained in the French exam were more spread out than the Maths marks. The French marks were distributed fairly evenly over the range from 0 to 100% whereas the Maths marks were mostly between 0 and 40%.

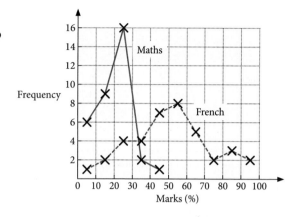

Exercise 3

1. Draw a frequency polygon for the distribution of masses of children drawn in the diagram.

2. In a supermarket survey, shoppers were asked two questions as they left:

   a) How much have you just spent?

   b) How far away do you live?

The results were separated into two groups: shoppers who lived less than 2 miles from the supermarket and shoppers who lived further away. The frequency polygons show how much shoppers in each group had spent.

Decide which polygon, P or Q, is most likely to represent shoppers who lived less than 2 miles from the supermarket. Give your reasons.

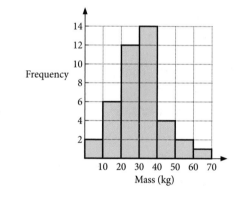

3. Scientists doing research in genetic engineering altered the genes of a certain kind of rabbit. Over a period of several years, measurements were made of the adult weight of the rabbits and their lifespans. The frequency polygons show the results.

What can you deduce from the two frequency polygons?

Write one sentence about weight and one sentence about lifespan.

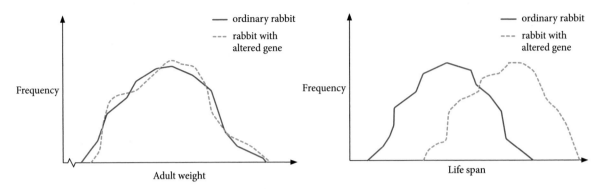

Histograms

In a histogram, the frequency of the data is shown by the *area* of each bar. Histograms resemble bar charts but are not to be confused with them: in bar charts the frequency is shown by the height of each bar. Histograms often have bars of varying widths. Because the area of the bar represents frequency, the height must be adjusted to correspond with the width of the bar. The vertical axis is not labelled frequency but frequency density.

$$\text{frequency density} = \frac{\text{frequency}}{\text{class width}}$$

Histograms can be used to represent both discrete data and continuous data, but their main purpose is for use with continuous data.

Example

Draw a histogram from the table shown for the distribution of ages of passengers travelling on a flight to New York.

Note that the data has been collected into class intervals of different widths.

Ages	Frequency
$0 \leqslant x < 20$	28
$20 \leqslant x < 40$	36
$40 \leqslant x < 50$	20
$50 \leqslant x < 70$	30
$70 \leqslant x < 100$	18

To draw the histogram, the heights of the bars must be adjusted by calculating frequency density.

Ages	Frequency	Frequency density (f.d.)
$0 \leqslant x < 20$	28	$28 \div 20 = 1.4$
$20 \leqslant x < 40$	36	$36 \div 20 = 1.8$
$40 \leqslant x < 50$	20	$20 \div 10 = 2$
$50 \leqslant x < 70$	30	$30 \div 20 = 1.5$
$70 \leqslant x < 100$	18	$18 \div 30 = 0.6$

Exercise 4

1. The lengths of 20 copper nails were measured. The results are
shown in the frequency table.

Length l (in mm)	Frequency	Frequency density (f.d.)
$0 \leqslant L < 20$	5	$5 \div 20 = 0.25$
$20 \leqslant L < 25$	5	
$25 \leqslant L < 30$	7	
$30 \leqslant L < 40$	3	

Calculate the frequency densities and draw the histogram as
started on the right.

2. The volumes of 55 containers were measured and the results presented in a frequency table as shown in the table.

Volume (mm³)	Frequency
$0 \leqslant V < 5$	5
$5 \leqslant V < 10$	3
$10 \leqslant V < 20$	12
$20 \leqslant V < 30$	17
$30 \leqslant V < 40$	13
$40 \leqslant V < 60$	5

Calculate the frequency densities and draw the histogram.

3. The masses of thirty students in a class are measured. Draw a histogram to represent this data.

Mass (kg)	Frequency
30–40	5
40–45	7
45–50	10
50–55	5
55–70	3

Note that the masses do not start a zero. This can be shown on the graph as follows:

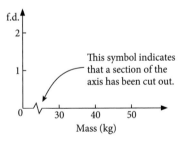

4. The ages of 120 people passing through a turnstyle were recorded and are shown in the frequency table.

Age (yrs)	Frequency
–10	18
–15	46
–20	35
–30	13
–40	8

The notation −10 means '0 < age ≤ 10' and similarly −15 means '10 < age ≤ 15'. The class boundaries are 0, 10, 15, 20, 30, 40. Draw the histogram for the data.

5. Another common notation is used here for the masses of plums picked in an orchard, shown in the table below.

Mass (g)	20–	30–	40–	60–	80–
Frequency	11	18	7	5	0

The notation 20– means 20 g ≤ mass < 30 g.

Draw a histogram with class boundaries at 20, 30, 40, 60, 80.

6. The heights of 50 Olympic athletes were measured as shown in the table.

Height (cm)	170–174	175–179	180–184	185–194
Frequency	8	17	14	11

These values were rounded off to the nearest cm. For example, an athlete whose height h is 181 cm could be entered anywhere in the class 180.5 cm ≤ h < 181.5 cm. So the table is as follows:

Height	169.5–174.5	174.5–179.5	179.5–184.5	184.5–194.5
Frequency	8	17	14	11

Draw a histogram with class boundaries at 169.5, 174.5, 179.5, …

7. The number of people travelling in 33 vehicles one day was as shown in the table below.

Number of people	1	2	3	4	5–6	7–10
Frequency	8	11	6	4	2	2

In this case, the data is discrete. To represent this information on a histogram, draw the column for the value 2, for example, from 1.5 to 2.5, and that for the values 5–6 from 4.5 to 6.5 as shown below.

Number of people	Frequency	Interval on histogram	Width of interval	Frequency density
1	8	0.5–1.5	1	8
2	11	1.5–2.5		
3	6			
4	4			
5–6	2	4.5–6.5	2	1
7–10	2			

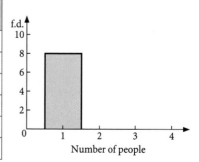

Copy and complete the above table and the histogram which has been started on the right.

9.2 Mean, median and mode

a) The *mean* of a series of numbers is obtained by adding the numbers and dividing the result by the number of numbers.

b) The *median* of a series of numbers is obtained by arranging the numbers in ascending order and then choosing the number in the 'middle'.
If there are *two* 'middle' numbers the median is the average (mean) of these two numbers.

c) The *mode* of a series of numbers is simply the number which occurs most often.

Example

Find the mean, median and mode of the following numbers:

5, 4, 10, 3, 3, 4, 7, 4, 6, 5.

a) Mean $= \dfrac{(5+4+10+3+3+4+7+4+6+5)}{10} = \dfrac{51}{10} = 5.1$

b) Median: arranging numbers in order of size

3, 3, 4, 4, 4, 5, 5, 6, 7, 10

The median is the 'average' of 4 and 5

∴ median $= 4.5$

c) Mode $= 4$ (there are more 4's than any other number).

Frequency tables

A frequency table shows a number x such as a mark or a score, against the frequency f or number of times that x occurs.

The symbol Σ (or sigma) means 'the sum of'.

The next example shows how these symbols are used in calculating the mean, the median and the mode.

Example

The marks obtained by 100 students in a test were as follows:

Mark (x)	0	1	2	3	4
Frequency (f)	4	19	25	29	23

Find:

a) the mean mark

b) the median mark

c) the modal mark

---

a) Mean $= \dfrac{\sum xf}{\sum f}$

where $\sum xf$ means 'the sum of the products'
i.e. $\sum$ (number $\times$ frequency)
and $\sum f$ means 'the sum of the frequencies'.

$$\text{Mean} = \frac{(0 \times 4) + (1 \times 19) + (2 \times 25) + (3 \times 29) + (4 \times 23)}{100}$$

$$= \frac{248}{100} = 2.48$$

b) The median mark is the number between the 50th and 51st numbers. By inspection, both the 50th and 51st numbers are 3.

$\therefore$ Median = 3 marks

c) The modal mark = 3

Exercise 5

1. Find the mean, median and mode of the following sets of numbers:
    a) 3, 12, 4, 6, 8, 5, 4
    b) 7, 21, 2, 17, 3, 13, 7, 4, 9, 7, 9
    c) 12, 1, 10, 1, 9, 3, 4, 9, 7, 9
    d) 8, 0, 3, 3, 1, 7, 4, 1, 4, 4

2. Find the mean, median and mode of the following sets of numbers:
    a) 3, 3, 5, 7, 8, 8, 8, 9, 11, 12, 12
    b) 7, 3, 4, 10, 1, 2, 1, 3, 4, 11, 10, 4
    c) −3, 4, 0, 4, −2, −5, 1, 7, 10, 5
    d) $1, \frac{1}{2}, \frac{1}{2}, \frac{3}{4}, \frac{1}{4}, 2, \frac{1}{2}, \frac{1}{4}, \frac{3}{4}$

3. The mean mass of five men is 76 kg. The masses of four of the men are 72 kg, 74 kg, 75 kg and 81 kg. What is the mass of the fifth man?

4. The mean length of 6 rods is 44.2 cm. The mean length of 5 of them is 46 cm. How long is the sixth rod?

5. a) The mean of 3, 7, 8, 10 and x is 6. Find x.
    b) The mean of 3, 3, 7, 8, 10, x and x is 7. Find x.

6. The mean height of 12 men is 1.70 m, and the mean height of 8 women is 1.60 m. Find:
    a) the total height of the 12 men
    b) the total height of the 8 women
    c) the mean height of the 20 men and women.

7. The total mass of 6 rugby players is 540 kg and the mean mass of 14 ballet dancers is 40 kg. Find the mean mass of the group of 20 rugby players and ballet dancers.

8. The mean mass of 8 boys is 55 kg and the mean mass of a group of girls is 52 kg. The mean mass of all the children is 53.2 kg. How many girls are there?

9. For the set of numbers below, find the mean and the median.

1, 3, 3, 3, 4, 6, 99

   Which average best describes the set of numbers?

10. In a history test, Andrew got 62%. For the whole class, the mean mark was 64% and the median mark was 59%. Which 'average' tells Andrew whether he is in the 'top' half or the 'bottom' half of the class?

11. The mean age of three people is 22 and their median age is 20.

    The range of their ages is 16. How old is each person?

12. A group of 50 people were asked how many books they had read in the previous year; the results are shown in the frequency table below. Calculate the mean number of books read per person.

Number of books	0	1	2	3	4	5	6	7	8
Frequency	5	5	6	9	11	7	4	2	1

13. A number of people were asked how many coins they had in their pockets; the results are shown below. Calculate the mean number of coins per person.

Number of coins	0	1	2	3	4	5	6	7
Frequency	3	6	4	7	5	8	5	2

14. The following tables give the distribution of marks obtained by different classes in various tests. For each table, find the mean, median and mode.

a)
Mark	0	1	2	3	4	5	6
Frequency	3	5	8	9	5	7	3

b)
Mark	15	16	17	18	19	20
Frequency	1	3	7	1	5	3

c)
Mark	0	1	2	3	4	5	6
Frequency	10	11	8	15	25	20	11

15. One hundred golfers play a certain hole and their scores are summarised below.

Score	2	3	4	5	6	7	8
Number of players	2	7	24	31	18	11	7

Find:

a) the mean score

b) the median score.

16. The number of goals scored in a series of football matches was as follows:

Number of goals	1	2	3
Number of matches	8	8	x

a) If the mean number of goals is 2.04, find x.

b) If the modal number of goals is 3, find the smallest possible value of x.

c) If the median number of goals is 2, find the largest possible value of x.

17. In a survey of the number of occupants in a number of cars, the following data resulted.

Number of occupants	1	2	3	4
Number of cars	7	11	7	x

a) If the mean number of occupants is $2\frac{1}{3}$, find x.

b) If the mode is 2, find the largest possible value of x.

c) If the median is 2, find the largest possible value of x.

18. The numbers 3, 5, 7, 8 and N are arranged in ascending order. If the mean of the numbers is equal to the median, find N.

19. The mean of 5 numbers is 11. The numbers are in the ratio $1:2:3:4:5$. Find the smallest number.

20. The mean of a set of 7 numbers is 3.6 and the mean of a different set of 18 numbers is 5.1. Calculate the mean of the 25 numbers.

21. The marks obtained by the members of a class are summarised in the table.

Mark	x	y	z
Frequency	a	b	c

Calculate the mean mark in terms of a, b, c, x, y and z.

Data in groups

Example

The results of 51 students in a test are given in the frequency table.

Find the   **a)** mean   **b)** median   **c)** modal class.

Mark	30–39	40–49	50–59	60–69
Frequency	7	14	21	9

In order to find the mean you approximate by saying each interval is represented by its midpoint. For the 30–39 interval you say there are 7 marks of 34.5 [that is $(30 + 39) \div 2 = 34.5$].

a) $\text{Mean} = \dfrac{(34.5 \times 7) + (44.5 \times 14) + (54.5 \times 21) + (64.5 \times 9)}{(7 + 14 + 21 + 9)}$

$= 50.7745098$

$= 51\,(2\text{ s.f.})$

Don't forget the mean is only an **estimate** because you do not have the raw data and you have made an assumption with the midpoint of each interval.

b) The median is the 26th mark, which is in the interval 50–59.

You cannot find the exact median.

c) The **modal class** is 50–59. You cannot find an exact mode.

Later you will find out how to get an estimate of the median by drawing a cumulative frequency curve.

Exercise 6

1. The table gives the number of words in each sentence of a page in a book.

   a) Copy and complete the table.

   b) Work out an estimate for the mean number of words in a sentence.

Number of words	Frequency f	Midpoint x	fx
1–5	6	3	18
6–10	5	8	40
11–15	4		
16–20	2		
21–25	3		
totals	20	–	

2. The results of 24 students in a test are given in the table.

Mark	Frequency
85–99	4
70–84	7
55–69	8
40–54	5

a) Find the midpoint of each group of marks and calculate an estimate of the mean mark.

b) Explain why your answer is an estimate.

3. The results of 24 students in a test are given in the table.

Mark	40–54	55–69	70–84	85–99
Frequency	5	8	7	4

Find the midpoint of each group of marks and calculate an estimate of the mean mark.

4. The table shows the number of letters delivered to the 26 houses in a street.

Calculate an estimate of the mean number of letters delivered per house.

Number of letters delivered	Number of houses (frequency)
0–2	10
3–4	8
5–7	5
8–12	3

5. The histogram shows the heights of the 60 athletes in the Indian athletics team.

a) Calculate an estimate for the mean height of the 60 athletes.

b) Explain why your answer is an **estimate** for the mean height.

c) What is the modal class for the heights of these athletes?

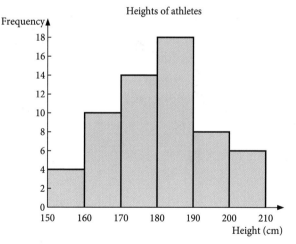

9.3 Scatter graphs

Sometimes it is important to discover if there is a connection or relationship between two sets of data.

Examples:

- Are more ice creams sold when the weather is hot?
- Do tall people have higher pulse rates?
- Are people who are good at maths also good at science?
- Does watching television improve examination results?

If there is a relationship, it will be easy to spot if your data is plotted on a scatter diagram – that is a graph in which one set of data is plotted on the horizontal axis and the other on the vertical axis.

Here is a scatter graph showing the price of pears and the quantity sold.

We can see a *connection* – when the price was high the sales were low and when the price went down the sales increased.

This scatter graph shows the sales of a newspaper and the temperature. We can see there is *no connection* between the two variables.

Correlation

The word correlation describes how things *co-relate*. There is correlation between two sets of data if there is a connection or relationship.

The correlation between two sets of data can be positive or negative and it can be strong or weak as indicated by the scatter graphs below.

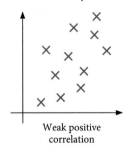

When the correlation is positive the points are around a line which slopes upwards to the right. When the correlation is negative the 'line' slopes downwards to the right.

When the correlation is strong the points are bunched close to a line through their midst. When the correlation is weak the points are more scattered.

It is important to realise that often there is *no* correlation between two sets of data.

If, for example, we take a group of students and plot their maths test results against their time to run 800 m, the graph might look like the one on the right. A common mistake in this topic is to 'see' a correlation on a scatter graph where none exists.

There is also *no* correlation in these two scatter graphs.

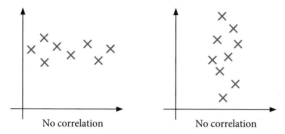

No correlation   No correlation

Line of best fit

When a scatter graph shows either positive or negative correlation, a *line of best fit* can be drawn. The sums of the distances to points on either side of the line are equal and there should be an equal number of points on each side of the line. The line is easier to draw when a transparent ruler is used.

Here are the marks obtained in two tests by 9 students.

Student	A	B	C	D	E	F	G	H	I
Maths mark	28	22	9	40	37	35	30	23	?
Physics mark	48	45	34	57	50	55	53	45	52

A line of best fit can be drawn as there is strong positive correlation between the two sets of marks.

The line of best fit can be used to estimate the maths result of student I, who missed the maths test but scored 52 in the physics test.

We can *estimate that student I would have scored about* 33 in the maths test. It is not possible to be *very* accurate using scatter graphs. It is reasonable to state that student I 'might have scored between 30 and 36' in the maths test.

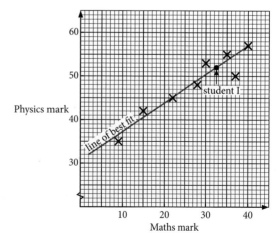

Here is a scatter graph in which the heights of boys of different ages is recorded. A line of best fit is drawn.

a) We can estimate that the height of an 8-year-old boy might be about 123 cm [say between 120 and 126 cm].

b) We can only predict a height within the range of values plotted. We could not extend the line of best and use it to predict the height of a 30-year-old! Why not?

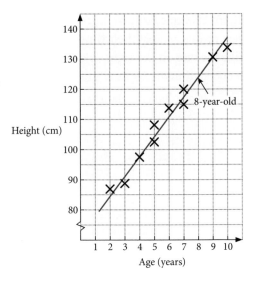

Exercise 7

1. Make the following measurements for everyone in your class:

height   (nearest cm)

arm span   (nearest cm)

head circumference   (nearest cm)

hand span   (nearest cm)

pulse rate   (beats/minute)

For greater consistency of measuring, one person (or perhaps two people) should do all the measurements of one kind (except on themselves!).

Enter all the measurements in a table, either on the board or on a sheet of paper.

Name	Height	Armspan	Head
Roger	161	165	56
Liz	150	148	49
Gill			

a) Draw the scatter graphs shown below:

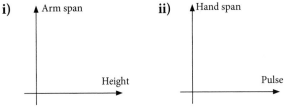

i) Arm span / Height

ii) Hand span / Pulse

b) Describe the correlation, if any, in the scatter graphs you drew in part (a).

c) **i)** Draw a scatter graph of two measurements where you think there might be positive correlation.

ii) Was there indeed a positive correlation?

2. Plot the points given on a scatter graph, with *s* across the page and *p* up the page. Draw axes with values from 0 to 20.

Describe the correlation, if any, between the values of *s* and *p*. [i.e. 'strong negative', 'weak positive' etc.]

a)

s	7	16	4	12	18	6	20	4	10	13
p	8	15	6	12	17	9	18	7	10	14

b)

s	3	8	12	15	16	5	6	17	9
p	4	2	10	17	5	10	17	11	15

c)

s	11	1	16	7	2	19	8	4	13	18
p	5	12	7	14	17	1	11	8	11	5

In questions **3**, **4** and **5** plot the points given on a scatter graph, with *s* across the page and *p* up the page.

Draw axes with the values from 0 to 20.

If possible draw a line of best fit on the graph.

Where possible estimate the value of *p* on the line of best fit where *s = 10*.

3.

s	2	14	14	4	12	18	12	6
p	5	15	16	6	12	18	13	7

4.

s	2	15	17	3	20	3	6
p	13	7	5	12	4	13	11

5.

s	4	10	15	18	19	4	19	5
p	19	16	11	19	15	3	1	9

6. The following data gives the marks of 11 students in a French test and in a German test.

French	15	36	36	22	23	27	43	22	43	40	26
German	6	28	35	18	28	28	37	9	41	45	17

a) Plot this data on a scatter graph, with French marks on the horizontal axis.

b) Draw the line of best fit.

c) Estimate the German mark of a student who got 30 in French.

d) Estimate the French mark of a student who got 45 in German.

7. The data below gives the petrol consumption figures of cars, with the same size engine, when driven at different speeds.

Speed (m.p.h.)	30	62	40	80	70	55	75
Petrol consumption (m.p.g.)	38	25	35	20	26	34	22

a) Plot a scatter graph and draw a line of best fit.

b) Estimate the petrol consumption of a car travelling at 45 m.p.h.

c) Estimate the speed of a car whose petrol consumption is 27 m.p.g.

9.4 Box-and-whisker plots

The *range* is a simple way to measure the *spread* or *dispersion* of a set of data, but one extreme value (very high or very low) can have a big effect on the range.

range = highest value – lowest value

A better measure of spread is the *interquartile range*.

The value at the *25th percentile* (one quarter of the way through the data set) is called the *lower quartile* (Q_1).

The value at the *75th percentile* (three quarters of the way through the data set) is called the *upper quartile* (Q_3).

The bigger the value of the interquartile range, the bigger the spread of the data.

The *median* is the value at the *50th percentile*.

interquartile range = upper quartile – lower quartile

Example

Find the quartiles and interquartile range for these numbers.

$$8 \quad 9 \quad 5 \quad 11 \quad 5 \quad 20 \quad 8 \quad 7 \quad 8 \quad 6 \quad 3 \quad 14$$

In order: 3 5 5 ┊ 6 7 8 ┊ 8 8 9 ┊ 11 14 20

lower quartile   median   upper quartile

is 5.5   is 8   is 10

Interquartile range = upper quartile – lower quartile

$$= 10 - 5.5$$

$$= 4.5$$

A **box-and-whisker plot** or **box plot** shows the spread of a set of data.

Here is a box plot.

A box plot can also be vertical.

The box, made from the upper and lower quartiles and the median, shows the interquartile range. The 'whiskers', extending to the lowest and highest values, show the range.

Example

Illustrate the following set of test scores using a box-and-whisker plot.

| 12 | 21 | 8 | 20 | 12 | 20 | 9 | 22 | 17 | 5 | 19 |

In order: 5   8   9   12   12   17   19   20   20   21   22

The median is 17.

Now find the medians of the two remaining halves of the data set.

If the median is one of the items of data, do not include it in the next step.

5   8   9   12   12   19   20   20   21   22

The lower quartile is 9.   The upper quartile is 20.

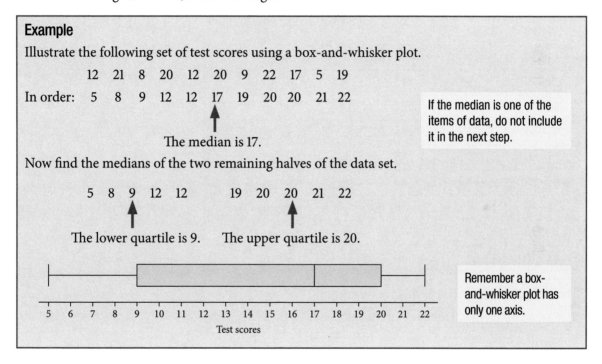

Test scores

Remember a box-and-whisker plot has only one axis.

Exercise 8

1. Illustrate each set of data using a box plot, and state the median and interquartile range.

   a) 9   18   1   8   10   8   6   4

   b) 9   3   4   12   7   12   10

   c) 14   8   11   8   21   7   19   25   5

2. A group of 10 students take a test that is marked out of 20. Here are their scores.

   9   9   1   4   14   20   3   15   12   6

   a) Illustrate these scores using a box-and-whisker plot.

   b) Calculate the interquartile range of the scores.

9.5 Cumulative frequency

Cumulative frequency is the total frequency up to a given point.

A cumulative frequency curve (or ogive) shows the *median* at the 50th percentile of the cumulative frequency.

Example

The marks obtained by 80 students in an examination are shown below.

Mark	Frequency	Cumulative frequency	Marks represented by cumulative frequency
1–10	3	3	$\leqslant 10$
11–20	5	8	$\leqslant 20$
21–30	5	13	$\leqslant 30$
31–40	9	22	$\leqslant 40$
41–50	11	33	$\leqslant 50$
51–60	15	48	$\leqslant 60$
61–70	14	62	$\leqslant 70$
71–80	8	70	$\leqslant 80$
81–90	6	76	$\leqslant 90$
91–100	4	80	$\leqslant 100$

The table also shows the cumulative frequency.

a) Plot a cumulative frequency curve and hence estimate:

   i) the median

   ii) the interquartile range.

The points on the graph are plotted at the upper limit of each group of marks.

From the cumulative frequency curve

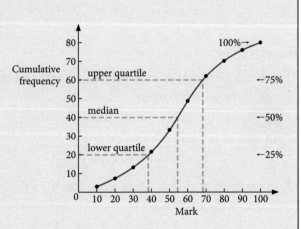

$$\text{median} = 55 \text{ marks}$$
$$\text{lower quartile} = 37.5 \text{ marks}$$
$$\text{upper quartile} = 68 \text{ marks}$$
$$\therefore \quad \text{interquartile range} = 68 - 37.5$$
$$= 30.5 \text{ marks}.$$

b) Illustrate this data using a box-and-whisker plot.

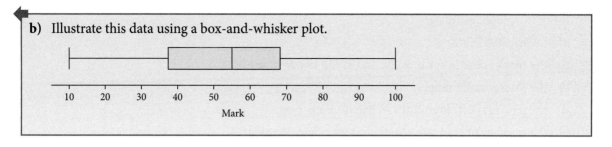

Exercise 9

1. Figure 1 shows the cumulative frequency curve for the marks of 60 students in an examination.

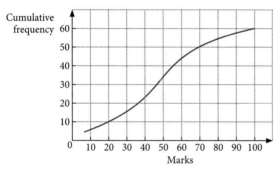

Figure 1

From the graph, estimate:

a) the median mark

b) the mark at the lower quartile and at the upper quartile

c) the interquartile range

d) the pass mark if two-thirds of the students passed

e) the number of students achieving less than 40 marks.

2. Figure 2 shows the cumulative frequency curve for the marks of 140 students in an examination.

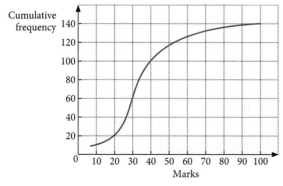

Figure 2

From the graph, estimate:

a) the median mark

b) the mark at the lower quartile and at the upper quartile

c) the interquartile range

d) the pass mark if three-fifths of the students passed

e) the number of students achieving more than 30 marks.

In questions **3** to **6**, draw a cumulative frequency curve, and find:

a) the median   b) the interquartile range.

Illustrate each set of data with a box-and-whisker plot.

3.

Mass (kg)	Frequency
1–5	4
6–10	7
11–15	11
16–20	18
21–25	22
26–30	10
31–35	5
36–40	3

4.

Length (cm)	Frequency
41–50	6
51–60	8
61–70	14
71–80	21
81–90	26
91–100	14
101–110	7
111–120	4

5.

Time (seconds)	Frequency
36–45	3
46–55	7
56–65	10
66–75	18
76–85	12
86–95	6
96–105	4

6.

Number of marks	Frequency
1–10	0
11–20	2
21–30	4
31–40	10
41–50	17
51–60	11
61–70	3
71–80	3

7. In an experiment, 50 people were asked to guess the mass of a bunch of flowers in grams. The guesses were as follows:

47	39	21	30	42	35	44	36	19	52
23	32	66	29	5	40	33	11	44	22
27	58	38	37	48	63	23	40	53	24
47	22	44	33	13	59	33	49	57	30
17	45	38	33	25	40	51	56	28	64

Construct a frequency table using intervals 0–9, 10–19, 20–29, etc.

Hence draw a cumulative frequency curve and estimate:

a) the median mass

b) the interquartile range

c) the number of people who guessed a mass within 10 grams of the median.

8. In a competition, 30 children had to pick up as many paper clips as possible in one minute using a pair of tweezers. The results were as follows:

3	17	8	11	26	23	18	28	33	38
12	38	22	50	5	35	39	30	31	43
27	34	9	25	39	14	27	16	33	49

Construct a frequency table using intervals 1–10, 11–20, etc. and hence draw a cumulative frequency curve.

a) From the curve, estimate the median number of clips picked up.

b) From the frequency table, estimate the mean of the distribution using the mid-interval values 5.5, 15.5, etc.

c) Calculate the exact value of the mean using the original data.

d) Why is it possible only to estimate the mean in part (b)?

9. The children in two schools took the same test in mathematics and their results are shown.

School A	School B	Note:
median mark = 52%	median mark = 51.8%	IQR is shorthand for interquartile range.
IQR = 7.2	IQR =11.2	

What can you say about these two sets of results?

10. As part of a health improvement programme, people from one town and from one village in Gambia were measured. Here are the results.

People in town	People in village
median height =171 cm	median height = 163 cm
IQR = 8.4	IQR = 3.7

What can you say about these two sets of results?

9.6 Comparing data sets

Graphs and charts can often be used to compare two different sets of data.

Exercise 10

1. Between finishing their dinner and going to bed, Zac and Lucy had 4 hours. These pie charts show how they spent their time.

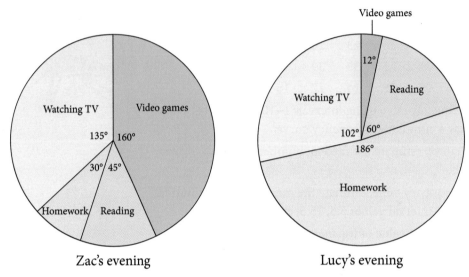

Zac's evening   Lucy's evening

a) Which one of them spent the most time reading?

b) How many minutes did Zac spend doing his homework?

c) How many more minutes did Zac spend watching TV than Lucy?

2. Two classes take a maths test and the scores from each class are recorded. Here are two box-and-whisker plots illustrating the data.

a) Write down the median for each class.

b) Work out the interquartile range for each class.

c) On average, which class did better in the test? Give a reason for your answer.

d) Which class was more consistent? Give a reason for your answer.

3. A group of 60 children and a group of 60 adults were asked to guess how many sweets there were in a jar. Their responses have been illustrated in the following cumulative frequency graph.

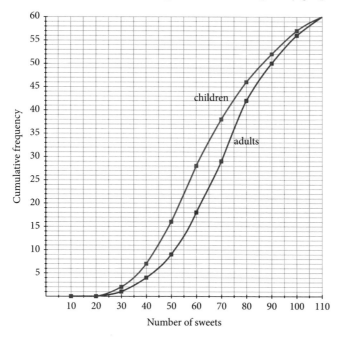

a) Work out estimates of the median and interquartile range for both groups.

b) Given that there were actually 70 sweets in the jar, which group was better at guessing?

4. The waiting times of 50 patients in two doctors' surgeries were measured to the nearest minute. They are illustrated here using box-and-whisker plots.

Compare the two surgeries, based on these waiting times.
Give reasons for your comments.

Revision exercise 9A

1. A pie chart is drawn with sectors to represent the following percentages:

   20%, 45%, 30%, 5%.

   What is the angle of the sector which represents 45%?

2. The pie chart shows the numbers of votes for candidates A, B and C in an election.

   What percentage of the votes were cast in favour of candidate C?

3. A pie chart is drawn showing the expenditure of a football club as follows:

Wages	$41000
Travel	$9000
Rates	$6000
Miscellaneous	$4000

   What is the angle of the sector showing the expenditure on travel?

4. The mean of four numbers is 21.

   a) Calculate the sum of the four numbers.

   Six other numbers have a mean of 18.

   b) Calculate the mean of the ten numbers.

5. Find:

   a) the mean

   b) the median

   c) the mode

   of the numbers 3, 1, 5, 4, 3, 8, 2, 3, 4, 1.

6.

Marks	3 4 5 6 7 8
Number of students	2 3 6 4 3 2

The table shows the number of students in a class who scored marks 3 to 8 in a test. Find:

a) the mean mark

b) the modal mark

c) the median mark.

7. The mean height of 10 boys is 1.60 m and the mean height of 15 girls is 1.52 m. Find the mean height of the 25 boys and girls.

8.

Mark	3 4 5
Number of students	3 x 4

The table shows the number of students who scored marks 3, 4 or 5 in a test. Given that the mean mark is 4.1, find x.

9. Two classes of 20 students take a maths test. The scores for the students in Class 1 are as follows:

11	14	16	17	18	22	26
28	34	39	41	42	44	44
46	46	48	49	49	50	

   a) Draw a stem-and-leaf diagram to illustrate these results.

   b) Use the stem-and-leaf diagram to find the median and interquartile range of these results.

   c) Draw a box-and-whisker plot to illustrate these results.

   Here is a summary of the results for students in Class 2.

Lowest score: 23	Lower quartile: 30
Median: 36	Upper quartile: 44
Highest score: 48	

   d) Compare the results from the two classes.

Examination-style exercise 9B

1. The mass of each of 200 tea bags was checked by an inspector in a factory.

The results are shown by the cumulative frequency curve.

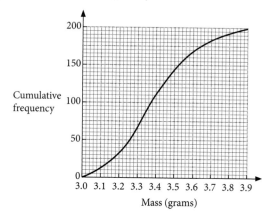

Use the cumulative frequency curve to find

(a) the median mass, [1]

(b) the interquartile range, [2]

(c) the number of tea bags with a mass greater than 3.5 grams. [1]

Cambridge IGCSE Mathematics 0580
Paper 2 Q19 November 2007

2. (a) Each student in a class is given a bag of sweets.

The students note the number of sweets in their bag. The results are shown in the table, where $0 \leqslant x < 10$.

Number of sweets	30	31	32
Frequency (number of bags)	10	7	x

i) State the mode. [1]

ii) Find the possible values of the median. [3]

iii) The mean number of sweets is 30.65.
Find the value of x. [3]

(b) The mass, m grams, of each of 200 chocolates is noted and the results are shown in the table.

Mass (m grams)	Frequency
$10 < m \leqslant 20$	35
$20 < m \leqslant 22$	115
$22 < m \leqslant 24$	26
$24 < m \leqslant 30$	24

i) Calculate an estimate of the mean mass of a chocolate. [4]

ii) On a histogram, the height of the column for the $20 < m \leqslant 22$ interval is 11.5 cm. Calculate the heights of the other three columns.
Do not draw the histogram. [5]

Cambridge IGCSE Mathematics 0580
Paper 4 Q6 November 2008

3. The speeds (v kilometres/hour) of 150 cars passing a 50 km/h speed limit sign are recorded. A cumulative frequency curve to show the results is drawn below.

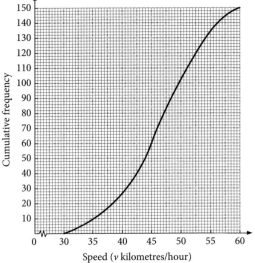

(a) Use the graph to find

i)   the median speed, [1]

ii) the interquartile range of the speeds, [2]

iii) the number of cars travelling with speeds of more than 50 km/h. [2]

(b) A frequency table showing the speeds of the cars is

Speed (v km/h)	Frequency
$30 < v \leqslant 35$	10
$35 < v \leqslant 40$	17
$40 < v \leqslant 45$	33
$45 < v \leqslant 50$	42
$50 < v \leqslant 55$	n
$55 < v \leqslant 60$	16

i)   Find the value of n. [1]

ii) Calculate an estimate of the mean speed. [4]

(c) **Answer this part of this question on a sheet of graph paper.**

Another frequency table for the same speeds is

Speed (v km/h)	$30 < v \leqslant 40$	$40 < v \leqslant 55$	$55 < v \leqslant 60$
Frequency	27	107	16

Draw an accurate histogram to show this information. Use 2 cm to represent 5 units on the speed axis and 1 cm to represent 1 unit on the frequency density axis (so that 1 cm² represents 2.5 cars). [5]

Cambridge IGCSE Mathematics 0580
Paper 4 Q7 June 2005

4. Here are the ages, in years, of 15 people who took part in a baking competition in 2010.

   12   14   19   23   31   35   42   44   46   49   52   54   58   60   65

(a) Draw a box-and-whisker plot for this data set on the grid below. [3]

The following box-and-whisker plot shows the distribution of the ages, in years, of the 25 people who took part in the same competition in 2015.

(b) Compare the distribution of the ages of the people who took part in 2010 with the distribution of the ages of the people who took part in 2015. [2]

10 Probability

Blaise Pascal (1623–1662) suffered the most appalling ill-health throughout his short life. He is best known for his work with Fermat on probability. This followed correspondence with a gentleman gambler who was puzzled as to why he lost so much in betting on the basis of the appearance of a throw of dice. Pascal's work on probability became of enormous importance and showed for the first time that absolute certainty is not a necessity in mathematics and science. He also studied physics, but his last years were spent in religious meditation and illness.

E8.1   Calculate the probability of a single event as either a fraction, decimal or percentage.

E8.2   Understand and use the probability scale from 0 to 1.

E8.3   Understand that the probability of an event occurring = 1 − the probability of the event not occurring.

E8.4   Understand relative frequency as an estimate of probability. Expected frequency of occurrences.

E8.5   Calculate the probability of simple combined events, using possibility diagrams, tree diagrams and Venn diagrams.

E8.6   Calculate conditional probability using Venn diagrams, tree diagrams and tables.

10.1 Simple probability

Probability theory is not the sole concern of people interested in betting, although it is true to say that a 'lucky' poker player is likely to be a player with a sound understanding of probability. All major airlines regularly overbook aircraft because they can usually predict with accuracy the probability that a certain number of passengers will fail to arrive for the flight.

Suppose a 'trial' can have n equally likely results and suppose that a 'success' can occur in s ways (from the n). Then the probability of a 'success' $= \dfrac{s}{n}$.

- If an event **cannot** happen the probability of it occurring is 0.

- If an event is **certain** to happen the probability of it occurring is 1.

- All probabilities lie between 0 and 1.

    You write probabilities using fractions or decimals.

Example 1

The numbers 1 to 20 are each written on a card.

The 20 cards are mixed together.

One card is chosen at random from the pack.

Find the probability that the number on the card is:

a) even   **b)** a factor of 24   **c)** prime.

....

We will use '$p(x)$' to mean 'the probability of x'.

a) $p(\text{even}) = \dfrac{10}{20}$
$= \dfrac{1}{2}$

b) $p(\text{factor of } 24)$
$= p(1, 2, 3, 4, 6, 8, 12)$
$= \dfrac{7}{20}$

c) $p(\text{prime})$
$= p(2, 3, 5, 7, 11, 13, 17, 19)$
$= \dfrac{8}{20} = \dfrac{2}{5}$

In each case, we have counted the number of ways in which a 'success' can occur and divided by the number of possible results of a 'trial'.

Example 2

A black die and a white die are thrown at the same time. Display all the possible outcomes. Find the probability of obtaining:

a) a total of 5

b) a total of 11

c) a 'two' on the black die and a 'six' on the white die.

It is convenient to display all the possible outcomes on a grid. This is called a 'possibility diagram'.

Number on black die

Number on white die

....

There are 36 possible outcomes, shown where the lines cross.

a) There are four ways of obtaining a total of 5 on the two dice.
They are shown circled on the diagram.

$\therefore$ Probability of obtaining a total of 5 $= \dfrac{4}{36}$

b) There are two ways of obtaining a total of 11. They are shown with a cross on the diagram.

$\therefore$ p (total of 11) $= \dfrac{2}{36} = \dfrac{1}{18}$

c) There is only one way of obtaining a 'two' on the black die and a 'six' on the white die.

$\therefore$ p (2 on black and 6 on white) $= \dfrac{1}{36}$

Exercise 1

In this exercise, all dice are normal cubic dice with faces numbered 1 to 6.

1. A fair die is thrown once. Find the probability of obtaining:

    a)   a six   **b)**   an even number

    c)   a number greater than 3   **d)**   a three or a five.

2. The two sides of a coin are known as 'head' and 'tail'. A 10c and a 5c coin are tossed at the same time. List all the possible outcomes.
Find the probability of obtaining:

    a)   two heads   **b)**   a head and a tail.

3. A bag contains 6 red balls and 4 green balls.

    a)   Find the probability of selecting at random:

        i)   a red ball   **ii)**   a green ball.

    b)   One red ball is removed from the bag. Find the new probability of selecting at random

        i)   a red ball   **ii)**   a green ball.

4. One letter is selected at random from the word 'UNNECESSARY'.
Find the probability of selecting:

    a)   an R   **b)**   an E

    c)   an O   **d)**   a C

5. Three coins are tossed at the same time. List all the possible outcomes. Find the probability of obtaining:

    a)   three heads   **b)**   two heads and one tail

    c)   no heads   **d)**   at least one head.

6. A bag contains 10 red balls, 5 blue balls and 7 green balls. Find the probability of selecting at random:

a) a red ball   **b)** a green ball

c) a blue *or* a red ball   **d)** a red *or* a green ball.

7. Cards with the numbers 2 to 101 are placed in a hat. Find the probability of selecting:

a) an even number   **b)** a number less than 14

c) a square number   **d)** a prime number less than 20.

8. A red die and a blue die are thrown at the same time. List all the possible outcomes in a systematic way. Find the probability of obtaining:

a) a total of 10   **b)** a total of 12

c) a total less than 6   **d)** the same number on both dice

e) a total more than 9.

What is the most likely total?

9. A die is thrown; when the result has been recorded, the die is thrown a second time. Display all the possible outcomes of the two throws. Find the probability of obtaining:

a) a total of 4 from the two throws

b) a total of 8 from the two throws

c) a total between 5 and 9 inclusive from the two throws

d) a number on the second throw which is double the number on the first throw

e) a number on the second throw which is four times the number on the first throw.

10. Find the probability of the following:

a) throwing a number less than 8 on a single die

b) obtaining the same number of heads and tails when five coins are tossed

c) selecting a square number from the set A = {4, 9, 16, 25, 36, 49}

d) selecting a prime number from the set A.

11. Four coins are tossed at the same time. List all the possible outcomes in a systematic way. Find the probability of obtaining:

a) two heads and two tails   **b)** four tails

c) at least one tail   **d)** three heads and one tail.

12. Cards numbered 1 to 1000 were put in a box. Ali selects a card at random. What is the probability that Ali selects a card containing at least one '3'?

13. One ball is selected at random from a bag containing 12 balls of which x are white.

    a) What is the probability of selecting a white ball?

       When a further 6 white balls are added the probability of selecting a white ball is doubled.

    b) Find x.

14. Two dice and two coins are thrown at the same time. Find the probability of obtaining:

    a) two heads and a total of 12 on the dice

    b) a head, a tail and a total of 9 on the dice

    c) two tails and a total of 3 on the dice.

    What is the most likely outcome?

15. A red, a blue and a green die are all thrown at the same time. Display all the possible outcomes in a suitable way. Find the probability of obtaining:

    a) a total of 18 on the three dice

    b) a total of 4 on the three dice

    c) a total of 10 on the three dice

    d) a total of 15 on the three dice

    e) a total of 7 on the three dice

    f) the same number on each die.

10.2 Relative frequency

To work out the probability of a drawing pin landing point up 📌 we can conduct an experiment in which a drawing pin is dropped many times. If the pin lands 'point up' on x occasions out of a total number of N trials, the **relative frequency** of landing 'point up' is $\dfrac{x}{N}$.

When an experiment is repeated many times we can use the relative frequency as an estimate of the probability of the event occurring.

Here are the results of an experiment in which a dice, suspected of being biased, was rolled 300 times. After each set of 25 rolls the number of sixes obtained was noted and the results were as follows:

    5 4 6 6 6 5 3 7 6 5 6 5

After 25 rolls the relative frequency of sixes $= \dfrac{5}{25} = 0.2$

After 50 rolls the relative frequency of sixes $= \dfrac{5+4}{50} = 0.18$

After 75 rolls the relative frequency

of sixes = $\dfrac{5+4+6}{75}$ = 0.173 and so on.

The results are plotted on this graph.

As we include more and more results, the average number of sixes per roll settles down at slightly over 0.21.

For this dice we say the **relative frequency** of sixes was just over 0.21.

If the dice was fair, we would expect

to get a six on $\dfrac{1}{6}$ of the throws. So the

relative frequency would be 0.1̇6̇.

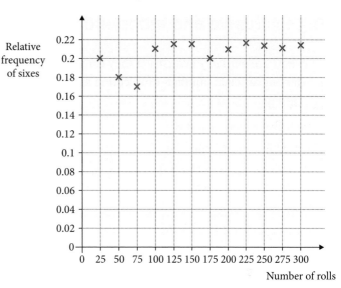

Relative frequency of sixes

Number of rolls

The **expected frequency** would be equal to one sixth of the total, so in 300 rolls you would expect to get (approximately) 50 sixes. The dice in the experiment does appear to be biased so that sixes occur more frequently than we would expect for a fair dice.

Exercise 2

1. Conduct an experiment where you cannot predict the result.
   You could roll a dice with a piece of 'Blu Tack' stuck to it.
   Or make a spinner where the axis is not quite in the centre.
   Or drop a drawing pin.

   Conduct the experiment many times and work out the relative frequency of a 'success' after every 10 or 20 trials.

   Plot a relative frequency graph like the one above to see if the results 'settle down' to a consistent value.

2. The spinner has an equal chance of giving any digit from 0 to 9. Four friends did an experiment when they spun the pointer a different number of times and recorded the number of zeros they got.

   Here are their results.

	Number of spins	Number of zeros	Relative frequency
Steve	10	2	0.2
Nick	150	14	0.093
Mike	200	41	0.205
Jason	1000	104	0.104

   One of the four recorded his results incorrectly. Say who you think this was and explain why.

10.3 Exclusive and independent events

Two events are *mutually exclusive* if they cannot occur at the same time:
e.g. Selecting an 'even number' or selecting a 'one' from a set of numbers.

The 'OR' rule:

For exclusive events A and B

$$p(A \text{ or } B) = p(A) + p(B)$$

Two events are *independent* if the occurrence of one event is unaffected by the occurrence of the other.

e.g. Obtaining a 'head' on one coin, and a 'tail' on another coin when the coins are tossed at the same time.

The 'AND' rule:

$$p(A \text{ and } B) = p(A) \times p(B)$$

where $p(A)$ = probability of A occurring etc. This is the multiplication law.

Example 1

One ball is selected at random from a bag containing 5 red balls,
2 yellow balls and 4 white balls. Find the probability of selecting a red ball or a white ball.

The two events are exclusive.

$$p \text{ (red ball } or \text{ white ball)} = p(\text{red}) + p(\text{white})$$

$$= \frac{5}{11} + \frac{4}{11}$$

$$= \frac{9}{11}$$

Example 2

A fair coin is tossed and a fair die is rolled. Find the probability of obtaining a 'head' and a 'six'.

The two events are independent.

$$p \text{ (head } and \text{ six)} = p(\text{head}) \times p(\text{six})$$

$$= \frac{1}{2} \times \frac{1}{6}$$

$$= \frac{1}{12}$$

Exercise 3

1. A coin is tossed and a die is thrown. Write down the probability of obtaining:

a) a 'head' on the coin

b) an odd number on the die

c) a 'head' on the coin and an odd number on the die.

2. A ball is selected at random from a bag containing 3 red balls, 4 black balls and 5 green balls. The first ball is replaced and a second is selected. Find the probability of obtaining:

a) two red balls   b) two green balls.

3. The letters of the word 'INDEPENDENT' are written on individual cards and the cards are put into a box. A card is selected and then replaced and then a second card is selected. Find the probability of obtaining:

a) the letter 'P' twice   b) the letter 'E' twice.

4. Three coins are tossed and two dice are thrown at the same time. Find the probability of obtaining:

a) three heads and a total of 12 on the dice

b) three tails and a total of 9 on the dice.

5. When a golfer plays any hole, he will take 3, 4, 5, 6, or 7 strokes with probabilities of $\frac{1}{10}, \frac{1}{5}, \frac{2}{5}, \frac{1}{5}$ and $\frac{1}{10}$ respectively. He never takes more than 7 strokes. Find the probability of the following events:

a) scoring 4 on each of the first three holes

b) scoring 3, 4 and 5 (in that order) on the first three holes

c) scoring a total of 28 for the first four holes

d) scoring a total of 10 for the first three holes

e) scoring a total of 20 for the first three holes.

6. A coin is biased so that it shows 'heads' with a probability of $\frac{2}{3}$. The same coin is tossed three times. Find the probability of obtaining:

a) two tails on the first two tosses

b) a head, a tail and a head (in that order)

c) two heads and one tail (in any order).

10.4 Tree diagrams

Example 1

A bag contains 5 red balls and 3 green balls. A ball is drawn at random and then replaced. Another ball is drawn.

What is the probability that both balls are green?

The branch marked * involves the selection of a green ball twice.

The probability of this event is obtained by simply multiplying the fractions on the two branches.

$$\therefore p \text{ (two green balls)} = \frac{3}{8} \times \frac{3}{8} = \frac{9}{64}$$

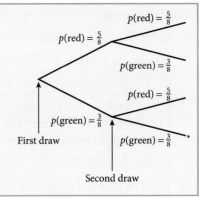

Example 2

A bag contains 5 red balls and 3 green balls. A ball is selected at random and not replaced. A second ball is then selected. Find the probability of selecting:

a) two green balls

b) one red ball and one green ball.

a) p(two green balls)

$$= \frac{3}{8} \times \frac{2}{7}$$

$$= \frac{3}{28}$$

b) p(one red, one green) $= \left(\frac{5}{8} \times \frac{3}{7}\right) + \left(\frac{3}{8} \times \frac{5}{7}\right)$

$$= \frac{15}{28}$$

Exercise 4

1. A bag contains 10 discs; 7 are black and 3 white. A disc is selected, and then replaced. A second disc is selected. Copy and complete the tree diagram showing all the probabilities and outcomes. Find the probability of the following:

a) both discs are black   **b)** both discs are white.

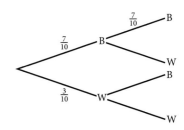

2. A bag contains 5 red balls and 3 green balls. A ball is drawn and then replaced before a ball is drawn again. Draw a tree diagram to show all the possible outcomes. Find the probability that:

a) two green balls are drawn

b) the first ball is red and the second is green.

3. A bag contains 7 green discs and 3 blue discs. A disc is drawn and *not* replaced.

A second disc is drawn. Copy and complete the tree diagram.

Find the probability that:

a) both discs are green

b) both discs are blue.

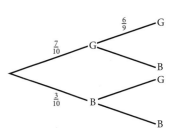

4. A bag contains 5 red balls, 3 blue balls and 2 yellow balls. A ball is drawn and not replaced. A second ball is drawn. Find the probability of drawing:

a) two red balls

b) one blue ball and one yellow ball

c) two yellow balls

d) two balls of the same colour.

5. A bag contains 4 red balls, 2 green balls and 3 blue balls. A ball is drawn and not replaced. A second ball is drawn. Find the probability of drawing:

a) two blue balls

b) two red balls

c) one red ball and one blue ball

d) one green ball and one red ball.

6. A six-sided die is thrown three times. Draw a tree diagram, showing at each branch the two events: 'six' and 'not six'.
What is the probability of throwing a total of:

a) three sixes

b) no sixes

c) one six

d) at least one six (use part (**b**)).

7. A bag contains 6 red marbles and 4 blue marbles. A marble is drawn at random and not replaced. Two further draws are made, again without replacement. Find the probability of drawing:

a) three red marbles   **b)** three blue marbles

c) no red marbles   **d)** at least one red marble.

8. When a cutting is taken from a geranium the probability that it grows is $\frac{3}{4}$. Three cuttings are taken. What is the probability that:

a) all three grow

b) none of them grow?

9. A die has its six faces marked 0, 1, 1, 1, 6, 6. Two of these dice are thrown together and the total score is recorded. Draw a tree diagram.

a) How many different totals are possible?

b) What is the probability of obtaining a total of 7?

10. A coin is biased so that the probability of a 'head' is $\frac{3}{4}$. Find the probability that, when tossed three times, it shows:

a) three tails

b) two heads and one tail

c) one head and two tails

d) no tails.

Write down the sum of the probabilities in (a), (b), (c) and (d).

11. A teacher decides to award exam grades A, B or C by a new method. Out of 20 children, three are to receive A's, five B's and the rest C's. She writes the letters A, B and C on 20 pieces of paper and invites the students to draw their exam result, going through the class in alphabetical order. Find the probability that:

a) the first three students all get grade 'A'

b) the first three students all get grade 'B'

c) the first three students all get different grades

d) the first four students all get grade 'B'.

(Do not cancel down the fractions.)

12. The probability that an amateur golfer actually hits the ball is $\frac{1}{10}$. If four separate attempts are made, find the probability that the ball will be hit:

a) four times   b) at least twice   c) not at all.

13. A box contains x milk chocolates and y plain chocolates. Two chocolates are selected at random. Find, in terms of x and y, the probability of choosing:

a) a milk chocolate on the first choice

b) two milk chocolates

c) one of each sort

d) two plain chocolates.

14. If a hedgehog crosses a certain road before 7.00 a.m., the probability of being run over is $\frac{1}{10}$. After 7.00 a.m., the corresponding probability is $\frac{3}{4}$. The probability of the hedgehog waking up early enough to cross before 7.00 a.m., is $\frac{4}{5}$.

    What is the probability of the following events:

    a) the hedgehog waking up too late to reach the road before 7.00 a.m.

    b) the hedgehog waking up early and crossing the road in safety

    c) the hedgehog waking up late and crossing the road in safety

    d) the hedgehog waking up early and being run over

    e) the hedgehog crossing the road in safety.

15. Bag A contains 3 red balls and 3 blue balls.

    Bag B contains 1 red ball and 3 blue balls.

    A ball is taken at random from bag A and placed in bag B. A ball is then chosen from bag B. What is the probability that the ball taken from B is red?

A

B

16. On a Monday or a Thursday, Ceren paints a 'masterpiece' with a probability of $\frac{1}{5}$. On any other day, the probability of producing a 'masterpiece' is $\frac{1}{100}$. Find the probability that on one day chosen at random, she will paint a masterpiece.

17. Two dice, each with four faces marked 1, 2, 3 and 4, are thrown together.

    a) What is the most likely total score on the faces pointing downwards?

    b) What is the probability of obtaining this score on three successive throws of the two dice?

18. A bag contains 3 red, 4 white and 5 green balls. Three balls are selected without replacement. Find the probability that the three balls chosen are:

    a) all red

    b) all green

    c) one of each colour.

    If the selection of the three balls was carried out 1100 times, how often would you expect to choose:

    d) three red balls

    e) one of each colour?

19. There are 1000 components in a box of which 10 are known to be defective. Two components are selected at random. What is the probability that:

a) both are defective   **b)** neither are defective

c) just one is defective?

(Do *not* simplify your answers.)

20. There are 10 boys and 15 girls in a class. Two children are chosen at random. What is the probability that:

a) both are boys   **b)** both are girls

c) one is a boy and one is a girl?

21. There are 500 ball bearings in a box of which 100 are known to be undersize. Three ball bearings are selected at random. What is the probability that:

a) all three are undersize   **b)** none are undersize?

Give your answers as decimals correct to three significant figures.

22. There are 9 boys and 15 girls in a class. Three children are chosen at random. What is the probability that:

a) all three are boys   **b)** all three are girls

c) one is a boy and two are girls?

Give your answers as fractions.

10.5 Probability from Venn diagrams

Venn diagrams can also be used to solve probability questions.

Example 3

A group of 30 cats were given two different types of food.
7 cats liked only food A, 5 cats liked only food B, 16 liked
both and 2 liked neither. This information is displayed
in the Venn diagram.

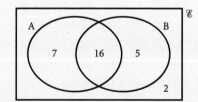

a) What is the probability that a randomly selected
cat will like both foods A and B?

b) What is the probability that a randomly selected cat will like only food A?

c) What is the probability that a randomly selected cat does not like food B?

. . . .

a) p(the cat likes both foods) $= \dfrac{16}{30} = \dfrac{8}{15}$

b) p(the cat likes only food A) $= \dfrac{7}{30}$

c) p(the cat does not like food B) $= \dfrac{9}{30}$

You don't have to simplify your
fractions in probability questions if
you would rather not.

Exercise 5

1. In a class of 25 students, some study French, some study German, some study both, and some study neither. This information is illustrated in the following Venn diagram.

   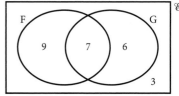

   ε = {students in the class}

   F = {students who study French}

   G = {students who study German}

   What is the probability that a student, chosen randomly from the class,

   a) studies French

   b) studies French and German

   c) studies neither French nor German

   d) studies German but does not study French?

2. A group of 30 children were asked whether they liked eating carrots. Some said they liked eating them, some said they didn't like them but ate them anyway, and some said they refused to eat them. This information is illustrated in the following Venn diagram.

   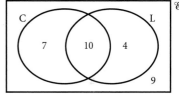

   ε = {the group of children}

   C = {those who eat carrots}

   L = {those who like carrots}

   a) What is the probability that a randomly selected student

       i) likes carrots

       ii) does not like carrots but does eat them

       iii) does not like carrots and refuses to eat them?

   b) What type of person does the number 4 in the diagram represent?

3. A group of 50 students have the option of going on two different school outings. 20 of them are going to the museum and to the theme park. 18 of them are going to the museum but not to the theme park. 3 are not going on either outing.

   a) Illustrate this information in a Venn diagram.

   b) What is the probability that a randomly selected member of the group

       i) is going to the theme park but not the museum

       ii) is going to the museum

       iii) is going to the theme park?

4. A group of 12 friends were discussing the various places they had visited. 2 had been to America but not Italy. 4 had been to Italy but not America. The number of people who had been to both countries was twice the number of people who had been to neither.

a) Illustrate this information in a Venn diagram.

b) What is the probability that a randomly selected member of the group

    i) had been to Italy and America

    ii) had been to Italy

    iii) had not been to Italy?

5. A book club has 30 members. Some of them like detective stories (D), some like historical fiction (H), some like science fiction (S) and one member does not like any of these types of book. This information is illustrated in the Venn diagram.

What is the probability that a randomly selected member of the group

a) likes detective stories

b) likes historical fiction and science fiction

c) likes science fiction but not detective stories

d) does not like historical fiction

e) likes all three types of book?

6. In a school year group consisting of 120 students, each student studies one or more of the three sciences, Biology, Chemistry and Physics. Here is a Venn diagram illustrating this.

$\varepsilon = \{$students in the year group$\}$

$B = \{$students who study Biology$\}$

$C = \{$students who study Chemistry$\}$

$P = \{$students who study Physics$\}$

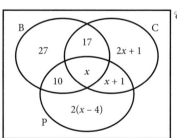

a) Work out the value of x.

b) What is the probability that a randomly selected student

    i) studies Biology

    ii) studies Chemistry and Physics

    iii) studies Chemistry but not Biology

    iv) does not study Physics?

7. ε = {positive whole numbers from 1 to 20}. F, P and T are sets of positive whole numbers, such that F = {1, 2, 3, 5, 8, 13}, P = {2, 3, 5, 7, 11, 13, 17, 19}, and T = {3, 6, 9, 12, 15, 18}.

a) Illustrate these three sets in a Venn diagram.

b) Calculate

    i) $p(F \cap P)$ **ii)** $p(F \cup T)$ **iii)** $p(P \cap T')$

    iv) $p(F' \cup P')$ **v)** $p(F \cup T')$

10.6 Conditional probability

A *conditional probability* is the probability of an event, given that another event has occurred. The probability of event A, given that event B has already occurred, is called the probability of 'A given B' and is written $p(A|B)$. There are many ways to calculate conditional probabilities, including tree diagrams, Venn diagrams, and just common sense combined with a basic knowledge of probability.

Sometimes it can be useful to use the formula $p(A|B) = \dfrac{p(A \cap B)}{p(B)}$

Example

On one floor of a bookshop is a café. Some people go into the shop just to use the café, some just to buy a book, some to do both, and some do not do either. The Venn diagram shows what a group of 50 people did in the bookshop.

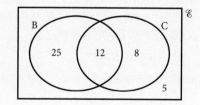

ε = {the group of 50 people}

B = {those who bought a book}

C = {those who used the café}

Work out

a) $p(B|C)$ b) $p(C|B)$

- -

a) $p(B|C) = \dfrac{\text{the number of people who buy a book and use the café}}{\text{the number of people who use the café}} = \dfrac{12}{20}$

b) $p(C|B) = \dfrac{\text{the number of people who buy a book and use the café}}{\text{the number of people who buy a book}} = \dfrac{12}{37}$

Notice that $p(B|C)$ and $p(C|B)$ are not the same.

Exercise 6

1. A regular pack of playing cards contains 26 red cards and 26 black cards.

   If you are asked to pick a card at random, what is the probability that you will choose a red card, given that one black card has already been removed from the pack and not replaced?

2. A bag of sweets contains 3 red sweets, 4 green sweets and 2 orange sweets. Harjit chooses a sweet at random and eats it. Satpal then chooses a sweet.

   a) What is the probability that Satpal chooses a green sweet, given that

   i) Harjit's sweet was orange

   ii) Harjit's sweet was red?

   b) What is the probability that they both chose green sweets?

3. A group of 50 people went to a restaurant for a meal. They each chose a main course and a dessert. Their choices are shown in the following table.

	Cheesecake	Ice-cream	Total
Pizza	17	9	26
Chicken curry	10	14	24
Total	27	23	50

   What is the probability that a randomly selected member of the group will have chosen

   a) chicken curry

   b) ice-cream

   c) cheesecake, given that they chose pizza

   d) chicken curry, given that they chose ice-cream

   e) ice-cream, given that they chose chicken curry?

4. If Kebe is late for school, the probability that Lilian is late for school is 0.7.

   If Kebe is not late for school, there is still a probability of 0.2 that Lilian will be late.

   The probability that Kebe will be late for school is 0.2.

   Here is a tree diagram illustrating this information.

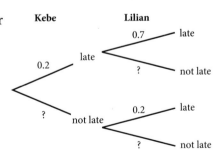

a) Copy and complete the tree diagram.

b) What is the probability that Lilian will not be late, given that Kebe is late?

c) What is the probability that Lilian will be late for school?

5. When Tanawat goes on holiday, he asks his friend Niran to water his plant for him while he is away.

If Niran does not water the plant correctly, the probability that the plant will die is 0.8.

If Niran does water the plant correctly, there is still a probability of 0.2 that it will die.

The probability that Niran will water the plant correctly is 0.7.

a) Use a tree diagram to work out the probability that the plant will be alive when Tanawat returns.

b) What is the probability that Niran did not water the plant properly, given that Tanawat returns to find that his plant is dead?

6. A coffee shop asked 60 customers whether they drank coffee or tea. Some drank only coffee, some drank only tea, some drank both and some drank neither. This information is illustrated in the following Venn diagram.

ε = {the 60 customers}

C = {those who drink coffee}

T = {those who drink tea}

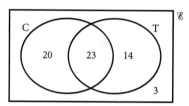

What is the probability that a customer, chosen at random,

a) drinks coffee, given that they also drink tea

b) does not drink tea, given that they drink coffee

c) does not drink coffee, given that they do not drink tea?

7. Let A and B be two events, such that $p(A) = 0.8$, $p(B) = 0.7$, and $p(A \cap B) = 0.5$. We can use a Venn diagram to illustrate these probabilities.

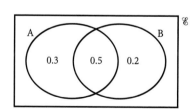

Find

a) $p(A|B)$ **b)** $p(B|A)$ **c)** $p(A|B')$

d) $p(B'|A')$

Revision exercise 10A

1. When two dice are thrown simultaneously, what is the probability of obtaining the same number on both dice?

2. A bag contains 20 discs of equal size of which 12 are red, x are blue and the rest are white.
   a) If the probability of selecting a blue disc is $\frac{1}{4}$, find x.
   b) A disc is drawn and then replaced. A second disc is drawn. Find the probability that neither disc is red.

3. Three dice are thrown. What is the probability that none of them shows a 1 or a 6?

4. A coin is tossed four times. What is the probability of obtaining at least three 'heads'?

5. A bag contains 8 balls of which 2 are red and 6 are white. A ball is selected and not replaced. A second ball is selected. Find the probability of obtaining:
   a) two red balls
   b) two white balls
   c) one ball of each colour.

6. A bag contains x green discs and 5 blue discs. A disc is selected. A second disc is drawn. Find, in terms of x, the probability of selecting:
   a) a green disc on the first draw
   b) a green disc on the first and second draws, if the first disc is replaced
   c) a green disc on the first and second draws, if the first disc is *not* replaced.

7. In a group of 20 people, 5 cannot swim. If two people are selected at random, what is the probability that neither of them can swim?

8. a) What is the probability of winning the toss in five consecutive hockey matches?
   b) What is the probability of winning the toss in all the matches in the FA cup from the first round to the final (i.e. 8 matches)?

9. Mr and Mrs Singh have three children. What is the probability that:
   a) all the children are boys
   b) there are more girls than boys?
   (Assume that a boy is as likely as a girl.)

10. The probability that it will be wet today is $\frac{1}{6}$. If it is dry today, the probability that it will be wet tomorrow is $\frac{1}{8}$. What is the probability that both today and tomorrow will be dry?

11. Two dice are thrown. What is the probability that the *product* of the numbers on top is:
    a) 12   b) 4   c) 11?

12. The probability of snow on January 1st is $\frac{1}{20}$. What is the probability that snow will fall on the next three January 1st?

13. In the Venn diagram:
    ε = {students in a class of 15}
    G = {girls}
    S = {swimmers}
    F = {students who were born on a Friday}.

    A student is chosen at random. Find the probability that the student:

    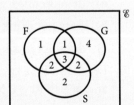

    a) can swim
    b) is a girl swimmer
    c) is a boy swimmer who was born on a Friday.

    Two students are chosen at random. Find the probability that:
    d) both are boys
    e) neither can swim
    f) both are girl swimmers who were born on a Friday.

Examination-style exercise 10B

1. Rooms in a hotel are numbered from 1 to 19. Rooms are allocated at random as guests arrive.

   (a) What is the probability that the first guest to arrive is given a room which is a prime number? [2]

   (b) The first guest to arrive is given a room which is a prime number. What is the probability that the second guest to arrive is given a room which is a prime number? [1]

Cambridge IGCSE Mathematics 0580
Paper 2 Q10 June 2005

2. (a)

Grade	1	2	3	4	5	6	7
Number of students	1	2	4	7	4	8	2

   The table shows the grades gained by 28 students in a history test.

   i) Write down the mode. [1]

   ii) Find the median. [1]

   iii) Calculate the mean. [3]

   iv) Two students are chosen at random.

   Calculate the probability that they both gained grade 5. [2]

   v) From all the students who gained grades 4 or 5 or 6 or 7, two are chosen at random.

   Calculate the probability that they both gained grade 5. [2]

   vi) Students are chosen at random, one by one, from the original 28, until the student chosen has a grade 5. Calculate the probabilty that this is the third student chosen. [2]

   (b) Claude goes to school by bus.

   The probability that the bus is late is 0.1. If the bus is late, the probability that Claude is late to school is 0.8.

   If the bus is not late, the probability that Claude is late to school is 0.05.

   i) Calculate the probability that the bus is late and Claude is late to school. [1]

   ii) Calculate the probability that Claude is late to school. [3]

   iii) The school term lasts 56 days.

   How many days would Claude expect to be late? [1]

Cambridge IGCSE Mathematics 0580
Paper 4 Q2 November 2007

3.

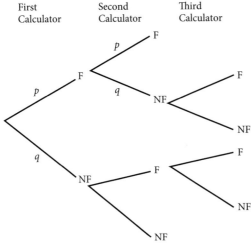

First Calculator   Second Calculator   Third Calculator

F = faulty
NF = not faulty

The tree diagram shows a testing procedure on calculators, taken from a large batch.

Each time a calculator is choosen at random, the probability that it is faulty (F) is $\frac{1}{20}$.

(a) Write down the values of p and q.   [1]

(b) Two calculators are chosen at random. Calculate the probability that

   i) both are faulty,   [2]

   ii) exactly one is faulty.   [2]

(c) If **exactly one** out of two calculators tested is faulty, then a third calculator is chosen at random.

Calculate the probability that exactly one of the first two calculators is faulty **and** the third one is faulty.   [2]

(d) The whole batch of calculators is rejected

   either if the first two chosen are both faulty

   or if a third one needs to be chosen and it is faulty.

Calculate the probability that the whole batch is rejected.   [2]

(e) In one month, 1000 batches of calculators are tested in this way.

How many batches are expected to be rejected?   [1]

Cambridge IGCSE Mathematics 0580
Paper 4 Q8 June 2009

4. (a) All 24 students in a class are asked whether they like football and whether they like basketball. Some of the results are shown in the Venn diagram below.

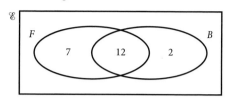

ε = {students in the class}.
F = {students who like football}.
B = {students who like basketball}.

i) How many students like both sports? [1]

ii) How many students do not like either sport? [1]

iii) Write down the value of $n(F \cup B)$. [1]

iv) Write down the value of $n(F' \cap B)$. [1]

v) A student from the class is selected at random.

What is the probability that this student likes basketball? [1]

vi) A student who likes football is selected at random.

What is the probability that this student likes basketball? [1]

(b) Two students are selected at random from a group of 10 boys and 12 girls.

Find the probability that

i) they are both girls, [2]

ii) one is a boy and one is a girl. [3]

Cambridge IGCSE Mathematics 0580
Paper 4 Q4 November 2005

5. A play is being performed twice; first on a Friday and again on a Saturday. 100 people who wanted to see the play were asked which of the two performances they could attend. 58 people said they could attend the Friday performance, 74 said they could attend the Saturday performance, and 4 said they could attend neither.

a) Complete the Venn diagram to illustrate this information. [3]

ε = {the 100 people questioned}

F = {those who could attend on Friday}

S = {those who could attend on Saturday}

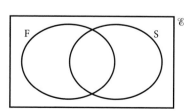

b) What is the probability that a randomly selected person from the 100 questioned

    i) could attend either performance   [1]

    ii) could only attend the Saturday performance   [1]

    iii) could not attend the Saturday performance?   [1]

c) If one customer who wanted a ticket for the Saturday performance accidentally bought a ticket for the Friday performance, what is the probability that they would still be able to go?   [2]

11 Investigations, Practical Problems, Puzzles

William Shockley (1910–1989), along with two other scientists, was awarded the Nobel Prize in Physics in 1956 for inventing the transistor. This is a good example of how mathematics can be used to solve practical problems.

Every time you use a calculator, you are making use of integrated circuits that were developed from the first transistors.

The first electronic computers did not make use of transistors or integrated circuits and they were so big that they occupied entire rooms. The modern computers we use today are a direct result of Shockley's work.

11.1 Investigations

There are a large number of possible starting points for these investigations so it may be possible to allow students to choose investigations which appeal to them. On other occasions the same investigation may be set to a whole class.

Here are a few guidelines for you:

- If the set problem is too complicated try an easier case.
- Draw your own diagrams.
- Make tables of your results and be systematic.
- Look for patterns.
- Is there a rule or formula to describe the results?
- Can you *predict* further results?
- Can you *prove* any rules which you may find?

1. Opposite corners

Here the numbers are arranged in 10 columns.

1	2	3	4	5	6	7	8	9	10
11	12	13	14	15	16	17	18	19	20
21	22	23	24	25	26	27	28	29	30
31	32	33	34	35	36	37	38	39	40
41	42	43	44	45	46	47	48	49	50
51	52	53	54	55	56	57	58	59	60
61	62	63	64	65	66	67	68	69	70
71	72	73	74	75	76	77	78	79	80
81	82	83	84	85	86	87	88	89	90
91	92	93	94	95	96	97	98	99	100

In the 2×2 square

$7 \times 18 = 126$

$8 \times 17 = 136$

7	8
17	18

the difference between them is 10.

In the 3×3 square

$12 \times 34 = 408$

$14 \times 32 = 448$

12	13	14
22	23	24
32	33	34

the difference between them is 40.

Investigate to see if you can find any rules or patterns connecting the size of square chosen and the difference.

If you find a rule, use it to *predict* the difference for larger squares.

Test your rule by looking at squares like 8×8 or 9×9.

Can you *generalise* the rule?

[What is the difference for a square of size $n \times n$?]

Can you prove the rule?

What happens if the numbers are arranged in six columns or seven columns?

In a 3×3 square …

x		?
?		?

1	2	3	4	5	6
7	8	9	10	11	12
13	14	15	16	17	18
19	–	–	–	–	–

1	2	3	4	5	6	7
8	9	10	11	12	13	14
15	16	17	18	19	20	21
22	–	–	–	–	–	–

2. Scales

In the diagram we are measuring the mass of the package x using two masses.

If the scales are balanced, x must be 2 kg.

Show how you can measure all the masses from 1 kg to 10 kg using three masses: 1 kg, 3 kg, 6 kg.

It is possible to measure all the masses from 1 kg to 13 kg using a different set of three masses. What are the three masses?

It is possible to measure all the masses from 1 kg to 40 kg using four masses. What are the masses?

3. Buying stamps

You have one 1c, one 2c, one 5c and one 10c coin.

You can buy stamps of any value you like, but you must give the exact money.

How many different value stamps can you buy?

Suppose you now have one 1c, one 2c, one 5c, one 10c, one 20c, one 50c and one $1 note.

How many different value stamps can you buy now?

4. Frogs

This is a game invented by a French mathematician called Lucas.

Aim: To swap the positions of the discs so that they end up the other way round (with a space in the middle).

Rules 1. A disc can slide one square in either direction onto an empty square.

2. A disc can hop over one adjacent disc of the other colour provided it can land on an empty square.

Example **a)** Slide Ⓐ one square to the right.

b) Ⓑ hops over Ⓐ to the left.

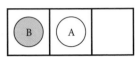

c) Slide Ⓐ one square to the right.

We took 3 moves.

1. Look at the diagram. What is the smallest number of moves needed for two discs of each colour?

2. Now try three discs of each colour. Can you complete the task in 15 moves?

3. Try four discs of each colour.

   Now look at your results and try to find a formula which gives the least number of moves needed for any number of discs *x*. It may help if you count the number of 'hops' and 'slides' separately.

4. Try the game with a different number of discs on each side. Say two reds and three blues. Play the game with different combinations and again try to find a formula giving the number of moves for *x* discs of one colour and *y* discs of another colour.

5. Triples

In this investigation a *triple* consists of three whole numbers in a definite order. For example, (4, 2, 1) is a triple and (1, 4, 2) is a different triple.

The three numbers in a triple do not have to be different. For example, (2, 2, 3) is a triple but (2, 0, 1) is not a triple because 0 is not allowed.

The *sum* of a triple is found by adding the three numbers together. So the sum of (4, 2, 1) is 7.

Investigate how many different triples there are with a given sum. See what happens to the number of different triples as the sum is changed.

If you find any pattern, try to explain why it occurs.

How many different triples are there whose sum is 22?

6. Mystic rose

Straight lines are drawn between each of the 12 points on the circle. Every point is joined to every other point. How many straight lines are there?

Suppose we draw a mystic rose with 24 points on the circle. How many straight lines are there?

How many straight lines would there be with n points on the circle?

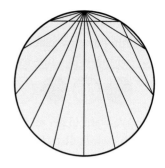

7. Knockout competition

Eight teams reach the 'knockout' stage of the World Cup.

```
England    2 ⎤
             ⎬──── England   1 ⎤
Germany    1 ⎦                 ⎬──── Brazil   1
France     0 ⎤                 ⎟
             ⎬──── Brazil    3 ⎦
Brazil     1 ⎦

Argentina  3 ⎤
             ⎬──── Argentina 0 ⎤
Italy      0 ⎦                 ⎬──── Morocco  2
Scotland   2 ⎤                 ⎟
             ⎬──── Morocco   1 ⎦
Morocco    3 ⎦
```

How would you organise a knockout competition if there were 12 teams? Or 15?

How many matches are played up to and including the final if there are:

a) 8 teams,

b) 12 teams,

c) 15 teams,

d) 23 teams,

e) n teams?

In a major tournament like Wimbledon, the better players are seeded from 1 to 16. Can you organise a tournament for 32 players so that, if they win all their games:

a) seeds 1 and 2 can meet in the final

b) seeds 1, 2, 3 and 4 can meet in the semi-finals

c) seeds 1, 2, 3, 4, 5, 6, 7, 8 can meet in the quarter-finals?

8. Discs

a) You have five black discs and five white discs which are arranged in a line as shown.

We want to get all the black discs to the right-hand end and all the white discs to the left-hand end.

The only move allowed is to interchange two neighbouring discs.

 becomes

How many moves does it take?

How many moves would it take if we had fifty black discs and fifty white discs arranged alternately?

b) Suppose the discs are arranged in pairs

 … etc.

How many moves would it take if we had fifty black discs and fifty white discs arranged like this?

> In both cases work with a smaller number of discs until you can see a pattern.

c) Now suppose you have three colours, black, white and green, arranged alternately.

 … etc.

You want to get all the black discs to the right, the green discs to the left and the white discs in the middle.

How many moves would it take if you have 30 discs of each colour?

9. Chessboard

Start with a small board, just 4 × 4.

How many squares are there? [It is not just 16!]

How many squares are there on an 8 × 8 chessboard?

How many squares are there on an $n \times n$ chessboard?

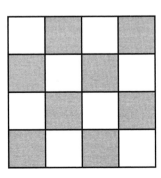

10. Area and perimeter

This is about finding different shapes in which the area is numerically equal to the perimeter.

This rectangle has an area of 10 square units and a perimeter of 14 units, so we will have to try another one.

There are some suggestions below but you can investigate shapes of your own choice if you prefer.

a) Find rectangles with equal area and perimeter. After a while you can try adding on bits like this.

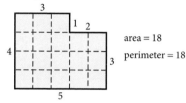

area = 18
perimeter = 18

b) Suppose one dimension of the rectangle is fixed. In this rectangle the length is 5 units.

c) Try right-angled triangles and equilateral triangles.

d) Try circles, semi-circles and so on.

e) How about three-dimensional shapes? Now we are looking for cuboids, spheres, cylinders in which the volume is numerically equal to the surface area.

f) Can you find any connection between the square with equal area and perimeter and the circle with equal area and perimeter? How about the equilateral triangle with equal area and perimeter?

11. Happy numbers (and more)

a) Take the number 23.

Square the digits and add.

2   3

$2^2 + 3^2 = 1$ 3

$1^2 + 3^2 = 1$ 0

$1^2 + 0^2 = 1$

The sequence ends at 1 and we call 23 a 'happy' number.

Investigate for other numbers. Here are a few suggestions:
70, 85, 49, 44, 14, 15, 94.

b) Now change the rule. Instead of squaring the digits we will cube them.

$$2 \quad 1$$
$$2^3 + 1^3 = 0 \quad 9$$
$$0^3 + 9^3 = 7 \quad 2 \quad 9$$
$$7^3 + 2^3 + 9^3 = 1 \quad 0 \quad 8 \quad 0$$
$$1^3 + 0^3 + 8^3 + 0^3 = 5 \quad 1 \quad 3$$
$$5^3 + 1^3 + 3^3 = 153$$

And now we are stuck because 153 leads to 153 again.

Investigate for numbers of your own choice. Do any numbers lead to 1?

12. Prime numbers

Write all the numbers from 1 to 104 in eight columns and draw a
ring around the prime numbers 2, 3, 5 and 7.

1	②	③	4	⑤	6	⑦	8
9	10	11	12	13	14	15	16
17	18	19	20	21	22	23	24
25							

If we cross out all the multiples of 2, 3, 5 and 7, we will be left with
all the prime numbers below 104. Can you see why this works?

Draw *four* lines to eliminate the multiples of 2.

Draw *six* lines to eliminate the multiples of 3.

Draw *two* lines to eliminate the multiples of 7.

Cross out all the numbers ending in 5.

Put a ring around all the prime numbers less than 104.

[Check there are 27 numbers.]

Many prime numbers can be written as the sum of two squares.

For example $5 = 2^2 + 1^2$, $13 = 3^2 + 2^2$. Find all the prime numbers
in your table which can be written as the sum of two squares.
Draw a red ring around them in the table.

What do you notice?

Check any 'gaps' you may have found.

Extend the table up to 200 and see if the pattern continues. In this
case you will need to eliminate the multiples of 11 and 13 as well.

13. Squares

For this investigation you need either dotted paper or squared paper.

The shaded square has an area of 1 unit.

Can you draw a square, with its corners on the dots, with an area of 2 units?

Can you draw a square with an area of 3 units?

Can you draw a square with an area of 4 units?

Investigate for squares up to 100 units.

For which numbers x can you draw a square of area x units?

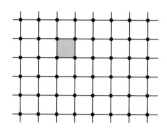

14. Painting cubes

The large cube below consists of 27 unit cubes.

All six faces of the large cube are painted green.

How many unit cubes have 3 green faces?

How many unit cubes have 2 green faces?

How many unit cubes have 1 green face?

How many unit cubes have 0 green faces?

Suppose the large cube is $20 \times 20 \times 20$.

Answer the four questions above.

Answer the four questions for the cube which is $n \times n \times n$.

15. Final score

The final score in a football match was 3–2. How many different scores were possible at half-time?

Investigate for other final scores where the difference between the teams is always one goal [1–0, 5–4, etc]. Is there a pattern or rule which would tell you the number of possible half-time scores in a game which finished 58–57?

Suppose the game ends in a draw. Find a rule which would tell you the number of possible half-time scores if the final score was 63–63.

Investigate for other final scores [3–0, 5–1, 4–2, etc].

16. Cutting paper

The rectangle ABCD is cut in half to give two smaller rectangles.

Each of the smaller rectangles is mathematically similar to the large rectangle. Find a rectangle which has this property.

What happens when the small rectangles are cut in half? Do they have the same property?

Why is this a useful shape for paper used in business?

17. Matchstick shapes

a) Here we have a sequence of matchstick shapes

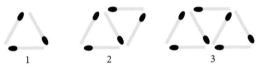

Can you work out the number of matches in the 10th member of the sequence? Or the 20th member of the sequence?

How about the nth member of the sequence?

b) Now try to answer the same questions for the patterns below. Or you may prefer to design patterns of your own.

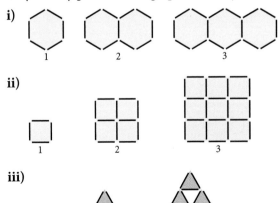

i)

ii)

iii)

18. Maximum box

a) You have a square sheet of card 24 cm by 24 cm.

You can make a box (without a lid) by cutting squares from the corners and folding up the sides.

What size corners should you cut out so that the volume of the box is as large as possible?

Try different sizes for the corners and record the results in a table:

length of the side of the corner square (cm)	dimensions of the open box (cm)	volume of the box (cm³)
1	$22 \times 22 \times 1$	484
2		
–		
–		

Now consider boxes made from different-sized cards: 15 cm by 15 cm and 20 cm by 20 cm.

What size corners should you cut out this time so that the volume of the box is as large as possible?

Is there a connection between the size of the corners cut out and the size of the square card?

b) Investigate the situation when the card is not square.

Take rectangular cards where the length is twice the width (20×10, 12×6, 18×9, etc).

Again, for the maximum volume is there a connection between the size of the corners cut out and the size of the original card?

19. Digit sum

Take the number 134.

Add the digits $1 + 3 + 4 = 8$.

The digit sum of 134 is 8.

Take the number 238.

$2 + 3 + 8 = 13$ [We continue if the sum is more than 9].

$\quad 1 + 3 = 4$

The digit sum of 238 is 4.

Consider the multiples of 3:

Number	3	6	9	12	15	18	21	24	27	30	33	36
Digit sum	3	6	9	3	6	9	3	6	9	3	6	9

The digit sum is always 3, 6, or 9.

These numbers can be shown on a circle.

Investigate the pattern of the digit sums for multiples of:

a) 2   **b)** 5   **c)** 6   **d)** 7   **e)** 8

f) 9   **g)** 11   **h)** 12   **i)** 13

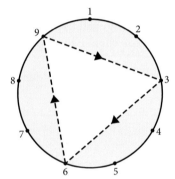

Is there any connection between numbers where the pattern of the digit sums is the same?

Can you (without doing all the usual working) predict what the pattern would be for multiples of 43? Or 62?

20. An expanding diagram

Look at the series of diagrams below.

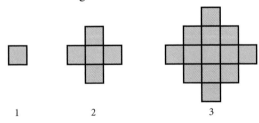

1   2   3

Each time new squares are added all around the outside of the previous diagram.

Draw the next few diagrams in the series and count the number of squares in each one.

How many squares are there in diagram number 15 or in diagram number 50?

What happens if we work in three dimensions? Instead of adding squares we add cubes all around the outside. How many cubes are there in the fifth member of the series or the fifteenth?

21. Fibonacci sequence

Fibonacci was the nickname of the Italian mathematician Leonardo de Pisa (A.D. 1170–1250). The sequence which bears his name has fascinated mathematicians for hundreds of years. You can if you like join the Fibonacci Association which was formed in 1963.

Here is the start of the sequence

1, 1, 2, 3, 5, 8, 13, 21, 34, 55, 89, 144, …

There are no prizes for working out the next term!

The sequence has many interesting properties to investigate. Here are a few suggestions.

a) Add three terms.

$1 + 1 + 2, 1 + 2 + 3$, etc.

Add four terms.

b) Add squares of terms

$1^2 + 1^2, 1^2 + 2^2, 2^2 + 3^2, …$

c) Ratios

$\frac{1}{1} = 1, \frac{2}{1} = 2, \frac{3}{2} = 1.5, …$

d) In fours $\boxed{2 \ \ 3 \ \ 5 \ \ 8}$

$2 \times 8 = 16, 3 \times 5 = 15$

e) In threes $\boxed{3 \ \ 5 \ \ 8}$

$3 \times 8 = 24, 5^2 = 25$

f) In sixes $\boxed{1 \ \ 1 \ \ 2 \ \ 3 \ \ 5 \ \ 8}$

square and add the first five numbers

$1^2 + 1^2 + 2^2 + 3^2 + 5^2 = 40$

$\qquad\qquad 5 \times 8 = 40.$

Now try seven numbers from the sequence, or eight …

g) Take a group of 10 consecutive terms. Compare the sum of the 10 terms with the seventh member of the group.

22. Alphabetical order

A teacher has four names on a piece of paper which are in no particular order (say Smith, Jones, Biggs, Eaton). He wants the names in alphabetical order.

One way of doing this is to interchange each pair of names which are clearly out of order.

So he could start like this; S J   B E

the order becomes   J   S   B   E

He would then interchange S and B.

Using this method, what is the largest number of interchanges he could possibly have to make?

What if he had thirty names, or fifty?

23. Tiles

Gao counts the tiles by placing them in a pattern consisting of alternate red and white tiles. This one is five tiles across and altogether there are 13 tiles in the pattern.

He makes the pattern so that there are always red tiles all around the outside. Draw the pattern which is nine tiles across. You should find that there are 41 tiles in the pattern.

How many tiles are there in the pattern which is 101 tiles across?

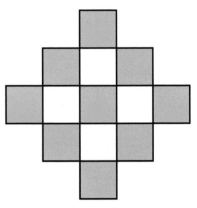

24. Diagonals

In a 4×7 rectangle the diagonal passes through 10 squares.

Draw rectangles of your own choice and count the number of squares through which the diagonal passes.

A rectangle is 640×250. How many squares will the diagonal pass through?

25. Biggest number

A calculator has the following buttons:

$$+ \quad - \quad \times \quad \div \quad (\quad) \quad y^x \quad =$$

Also the only digits buttons which work are the '1', '2' and '3'.

a)   You can press any button, but only once.

   What is the biggest number you can get?

b)   Now the '1', '2', '3' and '4' buttons are working.

   What is the biggest number you can get?

c)   Investigate what happens as you increase the number of digits which you can use.

26. What shape tin?

We need a cylindrical tin which will contain a volume of 600 cm³ of drink.

600 cm³

COLA

What shape should we make the tin so that we use the minimum amount of metal?

In other words, for a volume of 600 cm³, what is the smallest possible surface area?

What shape tin should we design to contain a volume of 1000 cm³?

Make a table.

r	h	A
2	?	?
3	?	?
⋮		

27. Spotted shapes

For this investigation you need dotted paper. If you have not got any, you can make your own using a felt tip pen and squared paper.

The rectangle in Diagram 1 has 10 dots on the perimeter ($p = 10$) and 2 dots inside the shape ($i = 2$). The area of the shape is 6 square units ($A = 6$).

The triangle in Diagram 2 has 9 dots on the perimeter ($p = 9$) and 4 dots inside the shape ($i = 4$). The area of the triangle is $7\frac{1}{2}$ square units $\left(A = 7\frac{1}{2} \right)$.

Draw more shapes of your own design and record the values for p, i and A in a table. Make some of your shapes more difficult like the one in Diagram 3.

Can you find a formula connecting p, i and A?

Try out your formula with some more shapes to see if it always works.

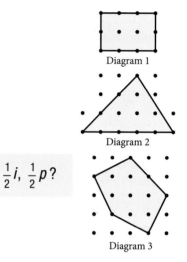

Diagram 1

Diagram 2

$\frac{1}{2}i, \frac{1}{2}p$?

Diagram 3

28. Stopping distances

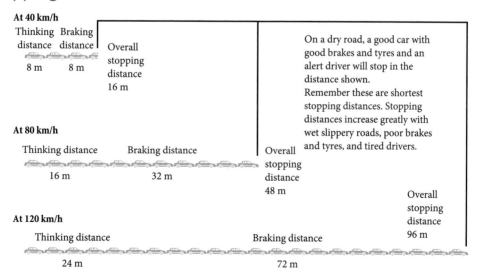

At 40 km/h

Thinking distance   Braking distance

8 m   8 m

Overall stopping distance 16 m

On a dry road, a good car with good brakes and tyres and an alert driver will stop in the distance shown.
Remember these are shortest stopping distances. Stopping distances increase greatly with wet slippery roads, poor brakes and tyres, and tired drivers.

At 80 km/h

Thinking distance   Braking distance

16 m   32 m

Overall stopping distance 48 m

At 120 km/h

Thinking distance   Braking distance

24 m   72 m

Overall stopping distance 96 m

This diagram from the Highway Code (see previous page) gives the overall stopping distances for cars travelling at various speeds.

What is meant by 'thinking distance'?

Work out the thinking distance for a car travelling at a speed of 90 km/h. What is the formula which connects the speed of the car and the thinking distance?

(More difficult)

Try to find a formula which connects the speed of the car and the *overall* stopping distance. It may help if you draw a graph of speed (across the page) against *braking* distance (up the page).

What curve are you reminded of?

Check that your formula gives the correct answer for the overall stopping distance at a speed of:

a) 40 km/h   b) 120 km/h.

29. Maximum cylinder

A rectangular piece of paper has a fixed perimeter of 40 cm. It could for example be 7 cm × 13 cm.

This paper can make a hollow cylinder of height 7 cm or of height 13 cm.

Work out the volume of each cylinder.

What dimensions should the paper have so that it can make a cylinder of the maximum possible volume?

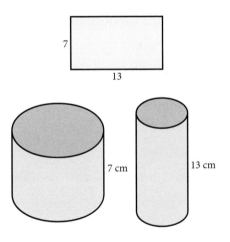

11.2 Practical problems

1. Timetabling

a) Every year a new timetable has to be written for the school. We will look at the problem of writing the timetable for one department (mathematics). The department allocates the teaching periods as follows:

Upper 6   2 sets (at the same times); 8 periods in 4 doubles.
Lower 6   2 sets (at the same times); 8 periods in 4 doubles.
Year   5   6 sets (at the same times); 5 single periods.
Year   4   6 sets (at the same times); 5 single periods.
Year   3   6 sets (at the same times); 5 single periods.
Year   2   6 sets (at the same times); 5 single periods.

Year   1   5 mixed ability forms; 5 single periods not
              necessarily at the same times.

Here are the teachers and the maximum number of maths periods which they can teach.

A   33
B   33
C   33
D   20
E   20
F   15   (must be years 5, 4, 3)
G   10   (must be years 2, 1)
H   10   (must be years 2, 1)
I   5   (must be year 3)

Furthermore, to ensure some continuity of teaching, teachers B and C must teach the U6 (Upper Sixth) and teachers A, B, C, D, E, F must teach year 5.

Here is a timetable form which has been started:

M	5				U6 B, C	U6 B, C		
Tu		5	U6 B, C	U6 B, C				
W					5			
Th						5	U6 B, C	U6 B, C
F	U6 B, C	U6 B, C		5				

Your task is to write a complete timetable for the mathematics department subject to the restrictions already stated.

b) If that was too easy, here are some changes.

U6 and L6 have 4 sets each (still 8 periods).

Two new teachers: J   20 periods maximum
                    K   15 periods maximum but cannot teach on Mondays.

Because of games lessons: A cannot teach Wednesday afternoon
                            B cannot teach Tuesday afternoon
                            C cannot teach Friday afternoon.

Also: A, B, C and E must teach U6

A, B, C, D, E, F must teach year 5.

For the students, games afternoons are as follows:

Monday year 2; Tuesday year 3; Wednesday year 5 L6, U6;

Thursday year 4; Friday year 1.

2. Hiring a car

You are going to hire a car for one week (seven days).

Which of the firms below should you choose?

Car rental

Gibson car hire	Snowdon rent-a-car	Hav-a-car
$170 per week	$10 per day	$60 per week
no charge up to 10 000 km	6.5c per km	500 km without charge
		22c per km over 500 km

Work out as detailed an answer as possible.

3. Running a business

Mr Singh runs a small business making two sorts of steam cleaner: the basic model B and the deluxe model D.

Here are the details of the manufacturing costs:

	Model B	Model D
Assembly time (in man-hours)	20 hours	30 hours
Component costs	$35	$25
Selling price	$195	$245

He employs 10 people and pays them each $160 for a 40-hour week. He can spend up to $525 per week on components.

a) In one week the firm makes and sells six cleaners of each model. Does he make a profit?

[Remember he has to pay his employees for a full week.]

b) What number of each model should he make so that he makes as much profit as possible? Assume he can sell all the machines which he makes.

4. How many of each?

A shop owner has room in her shop for up to 20 televisions. She can buy either type A for $150 each or type B for $300 each.

She has a total of $4500 she can spend and she must have at least 6 of each type in stock. She makes a profit of $80 on each television of type A and a profit of $100 on each of type B.

A cost $150

B cost $300

How many of each type should she buy so that she makes the maximum profit?

11.3 Puzzles and experiments

1. Cross numbers

a) Copy out the cross number pattern.

b) Fit all the given numbers into the correct spaces. Tick off the numbers from the lists as you write them in the square.

1.

(grid with shaded cells, containing the clue number 6)

2 digits	3 digits	4 digits	5 digits	6 digits
11	121	2104	14 700	216 841
17	147	2356	24 567	588 369
18	170	2456	25 921	846 789
19	174	3714	26 759	861 277
23	204	4711	30 388	876 452
31	247	5548	50 968	
37	287	5678	51 789	
58	324	6231	78 967	
61	431	6789	98 438	
62	450	7630		*7 digits*
62	612	9012		6 645 678
70	678	9921		
74	772			
81	774			
85	789			
94	870			
99				

2.

2 digits		3 digits	4 digits	5 digits	6 digits
12	47	129	2096	12 641	324 029
14	48	143	3966	23 449	559 641
16	54	298	5019	33 111	956 782
18	56	325	5665	33 210	
20	63	331	6462	34 509	
21	67	341	7809	40 551	
23	81	443	8019	41 503	
26	90	831	8652	44 333	*7 digits*
27	91	923		69 786	1 788 932
32	93			88 058	5 749 306
38	98			88 961	
39	99			90 963	
46				94 461	
				99 654	

2. Estimating game

This is a game for two players. On squared paper draw an answer grid with the numbers shown below.

Answer grid

891	7047	546	2262	8526	429
2548	231	1479	357	850	7938
663	1078	2058	1014	1666	3822
1300	1950	819	187	1050	3393
4350	286	3159	442	2106	550
1701	4050	1377	4900	1827	957

The players now take turns to choose two numbers from the question grid below and multiply them on a calculator.

Question grid

11	26	81
17	39	87
21	50	98

The game continues until all the numbers in the answer grid have been crossed out. The object is to get four answers in a line (horizontally, vertically or diagonally). The winner is the player with most lines of four.

A line of *five* counts as *two* lines of four.

A line of *six* counts as *three* lines of four.

3. The chessboard problem

a) On the 4×4 square shown we have placed four objects subject to the restriction that nowhere are there two objects on the same row, column or diagonal.

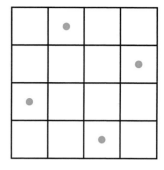

Subject to the same restrictions:

   i) find a solution for a 5×5 square, using five objects

   ii) find a solution for a 6×6 square, using six objects

   iii) find a solution for a 7×7 square, using seven objects

   iv) find a solution for a 8×8 square, using eight objects.

It is called the chessboard problem because the objects could be 'Queens' which can move any number of squares in any direction.

b) Suppose we remove the restriction that no two Queens can be on the same row, column or diagonal. Is it possible to attack every square on an 8×8 chessboard with fewer than eight Queens?

Try the same problem with other pieces like knights or bishops.

4. Creating numbers

Using only the numbers 1, 2, 3 and 4 once each and the operations $+, -, \times, \div, !$ create every number from 1 to 100.

You can use the numbers as powers and you must use all of the numbers 1, 2, 3 and 4.

[4! is pronounced 'four factorial' and means $4 \times 3 \times 2 \times 1$ (i.e. 24)

Similarly $3! = 3 \times 2 \times 1 = 6$
                 $5! = 5 \times 4 \times 3 \times 2 \times 1 = 120]$

Examples: $1 = (4-3) \div (2-1)$
                 $20 = 4^2 + 3 + 1$
                 $68 = 34 \times 2 \times 1$
                 $100 = (4!+1)(3!-2!)$

5. Pentominoes

A pentomino is a set of five squares joined along their edges. Here are three of the twelve different pentomino designs.

a) Find the other nine pentomino designs to make up the complete set of twelve. Reflections or rotations of other pentominoes are not allowed.

b) On squared paper draw an 8 × 8 square. It is possible to fill up the 8 × 8 square with the twelve different pentominoes together with a 2 × 2 square. Here we have made a possible start.

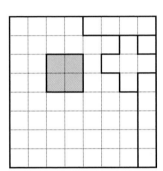

There are in fact many different ways in which this can be done.

c) Now draw a 10 × 6 rectangle.

Try to fill up the rectangle with as many different pentominoes as you can. This problem is more difficult than the previous one but it is possible to fill up the rectangle with the twelve different pentominoes.

6. Calculator words

On a calculator work out $9508^2 + 192^2 + 10^2 + 6$. If you turn the calculator upside down and use a little imagination, you can see the word 'HEDGEHOG'.

Find the words given by the clues below.

1. $19 \times 20 \times 14 - 2.66$ (not an upstanding man)

2. $(84 + 17) \times 5$ (dotty message)

3. $904^2 + 89\,621\,818$ (prickly customer)

4. $(559 \times 6) + (21 \times 55)$ (what a surprise!)

5. $566 \times 711 - 23\,617$ (bolt it down)

6. $\dfrac{9999 + 319}{8.47 + 2.53}$ (sit up and plead)

7. $\dfrac{2601 \times 6}{4^2 + 1^2}$; $(401 - 78) \times 5^2$ (two words) (not a great man)

8. $0.4^2 - 0.1^2$ (little Sidney)

9. $\dfrac{(27 \times 2000 - 2)}{(0.63 \div 0.09)}$ (not quite a mountain)

10. $(5^2 - 1^2)^4 - 14\,239$ (just a name)

11. $48^4 + 102^2 - 4^2$ (pursuits)

12. $615^2 + (7 \times 242)$ (almost a goggle)

13. $(130 \times 135) + (23 \times 3 \times 11 \times 23)$ (wobbly)

14. $164 \times 166^2 + 734$ (almost big)

15. $8794^2 + 25 \times 342.28 + 120 \times 25$ (thin skin)

16. $0.08 - (3^2 \div 10^4)$ (ice house)

17. $235^2 - (4 \times 36.5)$ (shiny surface)

18. $(80^2 + 60^2) \times 3 + 81^2 + 12^2 + 3013$ (ship gunge)

19. $3 \times 17 \times (329^2 + 2 \times 173)$ (unlimited)

20. $230 \times 230\frac{1}{2} + 30$ (fit feet)

21. $33 \times 34 \times 35 + 15 \times 3$ (beleaguer)

22. $0.32^2 + \dfrac{1}{1000}$ (Did he or didn't he?)

23. $(23 \times 24 \times 25 \times 26) + (3 \times 11 \times 10^3) - 20$ (help)

24. $(16^2 + 16)^2 - (13^2 \div 2)$ (slander)

25. $(3 \times 661)^2 - (3^6 + 22)$ (pester)

26. $(22^2 + 29.4) \times 10$; $(3.03^2 - 0.02^2) \times 100^2$ (four words) (Goliath)

27. $1.25 \times 0.2^6 + 0.2^2$ (tissue time)

28. $(3^3)^2 + 2^2$ (wriggler)

29. $14 + (5 \times (83^2 + 110))$ (bigger than a duck)

30. $2 \times 3 \times 53 \times 10^4 + 9$ (opposite to hello, almost!)

31. $(177 \times 179 \times 182) + (85 \times 86) - 82$ (good salesman)

32. $6.2 \times 0.987 \times 1\,000\,000 - 860^2 + 118$ (flying ace)

33. $(426 \times 474) + (318 \times 487) + 22\,018$ (close to a bubble)

12 Revision Tests

Test 1

1. How many mm are there in 1 m 1 cm?

   A 1001   **B** 1110   **C** 1010   **D** 1100

2. The circumference of a circle is 16π cm. The radius, in cm, of the circle is

   A 2   **B** 4   **C** $\dfrac{4}{\pi}$ **D** 8

3. In the triangle below the value of $\cos x$ is

   A 0.8

   B 1.333

   C 0.75

   D 0.6

   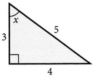

4. The line $y = 2x - 1$ cuts the x-axis at P. The coordinates of P are

   A $(0, -1)$ **B** $\left(\dfrac{1}{2}, 0\right)$ **C** $\left(-\dfrac{1}{2}, 0\right)$ **D** $(-1, 0)$

5. The formula $b + \dfrac{x}{a} = c$ is rearranged to make x the subject. What is x?

   A $a(c - b)$ **B** $ac - b$ **C** $\dfrac{c - b}{a}$ **D** $ac + ab$

6. The mean mass of a group of 11 men is 70 kg. What is the mean mass of the remaining group when a man of mass 90 kg leaves?

   A 80 kg   **B** 72 kg   **C** 68 kg   **D** 62 kg

7. How many lines of symmetry has this shape?

   A 0

   B 1

   C 2

   D 4

8. In standard form the value of $200 \times 80\,000$ is

   A 16×10^6 **B** 1.6×10^9 **C** 1.6×10^7 **D** 1.6×10^8

9. The solutions of the equation $(x - 3)(2x + 1) = 0$ are

   A $-3, \dfrac{1}{2}$ **B** $3, -2$ **C** $3, -\dfrac{1}{2}$ **D** $-3, -2$

10. In the triangle the size of angle x is

   A   35°

   B   70°

   C   110°

   D   40°

11. A man paid tax on $9000 at 30%. He paid the tax in 12 equal payments. Each payment was

   A $2.25   **B** $22.50   **C** $225   **D** $250

12. The approximate value of $\dfrac{3.96 \times (0.5)^2}{97.1}$ is

   A   0.01   **B**   0.02   **C**   0.04   **D**   0.1

13. Given that $\dfrac{3}{n} = 5$, then $n =$

   A   2   **B**   −2   **C** $1\frac{2}{3}$ **D**   0.6

14. Cube A has side 2 cm. Cube B has side 4 cm.

$$\left(\frac{\text{Volume of B}}{\text{Volume of A}} \right) =$$

   A   2   **B**   4   **C**   8   **D**   16

15. How many square tiles of side 50 cm will be needed to cover the floor shown?

   A   16

   B   32

   C   64

   D   84

16. The equation $ax^2 + x - 6 = 0$ has a solution $x = -2$. What is a?

   A   1   **B**   −2   **C** $\sqrt{2}$ **D**   2

17. Which of the following is/are correct?

   1. $\sqrt{0.16} = \pm 0.4$

   2. $0.2 \div 0.1 = 0.2$

   3. $\dfrac{4}{7} > \dfrac{3}{5}$

   A   *1* only   **B**   *2* only   **C**   *3* only   **D**   *1* and *2*

18. How many prime numbers are there between 30 and 40?

   A   0   **B**   1   **C**   2   **D**   3

19. A man is paid $600 per week after a pay rise of 20%. What was he paid before?

   A $480   **B** $500   **C** $540   **D** $580

20. A car travels for 20 minutes at 45 km/h and then for 40 minutes at 60 km/h. The average speed for the whole journey is

   A $52\frac{1}{2}$ km/h   **B** 50 km/h   **C** 54 km/h   **D** 55 km/h

21. The point $(3, -1)$ is reflected in the line $y = 2$. The new coordinates are

   A $(3, 5)$ **B** $(1, -1)$ **C** $(3, 4)$ **D** $(0, -1)$

22. Two discs are randomly taken without replacement from a bag containing 3 red discs and 2 blue discs. What is the probability of taking 2 red discs?

   A $\dfrac{9}{25}$ **B** $\dfrac{1}{10}$ **C** $\dfrac{3}{10}$ **D** $\dfrac{2}{5}$

23. The shaded area, in cm², is

   A $16 - 2\pi$

   B $16 - 4\pi$

   C $\dfrac{4}{\pi}$

   D $64 - 8\pi$

8 cm

8 cm

24. Given the equation $5^x = 120$, the best approximate solution is $x =$

   A 2   **B** 3   **C** 4   **D** 25

25. What is the sine of 45°?

   A 1

   B $\dfrac{1}{2}$

   C $\dfrac{1}{\sqrt{2}}$

   D $\sqrt{2}$

Test 2

1. What is the value of the expression $(x - 2)(x + 4)$ when $x = -1$?

   A 9   **B** -9   **C** 5   **D** -5

2. The perimeter of a square is 36 cm. What is its area?

   A 36 cm²   **B** 324 cm²   **C** 81 cm²   **D** 9 cm²

3. AB is a diameter of the circle. Find the angle **BCO**.

   A 70°

   B 20°

   C 60°

   D 50°

4. The gradient of the line $2x + y = 3$ is

   A 3   **B** -2 **C** $\frac{1}{2}$ **D** $-\frac{1}{2}$

5. A firm employs 1200 people, of whom 240 are men. The percentage of employees who are men is

   A 40%   **B** 10%   **C** 15%   **D** 20%

6. A car is travelling at a constant speed of 30 km/h. How far will the car travel in 10 minutes?

   A $\frac{1}{3}$ mile   **B** 3 km   **C** 5 km   **D** 6 km

7. What are the coordinates of the point $(1, -1)$ after reflection in the line $y = x$?

   A $(-1, 1)$ **B** $(1, 1)$ **C** $(-1, -1)$ **D** $(1, -1)$

8. $\frac{1}{3} + \frac{2}{5} =$

   A $\dfrac{2}{8}$ **B** $\dfrac{3}{8}$ **C** $\dfrac{3}{15}$ **D** $\dfrac{11}{15}$

9. In the triangle the size of the largest angle is

   A 30°

   B 90°

   C 120°

   D 80°

Not to scale

10. 800 decreased by 5% is

   A 795   **B** 640   **C** 760   **D** 400

11. Which of the statements is (are) true?

   1. $\tan 60° = 2$

   2. $\sin 60° = \cos 30°$

   3. $\sin 30° > \cos 30°$

   A *1* only   **B** *2* only   **C** *3* only   **D** *2* and *3*

12. Given $a = \frac{3}{5}, b = \frac{1}{3}, c = \frac{1}{2}$ then

   A $a < b < c$ **B** $a < c < b$ **C** $a > b > c$ **D** $a > c > b$

13. The *larger* angle between south-west and east is

   A 225°   **B** 240°   **C** 135°   **D** 315°

14. Each exterior angle of a regular polygon with n sides is 10°; $n =$

   A 9   **B** 18   **C** 30   **D** 36

15. What is the value of $1 - 0.05$ as a fraction?

   A $\dfrac{1}{20}$ **B** $\dfrac{9}{10}$ **C** $\dfrac{19}{20}$ **D** $\dfrac{5}{100}$

16. Find the length x.

   A 5

   B 6

   C 8

   D $\sqrt{50}$

17. Given that $m = 2$ and $n = -3$, what is mn^2?

   A -18 **B** 18   **C** -36 **D** 36

18. The graph of $y = (x - 3)(x - 2)$ cuts the y-axis at P.

The coordinates of P are

   A $(0, 6)$ **B** $(6, 0)$ **C** $(2, 0)$ **D** $(3, 0)$

19. $240 is shared in the ratio $2:3:7$. The largest share is

   A $130   **B** $140   **C** $150   **D** $160

20. Adjacent angles in a parallelogram are $x°$ and $3x°$.

The smallest angles in the parallelogram are each

   A $30°$ **B** $45°$ **C** $60°$ **D** $120°$

21. When the sides of a square are increased by 10% the area is increased by

   A 10%   **B** 20%   **C** 21%   **D** 15%

22. The volume, in cm³, of the cylinder is

   A 9π

   B 12π

   C 600π

   D 900π

23. A car travels for 10 minutes at 30 km/h and then for 20 minutes at 45 km/h. The average speed for the whole journey is

   A 40 km/h   **B** $37\frac{1}{2}$ km/h **C** 20 km/h   **D** 35 km/h

24. Four people each toss a coin. What is the probability that the fourth person will toss a 'tail'?

   A $\dfrac{1}{2}$ **B** $\dfrac{1}{4}$ **C** $\dfrac{1}{8}$ **D** $\dfrac{1}{16}$

25. A rectangle 8 cm by 6 cm is inscribed inside a circle.

What is the area, in cm², of the circle?

   A 10π **B** 25π **C** 49π **D** 100π

Test 3

1. The price of a television changed from $240 to $300. What is the percentage increase?

    A 15%   **B** 20%   **C** 60%   **D** 25%

2. Find the length x.

    A 6

    B 5

    C $\sqrt{44}$

    D $\sqrt{18}$

    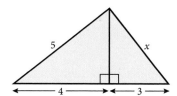

3. The bearing of A from B is 120°. What is the bearing of B from A?

    A 060°   **B** 120°   **C** 240°   **D** 300°

4. Numbers m, x and y satisfy the equation $y = mx^2$.

    When $m = \frac{1}{2}$ and $x = 4$ the value of y is

    A 4   **B** 8   **C** 1   **D** 2

5. A school has 400 students, of whom 250 are boys. The ratio of boys to girls is

    A 5:3   **B** 3:2   **C** 3:5   **D** 8:5

6. A train is travelling at a speed of 30 km per hour. How long will it take to travel 500 m?

    A 2 minutes   **B** $\frac{3}{50}$ hour   **C** 1 minute   **D** $\frac{1}{2}$ hour

7. The approximate value of $\dfrac{9.65 \times 0.203}{0.0198}$ is

    A 100   **B** 10   **C** 1   **D** 180

8. Which point does *not* lie on the curve $y = \dfrac{12}{x}$?

    A $(6, 2)$ **B** $(\frac{1}{2}, 24)$ **C** $(-3, -4)$ **D** $(3, -4)$

9. $t = \dfrac{c^3}{y}$, $y =$

    A $\dfrac{t}{c^3}$ **B** $c^3 t$ **C** $c^3 - t$ **D** $\dfrac{c^3}{t}$

10. The largest number of 1 cm cubes which will fit inside a cubical box of side 1 m is

    A 10^3 **B** 10^6 **C** 10^8 **D** 10^{12}

11. The shaded area in the Venn diagram represents

    A $A' \cup B$ **B** $A \cap B'$ **C** $A' \cap B$ **D** $(A \cap B)'$

12. Which of the following has the largest value?

   A $\sqrt{100}$ **B** $\sqrt{\dfrac{1}{0.1}}$ **C** $\sqrt{1000}$ **D** $\dfrac{1}{0.01}$

13. Two dice numbered 1 to 6 are thrown together and their scores are added. The probability that the sum will be 12 is

   A $\dfrac{1}{6}$ **B** $\dfrac{1}{12}$ **C** $\dfrac{1}{18}$ **D** $\dfrac{1}{36}$

14. The length, in cm, of the minor arc is

   A 2π

   B 3π

   C 6π

   D $13\frac{1}{2}\pi$

15. Metal of mass 84 kg is made into 40 000 pins. What is the mass, in kg, of one pin?

   A 0.0021   **B** 0.0036   **C** 0.021   **D** 0.21

16. What is the value of x which satisfies the simultaneous equations?

   $3x + y = 1$

   $x - 2y = 5$

   A −1   **B** 1   **C** −2   **D** 2

17. What is the new fare when the old fare of $250 is increased by 8%?

   A $258   **B** $260   **C** $270   **D** $281.25

18. What is the area of this triangle?

   A $12x^2$

   B $15x^2$

   C $16x^2$

   D $30x^2$

19. What values of x satisfy the inequality $2 - 3x > 1$?

   A $x < -\dfrac{1}{3}$ **B** $x > -\dfrac{1}{3}$ **C** $x > \dfrac{1}{3}$ **D** $x < \dfrac{1}{3}$

20. A right-angled triangle has sides in the ratio $5 : 12 : 13$. The tangent of the smallest angle is

   A $\dfrac{12}{5}$ **B** $\dfrac{12}{13}$ **C** $\dfrac{5}{13}$ **D** $\dfrac{5}{12}$

21. The area of ΔABE is 4 cm². The area of ΔACD is

A   10 cm²

B   6 cm²

C   25 cm²

D   16 cm²

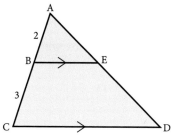

22. Given $2^x = 3$ and $2^y = 5$, the value of 2^{x+y} is

A   15   B   8   C   4   D   125

23. The probability of an event occurring is 0.35. The probability of the event *not* occurring is

A $\dfrac{1}{0.35}$ B   0.65   C   0.35   D   0

24. What fraction of the area of the rectangle is the area of the triangle?

A $\dfrac{1}{4}$

B $\dfrac{1}{8}$

C $\dfrac{1}{16}$

D $\dfrac{1}{32}$

25. On a map a distance of 36 km is represented by a line of 1.8 cm. What is the scale of the map?

A   1 : 2000   B   1 : 20 000   C   1 : 200 000   D   1 : 2 000 000

Test 4

1. What is the value of x satisfying the simultaneous equations

$3x + 2y = 13$

$x - 2y = -1$?

A   7   B   3   C $3\frac{1}{2}$ D   2

2. A straight line is 4.5 cm long. $\frac{2}{5}$ of the line is

A   0.4 cm   B   1.8 cm   C   2 cm   D   0.18 cm

3. The mean of four numbers is 12. The mean of three of the numbers is 13. What is the fourth number?

A 9   **B** 12.5   **C** 7   **D** 1

4. How many cubes of edge 3 cm are needed to fill a box with internal dimensions 12 cm by 6 cm by 6 cm?

A 8   **B** 18   **C** 16   **D** 24

For questions **5** to **7** use the diagram below.

5. The length of AB, in cm, is

A 6   **B** $\sqrt{116}$ **C** 8   **D** $\sqrt{84}$

6. The sine of angle DCB is

A 0.8   **B** 1.25   **C** 0.6   **D** 0.75

7. The tangent of angle CBD is

A 0.6   **B** 0.75   **C** 1.333   **D** 1.6

8. The value of 4865.355 correct to 2 significant figures is

A 4865.36   **B** 4865.35   **C** 4900   **D** 49

9. What values of y satisfy the inequality $4y - 1 < 0$?

A $y < 4$ **B** $y < -\frac{1}{4}$ **C** $y > \frac{1}{4}$ **D** $y < \frac{1}{4}$

10. The area of a circle is 100π cm². The radius, in cm, of the circle is

A 50   **B** 10   **C** $\sqrt{50}$ **D** 5

11. If $f(x) = x^2 - 3$, then $f(3) - f(-1) =$

A 5   **B** 10   **C** 8   **D** 9

12. In the triangle BE is parallel to CD. What is x?

A $6\frac{2}{3}$

B 6

C $7\frac{1}{2}$

D $5\frac{3}{4}$

13. The cube root of 64 is

A 2   **B** 4   **C** 8   **D** 16

14. Given $a + b = 10$

and $a - b = 4$

then $2a - 5b =$

A 0   **B** −1   **C** 1   **D** 3

15. Given $16^x = 4^4$, what is x?

A −2   **B** $-\dfrac{1}{2}$ **C** $\dfrac{1}{2}$ **D** 2

16. What is the area, in m², of a square with each side 0.02 m long?

A 0.0004   **B** 0.004   **C** 0.04   **D** 0.4

17. I start with x, then square it, multiply by 3 and finally subtract 4.
The final result is

A $(3x)^2 - 4$ **B** $(3x - 4)^2$ **C** $3x^2 - 4$ **D** $3(x - 4)^2$

18. How many prime numbers are there between 50 and 60?

A 1   **B** 2   **C** 3   **D** 4

19. What are the coordinates of the point $(2, -2)$ after reflection in the line $y = -x$?

A $(-2, 2)$ **B** $(2, -2)$ **C** $(-2, -2)$ **D** $(2, 2)$

20. The area of a circle is 36π cm². The circumference, in cm, is

A 6π **B** 18π **C** $12\sqrt{\pi}$ **D** 12π

21. The gradient of the line $2x - 3y = 4$ is

A $\dfrac{2}{3}$ **B** $1\dfrac{1}{2}$ **C** $-\dfrac{4}{3}$ **D** $-\dfrac{3}{4}$

22. When all three sides of a triangle are trebled in length, the area is increased by a factor of

A 3   **B** 6   **C** 9   **D** 27

23. $a = \sqrt{\left(\dfrac{m}{x}\right)}$

$x =$

A $a^2 m$ **B** $a^2 - m$ **C** $\dfrac{m}{a^2}$ **D** $\dfrac{a^2}{m}$

24. A coin is tossed three times. The probability of getting three 'heads' is

A $\dfrac{1}{3}$ **B** $\dfrac{1}{6}$ **C** $\dfrac{1}{8}$ **D** $\dfrac{1}{16}$

25. A triangle has sides of length 5 cm, 5 cm and 6 cm. What is the area, in cm²?

A 12   **B** 15   **C** 18   **D** 20

Examination-style Paper 2

TIME 1 h 30 m

Instructions to candidates

Answer **all** questions.

You must show all necessary working clearly.

The total mark for this paper is 70.

You should use a calculator where appropriate.

Give non-exact numerical answers correct to 3 significant figures, or 1 decimal place for angles in degrees, unless a different level of accuracy is specified in the question.

For π, use either your calculator value or 3.142.

The number of marks for each question or part question is shown in brackets [ ].

1. Find $\sqrt{\dfrac{16}{25}}$. [1]

2. How many minutes are there between 19:35 and midnight? [1]

3. For what range of values of x is $4x - 5 < 19$? [2]

4. Here is a sequence of numbers:

   $$2, \quad 5, \quad 10, \quad 17, \quad 26, \dots$$

   Find an expression for the nth term if this sequence. [2]

5. Find the value of $4ab$ when $a = 5 \times 10^4$ and $b = 7 \times 10^{-9}$.

   Give your answer in standard form. [2]

6. Find the value of $9^{\frac{1}{2}} \times 125^{\frac{1}{3}} \times 4^0$. [2]

7. An armchair is advertised for sale at $240. This is a 40% reduction on its original price.
   Work out the original price. [2]

8. Here is a list of numbers:

   $$0.45 \quad \frac{4}{9} \quad \frac{33}{74} \quad 44.5\%$$

   a) Write down the largest number. [1]
   b) Which one of the numbers is closest to $\dfrac{1}{\sqrt{5}}$? [1]

9. a) What is the gradient of the line $y = 8 - 3x$? [1]

b) Find the equation of the line perpendicular to $y = 8 - 3x$ which passes through $(1, 1)$. [2]

10. To the nearest half metre, a room is 4 metres long and $2\frac{1}{2}$ metres wide.

a) The actual length of the room is l metres.

Write down the upper and lower limits of l. [1]

b) The actual area of the floor of the room is A square metres.

Calculate the upper and lower limits of A. [2]

11. Solve the simultaneous equations:

$3x + 2y = 10$

$2x - 3y = 11$ [3]

12. A bicycle wheel has a radius of 40 cm.

How many times does it revolve during a journey of 10 km?

Give your answer to the nearest 100.

[For π, use either your calculator value or 3.142.] [3]

13. The number of bees in 10 randomly selected hives are recorded.

321	302	303	315	317
329	317	320	319	325

a) Draw a stem-and-leaf diagram for this data. [2]

b) Work out the median value. [1]

14. A hat of size N in Britain is equivalent to a hat of size C in mainland Europe.

a) Find the value of $8N$ when N equals: **i)** $6\frac{3}{4}$ **ii)** $7\frac{1}{8}$ [2]

b) $C = 55$ when $N = 6\frac{3}{4}$ and $C = 58$ when $N = 7\frac{1}{8}$.

Write down a formula connecting C and N. [1]

15. Find the turning point of the curve $y = x^2 + 6x - 3$ by completing the square. [3]

16. On graph paper, draw coordinate axes from -8 to $+8$ in both the x- and y-directions. Mark the point P(2, 0). Draw the triangle A with vertices $(2, 1)$, $(5, 2)$ and $(5, 4)$.

a) On the diagram enlarge triangle A with centre of enlargement P and scale factor -2. [2]

b) The area of triangle A is 3 square units.

What is the area of the enlarged triangle? [1]

Triangle A is mapped onto triangle B by reflecting it in the line $x = 0$ and then rotating the image by 90° clockwise about (0, 0).

c) On your diagram, draw triangle B. [2]

d) Describe fully the single transformation that maps triangle B back onto triangle A. [2]

17. y varies inversely with x.

a) Write this statement as an equation in x, y and k, where k is a constant. [1]

b) If x decreases by 20%, find the percentage change in y. [3]

18. The diagrams A, B, C and D are four graphs of different functions.

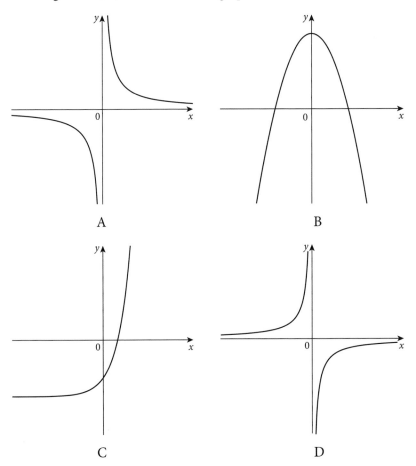

A

B

C

D

Complete the table to identify the correct graph for each function.

Function	$y = \dfrac{6}{x}$	$y = -3 + 2^x$
Diagram		

[2]

19. Write the recurring decimal 0.3$\dot{4}$ as a fraction. Show all your working. [2]

20.

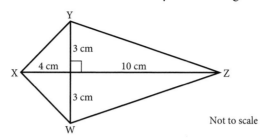

In the quadrilateral WXYZ, XZ is perpendicular to WY.

a) Calculate the lengths of the four sides of quadrilateral WXYZ. [2]

b) Calculate the size of angle YZW. [2]

21.

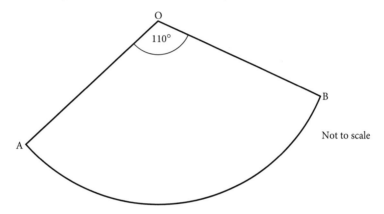

OAB is the sector of a circle, centre O, radius 5 cm and angle AOB = 110°.

a) Calculate the length of the arc AB. [2]

b) Calculate the area of the sector OAB. [2]

c) Write down the perimeter of the sector. [1]

22.

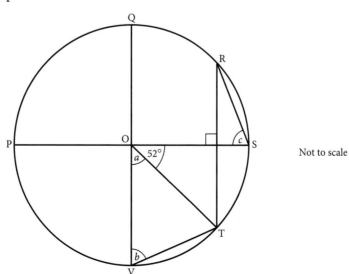

In the diagram, O is the centre of the circle.

QV is parallel to RT, PS is perpendicular to RT and angle SOT = 52°.

Find the angles marked a, b and c. [5]

23. The probability of a rugby team winning any single match is 0.6.

If the team plays three matches, work out the probability of the team winning all three. [2]

24. A curve has equation $y = x^3 - 3x^2 + 8$.

a) Find $\dfrac{dy}{dx}$. [2]

b) Find the x-coordinates of the two turning points on the curve. [2]

[70]

Examination-style Paper 4

TIME 2 h 30 m

Instructions to candidates

Answer **all** questions.

You must show all necessary working clearly.

The number of marks for each question or part question is shown in brackets [ ].

The total mark for this paper is 130.

You should use a calculator where appropriate.

Give non-exact numerical answers correct to 3 significant figures, or 1 decimal place for angles in degrees, unless a different level of accuracy is specified in the question.

For π, use either your calculator value or 3.142.

1. $r = \dfrac{2p^2}{q-3}$

    a) Find the value of r when

        i) $p = 6$ and $q = 5$,   [1]

        ii) $p = -4$ and $q = -1$.   [1]

    b) Find the value of q when $p = 3$ and $r = 12$.   [2]

    c) Find both possible values of p when $q = 8$ and $r = 10$.   [2]

    d) The value of p is tripled and q remains unchanged.

        What effect does this have on the value of r?   [2]

    e) Make p the subject of the formula.   [3]

2. Opposite sides of the hexagon in the diagram are parallel, and are in the ratio 2:1.

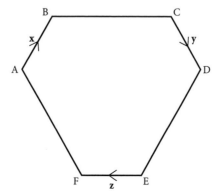

$\overrightarrow{AB} = \mathbf{x}$, $\overrightarrow{CD} = \mathbf{y}$, and $\overrightarrow{EF} = \mathbf{z}$.

a) i) Write down the vector $\overrightarrow{ED}$. [1]

ii) Hence show that $\overrightarrow{EC} = 2\mathbf{x} - \mathbf{y}$. [1]

iii) Find the vectors $\overrightarrow{AE}$ and $\overrightarrow{CA}$. [2]

b) Write down in terms of **x**, **y** and **z**:

$\overrightarrow{AE} + \overrightarrow{EC} + \overrightarrow{CA}$

expressing your answer in its simplest form. [2]

c) Write down a vector equation which follows from the result of part (b). [2]

d) Use the above results to determine whether or not BE is parallel to CD. [2]

3.

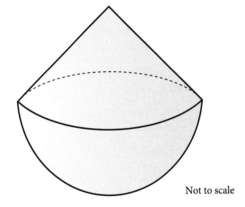

Not to scale

A glass paperweight consists of a cone mounted on a hemisphere. The common radius (r) is 3 cm; the height of the cone (h) is 4 cm.

You are given:

the volume of a cone is $\frac{1}{3}\pi r^2 h$; the volume of a sphere is

$\frac{4}{3}\pi r^3$; the curved surface area of a cone is $\pi r l$ (slant height l);

the surface area of a sphere is $4\pi r^2$.

a) Calculate **i)**   the volume of the paperweight, [4]

                ii)   the surface area of the paperweight. [5]

b) 1 cm³ of the glass of which the paperweight is made weighs 2.85 g. Calculate the mass of the paperweight. [2]

4. $f(x) = 3x - 1$ $g(x) = x^2 - 4$ $h(x) = 3^x$

    a) Find $f^{-1}(x)$. [2]

    b) Solve the equation $f(x) = g(3)$. [2]

    c) Solve the equation $h(x) = \frac{1}{9}$. [1]

    d) Show that $gf(x) = 9x^2 - 6x - 3$. [3]

    The graphs of $y = gf(x)$ and $y = f(x)$ are drawn on the same set of axes.

    e) Find, correct to 2 decimal places, the x-coordinates of the points of intersection of the two graphs. [3]

    f) Use differentiation to find the exact coordinates of the turning point on the graph of $y = gf(x)$. [3]

5. **a)** In triangle ABC, AB = 9 cm, BC = 7 cm and angle ABC = 128°.

    Calculate   **i)** the length of AC, [4]

                  ii) the area of triangle ABC. [3]

    b) The market place in Newark, Nottinghamshire is a rectangle PQRS. PQ = 105 m and QR = 65 m. In corner S stands the church. It is 40 m high.

      Work out the angle of elevation of the top of the church

      i) from P, [2]

      ii) from Q. [4]

6. A rectangle has length $(3x - 8)$ cm and width $(2x - 7)$ cm.

    a) Write down and simplify an expression for the perimeter of the rectangle. [2]

    b) Write down an expression for the area of the rectangle. [1]

    c) If the area of the rectangle is 91 cm², show that $6x^2 - 37x - 35 = 0$. [3]

    d) **i)** Factorise $6x^2 - 37x - 35$. [3]

      ii) Solve the quadratic equation $6x^2 - 37x - 35 = 0$. [3]

    e) Write down the length and width of the rectangle when its area is 91 cm². [2]

7. **a)** On each of the first two holes on his golf course, a golfer can take 3, 4, 5, 6, 7 or 8 strokes. All outcomes are equally likely. Consider these two holes only.

    i) Draw a possibility diagram, showing all his possible scores and totals. [2]

    ii) What is the probability that he takes a total of 16 strokes? [1]

     iii) What is the probability that he takes a total
        of 10 strokes? [2]

     iv) What is his most likely total? [1]

b) If the weather is fine today, the probability that it will
be fine tomorrow is 0.7.

This and the other probabilities are shown in this matrix.

TOMORROW

$$\text{TODAY} \begin{array}{cc} & \begin{array}{cc} \text{fine} & \text{wet} \end{array} \\ \begin{array}{c} \text{fine} \\ \text{wet} \end{array} & \begin{pmatrix} 0.7 & 0.3 \\ 0.4 & 0.6 \end{pmatrix} \end{array}$$

The probability of the weather being fine on any one day is
0.6. Copy and complete the tree diagram below, to
represent all this information. [3]

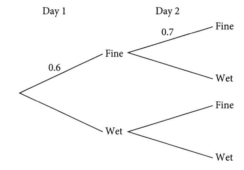

Calculate the probability of: [3]

i)   two fine days, [2]

ii) a wet day followed by a fine day, [2]

iii) one fine day and one wet day. [2]

8. The table shows the number of hours of sunshine each
day over a six-week period in a seaside town.

Number of hours of sunshine (N)	$0 \leqslant N \leqslant 2$	$2 < N \leqslant 4$	$4 < N \leqslant 6$	$6 < N \leqslant 8$	$8 < N \leqslant 10$	$10 < N \leqslant 12$
Frequency	9	8	6	2	4	13

a) Work out an estimate of the mean number of hours of
sunshine each day. [4]

b) i) Which is the modal class? [1]

    ii) Find an estimate for the median number of hours of sunshine. [2]

c) Would you choose the mean, median or mode for
publicity to attract visitors to the town?   [1]

d) Draw a histogram for the data, using the three class intervals
$0 \leqslant N \leqslant 4$, $4 < N \leqslant 10$ and $10 < N \leqslant 12$.   [5]

9. **Graph paper must be used for the whole of this question.**

A new model of bicycle is about to be marketed. It is estimated
that if the selling price is fixed at $80, then 5000 bicycles will be
sold; if it is fixed at $120, then only 3000 bicycles will be sold.

These two points are plotted and connected with a straight line, as below:

a) Copy and complete the following table, by reading
values from the graph and by calculation.

Selling price ($)	Number of bicycles sold	Sales revenue ($)
60		
70		
80	5000	400 000
90		
100		
110		
120	3000	360 000

[4]

b) Using a horizontal scale of 2 cm to represent $10
(starting at $60) and a vertical scale of 2 cm to represent $20 000,
draw the graph of selling price against sales revenue.   [5]

c) i) Use your graph to find what the selling price
should be in order to achieve the greatest sales revenue. [2]

ii) How many bicycles should be made at that price? [2]

10. The grid shows the graph of $y = \sin x$ for $0° \leqslant x \leqslant 360°$.

a) Solve the equation $4 \sin x = -1$ for $0° \leqslant x \leqslant 360°$. Give your
answers correct to 1 decimal place. [4]

b) On the same grid, sketch the graph of $y = \cos x$ for $0° \leqslant x \leqslant 360°$. [2]

11. At a science fair, students are invited to guess the volume of air in a balloon.
The cumulative frequency diagram shows the results.

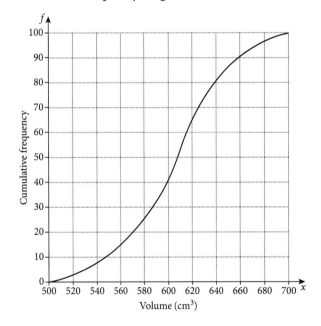

Use the graph to find an estimate of

a) the median, [1]

b) the interquartile range, [2]

c) the 67th percentile, [1]

d) the number of students who estimated the volume to be
between 590 cm³ and 630 cm³. [3]

[130]

Answers

1 Number

Exercise 1   page 2

1. 7.91	**2.** 22.22	**3.** 7.372	**4.** 0.066	**5.** 466.2
6. 1.22	**7.** 1.67	**8.** 1.61	**9.** 16.63	**10.** 24.1
11. 26.7	**12.** 3.86	**13.** 0.001	**14.** 1.56	**15.** 0.0288
16. 2.176	**17.** 0.02	**18.** 0.0001	**19.** 7.56	**20.** 0.7854
21. 360	**22.** 34 000	**23.** 18	**24.** 0.74	**25.** 2.34
26. 1620	**27.** 8.8	**28.** 1200	**29.** 0.00175	**30.** 13.2
31. 200	**32.** 0.804	**33.** 0.8	**34.** 0.077	**35.** 0.0009
36. 0.01	**37.** 184	**38.** 20	**39.** 0.099	**40.** 3

Exercise 2   page 3

1. 20   **2.** 256; 65 536

3. $6^2 + 7^2 + 42^2 = 43^2$; $x^2 + (x+1)^2 + [x(x+1)]^2 = (x^2 + x + 1)^2$

4. a) $54 \times 9 = 486$ **b)** $57 \times 8 = 456$ **c)** $52 \times 2 = 104$, $57 \times 2 = 114$ or $58 \times 3 = 174$

5. 5, 28; total 32   **7.** 12 units long, marks at 1, 4, 5 and 10   **8.** 21   **11.** 37

Exercise 3   page 4

1. $1\frac{11}{20}$	**2.** $\frac{11}{24}$	**3.** $1\frac{1}{2}$	**4.** $\frac{5}{12}$	**5.** $\frac{4}{15}$
6. $\frac{1}{10}$	**7.** $\frac{8}{15}$	**8.** $\frac{5}{42}$	**9.** $\frac{15}{26}$	**10.** $\frac{5}{12}$
11. $4\frac{1}{2}$	**12.** $1\frac{2}{3}$	**13.** $\frac{23}{40}$	**14.** $\frac{3}{40}$	**15.** $1\frac{7}{8}$
16. $1\frac{1}{12}$	**17.** $1\frac{1}{6}$	**18.** $2\frac{5}{8}$	**19.** $6\frac{1}{10}$	**20.** $9\frac{1}{10}$
21. $1\frac{9}{26}$	**22.** $\frac{1}{9}$	**23.** $\frac{2}{3}$	**24.** $5\frac{1}{4}$	**25.** $2\frac{2}{25}$

26. a) $\frac{1}{2}, \frac{7}{12}, \frac{2}{3}$ **b)** $\frac{2}{3}, \frac{3}{4}, \frac{5}{6}$ **c)** $\frac{1}{3}, \frac{5}{8}, \frac{17}{24}, \frac{3}{4}$ **d)** $\frac{5}{6}, \frac{8}{9}, \frac{11}{12}$

27. a) $\frac{1}{2}$ **b)** $\frac{3}{4}$ **c)** $\frac{17}{24}$ **d)** $\frac{7}{18}$ **e)** $\frac{3}{10}$ **f)** $\frac{5}{12}$

28. 5   **29.** 9   **30.** same

Exercise 4   page 6

1. 0.25	**2.** 0.4	**3.** 0.8	**4.** 0.75	**5.** $0.\dot{5}$
6. 0.375	**7.** 0.9	**8.** 0.625	**9.** $0.41\dot{6}$	**10.** $0.1\dot{6}$
11. $0.\dot{6}$	**12.** $0.8\dot{3}$	**13.** $0.\dot{2}8571\dot{4}$	**14.** $0.\dot{4}2857\dot{1}$	**15.** $0.\dot{4}$
16. $0.4\dot{5}$	**17.** 1.2	**18.** 2.625	**19.** $2.\dot{3}$	**20.** 1.7
21. 2.1875	**22.** $2.\dot{2}8571\dot{4}$	**23.** $2.\dot{8}5714\dot{2}$	**24.** 3.19	**25.** $\frac{1}{5}$
26. $\frac{7}{10}$	**27.** $\frac{1}{4}$	**28.** $\frac{9}{20}$	**29.** $\frac{9}{25}$	**30.** $\frac{13}{25}$
31. $\frac{1}{8}$	**32.** $\frac{5}{8}$	**33.** $\frac{21}{25}$	**34.** $2\frac{7}{20}$	**35.** $3\frac{19}{20}$
36. $1\frac{1}{20}$	**37.** $3\frac{1}{5}$	**38.** $\frac{27}{100}$	**39.** $\frac{7}{1000}$	**40.** $\frac{11}{100\,000}$
41. 0.58	**42.** 1.42	**43.** 0.65	**44.** 1.61	**45.** 0.07
46. 0.16	**47.** 3.64	**48.** 0.60	**49.** $\frac{4}{15}, 0.33, \frac{1}{3}$	**50.** $\frac{2}{7}, 0.3, \frac{4}{9}$
51. $\frac{7}{11}, 0.705, 0.71$	**52.** $\frac{5}{18}, 0.3, \frac{4}{13}$	**53.** $\frac{2}{3}$	**54.** $\frac{4}{9}$	**55.** $\frac{4}{33}$
56. $\frac{43}{99}$	**57.** $\frac{134}{999}$	**58.** $\frac{731}{999}$	**59.** $\frac{23}{90}$	**60.** $\frac{611}{990}$

Exercise 5   page 8

1. 3, 11, 19, 23, 29, 31, 37, 47, 59, 61, 67, 73

2. a) 4, 8, 12, 16, 20   **b)** 6, 12, 18, 24, 30   **c)** 10, 20, 30, 40, 50   **d)** 11, 22, 33, 44, 55   **e)** 20, 40, 60, 80, 100

3. 12 and 24   **4.** 15

5. a) 1, 2, 3, 6   **b)** 1, 3, 9   **c)** 1, 2, 5, 10,   **d)** 1, 3, 5, 15   **e)** 1, 2, 3, 4, 6, 8, 12, 24

    f) 1, 2, 4, 8, 16, 32

6. a) Yes. Divide by 3, 5, 7, 11, 13, (i.e. odd prime numbers $< \sqrt{263}$)

    b) No   **c)** Prime numbers $< \sqrt{1147}$ **7.** 2, 3, 5, 41, 67, 89

8. a) $2^3 \times 3$ **b)** $2^2 \times 3 \times 5$ **c)** $2 \times 3^2 \times 5$ **d)** $2^4 \times 3^2$ **e)** $2^3 \times 5^3$ **f)** $2^4 \times 5 \times 11$

9. a) 12   **b)** 18   **c)** 20   **d)** 8   **e)** 10   **f)** 12

10. a) 120   **b)** 180   **c)** 18 000   **d)** 2640   **e)** 9000   **f)** 3000

11. a) 16   **b)** 36   **c)** 100   **d)** 27   **e)** 1000

12. a) 81   **b)** 441   **c)** 1.44   **d)** 0.04   **e)** 9.61

    f) 10 000   **g)** 625   **h)** 75.69   **i)** 0.81   **j)** 6625.96

13. a) 4.41 cm²   **b)** 0.36 cm²   **c)** 196 m²

14. 10^{10} **15.** 2^7 **16.** $\frac{1}{2}$ or 0.5   **17.** $\frac{1}{10}$ or 0.1

18. $\frac{1}{5}$ or 0.2   **19.** $\frac{1}{4}$ or 0.25   **20.** $\frac{1}{8}$ or 0.125

Exercise 6   *page 10*

1. Rational: **c)** $\left(\sqrt{17}\right)^2$ **e)** 3.14   **f)** $\dfrac{\sqrt{12}}{\sqrt{3}}$ **h)** $3^{-1} + 3^{-2}$ **j)** $\dfrac{22}{7}$ **l)** $\sqrt{2.25}$

3. a) both irrational   **b)** both rational

4. a) 6π cm, irrational   **b)** 6 cm, rational   **c)** 36 cm², rational

    d) 9π cm², irrational   **e)** $36 - 9\pi$ cm², irrational

6. A rational number can always be written exactly in the form $\frac{a}{b}$ where a and b are whole numbers. An irrational number cannot be written in the form $\frac{a}{b}$.

7. a) No   **b)** Yes e.g. $\sqrt{8} \times \sqrt{2} = 4$

Exercise 7   *page 11*

1. 18, 22; Add 4   **2.** 30, 37; Add 7   **3.** 63, 55; Subtract 8   **4.** −7, −12; Subtract 5

5. 21, 27   **6.** 2, −5   **7.** 16, 22   **8.** 16, 32

9. 25, 15   **10.** −4, −10   **11.** −4, −3   **12.** $7\frac{1}{2}, 3\frac{3}{4}$

13. $\frac{1}{3}, \frac{1}{9}$ **14.** $2, \frac{2}{3}$ **15.** 32, 47   **16.** 840, 6720

17. 5, −1   **18.** 2, 1

Exercise 8   *page 11*

1. a) $2n$ **b)** $10n$ **c)** $3n$ **d)** $11n$ **e)** $100n$ **f)** n^2

    g) 10^n **h)** n^3

2. $n^2 + 4$ **3.** 9, 11, 13, 15, 17

4. a) 3, 4, 5, 6, 7   **b)** 5, 10, 15, 20, 25   **c)** 9, 19, 29, 39, 49   **d)** 97, 94, 91, 88, 85   **e)** $1, \frac{1}{2}, \frac{1}{3}, \frac{1}{4}, \frac{1}{5}$ **f)** 1, 4, 9, 16, 25

Exercise 9   *page 12*

1. $4n + 1$ **2.** $3n + 4$ **3.** $5n - 1$ **4.** $4n + 2$ **5.** $3n + 2$ **6.** $28 - 3n$

7. $5n$ **8.** 2^n **9.** $n(n + 2)$ **10.** $\dfrac{n}{n+1}$ **11.** $7n$ **12.** n^2

13. $\dfrac{5}{n^2}$ **14.** $\dfrac{n+2}{n}$ **15.** $4n - 1$ **16.** $2n + 3$ **17.** $9 - 2n$ **18.** $4n - 9$

19. a) $2n + 6$ **b)** $4n - 1$ **c)** $5n + 3$

20. a) $8n + 3$ **b)** $2n + \frac{1}{2}$ **c)** $3n - 10$

21. a) $3n + 1$ **b)** 3001

Exercise 10   *page 13*

1. $n^2 + 3$ **2.** $2n^2$ **3.** $n^2 - 1$ **4.** $\frac{1}{2}n^2$ **5.** $n^2 - 7$ **6.** $-n^2$

7. $-n^2 + 1$ **8.** $n^2 + 4n$ **9.** $2n^2 - n$ **10.** $n^2 + 3n - 1$ **11.** $n^3 + 1$ **12.** $2n^3$

13. $n^3 - 2$ **14.** $2n - 1$ **15.** 3^n

Exercise 11 *page 14*

1. a) 8   **b)** 8.17   **c)** 8.17   **2. a)** 20   **b)** 19.6   **c)** 19.62
3. a) 20   **b)** 20.0   **c)** 20.04   **4. a)** 1   **b)** 0.815   **c)** 0.81
5. a) 311   **b)** 311   **c)** 311.14   **6. a)** 0   **b)** 0.275   **c)** 0.28
7. a) 0   **b)** 0.00747   **c)** 0.01   **8. a)** 16   **b)** 15.6   **c)** 15.62
9. a) 900   **b)** 900   **c)** 900.12   **10. a)** 4   **b)** 3.56   **c)** 3.56
11. a) 5   **b)** 5.45   **c)** 5.45   **12. a)** 21   **b)** 21.0   **c)** 20.96
13. a) 0   **b)** 0.0851   **c)** 0.09   **14. a)** 1   **b)** 0.515   **c)** 0.52
15. a) 3   **b)** 3.07   **c)** 3.07   **16.** 5.7   **17.** 0.8   **18.** 11.2
19. 0.1   **20.** 0.0   **21.** 11.1

Exercise 12 *page 16*

1. 195.5 cm   **2.** 36.5 kg   **3.** 3.25 kg   **4.** 95.55 m   **5.** 28.65 s
6. a) 1.5, 2.5   **b)** 2.25, 2.35   **c)** 63.5, 64.5   **d)** 13.55, 13.65
7. B   **8.** C   **9. a)** Not necessarily   **b)** 1 cm
10. a) $16.5 \leqslant m < 17.5$ **b)** $255.5 \leqslant d < 256.5$ **c)** $2.35 \leqslant l < 2.45$
d) $0.335 \leqslant m < 0.345$ **e)** $2.035 \leqslant v < 2.045$ **f)** $11.95 \leqslant x < 12.05$
g) $81.35 \leqslant T < 81.45$ **h)** $0.25 \leqslant M < 0.35$ **i)** $0.65 \leqslant m < 0.75$
j) $51\,500 \leqslant n < 52\,500$
11. No, max. card length 11.55 cm, min. envelope length 11.5 cm

Exercise 13 *page 17*

1. a) 7.5, 8.5, 10.5 cm   **b)** 26.5 cm   **2.** 46.75 cm^2
3. a) 7   **b)** 5   **c)** 10   **d)** 4   **e)** 2   **f)** 5
g) 2   **h)** 24
4. a) 13   **b)** 11   **c)** 3   **d)** 12.5
5. i) 10.5   **ii)** 4.3   **6. i)** 13, 11   **ii)** 3, 1   **iii)** 0.8, 0.6
7. 56 cm^2 **8.** 55.7

Exercise 14 *page 18*

1. 70.56   **2.** 118.958   **3.** 451.62   **4.** 33 678.8   **5.** 0.6174
6. 1068   **7.** 19.53   **8.** 18 914.4   **9.** 38.72   **10.** 0.009 79
11. 2.4   **12.** 11   **13.** 41   **14.** 8.9   **15.** 4.7
16. 56   **17.** 0.0201   **18.** 30.1   **19.** 1.3   **20.** 0.31
21. 210.21   **22.** 294   **23.** 282.131   **24.** 35   **25.** 242

Exercise 15 *page 20*

1. 4×10^3 **2.** 5×10^2 **3.** 7×10^4 **4.** 6×10 **5.** 2.4×10^3
6. 3.8×10^2 **7.** 4.6×10^4 **8.** 4.6×10 **9.** 9×10^5 **10.** 2.56×10^3
11. 7×10^{-3} **12.** 4×10^{-4} **13.** 3.5×10^{-3} **14.** 4.21×10^{-1} **15.** 5.5×10^{-5}
16. 1×10^{-2} **17.** 5.64×10^5 **18.** 1.9×10^7 **19.** 1.1×10^9 **20.** 1.67×10^{-24}
21. 5.1×10^8 **22.** 2.5×10^{-10} **23.** 6.023×10^{23} **24.** 3×10^{10} **25.** $\$3.6 \times 10^6$

Exercise 16 *page 20*

1. 1.5×10^7 **2.** 3×10^8 **3.** 2.8×10^{-2} **4.** 7×10^{-9} **5.** 2×10^6
6. 4×10^{-6} **7.** 9×10^{-2} **8.** 6.6×10^{-8} **9.** 3.5×10^{-7} **10.** 1×10^{-16}
11. 8×10^9 **12.** 7.4×10^{-7} **13.** c, a, b **14.** 13   **15.** 16
16. i) $9 \times 10^2, 4 \times 10^2$ **ii)** $1 \times 10^8, 4 \times 10^7$
17. 50 min   **18.** 6×10^2 **19. a)** 20.5 s   **b)** 6.3×10^{91} years

Exercise 17 *page 22*

1. $1 : 3$ **2.** $1 : 6$ **3.** $1 : 50$ **4.** $1 : 1.6$ **5.** $1 : 0.75$
6. $1 : 0.375$ **7.** $1 : 25$ **8.** $1 : 8$ **9.** $2.4 : 1$ **10.** $2.5 : 1$
11. $0.8 : 1$ **12.** $0.02 : 1$ **13.** $\$15, \$25$ **14.** $\$36, \$84$ **15.** 140 m 110 m
16. $\$18, \$27, \$72$ **17.** 15 kg, 75 kg, 90 kg   **18.** 46 min, 69 min, 69 min
19. £39   **20.** 18 kg, 36 kg, 54 kg, 72 kg   **21.** $\$400, \$1000, \$1000, \$1600$
22. $5 : 3$ **23.** $\$200$ **24.** $3 : 7$ **25.** $\frac{1}{7}x$ **26.** 6
27. 12   **28.** $\$120$ **29.** 300 g   **30.** 625

Exercise 18   page 23

1. $1.68   **2.** $84   **3.** 6 days   **4.** $2\frac{1}{2}$ litres   **5.** 60 km   **6.** 119 g

7. $68.40   **8.** $2\frac{1}{4}$ weeks   **9.** 80 c   **10. a)** 12   **b)** 2100   **11.** 4

12. 5.6 days   **13.** $175   **14.** 540°   **15.** $1.20   **16.** 190 m   **17.** 1250
18. 11.2 h   **19.** 57.1 min   **20.** 243 kg   **21.** 12 days

Exercise 19   page 25

1. a) €18.60   **b)** £44.10   **c)** 758 pesos   **d)** 69.75 rupees   **e)** 209.76 yen   **f)** 0.27 dinars
2. a) $537.63   **b)** $3968.25   **c)** $0.16   **d)** $3000   **e)** $33.04   **f)** $663.72
3. £3.39   **4.** Cheaper in UK by $9.23   **5.** €494.67
6. Kuwait £325.86, France £495, Japan £706.14   **7.** €433.63

Exercise 20   page 26

1. a) 70 m   **b)** 16 m   **c)** 3.55 m   **d)** 108.5 m
2. a) 5 cm   **b)** 3.5 cm   **c)** 0.72 cm   **d)** 2.86 cm
3. a) 450 000 cm   **b)** 4500 m   **c)** 4.5 km
4. 12.3 km   **5.** 4.71 km   **6.** 50 cm   **7.** 64 cm   **8.** 5.25 cm

Exercise 21   page 27

1. 40 m by 30 m; 12 cm²; 1200 m²   **2.** 1 m², 6 m²   **3.** 0.32 km²   **4.** 50 cm²
5. 150 km²   **6.** 0.75 hectares   **7.** 240 cm²   **8.** 1 : 50 000

Exercise 22   page 28

1. a) $\frac{3}{5}$ **b)** $\frac{6}{25}$ **c)** $\frac{7}{20}$ **d)** $\frac{1}{50}$

2. a) 25%   **b)** 10%   **c)** $87\frac{1}{2}$%   **d)** $33\frac{1}{3}$%   **e)** 72%   **f)** 31%

3. a) 0.36   **b)** 0.28   **c)** 0.07   **d)** 0.134   **e)** 0.6   **f)** 0.875

4. a) 45%; $\frac{1}{2}$; 0.6   **b)** 4%; $\frac{6}{16}$; 0.38   **c)** 11%; 0.111; $\frac{1}{9}$ **d)** 0.3; 32%; $\frac{1}{3}$

5. a) 85%   **b)** 77.5%   **c)** 23.75%   **d)** 56%   **e)** 10%   **f)** 37.5%

Exercise 23   page 29

1. a) $15   **b)** 900 kg   **c)** $2.80   **d)** 125
2. $32   **3.** 13.2c   **4.** 52.8 kg
5. a) $1.02   **b)** $21.58   **c)** $2.22   **d)** $0.53
6. $289.28   **7.** $26 182   **8.** 53.9%   **9.** 77.5%   **10.** $71.48
11. 200   **12.** 29 000   **13.** 500 cm   **14.** $6.30   **15.** 400 kg
16. 325   **17.** $35.25   **18.** $8425.60

Exercise 24   page 31

1. a) 25%, profit **b)** 25%, profit   **c)** 10%, loss   **d)** 20%, profit
     e) 30%, profit **f)** 7.5%, profit   **g)** 12%, loss   **h)** 54%, loss

2. 28%   **3.** $44\frac{4}{9}$%   **4.** 46.9%   **5.** 12%   **6.** $5\frac{1}{3}$%

7. a) $50   **b)** $450   **c)** $800   **d)** $12.40
8. $50   **9.** $12   **10.** $5   **11.** 60c   **12.** $2200
13. 14.3%   **14.** 20%   **15.** 8 : 11   **16.** 21%   **17.** 20%

Exercise 25   page 33

1. a) $216   **b)** $115.50   **c)** 2 years   **d)** 5 years
2. $2295, $9045 **3.** 7.5%

Exercise 26   page 34

1. a) $2180   **b)** $2376.20   **c)** $2590.06   **2. a)** $5550   **b)** $6838.16   **c)** $8425.29
3. $13 107.96   **4. a)** $36 465.19 **b)** $40 202.87
5. a) $9 540   **b)** $107 19.10   **c)** $161 17.60
6. a) $14 033.01 **b)** $734.03   **c)** $107 946.25
7. $9211.88   **8.** 8 years   **9.** 12 years   **10.** 13 years   **11.** $30 000 at 8%

Exercise 27 *page 35*
1. $7200 **2.** $8800 **3.** $18 800 **4.** $3640

Exercise 28 *page 37*

1. a) $2\frac{1}{2}$ h **b)** $3\frac{1}{8}$ h **c)** 75 s **d)** 4 h

2. a) 20 m/s **b)** 30 m/s **c)** $83\frac{1}{3}$ m/s **d)** 108 km/h **e)** 79.2 km/h

f) 1.2 cm/s **g)** 90 m/s **h)** 25 mph **i)** 0.03 miles per second
3. a) 75 km/h **b)** 4.52 km/h **c)** 7.6 m/s **d)** 4×10^6 m/s **e)** 2.5×10^8 m/s
f) 200 km/h **g)** 3 km/h
4. a) 110 000 m **b)** 10 000 m **c)** 56 400 m **d)** 4500 m **e)** 50 400 m
f) 80 m **g)** 960 000 m
5. a) 3.125 h **b)** 76.8 km/h **6. a)** 4.45 h **b)** 23.6 km/h
7. 46 km/h **8. a)** 8 m/s **b)** 7.6 m/s **c)** 102.63 s **d)** 7.79 m/s

9. 1230 km/h **10.** 3 h **11.** 100 s **12.** $1\frac{1}{2}$ minutes **13.** 600 m

14. $53\frac{1}{3}$ s **15.** 5 cm/s **16.** 60 s **17.** 120 km/h

Exercise 29 *page 39*
1. a) 0.8 **b)** 16 **c)** 390 **d)** 4800 **e)** 1460
2. a) 1.5 **b)** 2.5 **c)** 90 **d)** 36
3. 13.3 litres per minute **4.** 12.6 kwh/day **5.** 8.33 minutes
6. a) 2500 **b)** 66.7

Exercise 30 *page 40*

1. $\frac{7}{25}$, 0.28, 28%; $\frac{16}{25}$, 0.64, 64%; $\frac{5}{8}$, 0.625, $62\frac{1}{2}$% **2.** 12.4 m

3. 3.08 kg **4.** $56\frac{1}{4}$ km **5.** $820 **6.** A

7. a) 19:17 **b)** 23:49 **8.** $36 **9.** 1.32

Exercise 31 *page 41*
1. 1.08×10^9 km **2.** 167 days **3.** 3 h 21 min **4.** 17
5. a) $4.95 **b)** 25 **c)** $11.75 **6.** 30 g zinc, 2850 g copper, 3000 g total

Exercise 32 *page 41*
1. 2 : 1 **2. a)** 9.85 **b)** 76.2 **c)** 223 512 **d)** 1678.1
3. 252 000 **4. a)** 8 **b)** 24 **c)** 8 **d)** 8
5. 0.18 s **6.** $140 **7.** 5 **8.** THIS IS A VERY SILLY CODE **9.** 29

Exercise 33 *page 43*
1. 3.041 **2.** 1460 **3.** 0.030 83 **4.** 47.98 **5.** 130.6
6. 0.4771 **7.** 0.3658 **8.** 37.54 **9.** 8.000 **10.** 0.6537
11. 0.037 16 **12.** 34.31 **13.** 0.7195 **14.** 3.598 **15.** 0.2445
16. 2.043 **17.** 0.3798 **18.** 0.7683 **19.** −0.5407 **20.** 0.070 40
21. 2.526 **22.** 0.094 78 **23.** 0.2110 **24.** 3.123 **25.** 2.230
26. 128.8 **27.** 4.268 **28.** 3.893 **29.** 0.6290 **30.** 0.4069
31. 9.298 **32.** 0.1010 **33.** 0.3692 **34.** 1.125 **35.** 1.677
36. 0.9767 **37.** 0.8035 **38.** 0.3528 **39.** 2.423 **40.** 1.639
41. 0.000 465 9 **42.** 0.3934 **43.** −0.7526 **44.** 2.454

Exercise 34 *page 44*
1. 40 000 **2.** 0.070 49 **3.** 405 400 **4.** 471.3 **5.** 20 810
6. 2.218×10^6 **7.** 1.237×10^{-24} **8.** 3.003 **9.** 0.035 81 **10.** 47.40
11. −1748 **12.** 0.011 38 **13.** 1757 **14.** 0.026 35 **15.** 0.1651
16. 5447 **17.** 0.006 562 **18.** 0.1330 **19.** 0.4451 **20.** 0.036 16
21. 19.43 **22.** 1.296×10^{-15} **23.** 5.595×10^{14} **24.** 1.022×10^{-8} **25.** 0.019 22
26. 0.9613

Exercise 35   page 46

1. a) 1850, 1850, 12.5   **b)** 4592, 4592, 14   **c)** 50.4, 50.4, 63   **d)** 31.6, 31.6, 221.2   **e)** 42.3, 42.3, 384.93
f) 39.51, 39.51, 13{\cdot}71   **g)** 21.2, 21.2, 95.4
h) 42.4, 42.4   **i)** 6.2449 ..., 6.2449 ...   **j)** 29.63, 29.63
2. a) A–T, B–P, C–S, D–R, E–Q
3. a) 281   **b)** 36   **c)** 101:16
4. $1000
5. 6 times
6. a) 5   **b)** 100   **c)** £3000   **d)** 1   **e)** 0.2   **f)** 2   **g)** 100   **h)** £2000   **i)** 400

Revision exercise 1A   page 47

1. a) 185   **b)** 150   **c)** 40   **d)** $\frac{11}{12}$ **e)** $2\frac{4}{5}$ **f)** $\frac{2}{5}$

2. 128 cm   **3.** $\frac{2}{5}$ **4.** $\frac{a}{b}$ **5. a)** 0.0547   **b)** 0.055   **c)** 5.473×10^{-2}

6. 1.238   **7. a)** 3×10^7 **b)** 3.7×10^4 **c)** 2.7×10^{13}
8. a) $26   **b)** $6:5$ **c)** 6   **9.** $75

10. a) i) 57.2%   **ii)** $87\frac{1}{2}\%$ **b)** 40%   **c)** 80 c   **11.** 5%

12. a) $500   **b)** $37\frac{1}{2}\%$ **13.** $357.88   **14.** 3.05

15. a) 2.4 km   **b)** 1 km²   **16. a)** 300 m   **b)** 60 cm   **c)** 150 cm²
17. a) 1 : 50 000   **b)** 1 : 4 000 000   **18. a)** 22%   **b)** 20.8%   **c)** $240
19. a) i) 7 m/s   **ii)** 200 m/s   **iii)** 5 m/s   **b) i)** 144 km/h   **ii)** 2.16 km/h

20. a) 0.005 m/s   **b)** 1.6 s   **c)** 172.8 km   **21.** $33\frac{1}{3}$ km/h

22. a) 3   **b)** 10   **c)** 1, 9   **d)** 1, 8   **e)** $m = 3, n = 9$
f) $p = 1, q = 3, r = 9, s = 8, t = 10$ **23.** About 3   **24.** 2.3×10^9
25. a) 600   **b)** 10 000   **c)** 3   **d)** 20
26. a) 0.5601   **b)** 3.215   **c)** 0.6161   **d)** 0.4743
27. a) 0.340   **b)** 4.08×10^{-6} **c)** 64.9   **d)** 0.119

28. 33.1%   **29. a)** $\frac{1}{20}$ or 0.05   **b)** 3   **c)** 2.5   **d)** $\frac{2}{3}$

30. 2^8

Examination-style exercise 1B   page 49

1. a) $\frac{25}{32}$ **b)** 0.781   **2.** $\frac{37}{25}$ or $1\frac{12}{25}$ or 0.48

3. a) any irrational square root, π or e   **b)** 61 or 67   **4. a)** 0641   **b)** $204
5. a) −1.8   **b)** 21   **6. a)** 1170   **b)** $(n + 2)^2 + 10$
7. a) $21.5 \leqslant d$ km < 22.5 **b)** 172   **8.** 75 000   76 200   **9.** 50.1225
10. 62 225 000   **11.** 5.7×10^{26}
12. a) 350, 250, 200   **b)** 275   **c)** 200   **d)** 11 : 8 : 4   **e)** 110.25
13. a) $6000   **b)** 12.5%   **14.** 20   **15. a)** $2300   **b)** $8.64
16. a) 5   **b)** 1   **17. a)** 950 kg   **b)** $405   **c)** $0.43 or $0.426
d) i) $0.21   **ii)** $0.28   **18. a) i)** 2400   **ii)** 520 000
b) i) 1 : 5 000 000 or $n = 5 000 000$ **ii)** Time = 2 hours 8 minutes or
128 (minutes) = 2.13(33..) (hours) oe soi 1580 ÷ their time 738 − 742 cso
19. a) ii) 80 200   **b) ii)** 40 200   **iii)** 40 000   **c) i)** $n(2n + 1)$ **ii)** n^2
20. a) i) $346.50   **ii)** $350   **b) i)** 115   **ii)** $430   **iii)** 4.88%   **c)** 55
21. a) 22 500 ml   **b)** 2250 seconds or 37.5 minutes

2 Algebra 1

Exercise 1   *page 56*
1. 5°   **2.** −4°   **3.** −1°   **4.** 4°   **5.** −4°
6. 12°   **7.** −7°   **8.** −5°   **9.** −4°   **10.** 0°
11. a) C   **b)** B   **12.** −17 m

Exercise 2   *page 57*
1. 13   **2.** 211   **3.** −12   **4.** −31   **5.** −66   **6.** 6.1
7. 9.1   **8.** −35   **9.** 18.7   **10.** −9   **11.** −3   **12.** 3
13. −2   **14.** −14   **15.** −7   **16.** 3   **17.** 181   **18.** −2.2
19. 8.2   **20.** 17   **21.** 2   **22.** −6   **23.** −15   **24.** −14
25. −2   **26.** −12   **27.** −80   **28.** −13.1   **29.** −4.2   **30.** 12.4
31. −7   **32.** 8   **33.** 4   **34.** −10   **35.** 11   **36.** 4
37. −20   **38.** 8   **39.** −5   **40.** −10   **41.** −26   **42.** −21
43. 8   **44.** 1   **45.** −20.2   **46.** −50   **47.** −508   **48.** −29
49. 0   **50.** −21   **51.** −0.1   **52.** −4   **53.** 6.7   **54.** 1
55. −850   **56.** 4   **57.** 6   **58.** −4   **59.** −12   **60.** −31

Exercise 3   *page 58*
1. −8   **2.** 28   **3.** 12   **4.** 24   **5.** 18   **6.** −35
7. 49   **8.** −12   **9.** −2   **10.** 9   **11.** −4   **12.** 4
13. −4   **14.** 8   **15.** 70   **16.** −7   **17.** $\frac{1}{4}$ **18.** $-\frac{3}{5}$
19. −0.01   **20.** 0.0002   **21.** 121   **22.** 6   **23.** −600   **24.** −1
25. −20   **26.** −2.6   **27.** −700   **28.** 18   **29.** −1000   **30.** 640
31. −6   **32.** −42   **33.** −0.4   **34.** −0.4   **35.** −200   **36.** −35
37. −2   **38.** $\frac{1}{2}$ **39.** $-\frac{1}{4}$ **40.** −90

Exercise 4   *page 59*
1. −10   **2.** 1   **3.** 12   **4.** −28   **5.** −2   **6.** 16
7. −3   **8.** 14   **9.** −28   **10.** 4   **11.** $-\frac{1}{6}$ **12.** 9
13. −30   **14.** 24   **15.** −1   **16.** −2   **17.** −30   **18.** 7
19. 3   **20.** 16   **21.** 93   **22.** 2400   **23.** 10   **24.** 1
25. −4   **26.** 48   **27.** −1   **28.** 0   **29.** −8   **30.** 170
31. −3   **32.** 1   **33.** 1   **34.** 0   **35.** 15   **36.** 5
37. −2.4   **38.** −180   **39.** 5   **40.** −994   **41.** 2   **42.** −48
43. 60   **44.** −2.5   **45.** −32   **46.** 0   **47.** −0.1   **48.** −16
49. −4.3   **50.** $-\frac{1}{16}$

Exercise 5   *page 59*
1. 21   **2.** 1.62   **3.** 396   **4.** 650   **5.** 63.8   **6.** 9×10^{12}
7. 800   **8.** $ac + ab - a^2$ **9.** $r - p + q$ **10.** 802; $4n + 2$ **11.** $2n + 6$

Exercise 6   *page 61*
1. 7   **2.** 13   **3.** 13   **4.** 22   **5.** 1   **6.** −1
7. 18   **8.** −4   **9.** −3   **10.** 37   **11.** 0   **12.** −4
13. −7   **14.** −2   **15.** −3   **16.** −8   **17.** −30   **18.** 16
19. −10   **20.** 0   **21.** 7   **22.** −6   **23.** −2   **24.** −7
25. −5   **26.** 3   **27.** 4   **28.** −8   **29.** −2   **30.** 2
31. 0   **32.** 4   **33.** −4   **34.** −3   **35.** −9   **36.** 4

Exercise 7   *page 62*
1. 9   **2.** 27   **3.** 4   **4.** 16   **5.** 36   **6.** 18
7. 1   **8.** 6   **9.** 2   **10.** 8   **11.** −7   **12.** 15

13. −23	14. 3	15. 32	16. 36	17. 144	18. −8
19. −7	20. 13	21. 5	22. −16	23. 84	24. 17
25. 6	26. 0	27. −25	28. −5	29. 17	30. $-1\frac{1}{2}$
31. 19	32. 8	33. 19	34. 16	35. −16	36. 12
37. 36	38. −12	39. 2	40. 11	41. −23	42. −26
43. 5	44. 31	45. $4\frac{1}{2}$			

Exercise 8 *page 63*

1. −20	2. 16	3. −42	4. −4	5. −90	6. −160
7. −2	8. −81	9. 4	10. 22	11. 14	12. 5 or − 5
13. 1 or − 1	14. $\sqrt{5}$	15. 4	16. $-6\frac{1}{2}$	17. 54	18. 25
19. 4 or − 4	20. 312	21. 45	22. 22	23. 14	24. −36
25. −7	26. 1 or − 1	27. 901	28. −30	29. −5	30. $7\frac{1}{2}$
31. −7	32. $-\frac{3}{13}$	33. 7	34. −2	35. 0	36. $-4\frac{1}{2}$
37. 6 or − 6	38. 2 or − 2	39. 26	40. −9	41. $3\frac{1}{4}$	42. $-\frac{5}{6}$
43. 4	44. $2\frac{2}{3}$	45. $3\frac{1}{4}$	46. $-2\frac{1}{6}$	47. −13	48. 12
49. $1\frac{1}{3}$	50. $-\frac{5}{36}$				

Exercise 9 *page 64*

1. $3x + 11y$	2. $2a + 8b$	3. $3x + 2y$	4. $5x + 5$	5. $9 + x$
6. $3 - 9y$	7. $5x - 2y - x^2$	8. $2x^2 + 3x + 5$	9. $-10y$	10. $3a^2 + 2a$
11. $7 + 7a - 7a^2$	12. $5x$	13. $\frac{10}{a} - b$	14. $\frac{5}{x} - \frac{5}{y}$	15. $\frac{3m}{x}$
16. $\frac{1}{2} - \frac{2}{x}$	17. $\frac{5}{a} + 3b$	18. $-\frac{n}{4}$	19. $7x^2 - x^3$	20. $2x^2$
21. $x^2 + 5y^2$	22. $-12x^2 - 4y^2$	23. $5x - 11x^2$	24. $\frac{8}{x^2}$	25. $5x + 2$
26. $12x - 7$	27. $3x + 4$	28. $11 - 6x$	29. $-5x - 20$	30. $7x - 2x^2$
31. $3x^2 - 5x$	32. $x - 4$	33. $5x^2 + 14x$	34. $-4x^2 - 3x$	35. $5a + 8$
36. $a + 9$	37. $ab + 4a$	38. $y^2 + y$	39. $2x - 2$	40. $6x + 3$
41. $x - 4$	42. $7x + 5y$	43. $4x^2 - 11x$	44. $2x^2 + 14x$	45. $3y^2 - 4y + 1$
46. $12x + 12$	47. $4ab - 3a + 14b$	48. $2x - 4$		

Exercise 10 *page 65*

1. $x^2 + 4x + 3$	2. $x^2 + 5x + 6$	3. $y^2 + 9y + 20$	4. $x^2 + x - 12$
5. $x^2 + 3x - 10$	6. $x^2 - 5x + 6$	7. $a^2 - 2a - 35$	8. $z^2 + 7z - 18$
9. $x^2 - 9$	10. $k^2 - 121$	11. $2x^2 - 5x - 3$	12. $3x^2 - 2x - 8$
13. $2y^2 - y - 3$	14. $49y^2 - 1$	15. $9x^2 - 4$	16. $6a^2 + 5ab + b^2$
17. $3x^2 + 7xy + 2y^2$	18. $6b^2 + bc - c^2$	19. $-5x^2 + 16xy - 3y^2$	20. $15b^2 + ab - 2a^2$
21. $2x^2 + 2x - 4$	22. $6x^2 + 3x - 9$	23. $24y^2 + 4y - 8$	24. $6x^2 - 10x - 4$
25. $4a^2 - 16b^2$	26. $x^3 - 3x^2 + 2x$	27. $8x^3 - 2x$	28. $3y^3 + 3y^2 - 18y$
29. $x^3 + x^2y + x^2z + xyz$	30. $3za^2 + 3zam - 6zm^2$		

Exercise 11 *page 66*

1. $x^2 + 8x + 16$	2. $x^2 + 4x + 4$	3. $x^2 - 4x + 4$	4. $4x^2 + 4x + 1$
5. $y^2 - 10y + 25$	6. $9y^2 + 6y + 1$	7. $x^2 + 2xy + y^2$	8. $4x^2 + 4xy + y^2$
9. $a^2 - 2ab + b^2$	10. $4a^2 - 12ab + 9b^2$	11. $3x^2 + 12x + 12$	12. $9 - 6x + x^2$
13. $9x^2 + 12x + 4$	14. $a^2 - 4ab + 4b^2$	15. $2x^2 + 6x + 5$	16. $2x^2 + 2x + 13$
17. $5x^2 + 8x + 5$	18. $2y^2 - 14y + 25$	19. $10x - 5$	20. $-8x + 8$
21. $-10y + 5$	22. $3x^2 - 2x - 8$	23. $2x^2 + 4x - 4$	24. $-x^2 - 18x + 15$

Answers

1. $x^3 - 5x^2 - 2x + 24$ **2.** $x^3 - 4x^2 - 7x + 10$ **3.** $x^3 + 8x^2 - 3x - 90$
4. $2x^3 - x^2 - 2x + 1$ **5.** $6x^3 - 7x^2 - 9x - 2$ **6.** $8x^3 + 22x^2 + 3x - 18$
7. $36x^3 - 361x + 280$ **8.** $x^3 - 2x^2 - 7x - 4$ **9.** $x^3 - 7x^2 + 16x - 12$
10. $4x^3 + 8x^2 - 3x - 9$ **11.** $x^3 - 3x^2 + 3x - 1$ **12.** $27x^3 + 54x^2 + 36x + 8$
13. $-9x^2 + 9x - 9$ **14.** $21x^2 - 21x + 91$ **15.** $11x^3 + 21x^2 + 15x + 4$

1. 8 **2.** 9 **3.** 7 **4.** 10 **5.** $\frac{1}{3}$ **6.** 10

7. $1\frac{1}{2}$ **8.** -1 **9.** $-1\frac{1}{2}$ **10.** $\frac{1}{3}$ **11.** 35 **12.** 130

13. 14 **14.** $\frac{2}{3}$ **15.** $3\frac{1}{3}$ **16.** $-2\frac{1}{2}$ **17.** 3 **18.** $1\frac{1}{8}$

19. $\frac{3}{10}$ **20.** $-1\frac{1}{4}$ **21.** 10 **22.** 27 **23.** 20 **24.** 18

25. 28 **26.** -15 **27.** $\frac{99}{100}$ **28.** 0 **29.** 1000 **30.** $-\frac{1}{1000}$

31. 1 **32.** -7 **33.** -5 **34.** $1\frac{1}{6}$ **35.** 1 **36.** 2

37. -5 **38.** -3 **39.** $-1\frac{1}{2}$ **40.** 2 **41.** 1 **42.** $3\frac{1}{2}$

43. 2 **44.** -1 **45.** $10\frac{2}{3}$ **46.** 1.1 **47.** -1 **48.** 2

49. $2\frac{1}{2}$ **50.** $1\frac{1}{3}$

1. $-1\frac{1}{2}$ **2.** 2 **3.** $-\frac{2}{5}$ **4.** $-\frac{1}{3}$ **5.** $1\frac{2}{3}$ **6.** 6

7. $-\frac{2}{5}$ **8.** $-3\frac{1}{5}$ **9.** $\frac{1}{2}$ **10.** -4 **11.** 18 **12.** 5

13. 4 **14.** 3 **15.** $2\frac{3}{4}$ **16.** $-\frac{7}{22}$ **17.** $\frac{1}{4}$ **18.** 1

19. 4 **20.** -11 **21.** $-7\frac{1}{3}$ **22.** $1\frac{1}{4}$ **23.** -5 **24.** 6

25. 3 **26.** 6 **27.** 2 **28.** 3 **29.** 4 **30.** 3

31. $10\frac{1}{2}$ **32.** 5 **33.** 2 **34.** -1 **35.** -17 **36.** $-2\frac{9}{10}$

37. $2\frac{10}{21}$ **38.** $\frac{1}{3}$ **39.** 14 **40.** 15

1. $\frac{1}{4}$ **2.** -3 **3.** 4 **4.** $-7\frac{2}{3}$ **5.** -43

6. 11 **7.** $-\frac{1}{2}$ **8.** 0 **9.** 1 **10.** $-1\frac{2}{3}$

11. $\frac{1}{4}$ **12.** 0 **13.** $-\frac{6}{7}$ **14.** $1\frac{9}{17}$ **15.** $1\frac{22}{23}$

16. $\frac{2}{11}$ **17.** 4 cm **18.** 5 m **19.** 4

1. $\frac{1}{3}$ **2.** $\frac{1}{5}$ **3.** $1\frac{2}{3}$ **4.** -3

5. $\frac{5}{11}$ **6.** -2 **7.** 6 **8.** $3\frac{3}{4}$

9. -7 **10.** $-7\frac{2}{3}$ **11.** 2 **12.** 3

13. 4 **14.** -2 **15.** -3 **16.** 3

17. $1\frac{5}{7}$ **18.** $4\frac{4}{5}$ **19.** 10 **20.** 24

21. 2 **22.** 3 **23.** 5 **24.** -4

25. $6\frac{3}{4}$ **26.** −3   **27.** 0   **28.** 3

29. 0   **30.** 1   **31.** 2   **32.** 3

33. 4   **34.** $\frac{3}{5}$ **35.** $1\frac{1}{8}$ **36.** −1

37. 1   **38.** 1   **39.** $\frac{1}{4}$ **40.** $-\frac{1}{3}$

41. $\frac{9}{10}$ **42.** 1   **43.** 2   **44.** $-\frac{1}{7}$

45. 2   **46.** 3

Exercise 17   *page 73*

1. 91, 92, 93   **2.** 21, 22, 23, 24   **3.** 57, 59, 61   **4.** 506, 508, 510

5. $12\frac{1}{2}$ **6.** $12\frac{1}{2}$ **7.** $11\frac{2}{3}$ **8.** $8\frac{1}{3}, 41\frac{2}{3}$

9. $1\frac{1}{4}, 13\frac{3}{4}$ **10.** $3\frac{1}{3}$ cm   **11.** 12 cm   **12.** 20

13. 5 cm   **14.** 7 cm   **15.** $18\frac{1}{2}, 27\frac{1}{2}$ **16.** 20°, 60°, 100°

17. 45°, 60°, 75°   **18.** 5   **19.** 6, 8   **20.** 12, 24, 30

21. 5, 15, 8   **22.** $59\frac{2}{3}$ kg, $64\frac{2}{3}$ kg, $72\frac{2}{3}$ kg   **23.** 24, 22, 15

24. 48, 12   **25.** 40, 8   **26.** 6   **27.** 168.84 cm²

28. 14   **29.** $45, $31   **30.** $21.50

Exercise 18   *page 76*

1. $3700   **2.** 3   **3.** $1\frac{3}{7}$ m   **4.** 80°, 100°   **5.** 30°, 60°, 90°, 120°, 150°, 270°

6. 26, 58   **7.** 2 km   **8.** 8 km   **9.** 400 m   **10.** 21   **11.** 23

12. $3600   **13.** 15   **14.** 2 km   **15.** 7, 8, 9   **16.** 2, 3, 4, 5

Exercise 19   *page 78*

1. $x = 2, y = 1$ **2.** $x = 4, y = 2$ **3.** $x = 3, y = 1$ **4.** $x = -2, y = 1$

5. $x = 3, y = 2$ **6.** $x = 5, y = -2$ **1.** $x = 2, y = 1$ **8.** $x = 5, y = 3$

9. $x = 3, y = -1$ **10.** $a = 2, b = -3$ **11.** $a = 5, b = \frac{1}{4}$ **12.** $a = 1, b = 3$

13. $m = \frac{1}{2}, n = 4$ **14.** $w = 2, x = 3$ **15.** $x = 6, y = 3$ **16.** $x = \frac{1}{2}, z = -3$

17. $m = 1\frac{15}{17}, n = \frac{11}{17}$ **18.** $c = 1\frac{16}{23}, d = -2\frac{12}{23}$

Exercise 20   *page 79*

1. 1   **2.** −3   **3.** 2   **4.** 15

5. −12   **6.** −3   **7.** −2   **8.** −11

9. −21   **10.** 1   **11.** 0   **12.** 15

13. −10   **14.** 3   **15.** 6   **16.** −11

17. 2   **18.** 5   **19.** −19   **20.** −4

21. x **22.** $-3x$ **23.** $4x$ **24.** $4y$

25. $9y$ **26.** $3x$ **27.** $-8x$ **28.** $4x$

29. $2x$ **30.** $3y$

Exercise 21   *page 80*

1. $x = 2, y = 4$ **2.** $x = 1, y = 4$ **3.** $x = 2, y = 5$ **4.** $x = 3, y = 7$

5. $x = 5, y = 2$ **6.** $a = 3, b = 1$ **7.** $x = 1, y = 3$ **8.** $x = 1, y = 3$

9. $x = -2, y = 3$ **10.** $x = 4, y = 1$ **11.** $x = 1, y = 5$ **12.** $x = 0, y = 2$

13. $x = \frac{5}{7}, y = 4\frac{3}{7}$ **14.** $x = 1, y = 2$ **15.** $x = 2, y = -3$ **16.** $x = 4, y = -1$

17. $x = 3, y = 1$ **18.** $x = 1, y = 2$ **19.** $x = 2, y = 1$ **20.** $x = -2, y = 1$

21. $x = 1, y = 2$ **22.** $a = 4, b = 3$ **23.** $x = -23, y = -78$ **24.** $x = 3, \ y = \frac{1}{2}$

25. $x = 4, y = 3$ **26.** $x = 5, y = -2$ **27.** $x = \frac{1}{3}, y = -2$ **28.** $x = 5\frac{5}{14}, y = \frac{2}{7}$
29. $x = 3, y = -1$ **30.** $x = 5, y = 0.2$

Exercise 22   page 82

1. $5\frac{1}{2}, 9\frac{1}{2}$ **2.** 6, 3 or $2\frac{2}{5}, 5\frac{2}{5}$ **3.** 4, 10   **4.** $a = 2, c = 7$

5. $m = 4, c = -3$ **6.** $a = 1, b = -2$ **7.** $m = lc, w = 3c$ **8.** TV \$200, DVD player \$450

9. 7, 3   **10.** white 2 g, brown $3\frac{1}{2}$ g **11.** 120 cm, 240 cm   **12.** 150 m, 350 m

13. $2c \times 15, 5c \times 25$ **14.** $10c \times 14, 50c \times 7$ **15.** 20
16. man \$500, woman \$700   **17.** current 4 m/s, kipper 10 m/s
18. $\frac{5}{7}$ **19.** $\frac{3}{5}$ **20.** boy 10, mouse 3   **21.** 4, 7

22. $y = 3x - 2$ **23.** walks 4 m/s, runs 5 m/s   **24.** \$1 $\times$ 15, \$5 $\times$ 5

25. 36, 9   **26.** current $4\frac{1}{2}$ knots, submarine $20\frac{1}{2}$ knots   **27.** $a = 1, b = 2, c = 5$

28. $y = 2x^2 - 3x + 5$ **29.** $y = x^2 + 3x + 4$ **30.** $y = x^2 + 2x - 3$

Exercise 23   page 84
1. $5(a + b)$ **2.** $7(x + y)$ **3.** $x(7 + x)$ **4.** $y(y + 8)$
5. $y(2y + 3)$ **6.** $2y(3y - 2)$ **7.** $3x(x - 7)$ **8.** $2a(8 - a)$
9. $3c(2c - 7)$ **10.** $3x(5 - 3x)$ **11.** $7y(8 - 3y)$ **12.** $x(a + b + 2c)$
13. $x(x + y + 3z)$ **14.** $y(x^2 + y^2 + z^2)$ **15.** $ab(3a + 2b)$ **16.** $xy(x + y)$
17. $2a(3a + 2b + c)$ **18.** $m(a + 2b + m)$ **19.** $2k(x + 3y + 2z)$ **20.** $a(x^2 + y + 2b)$
21. $xk(x + k)$ **22.** $ab(a^2 + 2b)$ **23.** $bc(a - 3b)$ **24.** $ae(2a - 5e)$
25. $ab(a^2 + b^2)$ **26.** $x^2y(x + y)$ **27.** $2xy(3y - 2x)$ **28.** $3ab(b^2 - a^2)$
29. $a^2b(2a + 5b)$ **30.** $ax^2(y - 2z)$ **31.** $2ab(x + b + a)$ **32.** $yx(a + x^2 - 2yx)$

Exercise 24   page 85
1. $(a + b)(x + y)$ **2.** $(a + b)(y + z)$ **3.** $(x + y)(b + c)$ **4.** $(x + y)(h + k)$
5. $(x + y)(m + n)$ **6.** $(a + b)(h - k)$ **7.** $(a + b)(x - y)$ **8.** $(m + n)(a - b)$
9. $(h + k)(s + t)$ **10.** $(x + y)(s - t)$ **11.** $(a - b)(x - y)$ **12.** $(x - y)(s - t)$
13. $(a - x)(s - y)$ **14.** $(h - b)(x - y)$ **15.** $(m - n)(a - b)$ **16.** $(x - z)(k - m)$
17. $(2a + b)(x + 3y)$ **18.** $(2a+b)(x + y)$ **19.** $(2m + n)(h - k)$ **20.** $(m-n)(2h + 3k)$
21. $(2x + y)(3a + b)$ **22.** $(2a - b)(x - y)$ **23.** $(x^2 + y)(a + b)$ **24.** $(m - n)(s + 2t^2)$

Exercise 25   page 86
1. $(x + 2)(x + 5)$ **2.** $(x + 3)(x + 4)$ **3.** $(x + 3)(x + 5)$ **4.** $(x + 3)(x + 7)$
5. $(x + 2)(x + 6)$ **6.** $(y + 5)(y + 7)$ **7.** $(y + 3)(y + 8)$ **8.** $(y + 5)(y + 5)$
9. $(y + 3)(y + 12)$ **10.** $(a + 2)(a - 5)$ **11.** $(a + 3)(a - 4)$ **12.** $(z + 3)(z - 2)$
13. $(x + 5)(x - 7)$ **14.** $(x + 3)(x - 8)$ **15.** $(x - 2)(x - 4)$ **16.** $(y - 2)(y - 3)$
17. $(x - 3)(x - 5)$ **18.** $(a + 2)(a - 3)$ **19.** $(a + 5)(a + 9)$ **20.** $(b + 3)(b - 7)$
21. $(x - 4)(x - 4)$ **22.** $(y + 1)(y + 1)$ **23.** $(y - 7)(y + 4)$ **24.** $(x - 5)(x + 4)$
25. $(x - 20)(x + 12)$ **26.** $(x - 15)(x - 11)$ **27.** $(y + 12)(y - 9)$ **28.** $(x - 7)(x + 7)$
29. $(x - 3)(x + 3)$ **30.** $(x - 4)(x + 4)$

Exercise 26   page 86
1. $(2x + 3)(x + 1)$ **2.** $(2x + 1)(x + 3)$ **3.** $(3x + 1)(x + 2)$ **4.** $(2x + 3)(x + 4)$
5. $(3x + 2)(x + 2)$ **6.** $(2x + 5)(x + 1)$ **7.** $(3x + 1)(x - 2)$ **8.** $(2x + 5)(x - 3)$
9. $(2x + 7)(x - 3)$ **10.** $(3x + 4)(x - 7)$ **11.** $(2x + 1)(3x + 2)$ **12.** $(3x + 2)(4x + 5)$
13. $(3x - 2)(x - 3)$ **14.** $(y - 2)(3y - 5)$ **15.** $(4y - 3)(y - 5)$ **16.** $(2y + 3)(3y - 1)$
17. $(2x - 5)(3x - 6)$ **18.** $(5x + 2)(2x + 1)$ **19.** $(6x - 1)(x - 3)$ **20.** $(4x + 1)(2x - 3)$
21. $(6x + 5)(2x - 1)$ **22.** $(16x + 3)(x + 1)$ **23.** $(2a - 1)(2a - 1)$ **24.** $(x + 2)(12x - 7)$
25. $(x + 3)(15x - 1)$ **26.** $(8x + 1)(6x + 5)$ **27.** $(16y - 3)(4y + 1)$ **28.** $(15x - 1)(8x + 5)$
29. $(3x - 1)(3x + 1)$ **30.** $(2a - 3)(2a + 3)$

Exercise 27 page 87

1. $(y-a)(y+a)$ **2.** $(m-n)(m+n)$ **3.** $(x-t)(x+t)$ **4.** $(y-1)(y+1)$

5. $(x-3)(x+3)$ **6.** $(a-5)(a+5)$ **7.** $\left(x-\frac{1}{2}\right)\left(x+\frac{1}{2}\right)$ **8.** $\left(x-\frac{1}{3}\right)\left(x+\frac{1}{3}\right)$

9. $(2x-y)(2x+y)$ **10.** $(a-2b)(a+2b)$ **11.** $(5x-2y)(3x+2y)$ **12.** $(3x-4y)(3x+4y)$

13. $\left(x-\dfrac{y}{2}\right)\left(x+\dfrac{y}{2}\right)$ **14.** $\left(3m-\frac{2}{3}n\right)\left(3m+\frac{2}{3}n\right)$ **15.** $\left(4t-\frac{2}{5}s\right)\left(4t+\frac{2}{5}s\right)$ **16.** $\left(2x-\dfrac{z}{10}\right)\left(2x+\dfrac{z}{10}\right)$

17. $x(x-1)(x+1)$ **18.** $a(a-b)(a+b)$ **19.** $x(2x-1)(2x+1)$
20. $2x(2x-y)(2x+y)$ **21.** $3x(2x-y)(2x+y)$ **22.** $2m(3m-2n)(3m+2n)$

23. $5\left(x-\frac{1}{2}\right)\left(x+\frac{1}{2}\right)$ **24.** $2a(5a-3b)(5a+3b)$ **25.** $3y(2x-z)(2x+z)$

26. $4ab(3a-b)(3a+b)$ **27.** $2a^3(5a-2b)(5a+2b)$ **28.** $9xy(2x-5y)(2x+5y)$
29. 161 **30.** 404 **31.** 4400 **32.** 2421
33. 4329 **34.** 0.75 **35.** 4.8 **36.** –2469
37. 0.0761 **38.** –10 900 **39.** 53.6 **40.** 0.000 005

Exercise 28 page 88

1. $-3, -4$ **2.** $-2, -5$ **3.** $3, -5$ **4.** $2, -3$ **5.** $2, 6$

6. $-3, -7$ **7.** $6, -1$ **8.** $5, -1$ **9.** $-7, 2$ **10.** $-\frac{1}{2}, 2$

11. $\frac{2}{3}, -4$ **12.** $1\frac{1}{2}, -5$ **13.** $\frac{2}{3}, 1\frac{1}{2}$ **14.** $\frac{1}{4}, 7$ **15.** $\frac{2}{5}, -\frac{1}{2}$

16. $7, 8$ **17.** $\frac{5}{6}, \frac{1}{2}$ **18.** $7, -9$ **19.** $-1, -1$ **20.** $3, 3$

21. $-5, -5$ **22.** $7, 7$ **23.** $-\frac{1}{3}, \frac{1}{2}$ **24.** $-1\frac{1}{4}, 2$ **25.** $13, -5$

26. $-3, \frac{1}{6}$ **27.** $\frac{1}{10}, -2$ **28.** $1, 1$ **29.** $\frac{2}{9}, -\frac{1}{4}$ **30.** $-\frac{1}{4}, \frac{3}{5}$

Exercise 29 page 89

1. $0, 3$ **2.** $0, -7$ **3.** $0, 1$ **4.** $0, \frac{1}{3}$ **5.** $4, -4$

6. $7, -7$ **7.** $\frac{1}{2}, -\frac{1}{2}$ **8.** $\frac{2}{3}, -\frac{2}{3}$ **9.** $0, -1\frac{1}{2}$ **10.** $0, -1\frac{1}{2}$

11. $0, 5\frac{1}{2}$ **12.** $\frac{1}{4}, -\frac{1}{4}$ **13.** $\frac{1}{2}, -\frac{1}{2}$ **14.** $0, \frac{5}{8}$ **15.** $0, \frac{1}{12}$

16. $0, 6$ **17.** $0, 11$ **18.** $0, \frac{1}{2}$ **19.** $0, 1$ **20.** $0, 4$

21. $0, 3$ **22.** $\frac{1}{2}, -\frac{1}{2}$ **23.** $1\frac{1}{3}, -1\frac{1}{3}$ **24.** $3, -3$ **25.** $0, 2\frac{2}{5}$

26. $\frac{1}{3}, -\frac{1}{3}$ **27.** $0, \frac{1}{4}$ **28.** $0, \frac{1}{6}$ **29.** $\frac{1}{4}, -\frac{1}{4}$ **30.** $0, \frac{1}{5}$

Exercise 30 page 90

1. $-\frac{1}{2}, -5$ **2.** $-\frac{2}{3}, -3$ **3.** $-\frac{1}{2}, -\frac{2}{3}$ **4.** $\frac{1}{3}, 3$

5. $\frac{2}{5}, 1$ **6.** $\frac{1}{3}, 1\frac{1}{2}$ **7.** $-0.63, -2.37$ **8.** $-0.27, -3.73$

9. $0.72, 0.28$ **10.** $6.70, 0.30$ **11.** $0.19, -2.69$ **12.** $0.85, -1.18$

13. $0.61, -3.28$ **14.** $-1\frac{2}{3}, 4$ **15.** $-1\frac{1}{2}, 5$ **16.** $3.56, -0.56$

17. $0.16, -3.16$ **18.** $-\frac{1}{2}, 2\frac{1}{3}$ **19.** $-\frac{1}{3}, -8$ **20.** $-\frac{2}{3}, -1$

21. $2.28, 0.22$ **22.** $-0.35, -5.65$ **23.** $-\frac{2}{3}, \frac{1}{2}$ **24.** $-0.58, 2.58$

25. $-2.69, 0.19$ **26.** $0.22, -1.55$ **27.** $-0.37, 5.37$ **28.** $-\frac{5}{6}, 1\frac{3}{4}$

29. $-\frac{7}{9}, 1\frac{1}{4}$ **30.** $1\frac{2}{5}, 2\frac{1}{4}$ **31.** $-4, 1\frac{1}{2}$ **32.** $-3, 1\frac{2}{3}$

33. $-2, 1\frac{2}{3}$ **34.** $-3\frac{1}{2}, \frac{1}{5}$ **35.** $-3, \frac{4}{5}$ **36.** $-8\frac{1}{2}, 11$

Exercise 31   page 91

1. $-3, 2$ **2.** $-3, -7$ **3.** $-\frac{1}{2}, 2$ **4.** $1, 4$ **5.** $-1\frac{2}{3}, \frac{1}{2}$

6. $-0.39, -4.28$ **7.** $-0.16, 6.16$ **8.** 3 **9.** $2, -1\frac{1}{3}$ **10.** $-3, -1$

11. $0.66, -22.66$ **12.** $-7, 2$ **13.** $\frac{1}{4}, 7$ **14.** $-\frac{1}{2}, \frac{3}{5}$ **15.** $0, 3\frac{1}{2}$

16. $-\frac{1}{4}, \frac{1}{4}$ **17.** $-2.77, 1.27$ **18.** $-\frac{2}{3}, 1$ **19.** $-\frac{1}{2}, 2$ **20.** $0, 3$

21. a) -1 **b)** 0.6258 **c)** 0.5961 **d)** 0.2210

Exercise 32   page 93

1. $(x+4)^2 - 16$ **2.** $(x-6)^2 - 36$ **3.** $\left(x+\frac{1}{2}\right) - \frac{1}{4}$ **4.** $(x+2)^2 - 3$ **5.** $(x-3)^2$

6. $(x+1)^2 - 16$ **7.** $2(x+4)^2 - 27$ **8.** $2(x-2.5)^2 - 6.25$ **9.** $10 - (x-2)^2$ **10.** $4 - (x+1)^2$

11. a) $x = \pm\sqrt{7} - 2$ **b)** $x = 1.5 \pm \sqrt{4.25}$ **c)** $x = \pm\sqrt{37} - 6$ **12.** $(x+3)^2 + 3$ requires finding $\sqrt{-1}$

13. $f(x) = (x+3)^2 + 3$ **14.** $g(x) = (x-3.5)^2 - 12$ **15. a)** 3 **b)** $x = -2$ **c)** $\frac{1}{3}$

Exercise 33   page 95

1. $8, 11$ **2.** $11, 13$ **3.** 12 cm   **4.** 6 cm

5. $x = 11$ **6.** 10 cm $\times 24$ cm   **7.** 8 km north, 15 km east   **8.** 12 eggs

9. 13 eggs   **10.** 4 or -1 **11.** $2, 5$ **12.** $\frac{40}{x}$h, $\frac{40}{x-2}$h, 10 km/h

13. 4 km/h   **14.** 60 km/h   **15.** 5 km/h   **16.** 157 km   **17.** $x = 2$

18. $x = 3$ or 9.5 **19.** $\frac{3}{4}$ **20.** 9 cm or 13 cm

Exercise 34   page 97

1. $x = 6, y = 8$ and $x = 8, y = 4$ **2.** $x = 1, y = -2$ and $x = 3, y = 10$
3. $x = 1, y = 0$ **4.** $x = 1, y = 7$ and $x = 3, y = 3$
5. $x = -5, y = 19$ **6.** $x = 0.59, y = 33.31$ and $x = 3.41, y = 10.69$
7. $x = -0.73, y = 6.07$ and $x = 2.73, y = 19.93$ **8.** $x = -6.24, y = 5.58$ and $x = -1.76, y = 32.42$
9. $x = -5.73. y = 8.46$ and $x = -2.27, y = 1.54$ **10.** $x = -3.59, y = -4.88$ and $x = 2.09, y = 3.63$
11. $x = 0, y = 5$ and $x = 0.83, y = 3.89$ **12.** $x = -2.20, y = -3.13$ and $x = 1.31, y = -0.79$

Revision exercise 2A   page 98

1. a) $-2\frac{1}{2}$ **b)** $2\frac{2}{3}$ **c)** $0, -5$ **d)** $2, -2$ **e)** $-5, 2\frac{2}{3}$

2. a) 14 **b)** 18 **c)** 28

3. a) $(2x - y)(2x + y)$ **b)** $2(x+3)(x+1)$ **c)** $(2 - 3k)(3m + 2n)$ **d)** $(2x+1)(x-3)$

4. a) $x = 3, y = -2$ **b)** $m = 1\frac{1}{2}, n = -3$ **c)** $x = 7, y = \frac{1}{2}$ **d)** $x = -1, y = -2$

5. a) 8 **b)** 140 **c)** 29 **d)** 42 **e)** 6 **f)** -6
6. a) $2x - 21$ **b)** $(1 - 2x)(2a - 3b)$ **c)** 23 **d)** $x^3 - 9x^2 + 26x - 24$ **e)** $8x^3 - 36x^2 + 54x - 27$
7. a) 1 **b)** $10\frac{1}{2}$ **c)** $0, 3\frac{1}{2}$ **d)** $-3, -2$ **e)** 12

8. a) $z(z - 4)(z + 4)$ **b)** $(x^2 + 1)(y^2 + 1)$ **c)** $(2x + 3)(x + 4)$ **9.** $\frac{7}{8}$

10. a) $c = 5, d = -2$ **b)** $x = 2, y = -1$ **c)** $x = 9, y = -14$ **d)** $s = 5, t = -3$
     e) $x = 0, y = 4$ and $x = -3, y = 1$ **f)** $x = 0.57, y = 1.36$ and $x = 2.18, y = 3.76$
11. a) $\frac{1}{2}, -\frac{1}{2}$ **b)** $\frac{7}{11}$ **c)** 3 **d)** $0, 5$

12. a) $1.78, -0.28$ **b)** $1.62, -0.62$ **c)** $0.87, -1.54$ **d)** $1.54, -4.54$
13. a) $x = 9$ **b)** $x = 10$

14. a) 2   **b)** −3   **c)** 36   **d)** 0   **e)** 36   **f)** 4

15. speed = 5 km/h   **16.** 8 cm × 6.5 cm   **17. a)** −2, 4   **b)** 16   **c)** 6.19, 0.81

18. $-\frac{1}{5}$, 3   **19.** 8   **20.** $x = 13$ **21.** 21

22. 18   **23.** 6 cm   **24.** −4

Examination-style exercise 2B   *page 100*

  1. a) 3   **b)** 8   **2.** (4, 1)

  3. a) 13.5   **b)** −1 and 4

  4. $x = 10, y = 3$ **5.** $p = 2, q = -12$

  6. a) i) $4x(x + 4)$ **b)** 1.1

  7. a) i) $(x + 4)(x - 5)$ **ii)** −4, 5   **b)** −0.55, 1.22

    c) i) $(m - 2n)(m + 2n)$ **ii)** −12   **iii)** $y = 20x + 5$ **iv)** $n = \sqrt{\dfrac{m^2 - y}{4}}$

    d) i) ± 4   **ii)** $n(m - 2n)(m + 2n)(m^2 + 4n^2)$

  8. a) ii) −9, 4   **iii)** 7.81 cm   **b) iii)** $y = 4.5$ **iv)** 2.55 km/h

  9. a) $3x^3 - 17x^2 + 21x + 9$ **b)** $3x^3 - 18x^2 + 17x + 5$

  10. $x = -1.14, y = 0.43$ and $x = 2.64, y = 2.32$

3 Mensuration

Exercise 1   *page 104*

  1. 10.2 m²   **2.** 22 cm²   **3.** 103 m²   **4.** 9 cm²

  5. 31 m²   **6.** 6000 cm² or 0.6 m²   **7.** 26 m²   **8.** 18 cm²

  9. 20 cm²   **10.** 13 m   **11.** 15 cm   **12.** 56 m

  13. 8 m, 10 m   **14.** 12 cm   **15.** 2500   **16.** 6 square units

  17. 14 square units   **18.** 1849   **20.** 1100 m

Exercise 2   *page 106*

  1. 48.3 cm²   **2.** 28.4 cm²   **3.** 66.4 m²   **4.** 3.1 cm²

  5. 18.2 cm²   **6.** 12.3 cm²   **7.** 2.78 cm²   **8.** 36.4 m²

  9. 62.4 m²   **10.** 30.4 m²   **11.** 44.9 cm²   **12.** 0.28 m²

  13. 63 m²   **14.** 70.7 m²   **15.** 14 m²   **16.** 65.8 cm²

  17. 18.1 cm²   **18.** 8.0 m²   **19.** 14 m²   **20.** 52.0 cm²

  21. 124 cm²   **22.** 69.8 m²   **23.** 57.1 cm²   **24.** 10.7 cm

  25. 50.9°   **26.** 4.10 m   **27.** 4.85 m   **28.** 7.23 cm

  29. 60°; 23.4 cm²   **30.** 292   **31.** 110 cm²

  32. a) $\dfrac{360°}{n}$ **b)** $\dfrac{n}{2}\sin\dfrac{360°}{n}$ **c)** 2.6, 2.94, 3.1414, 3.1416, 3.1416 as n increases, $A \to \pi$ **33.** 18.7 cm

Exercise 3   *page 109*

  1. a) 31.4 cm   **b)** 78.5 cm²   **2. a)** 18.8 cm   **b)** 28.3 cm²

  3. a) 51.4 cm   **b)** 157 cm²   **4. a)** 26.6 cm   **b)** 49.1 cm²

  5. a) 26.3 cm   **b)** 33.3 cm²   **6. a)** 25.0 cm   **b)** 38.5 cm²

  7. a) 35.7 cm   **b)** 21.5 cm²   **8. a)** 50.3 cm   **b)** 174 cm²

  9. a) 22.0 cm   **b)** 10.5 cm²   **10. a)** 9.42 cm   **b)** 6.44 cm²

  11. a) 25.1 cm   **b)** 25.1 cm²   **12. a)** 18.8 cm   **b)** 12.6 cm²

Exercise 4   *page 110*

  1. 2.19 cm   **2.** 30.2 m   **3.** 2.65 km   **4.** 9.33 cm

  5. 14.2 mm   **6.** 497 000 km²   **7.** 21.5 cm²

  8. a) 40.8 m²   **b)** 6   **9. a)** 30   **b)** 1508 cm²   **c)** 508 cm²

  10. 5305   **11.** 29   **12.** 970   **13. a)** 80   **b)** 7

  14. 5.39 cm $\left(\sqrt{29}\right)$ **15. a)** 33.0 cm   **b)** 70.9 cm²   **16. a)** 98 cm²   **b)** 14.0 cm²

  17. 1 : 3 : 5   **18.** 796 m²   **19.** 57.5°   **20.** Yes   **21.** 1.716 cm

Exercise 5 *page 113*
  1. a) 2.09 cm; 4.19 cm²   **b)** 7.85 cm; 39.3 cm²   **c)** 8.20 cm; 8.20 cm²
  2. 31.9 cm²   **3.** 31.2 cm²
  4. a) 7.07 cm²   **b)** 19.5 cm²   **5. a)** 85.9°   **b)** 57.3°   **c)** 6.25 cm
  6. a) 12 cm   **b)** 30°   **7. a)** 3.98 cm   **b)** 74.9°
  8. a) 30°   **b)** 10.5 cm   **9. a)** 18 cm   **b)** 38.2°
  10. a) 10 cm   **b)** 43.0°   **11. a)** 6.14 cm   **b)** 27.6 m   **c)** 28.6 cm²
  12. 15.14 km²

Exercise 6 *page 116*
  1. a) 14.5 cm   **b)** 72.6 cm²   **c)** 24.5 cm²   **d)** 48.1 cm²
  2. a) 5.08 cm²   **b)** 82.8 m²   **c)** 5.14 cm²
  4. a) 60°, 9.06 cm²   **b)** 106.3°, 11.2 cm²
  4. 3 cm   **5.** 3.97 cm   **6.** 13.5 cm², 405 cm³   **7.** 129.9 cm²; 184.3 cm²
  8. 459 cm², 651 cm³   **9.** 19.6 cm²   **10.** 0.313r²
  11. a) 8.37 cm   **b)** 54.5 cm   **c)** 10.4 cm   **12.** 81.2 cm²

Exercise 7 *page 118*
  1. a) 30 cm³   **b)** 168 cm³   **c)** 110 cm³   **d)** 94.5 cm³   **e)** 754 cm³   **f)** 283 cm³
  2. a) 503 cm³   **b)** 760 m³   **c)** 12.5 cm³
  3. 3.98 cm   **4.** 6.37 cm   **5.** 1.89 cm   **6.** 5.37 cm
  7. 9.77 cm   **8.** 7.38 cm   **9.** 12.7 m   **10.** 4.24 litres
  11. 106 cm/s   **12.** 1570 cm³, 12.6 kg   **13.** 3 : 4   **14.** cubes by 77 cm³
  15. No   **16.** l.19 cm   **17.** 53 times   **18.** 191 cm

Exercise 8 *page 121*
  1. 20.9 cm³   **2.** 524 cm³   **3.** 4189 cm³   **4.** 101 cm³   **5.** 268 cm³   **6.** 4.19x³ cm³
  7. 0.004 19 m³   **8.** 3 cm³   **9.** 93.3 cm³   **10.** 48 cm³   **11.** 92.4 cm³   **12.** 262 cm³
  13. 235 cm³   **14.** 415 cm³   **15.** 5 m   **16.** 2.43 cm   **17.** 23.9 cm   **18.** 6 cm
  19. 3.72 cm   **20.** 1.93 kg   **21.** 106 s   **22. a)** 125   **b)** 2744   **c)** 2.7×10^7
  23. a) 0.36 cm   **b)** 0.427 cm   **24. a)** 6.69 cm   **b)** 39.1 cm

  25. $10\frac{2}{3}$ cm³   **26.** 1.05 cm³   **27.** 488 cm³   **28.** 4 cm   **29.** 53.6 cm³   **30.** 74.5 cm³

  31. 4.24 cm   **32.** 123 cm³   **33.** 54.5 litres   **34. a)** 16π   **b)** 8 cm   **c)** 6 cm
  35. 471 cm³   **36.** 2720 cm³   **37.** 943 cm³   **38.** 5050 cm³

Exercise 9 *page 126*
  1. a) 36π cm²   **b)** 72π cm²   **c)** 60π cm²   **d)** 2.38π m²
      e) 400π m²   **f)** 65π cm²   **g)** 192π mm²   **h)** 10.2π cm²
      i) 0.000 4π m²   **j)** 98π cm², 147π cm²
  2. 1.64 cm   **3.** 2.12 cm   **4.** 3.46 cm
  5. a) 3 cm   **b)** 4 cm   **c)** 5 cm   **d)** 0.2 m   **e)** 6 cm   **f)** 0.25 cm   **g)** 7 m
  6. 303 cm²   **7.** $1178   **8.** $3870   **9.** 94.0 cm³
  10. 44.6 cm²   **11.** 675 cm²   **12.** 1.62×10^8 years   **13.** 377 cm²
  14. 20 cm, 10 cm   **15.** 71.7 cm²   **16.** 147 cm²
  17. 336 cm²   **18.** 198 cm²   **19.** 592 cm²   **20.** 184 cm²

Exercise 10 *page 128*
  1. 200 mm²   **2.** 4500 mm²   **3.** 16 cm²   **4.** 0.48 cm²   **5.** 30 000 cm²
  6. 260 000 cm²   **7.** 0.86 m²   **8.** 0.076 m²   **9.** 5 000 000 m²   **10.** 4.5 km²
  11. 8000 mm³   **12.** 21 000 cm³   **13.** 48 cm³   **14.** 6 000 000 cm³   **15.** 28 m³
  16. a) 24 000 mm³   **b)** 5200 mm³   **17.** 0.32 m²
  18. a) 4 830 000 cm² (3 s.f.)   **b)** 998 m³   **c)** 998 000 000 cm³ (3 s.f.)
  19. 400 000 mm³   **20.** 95.4 mm (3 s.f.)

Revision exercise 3A *page 128*
  1. a) 14 cm²   **b)** 54 cm²   **c)** 50 cm²   **d)** 18 m²
  2. a) 56.5 m, 254 m²   **b)** 10.8 cm   **c)** 3.99 cm

3. a) $9\pi \, \text{cm}^2$ **b)** $8:1$ **4.** $3.43 \, \text{cm}^2$, $4.57 \, \text{cm}^2$
5. a) $12.2 \, \text{cm}$ **b)** $61.1 \, \text{cm}^2$
6. a) $11.2 \, \text{cm}$ **b)** $10.3 \, \text{cm}$ **c)** $44.7 \, \text{cm}^2$ **d)** $31.5 \, \text{cm}^2$ **e)** $13.2 \, \text{cm}^2$
7. $103.1°$ **8.** $9.95 \, \text{cm}$ **9. a)** $905 \, \text{cm}^3$ **b)** $5.76 \, \text{cm}$
10. $8.06 \, \text{cm}$ **11.** $99.5 \, \text{cm}^3$ **12.** $333 \, \text{cm}^3$, $201 \, \text{cm}^3$ **13.** $4 \, \text{cm}$
14. a) $15.6 \, \text{cm}^2$ **b)** $93.5 \, \text{cm}^2$ **c)** $3741 \, \text{cm}^3$
15. $0.370 \, \text{cm}$ **16.** $104 \, \text{cm}^2$ **17.** $5.14 \, \text{cm}^2$ **18.** $68c$ **19.** 25 **20.** $20 \, \text{cm}^2$
21. a) $1350 \, \text{cm}^3$ **b)** $1008 \, \text{cm}^2$

Examination-style exercise 3B   *page 131*
1. a) $45\,498 \, \text{km}$ **b)** $7240 \, \text{km}$ **2.** 23 **3.** $21.3 \, \text{cm}^2$
4. $170 \, \text{cm}^2$ **5. a)** $14.1 \, \text{cm}^2$ **b)** $24.8 \, \text{cm}$ **6.** $162 \, \text{cm}^2$
7. a) $6.93 \, \text{cm}$ **b)** $60.6 \, \text{cm}^2$
8. b) $42.6 \, \text{kg}$ **c)** $26.4 \, \text{cm}$
    d) i) $0.649 - 0.651$ **ii)** $5.31 \, \text{cm}^2$ **iii)** $501.9 - 503\%$
9. b) i) $8.49 \, \text{cm}$ **ii)** $29.0 \, \text{cm}$ **iii)** $36 \, \text{cm}^2$ **iv)** $695 \, \text{cm}^2$
    c) i) $14.5 \, \text{cm}$ **ii)** 94.8%
10. a) $325 \, \text{cm}^2$ **b)** $16\,250 \, \text{cm}^3$ **c)** $5650 \, \text{cm}^2$

4 Geometry

Exercise 1   *page 137*
1. $95°$ **2.** $49°$ **3.** $100°$ **4.** $77°$ **5.** $129°$ **6.** $95°$ **7.** $a = 30°$
8. $e = 30°, f = 60°$ **9.** $110°$ **10.** $x = 54°$ **11.** $a = 40°$
12. $a = 36°, b = 72°, c = 144°, d = 108°$ **13.** $105°$
14. $a = 30°, b = 120°, c = 150°$ **15.** $x = 20°, y = 140°$ **16.** $a = 120°, b = 34°, c = 26°$
17. $a = 68°, b = 58.5°$ **18.** $25°$ **19.** $44°$
20. $a = 30°, b = 60°, c = 150°, d = 120°$ **21.** $a = 10°, b = 76°$ **22.** $e = 71°, f = 21°$
23. $144°$ **24.** $70°$ **25.** $41°, 66°$ **26.** $46°, 122°$ **27.** $36°$

Exercise 2   *page 139*
1. $a = 72°, b = 108°$ **2.** $x = 60°, y = 120°$ **3.** $(n - 2)180°$ **4.** $110°$
5. $60°$ **6.** $128\frac{4}{7}°$ **7.** 15 **8.** 12
9. 9 **10.** 18 **11.** 12 **12.** $36°$

Exercise 3   *page 141*
1. $a = 116°, b = 64°, c = 64°$ **2.** $a = 64°, b = 40°$ **3.** $x = 68°$
4. $a = 40°, b = 134, c = 134°$ **5.** $m = 69°, y = 65°$ **6.** $t = 48°, u = 48°, v = 42°$
7. $a = 118°, b = 100°, c = 62°$ **8.** $a = 34°, b = 76°, c = 70°, d = 70°$ **9.** $72°, 108°$

Exercise 4   *page 142*
1. $10 \, \text{cm}$ **2.** $4.12 \, \text{cm}$ **3.** $4.24 \, \text{cm}$ **4.** $12.7 \, \text{cm}$ **5.** $8.72 \, \text{cm}$ **6.** $5.66 \, \text{cm}$
7. $6.63 \, \text{cm}$ **8.** $5 \, \text{cm}$ **9.** $17 \, \text{cm}$ **10.** $4 \, \text{cm}$ **11.** $9.85 \, \text{cm}$ **12.** $7.07 \, \text{cm}$
13. $3.46 \, \text{m}$ **14.** $40.3 \, \text{km}$ **15.** $13.6 \, \text{cm}$ **16.** $6.34 \, \text{m}$ **17.** $4.58 \, \text{cm}$ **18.** $84.9 \, \text{km}$
19. $24 \, \text{cm}$ **20.** $9.80 \, \text{cm}$ **21.** $5, 4, 3; 13, 12, 5; 25, 24, 7; 41, 40, 9; 61, 60, 11$
22. $x = 4 \, \text{m}, 20.6 \, \text{m}$ **23.** $9.49 \, \text{cm}$ **24.** $18.5 \, \text{km}$

Exercise 5   *page 145*
1. a) i) 1 **ii)** 1 **b) i)** 1 **ii)** 1 **c) i)** 2 **ii)** 2 **d) i)** 2 **ii)** 2 **e) i)** 4 **ii)** 4
   f) i) 0 **ii)** 2 **g) i)** 5 **ii)** 5 **h) i)** 0 **ii)** 1 **i) i)** 1 **ii)** 1 **j) i)** 0 **ii)** 2
   k) i) 0 **ii)** 2 **l) i)** 0 **ii)** 2 **m) i)** ∞ **ii)** ∞ **n) i)** 0 **ii)** 4
4. square 4, 4; rectangle 2, 2; parallelogram 0, 2; rhombus 2, 2; trapezium 0, 1; kite 1,1;
   equilateral triangle 3, 3; regular hexagon 6, 6
5. $34°, 56°$ **6.** $35°, 35°$ **7.** $72°, 108°, 80°$ **8.** $40°, 30°, 110°$ **9.** $116°, 32°, 58°$ **10.** $55°, 55°$
11. $26°, 26°, 77°$ **12.** $52°, 64°, 116°$ **13.** $70°, 40°, 110°$ **14.** $54°, 72°, 36°$ **15.** $60°, 15°, 75°, 135°$

Exercise 6 *page 147*

1. 3 **2. a)** 1 **b)** 1 **c)** 2

3. a) Multiple answers **b)** 9

4. 2 planes of symmetry are shown.
There are another 2 formed by
joining the diagonals of the base to
the vertex of the pyramid.

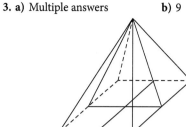

5. 4

6. a) an infinite number
b) an infinite number running through the tip of the cone to the centre of the base.

Exercise 7 *page 148*

1. $a = 2\frac{1}{2}$ cm, $e = 3$ cm **2.** $x = 6$ cm, $y = 10$ cm **3.** $x = 12$ cm, $y = 8$ cm

4. $m = 10$ cm, $a = 16\frac{2}{3}$ cm **5.** $y = 6$ cm **6.** $x = 4$ cm, $w = 1\frac{1}{2}$ cm

7. $e = 9$ cm, $f = 4\frac{1}{2}$ cm **8.** $x = 13\frac{1}{3}$ cm, $y = 9$ cm **9.** $m = 6$ cm, $n = 6$ cm

10. $m = 5\frac{1}{3}$ cm, $z = 4\frac{4}{5}$ cm **11.** $v = 5\frac{1}{3}$ cm, $w = 6\frac{2}{3}$ cm **12.** No

13. 2 cm, 6 cm **14.** 16 m

15. a) Yes **b)** No **c)** No **d)** Yes **e)** Yes **f)** No **g)** No **h)** Yes

18. 0.618; 1.618 : 1

Exercise 8 *page 151*

1. 16 cm² **2.** 27 cm² **3.** $11\frac{1}{4}$ cm² **4.** $14\frac{1}{2}$ cm² **5.** 128 cm² **6.** 12 cm²

7. 8 cm **8.** 18 cm **9.** $4\frac{1}{2}$ cm **10.** $7\frac{1}{2}$ cm **11.** $2\frac{1}{2}$ cm **12.** 6 cm

13. A = 32 cm² **14.** B = 279 cm² **15.** C = 40 cm² **16.** D = 225 cm²

17. a) $16\frac{2}{3}$ cm² **b)** $10\frac{2}{3}$ cm² **18. a)** 25 cm² **b)** 21 cm²

19. 8 cm² **20.** 6 cm **21.** 24 cm²

22. a) $1\frac{4}{5}$ cm **b)** 3 cm **c)** 3 : 5 **d)** 9 : 25

23. 150 **24.** 360 **25.** Less (for the same weight)

Exercise 9 *page 154*

1. 480 cm³ **2.** 540 cm³ **3.** 160 cm³ **4.** 4500 cm³ **5.** 81 cm³

6. 11 cm³ **7.** 16 cm³ **8.** $85\frac{1}{3}$ cm³ **9.** 4 cm **10.** 21 cm

11. 4.6 cm **12.** 9 cm **13.** 6.6 cm **14.** $4\frac{1}{2}$ cm **15.** $168\frac{3}{4}$ cm³

16. 106.3 cm³ **17.** 12 cm **18. a)** 2 : 3 **b)** 8 : 27 **19.** 8 : 125

20. $x_1^3 : x_2^3$ **21.** 54 kg **22.** 240 cm² **23.** $9\frac{3}{8}$ litres **24.** $2812\frac{1}{2}$ cm²

Exercise 10 *page 157*

1. A and G; B and E.

Exercise 11 *page 159*

1. $a = 27$, $b = 30°$ **2.** $c = 20°$, $d = 45°$ **3.** $c = 58°$, $d = 41°$, $e = 30°$

4. $f = 40°$, $g = 55°$, $h = 55°$ **5.** $a = 32°$, $b = 80°$, $c = 43°$ **6.** $x = 34°$, $y = 34°$, $z = 56°$

7. 43° **8.** 92° **9.** 42°

10. $c = 46°$, $d = 44°$ **11.** $e = 49°$, $f = 41°$ **12.** $g = 76°$, $h = 52°$

13. 48° **14.** 32° **15.** 22°

16. $a = 36°$, $x = 36°$

Exercise 12   *page 161*

1. $a = 94°, b = 75°$ **2.** $c = 101°, d = 84°$ **3.** $x = 92°, y = 116°$
4. $c = 60°, d = 45°$ **5.** $37°$ **6.** $118°$
7. $e = 36°, f = 72°$ **8.** $35°$ **9.** $18°$

10. $90°$ **11.** $30°$ **12.** $22\frac{1}{2}°$

13. $n = 58°, t = 64°, w = 45°$ **14.** $a = 32°, b = 40°, c = 40°$ **15.** $a = 18°, c = 72°$
16. $55°$ **17.** $e = 41°, f = 41°, g = 41°$ **18.** $8°$
19. $x = 30°, y = 115°$ **20.** $x = 80°, z = 10°$

Exercise 13   *page 163*

1. $a = 18°$ **2.** $x = 40°, y = 65°, z = 25°$
3. $c = 30°, e = 15°$ **4.** $f = 50°, g = 40°$
5. $h = 40°, i = 40°$ **6.** $n = 36°$
7. $k = 50°, m = 50°, n = 80°, p = 80°$ **8.** $n = 16°, p = 46°$
9. $x = 70°, y = 20°, z = 55°$

Exercise 14   *page 165*

1. $70°$ **2.** $23°$ **3.** $49°$ **4.** $85°$ **5.** $36°$
6. $57°$ **7.** $136°$ **8.** $44°$ **9.** $x = 56°, y = 85°, z = 39°$

Exercise 15   *page 166*

1. $63°$ **2.** $35°$ **3.** $62°$ **4.** $30°$
5. $37°$ **6.** $94°$ **7.** $93°$ **8.** $36°$

Exercise 16   *page 167*

1. a), b), d)
2. a) $a = 4$ cm, $x = 4$ cm, $y = 6$ cm   **b)** 240 cm³
3. a) $a = 10$ cm, $b = 6$ cm, $c = 10$ cm, $d = 10$ cm   **b)** 64 cm³
4. a) 168 mm²   **b)** $16\,800$ mm³
5. $a = \sqrt{2}, b = \sqrt{2}, c = \sqrt{3}, x = \sqrt{2}, y = \sqrt{3}$

Revision exercise 4A   *page 168*

2. $80°$ **3. a)** $30°$ **b)** $22\frac{1}{2}°$ **c)** 12

4. a) $40°$ **b)** $100°$ **5.** 4.12 cm

6. i) 3 cm   **ii)** 5.66 cm   **7. c)** $2\frac{4}{5}$ cm

8. b) 6 cm   **9.** $3\frac{2}{3}$ cm, $1\frac{1}{11}$ cm   **10.** 6 cm   **11.** 250 cm³

12. a) $3\frac{1}{3}$ cm   **b)** 1620 cm³   **13. a)** 1 m²   **b)** 1000 cm³

14. a) $50°$ **b)** $128°$ **c)** $c = 50°, d = 40°$
       d) $x = 10°, y = 40°$ **e)** $x = 62°, y = 56°, z = 68°$ **f)** $x = 36°, y = 54°, z = 72°$
15. a) $55°$ **b)** $45°$

Examination-style exercise 4B   *page 170*

1. a) $72°$ **b)** $36°$ **2. a)** 5.66 cm   **b)** 32.0 cm²

3. a) 320 cm³   **b)** 567 cm²   **4. a)** 55 cm by 40 cm   **b)** $\frac{16}{25}$

5. $r = 96$ cm, $h = 180$ cm   **6. a)** $62°$ **b)** $28°$ **c)** $62°$ **d)** $34°$
7. a) $54°$ **b)** $42°$ **c)** $78°$

5 Algebra 2

Exercise 1 *page 174*

1. $\frac{5}{7}$

2. $\frac{7}{8}$

3. $5y$

4. $\frac{1}{2}$

5. 4

6. $\frac{x}{2y}$

7. 2

8. $\frac{a}{2}$

9. $\frac{2b}{3}$

10. $\frac{a}{5b}$

11. a

12. $\frac{7}{8}$

13. $\frac{5+2x}{3}$

14. $\frac{3x+1}{x}$

15. $\frac{32}{25}$

16. $\frac{4+5a}{5}$

17. $\frac{3}{4-x}$

18. $\frac{b}{3+2a}$

19. $\frac{5x+4}{8x}$

20. $\frac{2x+1}{y}$

21. $\frac{x+2y}{3xy}$

22. $\frac{6-b}{2a}$

23. $\frac{2b+4a}{b}$

24. $x-2$

Exercise 2 *page 174*

1. $\frac{x+2}{x-3}$

2. $\frac{x}{x+1}$

3. $\frac{x+4}{2(x-5)}$

4. $\frac{x+5}{x-2}$

5. $\frac{x+3}{x+2}$

6. $\frac{x+5}{x-2}$

7. $\frac{x+2}{x}$

8. $\frac{3x}{x+5}$

9. $\frac{1}{2}$

10. $\frac{3x}{x-5}$

11. $\frac{3x-5}{x}$

12. $\frac{x-2}{x-1}$

Exercise 3 *page 175*

1. $\frac{3}{5}$

2. $\frac{3x}{5}$

3. $\frac{3}{x}$

4. $\frac{4}{7}$

5. $\frac{4x}{7}$

6. $\frac{4}{7x}$

7. $\frac{7}{8}$

8. $\frac{7x}{8}$

9. $\frac{7}{8x}$

10. $\frac{5}{6}$

11. $\frac{5x}{6}$

12. $\frac{5}{6x}$

13. $\frac{23}{20}$

14. $\frac{23x}{20}$

15. $\frac{23}{20x}$

16. $\frac{1}{12}$

17. $\frac{x}{12}$

18. $\frac{1}{12x}$

19. $\frac{5x+2}{6}$

20. $\frac{7x+2}{12}$

21. $\frac{9x+13}{10}$

22. $\frac{1-2x}{12}$

23. $\frac{2x-9}{15}$

24. $\frac{-3x-12}{14}$

25. $\frac{3x+1}{x(x+1)}$

26. $\frac{7x-8}{x(x-2)}$

27. $\frac{8x+9}{(x-2)(x+3)}$

28. $\frac{4x+11}{(x+1)(x+2)}$

29. $\frac{-3x-17}{(x+3)(x-1)}$

30. $\frac{11-x}{(x+1)(x-2)}$

Exercise 4 *page 177*

1. $2\frac{1}{2}$

2. 3

3. $\frac{B}{A}$

4. $\frac{T}{N}$

5. $\frac{K}{M}$

6. $\frac{4}{y}$

7. $\frac{C}{B}$

8. $\frac{D}{4}$

9. $\frac{T+N}{9}$

10. $\frac{B-R}{A}$

11. $\frac{R+T}{C}$

12. $\frac{N-R^2}{L}$

13. $\frac{R-S^2}{N}$

14. 2

15. -7

16. $T-A$

17. $S-B$

18. $N-D$

19. $M-B$

20. $L-D^2$

21. $T-N^2$

22. $N+M-L$

23. $R-S-Z$

24. 7

25. $A+R$

26. $E+A$

27. $F+B$

28. F^2+B^2

29. $A+B+D$

30. A^2+E

31. $L+B$

32. $N+T$

33. 2

34. $4\frac{1}{2}$

35. $\frac{N-C}{A}$

36. $\frac{L-D}{B}$

37. $\frac{F-E}{D}$

38. $\frac{H+F}{N}$

39. $\frac{T+Z}{Y}$

40. $\frac{B+L}{R}$

41. $\frac{Q-m}{V}$

42. $\frac{n+a+m}{t}$

43. $\frac{s-t-n}{q}$

44. $\frac{t+s^2}{n}$

45. $\frac{c-b}{V^2}$

46. $\dfrac{r+6}{n}$ **47.** $\dfrac{s-d}{m}$ **48.** $\dfrac{t+b}{m}$ **49.** $\dfrac{j-c}{m}$ **50.** 2

51. $2\frac{2}{3}$ **52.** $\dfrac{C-AB}{A}$ **53.** $\dfrac{F-DE}{D}$ **54.** $\dfrac{a-hn}{h}$ **55.** $\dfrac{q+bd}{b}$

56. $\dfrac{n-rt}{r}$ **57.** $\dfrac{b+4t}{t}$ **58.** $\dfrac{z-St}{S}$ **59.** $\dfrac{s+vd}{v}$ **60.** $\dfrac{g-mn}{m}$

Exercise 5 page 178

1. 12   **2.** 10   **3.** BD **4.** TB **5.** RN
6. bm **7.** 26   **8.** $BT+A$ **9.** $AN+D$ **10.** B^2N-Q

11. $ge+r$ **12.** $4\frac{1}{2}$ **13.** $\dfrac{DC-B}{A}$ **14.** $\dfrac{pq-m}{n}$ **15.** $\dfrac{vS+t}{r}$

16. $\dfrac{qt+m}{z}$ **17.** $\dfrac{bc-m}{A}$ **18.** $\dfrac{AE-D}{B}$ **19.** $\dfrac{nh+f}{e}$ **20.** $\dfrac{qr-b}{g}$

21. 4   **22.** −2   **23.** 2   **24.** $A-B$ **25.** $C-E$
26. $D-H$ **27.** $n-m$ **28.** $q-t$ **29.** $s-b$ **30.** $r-v$

31. $m-t$ **32.** 2   **33.** $\dfrac{T-B}{X}$ **34.** $\dfrac{M-Q}{N}$ **35.** $\dfrac{V-T}{M}$

36. $\dfrac{N-L}{R}$ **37.** $\dfrac{v^2-r}{r}$ **38.** $\dfrac{w-t^2}{n}$ **39.** $\dfrac{n-2}{q}$ **40.** $\frac{1}{4}$

41. $-\frac{1}{7}$ **42.** $\dfrac{B-DE}{A}$ **43.** $\dfrac{D-NB}{E}$ **44.** $\dfrac{h-bx}{f}$ **45.** $\dfrac{v^2-Cd}{h}$

46. $\dfrac{NT-MB}{M}$ **47.** $\dfrac{mB+ef}{fN}$ **48.** $\dfrac{TM-EF}{T}$ **49.** $\dfrac{yx-zt}{y}$ **50.** $\dfrac{k^2m-x^2}{k^2}$

Exercise 6 page 179

1. $\frac{1}{2}$ **2.** $1\frac{2}{3}$ **3.** $\dfrac{B}{C}$ **4.** $\dfrac{T}{X}$ **5.** $\dfrac{M}{B}$

6. $\dfrac{n}{m}$ **7.** $\dfrac{v}{t}$ **8.** $\dfrac{n}{\sin 20°}$ **9.** $\dfrac{7}{\cos 30°}$ **10.** $\dfrac{B}{x}$

11. $6\frac{2}{3}$ **12.** $\dfrac{ND}{B}$ **13.** $\dfrac{HM}{N}$ **14.** $\dfrac{et}{b}$ **15.** $\dfrac{vs}{m}$

16. $\dfrac{mb}{t}$ **17.** $1\frac{1}{2}$ **18.** $3\frac{1}{3}$ **19.** $\dfrac{B-DC}{C}$ **20.** $\dfrac{Q+TC}{T}$

21. $\dfrac{V+TD}{D}$ **22.** $\dfrac{L}{MB}$ **23.** $\dfrac{N}{BC}$ **24.** $\dfrac{m}{cd}$ **25.** $\dfrac{tc-b}{t}$

26. $\dfrac{xy-z}{x}$ **27.** 1   **28.** $\frac{5}{6}$ **29.** $\dfrac{A}{C-B}$ **30.** $\dfrac{V}{H-G}$

31. $\dfrac{r}{n+t}$ **32.** $\dfrac{b}{q-d}$ **33.** $\dfrac{m}{t+n}$ **34.** $\dfrac{b}{d-h}$ **35.** $\dfrac{d}{C-e}$

36. $\dfrac{m}{r-e^2}$ **37.** $\dfrac{n}{b-t^2}$ **38.** $\dfrac{d}{mn-b}$ **39.** $\dfrac{M-Nq}{N}$ **40.** $\dfrac{Y+Tc}{T}$

41. $\dfrac{N-2MP}{2M}$ **42.** $\dfrac{B-6Ac}{6A}$ **43.** $\dfrac{K}{(C-B)M}$ **44.** $\dfrac{z}{y(y+z)}$ **45.** $\dfrac{m^2}{n-p}$

46. $\dfrac{q}{w-t}$

Exercise 7 page 180

1. 4   **2.** 24   **3.** 11   **4.** $B^2 - A$ **5.** $D^2 - C$

6. $H^2 + E$ **7.** $\dfrac{c^2 - b}{a}$ **8.** $a^2 + m$ **9.** $\dfrac{b^2 + t}{g}$ **10.** $b - r^2$

11. $d - t^2$ **12.** $b^2 + d$ **13.** $n - c^2$ **14.** $b - f^2$ **15.** $c - g^2$

16. $\dfrac{M - P^2}{N}$ **17.** $\dfrac{D - B}{A}$ **18.** $A^4 + D$ **19.** $\pm\sqrt{g}$ **20.** ± 4

21. $\pm\sqrt{B}$ **22.** $\pm\sqrt{(B - A)}$ **23.** $\pm\sqrt{(M + A)}$ **24.** $\pm\sqrt{(b - a)}$ **25.** $\pm\sqrt{(C - m)}$

26. $\pm\sqrt{(d - n)}$ **27.** $\pm\sqrt{\dfrac{n}{m}}$ **28.** $\pm\sqrt{\dfrac{b}{a}}$ **29.** $\dfrac{at}{z}$ **30.** $\pm\sqrt{\left(\dfrac{m + t}{a}\right)}$

31. $\pm\sqrt{(a - n)}$ **32.** $\pm\sqrt{40}$ **33.** $\pm\sqrt{(B^2 + A)}$ **34.** $\pm\sqrt{(x^2 - y)}$ **35.** $\pm\sqrt{(t^2 - m)}$

36. 8   **37.** $\dfrac{M^2 - A^2 B}{A^2}$ **38.** $\dfrac{M}{N^2}$ **39.** $\dfrac{N}{B^2}$ **40.** $a - b^2$

41. $\pm\sqrt{(a^2 - t^2)}$ **42.** $\pm\sqrt{(m - x^2)}$ **43.** $\dfrac{4}{\pi^2} - t$ **44.** $\dfrac{B^2}{A^2} - 1$ **45.** $\pm\sqrt{\left(\dfrac{C^2 + b}{a}\right)}$

46. $\pm\sqrt{\left(\dfrac{b^2 + a^2 x}{a^2}\right)}$ **47.** $\pm\sqrt{(x^2 - b)}$ **48.** $\pm\sqrt{(c - b)a}$ **49.** $\dfrac{c^2 - b^2}{a}$ **50.** $\pm\sqrt{\left(\dfrac{m}{a + b}\right)}$

Exercise 8 page 181

1. $3\tfrac{2}{3}$ **2.** 3   **3.** $\dfrac{D - B}{2N}$ **4.** $\dfrac{E + D}{3M}$ **5.** $\dfrac{2b}{a - b}$

6. $\dfrac{e + c}{m + n}$ **7.** $\dfrac{3}{x + k}$ **8.** $\dfrac{C - D}{R - T}$ **9.** $\dfrac{z + x}{a - b}$ **10.** $\dfrac{nb - ma}{m - n}$

11. $\dfrac{d + xb}{x - 1}$ **12.** $\dfrac{a - ab}{b + 1}$ **13.** $\dfrac{d - c}{d + c}$ **14.** $\dfrac{M(b - a)}{b + a}$ **15.** $\dfrac{n^2 - mn}{m + n}$

16. $\dfrac{m^2 + 5}{2 - m}$ **17.** $\dfrac{2 + n^2}{n - 1}$ **18.** $\dfrac{e - b^2}{b - a}$ **19.** $\dfrac{3x}{a + x}$ **20.** $\dfrac{e - c}{a - d}$ or $\dfrac{c - e}{d - a}$

21. $\dfrac{d}{a - b - c}$ **22.** $\dfrac{ab}{m + n - a}$ **23.** $\dfrac{s - t}{b - a}$ or $\dfrac{t - s}{a - b}$ **24.** $2x$ **25.** $\dfrac{v}{3}$

26. $\dfrac{a(b + c)}{b - 2a}$ **27.** $\dfrac{5x}{3}$ **28.** $-\dfrac{4z}{5}$ **29.** $\dfrac{mn}{p^2 - m}$ **30.** $\dfrac{mn + n}{4 + m}$

Exercise 9 page 182

1. $-\left(\dfrac{by + c}{a}\right)$ **2.** $\pm\sqrt{\left(\dfrac{e^2 + ab}{a}\right)}$ **3.** $\dfrac{n^2}{m^2} + m$ **4.** $\dfrac{a - b}{1 + b}$ **5.** $3y$

6. $\dfrac{a}{e^2 + c}$ **7.** $-\left(\dfrac{a + lm}{m}\right)$ **8.** $\dfrac{t^2 g}{4\pi^2}$ **9.** $\dfrac{4\pi^2 d}{t^2}$ **10.** $\pm\sqrt{\dfrac{a}{3}}$

11. $\pm\sqrt{\left(\dfrac{t^2 e - ba}{b}\right)}$ **12.** $\dfrac{1}{a^2 - 1}$ **13.** $\dfrac{a + b}{x}$ **14.** $\pm\sqrt{(x^4 - b^2)}$ **15.** $\dfrac{c - a}{b}$

16. $\dfrac{a^2 - b}{a + 1}$ **17.** $\pm\sqrt{\left(\dfrac{G^2}{16\pi^2} - T^2\right)}$ **18.** $-\left(\dfrac{ax + c}{b}\right)$ **19.** $\dfrac{1 + x^2}{1 - x^2}$ **20.** $\pm\sqrt{\left(\dfrac{a^2 m}{b^2 + n}\right)}$

21. $\dfrac{P - M}{E}$ **22.** $\dfrac{RP - Q}{R}$ **23.** $\dfrac{z - t^2}{x}$ **24.** $(g - e)^2 - f$ **25.** $\dfrac{4np + me^2}{mn}$

Exercise 10   page 185

1. a) $S = ke$ **b)** $v = kt$ **c)** $x = kz^2$ **d)** $y = k\sqrt{x}$
   e) $T = k\sqrt{L}$ **f)** $C = kr$ **g)** $A = kr^2$ **h)** $V = kr^3$

2. a) 9   **b)** $2\frac{2}{3}$ **3. a)** 35   **b)** 11

5.

x	1	3	4	$5\frac{1}{2}$
z	4	12	16	22

6.

r	1	2	4	$1\frac{1}{2}$
V	4	32	256	$13\frac{1}{2}$

7.

h	4	9	25	$2\frac{1}{4}$
w	6	9	15	$4\frac{1}{2}$

8. a) 18   **b)** 2   **9. a)** 42   **b)** 4   **10.** $333\frac{1}{3}$ N/cm³

11. 180 m; 2 s   **12.** 675 J; $\sqrt{\frac{4}{3}}$ cm.   **13.** 4 cm; 49 h

14. $15\frac{5}{8}$ h   **15.** 9000 N; 25 m/s   **16.** $15^4 : 1$ (50 625 : 1)

Exercise 11   page 187

1. a) $x = \dfrac{k}{y}$ **b)** $s = \dfrac{k}{t^2}$ **c)** $t = \dfrac{k}{\sqrt{q}}$ **d)** $m = \dfrac{k}{w}$ **e)** $z = \dfrac{k}{t^2}$

2. a) 1   **b)** 4   **3. a)** $2\frac{1}{2}$ **b)** $\frac{1}{2}$

4. a) 36   **b)** ±4   **5. a)** 1.2   **b)** ±2
6. a) 16   **b)** ±10   **7. a)** 6   **b)** 16

8. a) $\frac{1}{2}$ **b)** $\frac{1}{20}$

9.

y	2	4	1	$\frac{1}{4}$
z	8	4	16	64

10.

t	2	5	20	10
v	25	4	$\frac{1}{4}$	1

11.

x	1	4	256	36
r	12	6	$\frac{3}{4}$	2

12. a) 6   **(b)** 50   **13. a)** 0.36   **b)** 6
14. $k = 100$, $n = 3$ **15.** $k = 12$, $n = 2$

x	1	2	4	10
z	100	$12\frac{1}{2}$	1.5625	$\frac{1}{10}$

v	1	4	36	10 000
y	12	6	2	$\frac{3}{25}$

16. 2.5 m³; 200 N/m²   **17.** 3 h; 48 men   **18. a)** 2 days   **b)** 200 days   **19.** 6 cm

Exercise 12   page 190

1. 3^4 **2.** $4^2 \times 5^3$ **3.** 3×7^3 **4.** $2^3 \times 7$ **5.** 10^{-3}

6. $2^{-2} \times 3^{-3}$ **7.** $15^{\frac{1}{2}}$ **8.** $3^{\frac{1}{3}}$ **9.** $10^{\frac{1}{5}}$ **10.** $5^{\frac{3}{2}}$
11. x^7 **12.** y^{13} **13.** z^4 **14.** z^{100} **15.** m
16. e^{-5} **17.** y^2 **18.** w^6 **19.** y **20.** x^{10}
21. 1   **22.** w^{-5} **23.** w^{-5} **24.** x^7 **25.** a^8
26. k^3 **27.** 1   **28.** x^{29} **29.** y^2 **30.** x^6
31. z^4 **32.** t^{-4} **33.** $4x^6$ **34.** $16y^{10}$ **35.** $6x^4$
36. $10y^5$ **37.** $15a^4$ **38.** $8a^3$ **39.** 3   **40.** $4y^2$

41. $\frac{5}{2}y$ **42.** $32a^4$ **43.** $108x^5$ **44.** $4z^{-3}$ **45.** $2x^{-4}$

46. $\frac{5}{2}y^5$ **47.** 1   **48.** $21w^{-3}$ **49.** $2n^4$ **50.** $2x$

1. 27   **2.** 1   **3.** $\frac{1}{9}$ **4.** 25   **5.** 2

6. 4   **7.** 9   **8.** 2   **9.** 27   **10.** 3

11. $\frac{1}{3}$ **12.** $\frac{1}{2}$ **13.** 1   **14.** $\frac{1}{5}$ **15.** 10

16. 8   **17.** 32   **18.** 4   **19.** $\frac{1}{9}$ **20.** $\frac{1}{8}$

21. 18   **22.** 10   **23.** 1000   **24.** $\frac{1}{1000}$ **25.** $\frac{1}{9}$

26. 1   **27.** $1\frac{1}{2}$ **28.** $\frac{1}{25}$ **29.** $\frac{1}{10}$ **30.** $\frac{1}{4}$

31. $\frac{1}{4}$ **32.** 100 000   **33.** 1   **34.** $\frac{1}{32}$ **35.** 0.1

36. 0.2   **37.** 1.5   **38.** 1   **39.** 9   **40.** $1\frac{1}{2}$

41. $\frac{3}{10}$ **42.** 64   **43.** $\frac{1}{100}$ **44.** $1\frac{2}{3}$ **45.** $\frac{1}{100}$

46. 1   **47.** 100   **48.** 6   **49.** 750   **50.** -7

1. $25x^4$ **2.** $49y^6$ **3.** $100a^2b^2$ **4.** $4x^2y^4$ **5.** $2x$ **6.** $\frac{1}{9y}$

7. x^2 **8.** $\frac{x^2}{2}$ **9.** 1   **10.** $\frac{2}{x}$ **11.** $36x^4$ **12.** $25y$

13. $16x^2$ **14.** $27y$ **15.** 25   **16.** 1   **17.** 49   **18.** 1

19. $8x^6y^3$ **20.** $100x^2y^6$ **21.** $\frac{3x}{2}$ **22.** $\frac{2}{x}$ **23.** x^3y^5 **24.** $12\,x^3y^2$

25. $10y^4$ **26.** $3x^3$ **27.** $x^3y^2z^4$ **28.** x **29.** $3y$ **30.** $27x^{\frac{3}{2}}$

31. $10x^3y^5$ **32.** $32x^2$ **33.** $\frac{5}{2}x^2$ **34.** $\frac{9}{x^2}$ **35.** $2a^2$ **36.** $a^3b^3c^2$

37. a) 2^5 **b)** 2^7 **c)** 2^6 **d)** 2^0

38. a) 3^{-3} **b)** 3^{-4} **c)** 3^{-1} **d)** 3^{-2}

39. 16   **40.** $\frac{1}{4}$ **41.** $\frac{1}{6}$ **42.** 1   **43.** $16\frac{1}{8}$ **44.** $\frac{3}{8}$

45. $\frac{1}{4}$ **46.** $\frac{5}{256}$ **47.** $1\frac{1}{16}$ **48.** 0   **49.** $\frac{1}{4}$ **50.** $\frac{1}{4}$

51. 3   **52.** 4   **53.** -1 **54.** -2 **55.** 3   **56.** 3

57. 1   **58.** $\frac{1}{5}$ **59.** 0   **60.** -4 **61.** 2   **62.** -5

63. 1   **64.** $\frac{1}{18}$ **65 a)** 3.60   **b)** 5.44

1. <   **2.** >   **3.** >   **4.** =

5. <   **6.** <   **7.** =   **8.** >

9. <   **10.** >   **11.** <   **12.** >

13. >   **14.** >   **15.** =   **16.** F

17. F   **18.** T   **19.** F   **20.** F

21. T   **22.** T   **23.** F   **24.** F

25. $x > 13$ **26.** $x < -1$ **27.** $x < 12$ **28.** $x \geqslant 2\frac{1}{2}$

29. $x > 3$ **30.** $x \geqslant 8$ **31.** $x < \frac{1}{4}$ **32.** $x \geqslant -3$

33. $x < -8$ **34.** $x < 4$ **35.** $x > -9$ **36.** $x < 8$

37. $x > 3$ **38.** $x \geqslant 1$ **39.** $x < 1$ **40.** $x > 2\frac{1}{3}$

Exercise 16   page 195

1. $x > 5$ 2. $x \leqslant 3$ 3. $x > 6$ 4. $x \geqslant 4$
5. $x < 1$ 6. $x < -3$ 7. $x > 0$ 8. $x > 4$
9. $x > 2$ 10. $x < -3$ 11. $1 < x < 4$ 12. $-2 \leqslant x \leqslant 5$
13. $1 \leqslant x < 6$ 14. $0 \leqslant x < 5$ 15. $-1 \leqslant x \leqslant 7$ 16. $0.2 < x < 2$
17. $x > 80$ 18. $x > 10$ 19. $x < -2.5$ 20. $0 < x < 4$

21. $5 \leqslant x \leqslant 9$ 22. $-1 < x < 4$ 23. $5.5 \leqslant x \leqslant 6$ 24. $\frac{1}{2} < x < 8$

25. $-8 < x < 2$ 26. $\{1, 2, 3, 4, 5, 6\}$ 27. $\{7, 11, 13, 17, 19\}$ 28. $\{2, 4, 6, 8, 10\}$
29. $\{4, 9, 16, 25, 36, 49\}$ 30. $\{5, 10\}$ 31. $\{-4, -3, -2, -1\}$ 32. $\{2, 3, 4, \ldots 12\}$
33. $\{1, 4, 9\}$ 34. $\{2, 3, 5, 7, 11\}$ 35. $\{2, 4, 6, \ldots 18\}$ 36. $n = 5$
37. $x = 7$ 38. $y = 5$ 39. $4 < z < 5$ 40. $4 < p < 5$

41. $\frac{1}{2}$ (or other values)   42. $1, 2, 3, \ldots 14$ 43. 19   44. $\frac{1}{2}$ (or other values)   45. 19

46. a) $-3 \leqslant x < 6$ b) $-2 < x < 2$ c) $-3 \leqslant x \leqslant 2$ d) $-3 \leqslant x < 7$ 47. 17
48. a) $21x + 75 \geqslant 330$ b) \$12.15   49. a) $12y + 300 \leqslant 700$ b) \$33.33
50. a) $30d + 240 \leqslant 470$ b) 7 days

Exercise 17   page 197

1. $x \leqslant 3$ 2. $y \geqslant 2\frac{1}{2}$ 3. $1 \leqslant x \leqslant 6$

4. $x < 7, y < 5$ 5. $y \geqslant x$ 6. $x + y < 10$
7. $x < 8, y > -2, y < x$ 8. $x \geqslant 0, y \geqslant x - 1, x + y \leqslant 7$ 9. $y \geqslant 0, y \leqslant x + 2, x + y \leqslant 6$

10.   11.   12.   13.

14.   15.   16.   17.

18.   19.   20.   21.

22.   23.   24.   25.

26.

27.

Exercise 18   *page 200*

1. a) maximum value $= 26$ at $(6, 5)$ **b)** minimum value $= 12$ at $(3, 3)$
2. a) maximum value $= 25$ at $(8, 3)$ **b)** minimum value $= 9$ at $(7, 2)$
3. a) maximum value $= 40$ at $(20, 0)$ **b)** minimum value $= 112$ at $(14, 8)$
4. $(3, 3), (4, 2), (4, 3), (4, 4), (5, 1), (5, 2), (6, 0)$
5. $(0, 6), (0, 7), (0, 8), (1, 5), (1, 6), (2, 4)$ **6.** $(3, 2), (2, 3), (2, 4), (2, 5), (1, 4), (1, 5), (0, 5), (0, 6)$
7. $(2, 4), (2, 5), (2, 6), (2, 7), (2, 8), (2, 9), (2, 10), (3, 6), (3, 7), (3, 8)$
8. a) $(6, 7), (7, 7), (8, 6), (7, 6), (6, 8)$ **b)** 7 defenders, 6 forwards have lowest wage bill ($190 000)
9. a) 18   **b)** €2.60   **10. a)** 14   **b)** $(7, 7), $154 000$ **c)** $(13, 3), $190 000$
11. a) 10   **b)** $250, (4, 7)$
12. a) $x \geqslant 6, y \geqslant 6, x + y \leqslant 20, 1.5x + 3y \leqslant 45$ **b)** $(6, 12), 14 **c)** $(10, 10), 18
13. $(14, 11), 1360 **14. a)** $(9, 7), 44 **b)** $(15, 5), 45

Revision exercise 5A   *page 203*

1. a) $\dfrac{9x}{20}$ **b)** $\dfrac{7}{6x}$ **c)** $\dfrac{5x-2}{6}$ **d)** $\dfrac{5x+23}{(x-1)(x+3)}$

2. a) $(x-2)(x+2)$ **b)** $\dfrac{3}{x+2}$

3. a) $s = t(r+3)$ **b)** $r = \dfrac{s-3t}{t}$ **c)** $t = \dfrac{s}{r+3}$

4. a) $z = x - 5y$ **b)** $m = \dfrac{11}{k+3}$ **c)** $z = \dfrac{T^2}{C^2}$

5. a) 50   **b)** 50   **6. a)** 16   **b)** ± 4

7. a) i) 3   **ii)** 4   **iii)** $\frac{1}{4}$ **b) i)** 4   **ii)** 0

8. a) 9, 10   **b)** 2, 3, 4, 5   **9.** $\dfrac{t^2}{k^2} - 5$ **10.** $\dfrac{z+2}{z-3}$

11. a) $\frac{3}{5}$ **b)** $\dfrac{k(1-y)}{y}$ **12.**

13. a) $1\frac{5}{6}$ **b)** 0.09   **14.** 21

15. a) $\dfrac{5+a^2}{2-a}$ **b)** $-\left(\dfrac{cz+b}{a}\right)$ **c)** $\dfrac{a^2+1}{a^2-1}$

16. a) $\dfrac{7}{2x}$ **b)** $\dfrac{3a+7}{a^2-4}$ **c)** $\dfrac{x-8}{x(x+1)(x-2)}$

17. $p = \dfrac{10t^2}{s}$ **18.** 6 or 7   **19.** $y \geqslant 2, x + y \leqslant 6, y \leqslant 3x$

20. $x \geqslant 0, y \geqslant x - 2, x + y \leqslant 7, y \geqslant 0$ **22. a)** 512   **b)** 6 h   **c)** 2^{21}

Examination-style exercise 5B   *page 204*

1. $\dfrac{x^2-6x+25}{4(x-3)}$ **2.** $\dfrac{-18}{(2x+3)(x-3)}$ **3. a)** 0.8^2 **b)** 0.8^{-1} **4.** $9x^2$

5. a) 0   **b)** 0.2   **c)** 0.6   **6. a)** $3x^2$ **b)** -6

7. $\dfrac{2}{c}$ **8.** $x < 7.4$ **9.** $b = 4(a+2)^2$

10. a) $p^3(c+d)$ **b)** $p = \sqrt[3]{\dfrac{b^3 + a^2}{c+d}}$ **11.** 1.25   **12.** 0.128

13. a) $y \propto \dfrac{1}{x^2}$ or $y = \dfrac{k}{x^2}$ **b)** 30   **c)** 3.46   **d)** 4.93   **e)** divided by 4

     f) increases by 25%   **g)** $x = \sqrt{\dfrac{120}{y}}$

14. a) $x + y \leqslant 12,\ x \geqslant 4$ **d) i)** \$18 [from (4,4)]   **ii)** \$27 [from (6,6)]

15. a) i) 439.8 to 440 cm²   **ii)** $h = \dfrac{A - 2\pi r^2}{2\pi r}$ **iii)** 3.99 to 4.01   **iv)** 9.77 to 9.78

     b) i) 134   **ii)** $\dfrac{x}{45}$ **iii)** $\dfrac{x-75}{48}$ **iv)** $x = 3915$

6 Trigonometry

Exercise 2   *page 210*

1. 4.54	**2.** 3.50	**3.** 3.71	**4.** 6.62	**5.** 8.01
6. 31.9	**7.** 45.4	**8.** 4.34	**9.** 17.1	**10.** 13.2
11. 38.1	**12.** 3.15	**13.** 516	**14.** 79.1	**15.** 5.84
16. 2.56	**17.** 18.3	**18.** 8.65	**19.** 11.9	**20.** 10.6
21. 119	**22.** 10.1	**23.** 3.36 cm	**24.** 4.05 cm	**25.** 4.10 cm
26. 11.7 cm	**27.** 9.48 cm	**28.** 5.74 cm	**29.** 9.53 cm	**30.** 100 m
31. 56.7 m	**32.** 16.3 cm	**33.** 0.952 cm	**34.** 8.27 m	

Exercise 3   *page 212*

1. 5, 5.55	**2.** 13.1, 27.8	**3.** 34.6, 41.3	**4.** 20.4, 11.7	**5.** 94.1, 94.1
6. 15.2, 10, 6.43	**7.** 4.26	**8.** 3.50	**9.** 26.2	**10.** 8.82
11. a) 17.4 cm	**b)** 11.5 cm	**c)** 26.5 cm	**12. a)** 6.82 cm	**b)** 6.01 cm **c)** 7.31 cm

Exercise 4   *page 214*

1. 36.9°	**2.** 44.4°	**3.** 48.2°	**4.** 60°	**5.** 36.9°	**6.** 50.2°
7. 29.0°	**8.** 56.4°	**9.** 38.9°	**10.** 43.9°	**11.** 41.8°	**12.** 39.3°
13. 60.3°	**14.** 50.5°	**15.** 13.6°	**16.** 34.8°	**17.** 60.0°	**18.** 42.0°
19. 36.9°	**20.** 51.3°	**21.** 19.6°	**22.** 17.9°	**23.** 32.5°	**24.** 59.6°
25. 54.8°	**26.** 46.3°				

Exercise 5   *page 217*

1. 19.5°	**2.** 4.1 m	**3. a)** 26.0 km	**b)** 23.4 km
4. a) 88.6 km	**b)** 179.3 km	**5.** 4.1 m	**6.** 8.6 m
7. a) 484 km	**b)** 858 km	**c)** 985 km, 060.6°	
8. 954 km, 133°	**9.** 56.3°	**10.** 35.5°	**11.** 71.6°
12. 91.8°	**13.** 180 m	**14.** 36.4°	**15.** 10.3 cm
16. 9.51 cm	**17.** 71.1°	**18.** 67.1 m	**19.** 138 m
20. 83.2 km	**21.** 60°	**22.** 13.9 cm	**23.** Yes
24. 11.1 m; 11.1 s; 222 m **25.** 4.4 m			

Exercise 6   *page 219*

1. 100 m	**2.** 89 n miles	**3.** 103 km	**4.** 99 km; 024°	**5.** 9190 km/h; 255°	**6.** 11 km

Exercise 7   *page 221*

1. a) 13 cm	**b)** 13.6 cm	**c)** 17.1°		
2. a) 4.04 m	**b)** 38.9°	**c)** 11.2 m	**d)** 19.9°	
3. a) 8.49 cm	**b)** 8.49 cm	**c)** 10.4 cm	**d)** 35.3°	**e)** 35.3°
4. a) 14.1 cm	**b)** 18.7 cm	**c)** 69.3°	**d)** 29.0°	**e)** 41.4°

5. a) 4.47 m   **b)** 7.48 m   **c)** 63.4°   **d)** 74.5°   **e)** 53.3°
6. 10.8 cm; 21.8°

7. a) $h \tan 65°$ or $\dfrac{h}{\tan 25°}$ **b)** $h \tan 57°$ or $\dfrac{h}{\tan 33°}$ **c)** 22.7 m

8. 22.6 m   **9.** 55.0 m   **10.** 7.26 m   **11.** 43.3°

Exercise 8   *page 224*

1. a) 1, 0.87, 0.5, 0, −0.5, −0.87, −1, −0.87, −0.5, 0, 0.5, 0.87, 1   **2.** 0, 0.5, 0.87, 1, 0.87, 0.5, 0, −0.5, −0.87, −1, −0.87, −0.5, 0

b)

3.

4. 162°   **5.** 153°   **6.** 310°   **7. a)** 140°   **b)** 50°   **c)** 240°
8. 290°   **9.** 255°   **10.** 160°, 200°   **11.** 216°   **12.** 292°
13. a) 60°, 120°   **b)** 25.8°, 334.2°   **c)** 26.6°, 206.6°   **d)** 135°, 225°   **e)** 228.6°, 311.4°   **f)** 99.5°, 279.5°
14. a) 30°, 150°   **b)** 48.2°, 311.8°   **c)** 74.1°, 254.1°   **d)** 199.5°, 340.5°   **e)** 143.1°, 216.9°   **f)** 126.9°, 306.9°
   g) 15°, 105°   **h)** 90°, 270°   **15.** 60°, 120°

Exercise 9   *page 226*

1. 6.38 m   **2.** 12.5 m   **3.** 5.17 cm   **4.** 40.4 cm   **5.** 7.81 m, 7.10 m
6. 3.55 m, 6.68 m   **7.** 8.61 cm   **8.** 9.97 cm   **9.** 8.52 cm   **10.** 15.2 cm
11. 35.8°   **12.** 42.9°   **13.** 32.3°   **14.** 37.8°   **15.** 35.5°, 48.5°
16. 68.8°, 80.0°   **17.** 64.6°   **18.** 34.2°   **19.** 50.6°   **20.** 39.1°
21. 39.5°   **22.** 21.6°

Exercise 10   *page 228*

1. 6.24 cm   **2.** 6.05 cm   **3.** 5.47 cm   **4.** 9.27 cm   **5.** 10.1 cm
6. 8.99 cm   **7.** 5.87 cm   **8.** 4.24 cm   **9.** 11.9 cm   **10.** 154 cm
11. 25.2°   **12.** 78.5°   **13.** 115.0°   **14.** 111.1°   **15.** 24.0°
16. 92.5°   **17.** 99.9°   **18.** 38.2°   **19.** 137.8°   **20.** 34.0°
21. 60.2°   **22.** 8.72 cm   **23.** 1.40 cm   **24.** 7.38 cm

Exercise 11   *page 230*

1. 6.7 cm   **2.** 10.8 m   **3.** 35.6 km   **4.** 25.2 m
5. 38.6°, 48.5°, 92.9°   **6.** 40.4 m   **7. a)** 9.8 km   **b)** 085.7°

8. a) 29.6 km   **b)** 050.5°   **9. a)** 10.8 m   **b)** 72.6°   **c)** 32.6°
10. 378 km, 048.4°   **11. a)** 62.2°   **b)** 2.33 km   **12.** 9.64 m   **13.** 8.6°

Revision exercise 6A *page 231*
1. a) 45.6°   **b)** 58.0°   **c)** 3.89 cm   **d)** 33.8 m   **2. a)** 1.75   **b)** 60.3°
3. a) 48.6°, 131.4°   **b)** 101.5°, 258.5°   **c)** 116.6°, 296.6°   **d)** 216.9°, 323.1°   **e)** 33.6°, 326.4°   **f)** 36.3°, 216.3°
4. a) 12.7 cm   **b)** 5.92 cm   **c)** 36.1°
5. 5.39 cm   **6. a)** 220°   **b)** 295°
7. 0.335 m
8. a) 6.61 cm   **b)** 12.8 cm   **c)** 5.67 cm   **9. a)** 86.9 cm   **b)** 53.6 cm   **c)** 133 cm
10. 52.4 m   **11. a)** 14.1 cm   **b)** 35.3°   **c)** 35.3°
12. a) 6.63 cm   **b)** 41.8°   **13. a)** 11.3 cm   **b)** 8.25 cm   **c)** 55.6°
14. 45.2 km, 33.6 km   **15.** 73.4°   **16.** 8.76 m, 9.99 m
17. 0.539   **18.** 4.12 cm, 9.93 cm   **19.** 26.4°
20. a) 10 m   **b)** 7.81 m   **c)** 9.43 m   **d)** 70.2°

Examination-style exercise 6B *page 233*
1. 0.276 m   **2. a)** 121 m   **b) i)** 280°   **ii)** 069°   **3. a)** 232°   **b)** 175.4°
4. b) 9.60 to 9.603 m   **5. a) i)** 60°   **ii)** 13 km   **b) i)** 145°   **ii)** 61.4°   **iii)** 15.3 km
   c) 139 to 140 km²   **6.** 210, 330   **7.** 7.94
8. a) 24.7 m   **b)** 11.5 m   **9. a)** 11.3°   **b)** 233°
10. a) 2   **b)** 30 cm³   **c)** 45°   **d)** 37.5°   **e)** 4.92 to 4.93 cm
11.

$x = 109.5°$ and $x = 250.5°$

7 Graphs

Exercise 1 *page 239*
For questions **1** to **10** end points of lines are given.
1. $(-3, -5)$ and $(3, 7)$ **2.** $(-3, -13)$ and $(3, 5)$ **3.** $(-3, -7)$ and $(3, 5)$
4. $(-2, 10)$ and $(4, 4)$ **5.** $(-2, 14)$ and $(4, 2)$ **6.** $(-3, 1)$ and $(3, 4)$
7. $(-3, -15)$ and $(3, 3)$ **8.** $\left(-3, 2\frac{1}{2}\right)$ and $\left(3, 5\frac{1}{2}\right)$ **9.** $(-2, -7)$ and $(4, 5)$
10. $(-2, 18)$ and $(4, 0)$ **11.** $(0, 0), (1, 4), (1.6, 1.6)$ **12.** $(0,1), \left(2\frac{1}{4}, 1\right), \left(4\frac{1}{2}, 10\right)$
13. $(-2, -6), (1.25, 3.75), (4.5, 0.5)$ **14.** $(-1.5, 1.5)(0.67, 8), (3.5, 8), (3.5, -3.5)$
15. $(4, -2), (0.33, 5.33), (-2.28, -5.14)$ **16.** $(-2, 3), (0.6, 8.2), (2.5, 2.5), (1.33, 1.33)$
17. a) $560   **b)** 2400 km   **18. a)** 3.4 kg   **b)** 3 h 20 m
19. a) $440   **b)** 42 km/h   **c)** $210   **20. a)** $4315   **b)** 26 000 km

Exercise 2 *page 242*
1. $1\frac{1}{2}$ **2.** 2   **3.** 3   **4.** $1\frac{1}{2}$ **5.** $\frac{1}{2}$ **6.** $-\frac{1}{6}$
7. -7 **8.** -1 **9.** 4   **10.** -4 **11.** 5   **12.** $-\frac{3}{7}$
13. 6   **14.** 0   **15.** 0   **16.** infinite   **17.** infinite   **18.** -8

19. $5\frac{1}{3}$ **20.** 0   **21.** $\dfrac{b-d}{a-c}$ or $\dfrac{d-b}{c-a}$ **22.** $\dfrac{n+b}{m-a}$ **23.** $\dfrac{2f}{a}$

24. -4 **25.** 0   **26.** $-\dfrac{6d}{c}$ **27. a)** $-1\frac{1}{5}$ **b)** $\dfrac{1}{10}$ **c)** $\frac{4}{5}$

28. a) infinite   **b)** $-\frac{3}{10}$ **c)** $\frac{3}{10}$ **29.** $3\frac{1}{2}$

30. a) $\dfrac{n+4}{2m-3}$ **b)** $n=-4$ **c)** $m=1\frac{1}{2}$ **31. b)** 7.2   **c)** $(4,4)$

32. b) yes, PQ = PR   **c)** $(3, 2.5)$

Exercise 3   *page 243*

1. 1, 3   **2.** 1, −2   **3.** 2, 1   **4.** 2, −5   **5.** 3, 4

6. $\frac{1}{2}$, 6   **7.** 3, −2   **8.** 2, 0   **9.** $\frac{1}{4}$, −4   **10.** −1, 3

11. −2, 6   **12.** −1, 2   **13.** −2, 3   **14.** −3, −4   **15.** $\frac{1}{2}$, 3

16. $-\frac{1}{3}$, 3   **17.** 4, −5   **18.** $1\frac{1}{2}$, −4   **19.** 10, 0   **20.** 0, 4

Exercise 4   *page 244*

1. $y=3x+7$ **2.** $y=2x-9$ **3.** $y=-x+5$ **4.** $y=2x-1$

5. $y=3x+5$ **6.** $y=-x+7$ **7.** $y=\frac{1}{2}x-3$ **8.** $y=2x-3$

9. $y=3x-11$ **10.** $y=-x+5$ **11.** $y=\frac{1}{3}x-4$

Exercise 5   *page 244*

1. A: $y=3x-4$ B: $y=x+2$ **2.** C: $y=\frac{2}{3}x-2$ D: $y=-2x+4$

3. a) $y=2x+5$ **b)** $y=-x+3$ **4. a)** $y=3x+1$ **b)** $y=x-2$

Exercise 6   *page 245*

1. $y=-x+7$ **2.** $y=2x-5$ **3.** $y=-\frac{1}{4}x+\frac{23}{4}$

4. $y=6x-30$ **5.** $y=-\frac{1}{5}x+\frac{17}{5}$ **6.** $y=-\frac{1}{3}x-\frac{1}{3}$

7. a) $y=-\frac{1}{2}x+4.5$ **b)** $(1.4, 3.8)$ **c)** 1.79

8. a) $y=-2x+1$ **b)** 4.02   **9.** 0.32   **10.** 4.31

Exercise 7   *page 247*

1.   **2.**   **3.**   **4.**

5.

6.

7.

8.

9.

10.

11.

12.

13.

14.

15.

16.

17.

18.

19.

20.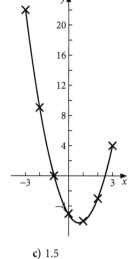

Exercise 8 *page 248*

1. a) 4   **b)** 8   **c)** 10.6   **2. a)** 3   **b)** −5   **c)** 1.5

3. a) 7.25   **b)** −2   **c)** −0.8, 3.8   **15. a)** 0.75   **b)** 1.23

16. a) 3.13 **b)** 3.35   **17. a)** −2.45   **b)** 1.4

18. a) 5   **b)** 10.1   **c)** −1.25   **20. a)** 245   **b)** 41   **c)** $25 < x < 67$

Exercise 9 *page 250*

1. a) 2   **2. a)** 600

b)

b)

c) 5.64 minutes

c) 1.26 hours

3.

4.

5. a) 996

b)

c) 5.6 hours   **d)** 950   **e)** The value of the function will be negative.

Exercise 10   *page 251*
 1. a) 10.7 cm²   **b)** 1.7 cm × 53 cm   **c)** 12.25 cm²
 d) 3.5 cm × 3.5 cm   **e)** square
 2. 15 m × 30 m   **3. a)** 2.5 s   **b)** 31.3 m   **c)** $2 < t < 3$
 4. a) 108 m/s   **b)** 1.4 s   **c)** $2.3 < t < 3.6$ **6.** 3.3
 10. d) 1.41 ± 0.02 **e)** $1.15 \leqslant x \leqslant 1.3 \ (\pm 0.02)$

Exercise 11   *page 254*
 1. a) i) 40 km   **ii)** 24 km   **iii)** 72 km   **iv)** 8 km
 b) i) 40 miles   **ii)** 35 miles   **iii)** 10 miles   **iv)** 20 miles
 2. a) i) €28   **ii)** €112   **iii)** €70
 b) i) £40   **ii)** £60   **iii)** £100   **c)** £110
 3. a) 180   **b)** $C = 0.2x + 35$
 4. a) 30 litres   **b) i)** 6 km/litre   **ii)** 30 km/litre   **c)** $6\frac{2}{3}$ km/litre; 6 litres
 5. a) 2000   **b)** 200   **c)** $1.6 \leqslant x \leqslant 2.4$
 6. a) Yes   **b)** No   **c)** About \$250 – \$270

Exercise 12   *page 257*
 1. a) −0.4, 2.4   **b)** −0.8, 3.8   **c)** −1, 3   **d)** −0.4, 2.4
 2. −0.3, 3.3   **3.** 0.6, 3.4   **4.** 0.3, 3.7
 5. a) $y = 3$ **b)** $y = -2$ **c)** $y = x + 4$ **d)** $y = x$ **e)** $y = 6$
 6. a) $y = 6$ **b)** $y = 0$ **c)** $y = 4$ **d)** $y = 2x$ **e)** $y = 2x + 4$
 7. a) $y = -4$ **b)** $y = 2x$ **c)** $y = x - 2$ **d)** $y = -3$ **e)** $y = 2$
 8. a) $y = 5$ **b)** $y = 2x$ **c)** $y = 0.2$ **d)** $y = 3 - x$ **e)** $y = 3$
 9. a) $y = 0$ **b)** $y = -2\frac{1}{2}$ **c)** $y = -8x$ **d)** $y = -3$ **e)** $y = -5\frac{1}{2}x$
 10. a) −1.65, 3.65   **b)** −1.3, 2.3   **c)** −1.45, 3.45
 11. a) 1.7, 5.3   **b)** 0.2, 4.8   **12. a)** −3.3, 0.3   **b)** −4.6, −0.4
 13. a) −2.35, 0.85   **b)** −2.8, 1.8   **14. a) i)** −0.4, 2.4   **ii)** −0.5, 2   **b)** $-1.3 < x < 2.8$
 15. a) 3.4, −5.4   **b)** 2.4, 7.6   **c)** ±4.2   **16. a)** ±3.7   **c)** ±2.8
 17. a) 1.75   **b)** 0, ±1.4   **18. a)** $1.6 < x < 7.4$ **b)** 6.9
 19. a) 2.6   **b)** 0.45   **c)** 0.64   **d)** 5.7
 20. a) −1.6, 0.6   **b)** $-\frac{1}{2}$, 1

Exercise 13   *page 260*
 1. a) 45 min   **b)** 09 : 15   **c)** 60 km/h   **d)** 100 km/h   **e)** 57.1 km/h
 2. a) 09 : 15   **b)** 64 km/h   **c)** 37.6 km/h   **d)** 47 km   **e)** 80 km/h

3. 11 : 05   **4.** 12 : 42   **5.** 12 : 35   **6.** $1\frac{1}{8}$ h   **7.** 1 h

8. a) i) B   **ii)** A   **b)** 8 s to 18 s   **c)** About 15 s   **d)** About 9 s
     e) B   **f)** A

9. Hanna started quickly, stood still for a while and then sped up quickly again before stopping and going backwards; Fateema started fairly slowly, sped up in the middle and then slowed down again; Carine started slowly and then gradually sped up so that she overtook the other two and won the race.

Exercise 14   *page 263*

1. a) $1\frac{1}{2}$ m/s²   **b)** 675 m   **c)** $11\frac{1}{4}$ m/s

2. a) 600 m   **b)** 20 m/s   **c)** 225 m   **d)** −2 m/s²

3. a) 600 m   **b)** $387\frac{1}{2}$ m   **c)** 0 m/s²

4. a) 20 m/s   **b)** 750 m
5. a) 8 s   **b)** 496 m   **c)** 12.4 m/s

6. a) 30 m/s   **b)** $-2\frac{1}{7}$ m/s²   **c)** 20 s

7. a) 15 m/s   **b)** $2\frac{1}{4}$ m/s²

8. a) 40 m/s   **b)** 10 s
9. a) 50 m/s   **b)** 20 s
10. a) 20 m/s   **b)** 20 s

Exercise 15   *page 264*

1. 225 m   **2.** 60 m   **3.** $\frac{2}{3}$ km

4. 10 s   **5.** 3 min   **6.** 50 m
7. 18.75 m   **8.** 1.39 km   **9.** 250 m
10. Yes. Stopping distance = 46.5 m
11. 94 375 m
12. a) 0.8 m/s²   **b)** 670 m
13. a) 0.35 m/s²   **b)** 260 m

Exercise 16   *page 266*

1. (3, −7)   **2.** (−2, −7)   **3.** (−2.5, −8.25)   **4.** (3.5, −7.25)   **5.** (−2, 10)
6. (−1.5, 6.25)   **7.** (1.5, 0.5)   **8.** (−1, −7)   **9.** (−0.75, 5.125)   **10.** (−0.625, 8.5625)

Exercise 17   *page 268*

1. $6x$ **2.** $6x^2 - 4$ **3.** $24x^3$ **4.** $10x^4 - 8x$ **5.** $16x^3 - 9x^2 + 10x$
6. $-6x - 12x^3$ **7.** $7x^6 + 6x^5 + 5x^4$ **8.** $\frac{3}{2}x^2 + \frac{4}{3}x$ **9.** $\frac{4}{5}x^3 + \frac{9}{4}x^2 - \frac{4}{5}x$ **10.** $\frac{1}{4}x^3 - x^2$
11. $15x^2 - 12x$ **12.** $30x^4 - 16x^3$ **13.** $40x - 25x^4 + 2$ **14.** $56x^7 - 13$ **15.** $\frac{7}{8}x^6 - \frac{5}{6}x^4$
16. $\frac{40}{9}x^4 + \frac{1}{5}x^2$ **17. a)** $70x^4 - 64x^3 - 13$ **b)** $72x^8 - 10x$ **c)** $\frac{1}{2}x^6 - 5x^5 + \frac{3}{4}x^2$

Exercise 18   *page 269*

1. a) −5   **b)** −128   **c)** −245   **2. a)** 43   **b)** 427   **c)** −2
3. a) 245   **b)** 329   **c)** $\frac{35}{3}$ **4.** $\frac{3}{2}$ **5.** −3   **6.** (−2, 5)
7. $1, -\frac{7}{3}$ **8.** $(1, -\frac{25}{6}), (-2, \frac{28}{3})$
9. (0, 0), (2, −14), (−2, −2)   **10.** $(4, -48), (-\frac{2}{3}, -\frac{76}{27})$

Exercise 19   *page 271*

1. a) (1.5, −7.25)   **b)** (0.875, −3.0625)   **c)** (−0.75, 3.125)
2. a) Min   **b)** Min   **c)** Max
3. a) (0.7, 3.55)   **4. a)** $(0, -3), (\frac{2}{3}, -\frac{89}{27})$ **b)** Max, Min
5. a) (−1, −1), (1, −9)   **b)** Max, Min   **6. a)** (−2, −13), (2, 19)   **b)** Min, Max

7. You show that the quadratic formed when you differentiate has no solutions = 0.

8. $k \leqslant -\frac{1}{3}$

Revision exercise 7 A   *page 272*

1. a) $y = x - 7$ **b)** $y = 2x + 5$ **c)** $y = -2x + 10$ **d)** $y = \dfrac{x+1}{2}$

2. a) 2   **b)** 1   **c)** $-3\frac{1}{2}$ **d)** 0   **e)** 10

3. a) 2, –7   **b)** –4, 5   **c)** $\frac{1}{2}$, 4   **d)** $-\frac{1}{2}$, 5   **e)** –2, 12   **f)** $-\frac{2}{3}$, 8

4. A: $y = 6$;   **B:** $y = \frac{1}{2}x - 3$;   **C:** $y = 10 - x$;   **D:** $y = 3x$

5. A: $4y = 3x - 16$;   **B:** $2y = x - 8$;   **C:** $2y + x = 8$;   **D:** $4y + 3x = 16$

6. a) $y = 2x - 3$ **b)** $y = 3x + 4$ **c)** $y = 10 - x$ **d)** $y = 7$

7. a) A(0, –8), B(4, 0)   **b)** 2   **c)** $y = 2x - 8$

8. 25 sq. units   **9.** 3.13   **10.** –3   **11.** 219

13. a) $y = 3x$ **b)** $y = 0$ **c)** $y = 11 - x$ **d)** $y = 5x$

14. a) 1.56, –2.56   **b)** ±2.24   **c)** ±2.65

15. a) 0.84, 4.15   **b)** $0.65 < x < 3.85$ **c)** 3.3

16. a) 9.2   **b)** 0.6   **c)** 1.4   **d)** 1.65

17. a)
    b) 2.8

18. a) 0.3 m/s²   **b)** 1050 m   **c)** 40 s

19. a) 30 m/s   **b)** 600 m

20. $12x^3 - 12x$ **21. a)** $\frac{3}{2}x^5 - \frac{6}{5}x^2 + \frac{7}{4}x$ **b)** 46.7   **22.** –0.52 (Max), 4.52 (Min)

Examination-style exercise 7B   *page 274*

1. a) $y = -2x - 5$ **b)** (–2.5, 0)

2. a) $y = \dfrac{8 - 3x}{2}$ **b)** $-\frac{3}{2}$ **c)** (0, 4)

3. $y = \frac{1}{2}x + 5$ **4. a)** 1000, 1400, 1960, 2744, 3842   **c)** 3.2 or 3.3

5. a) i) 3   **ii)** –4.25 to –4

    b) i) –1.6, 2.0, 8.6 to 8.63   **ii)** 9.2

    c) –9, 3   **d)** $0 < x < 6$

    e) i) $y = 1 - x$ **ii)** $y = 3$

6. a) $p = 5(.04), q = 0, r = 8.66$ **c) i)** –2.95 to –2.6, –0.75 to –0.6, 0.5 to 0.6

    ii) $a = 3\ b = -1$ **d)** –4.5 to –3

7. a) 1.05 m/s²   **b)** 3360 m   **c)** 18.7 m/s

8. a) i) 10.625 hours   **iii)** 10 hours 37 mins 30 secs

    b) i) 0608   **ii)** 78.7 km/h

    c) i) increasing (more slowly)   **ii)** decreasing   **iii)** 12.5 m/s²

    iv) 170 m   **v)** areas above and below broken line are approximately equal

    vi) 61.2 km/h

9. a) 0.9, –10.1   **c)** any integer $\geqslant 1$

    e) i) –0.45 to –0.3, 0.4 to 0.49, 2.9 to 2.99

       ii) $2x^3 - 6x^2 + 1 = 0$ **f) i)** tangent drawn with gradient ≈ 2

10. a) $y = -2x + 17$ **b)** 0.894

11. a) $3x^2 - 4x - 4$ **b)** $\left(-\frac{2}{3}, \frac{40}{27}\right)$ and (2, –8)

12. a) $6x^2 - 8x + 5$ **b)** 2.5   **c)** No, there are no solutions to the equation $\dfrac{dy}{dx} = 0$.

8 Sets, Vectors, Functions and Transformations

Exercise 1   *page 281*

1. a) 8	b) 3	c) 4	d) 18	e) 7	
2. a) 9	b) 5	c) 4	d) 20	e) 31	
3. a) 8	b) 3	c) 3	d) 2	e) 18	f) 0
4. a) 59	b) 11	c) 5	d) 40	e) 11	f) 124
5. a) 120	b) 120	c) 490	d) 80	e) 40	f) 10

5. g) 500

Exercise 2   *page 283*

1. a) {5, 7}   b) {1, 2, 3, 4, 5, 6, 7, 8, 9, 11, 13}   c) 5   d) 11
e) true   f) true   g) false   h) true
2. a) {2, 3, 5, 7}   b) {1, 2, 3, ..., 9}   c) 4   d) $\varnothing$ e) false
f) true   g) false   h) true
3. a) {2, 4, 6, 8, 10}   b) {16, 18, 20}   c) $\varnothing$ d) 15   e) 11
f) 21   g) false   h) false   i) true   j) true
4. a) {1, 3, 4, 5}   b) {1, 5}   c) 1   d) {1, 5}   e) {1, 3, 5, 10}
f) 4   g) true   h) false   i) true
5. a) 4   b) 3   c) {b, d}   d) {a, b, c, d, e}   e) 5   f) 2
6. a) 2   b) 4   c) {1, 2, 4, 6, 7, 8, 9}   d) {7, 9}   e) {1, 2, 4}
f) {1, 2, 4, 7, 9}   g) {1, 2, 4, 6, 8}   h) {6, 7, 8, 9}   i) {1, 2, 4, 7, 9}

Exercise 3   *page 284*

1. a)   b)   c)

d)   e)   f)

2. a)   b)   c)

d)

3. a)   b)   c)   d)

4. a)   b)   c)   d)

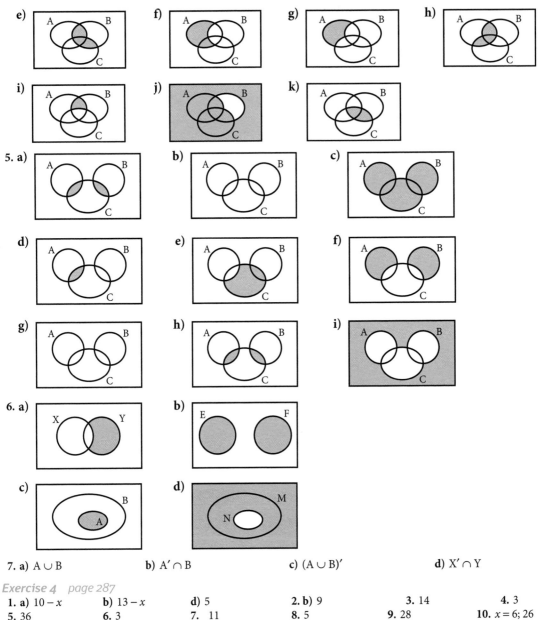

e) A B C

f) A B C

g) A B C

h) A B C

i) A B C

j) A B C

k) A B C

5. a) A B C

b) A B C

c) A B C

d) A B C

e) A B C

f) A B C

g) A B C

h) A B C

i) A B C

6. a) X Y

b) E F

c) A B

d) N M

7. a) $A \cup B$ **b)** $A' \cap B$ **c)** $(A \cup B)'$ **d)** $X' \cap Y$

Exercise 4   *page 287*

  1. a) $10 - x$ **b)** $13 - x$ **d)** 5   **2. b)** 9   **3.** 14   **4.** 3

  5. 36   **6.** 3   **7.** 11   **8.** 5   **9.** 28   **10.** $x = 6$; 26

  11. 34   **12. a)** 12   **b)** $\frac{1}{2}$ **13.** $x = 10$; 30   **14.** 2

  15. a) All good footballers are Serbian men.   **b)** No good footballers are Serbian men.
       c) There are some good footballers who are Serbian men.
  16. a) The football players are all boys.   **b)** The hockey players are all girls.
       c) There are some people who play both football and hockey.
       d) There are no boys who play hockey.   **e)** $B \cap F = \varnothing$ **f)** $H \cup F = \varepsilon$
  17. a) $S \cap T = \varnothing$ **b)** $F \subseteq T$ **c)** $S \cap F 6 \neq \varnothing$
       d) All living creatures are either spiders, animals that fly or animals which taste nice.
       e) Animals which taste nice are all spiders.
  18. a) All tigers who like lions also like elephants.
       b) All tigers who like lions or elephants are in hospital.

c) There are no tigers in hospital who like elephants.

d) $H \subseteq T$ **e)** $T \cap X \neq \varnothing$

19. a) There are no good bridge players called Peter.

     b) All school teachers are either called Peter or are good bridge players or are women.

     c) There are some women teachers called Peter.

     d) $W \cap B = \varnothing$ **e)** $B \subseteq (W \cap P)$

Exercise 5   *page 291*

1. d	**2.** 2c	**3.** 3c	**4.** 3d	**5.** 5d
6. 3c	**7.** −2d	**8.** −2c	**9.** −3c	**10.** −c
11. c + d	**12.** c + 2d	**13.** 2c + d	**14.** 3c + d	**15.** 2c + 2d
16. 2c + 3d	**17.** 2c − d	**18.** 3c − d	**19.** −c + 2d	**20.** −c + 3d
21. −c + d	**22.** −c − 2d	**23.** −2c − 2d	**24.** −3c − 6d	**25.** −2c + 3d
26. c + 6d	**27.** $\overrightarrow{QI}$	**28.** $\overrightarrow{QU}$	**29.** $\overrightarrow{QH}$	**30.** $\overrightarrow{QB}$
31. $\overrightarrow{QF}$	**32.** $\overrightarrow{QJ}$	**33.** $\overrightarrow{QZ}$	**34.** $\overrightarrow{QL}$	**35.** $\overrightarrow{QE}$
36. $\overrightarrow{QX}$	**37.** $\overrightarrow{QW}$	**38.** $\overrightarrow{QK}$		

39. a) −a   **b)** b − a   **c)** −b   **d)** a + b

40. a) a + b   **b)** a − 2b   **c)** −a + b   **d)** −a − b

41. a) −a − b   **b)** 3a − b   **c)** 2a − b   **d)** −2a + b

42. a) a − 2b   **b)** a − b   **c)** 2a   **d)** −2a + 3b

43. a) 2a − c   **b)** 2a − c   **c)** 3a   **d)** a + b + c   **e)** −3a − b

44. a) b − c   **b)** 2b + 2c   **c)** a + 2b + 2c   **d)** −a − b   **e)** c − a − b

45. a) a + c   **b)** −a + c   **c)** a + b + c   **d)** b − c   **e)** −a + 2c

Exercise 6   *page 293*

1. a) a   **b)** −a + b   **c)** 2b   **d)** −2a   **e)** −2a + 2b

     f) −a + b   **g)** a + b   **h)** b   **i)** −b + 2a   **j)** −2b + a

2. a) a   **b)** −a + b   **c)** 3b   **d)** −2a   **e)** −2a + 3b

     f) $-a + \frac{3}{2}b$ **g)** $a + \frac{3}{2}b$ **h)** $\frac{3}{2}b$ **i)** −b + 2a   **j)** −3b + a

3. a) 2a   **b)** −a + b   **c)** 2b   **d)** −3a   **e)** −3a + 2b

     f) $-\frac{3}{2}a + b$ **g)** $\frac{3}{2}a + b$ **h)** $\frac{1}{2}a + b$ **i)** −b + 3a   **j)** −2b + a

4. a) $\frac{1}{2}a$ **b)** −a + b   **c)** 4b   **d)** $-\frac{3}{2}a$ **e)** $-\frac{3}{2}a + 4b$

     f) $-a + \frac{8}{3}b$ **g)** $\frac{1}{2}a + \frac{8}{3}b$ **h)** $-\frac{1}{2}a + \frac{8}{3}b$ **i)** $\frac{3}{2}a - b$ **j)** a − 4b

5. a) 5a   **b)** b − a   **c)** $\frac{3}{2}b$ **d)** −6a   **e)** $\frac{3}{2}b - 6a$

     f) b − 4a   **g)** 2a + b   **h)** a + b   **i)** 6a − b   **j)** $a - \frac{3}{2}b$

6. a) 4a   **b)** b − a   **c)** 3b   **d)** −5a   **e)** 3b − 5a

     f) $\frac{3}{4}b - \frac{5}{4}a$ **g)** $\frac{15}{4}a + \frac{3}{4}b$ **h)** $\frac{11}{4}a + \frac{3}{4}b$ **i)** 5a − b   **j)** a − 3b

7. $\frac{1}{2}s - \frac{1}{2}t$ **8.** $\frac{1}{3}a + \frac{2}{3}b$ **9.** a + c − b   **10.** 2m + 2n

11. a) b − a   **b)** b − a   **c)** 2b − 2a   **d)** b − 2a   **e)** b − 2a

     f) 2b − 3a

12. a) y − z   **b)** $\frac{1}{2}y - \frac{1}{2}z$ **c)** $\frac{1}{2}y + \frac{1}{2}z$ **d)** $-x + \frac{1}{2}y + \frac{1}{2}z$

     e) $-\frac{2}{3}x + \frac{1}{3}y + \frac{1}{3}$ **f)** $\frac{1}{3}x + \frac{1}{3}y + \frac{1}{3}z$

1.

2.

3.

4.

5.

6.

7.

8.

9.

10.

11.

12.

13. $\begin{pmatrix} -11 \\ 9 \end{pmatrix}$ **14.** $\begin{pmatrix} -1 \\ -4 \end{pmatrix}$ **15.** $\begin{pmatrix} 4 \\ 8 \end{pmatrix}$ **16.** $\begin{pmatrix} 4 \\ 3 \end{pmatrix}$ **17.** $\begin{pmatrix} 8 \\ -7 \end{pmatrix}$ **18.** $\begin{pmatrix} 18 \\ -1 \end{pmatrix}$ **19.** $\begin{pmatrix} 7 \\ -4 \end{pmatrix}$ **20.** $\begin{pmatrix} -18 \\ -16 \end{pmatrix}$

21. $\begin{pmatrix} 13 \\ 19 \end{pmatrix}$ **22.** $\begin{pmatrix} 8 \\ 5 \end{pmatrix}$ **23.** $\begin{pmatrix} 10 \\ -13 \end{pmatrix}$ **24.** $\begin{pmatrix} 17 \\ 35 \end{pmatrix}$ **25.** $\begin{pmatrix} 4 \\ 8 \end{pmatrix}$ **26.** $\begin{pmatrix} 4 \\ 3 \end{pmatrix}$ **27.** $\begin{pmatrix} -1 \\ 1 \end{pmatrix}$ **28.** $\begin{pmatrix} -16 \\ 3 \end{pmatrix}$

29. $\begin{pmatrix} -2\frac{1}{2} \\ -3 \end{pmatrix}$ **30.** $\begin{pmatrix} -3\frac{1}{2} \\ \frac{1}{2} \end{pmatrix}$ **31.** $\begin{pmatrix} -3 \\ -7 \end{pmatrix}$ **32.** $\begin{pmatrix} -2 \\ 12 \end{pmatrix}$ **33.** $\begin{pmatrix} 4 \\ 8 \end{pmatrix}$ **34.** $\begin{pmatrix} -5\frac{1}{2} \\ 4\frac{1}{2} \end{pmatrix}$ **35.** $\begin{pmatrix} 0 \\ 0 \end{pmatrix}$ **36.** $\begin{pmatrix} -2\frac{1}{2} \\ -6 \end{pmatrix}$

37. b) l and s; n and r; p and t; m and q

38. a) true   **b)** true   **c)** true   **d)** true   **e)** false   **f)** false

39. a)

b)

40 a)

b)

c)

d)

Exercise 8   *page 298*

1. $\begin{pmatrix} 2 \\ -2 \end{pmatrix}$ **2.** $\begin{pmatrix} 6 \\ -2 \end{pmatrix}$ **3. b)** $\begin{pmatrix} 0 \\ 3 \end{pmatrix}; \begin{pmatrix} -5 \\ -5 \end{pmatrix}$ **4. b)** $\begin{pmatrix} 4 \\ 2 \end{pmatrix}; \begin{pmatrix} -7 \\ 0 \end{pmatrix}$

5. a) $\begin{pmatrix} 3 \\ -3 \end{pmatrix}$ **b)** $\begin{pmatrix} 1\frac{1}{2} \\ -1\frac{1}{2} \end{pmatrix}$ **c)** $\begin{pmatrix} 3\frac{1}{2} \\ 3\frac{1}{2} \end{pmatrix}; M\left(3\frac{1}{2}, 3\frac{1}{2}\right)$

6. a) $\begin{pmatrix} -1 \\ 6 \end{pmatrix}$ **b)** $\begin{pmatrix} -\frac{1}{2} \\ 3 \end{pmatrix}$ **c)** $\begin{pmatrix} 5\frac{1}{2} \\ -4 \end{pmatrix}; M\left(5\frac{1}{2}, -4\right)$

7. a) i) $\begin{pmatrix} -6 \\ 3 \end{pmatrix}$ **ii)** $\begin{pmatrix} -2 \\ 1 \end{pmatrix}$ **iii)** $\begin{pmatrix} 2 \\ 3 \end{pmatrix}$ **b) i)** $\begin{pmatrix} 0 \\ -9 \end{pmatrix}$ **ii)** $\begin{pmatrix} 0 \\ -3 \end{pmatrix}$ **iii)** $\begin{pmatrix} -2 \\ 2 \end{pmatrix}$

8. $\begin{pmatrix} 1 \\ -2 \end{pmatrix}$ or $\begin{pmatrix} -1 \\ 2 \end{pmatrix}$ **9.** $\begin{pmatrix} 0 \\ 2 \end{pmatrix}$ or $\begin{pmatrix} 0 \\ -2 \end{pmatrix}$

10. a) q − p   **b)** q + 2p   **c)** p + q

11. a) $\begin{pmatrix} 1 \\ -3 \end{pmatrix}$ **b)** $\begin{pmatrix} -1 \\ 3 \end{pmatrix}$ **c)** $\begin{pmatrix} 3 \\ 1 \end{pmatrix}$ **d)** $\begin{pmatrix} -3 \\ -1 \end{pmatrix}$

Exercise 9 page 300

1. 5
2. $\sqrt{17}$
3. 13
4. 3
5. 5
6. $\sqrt{45}$
7. $\sqrt{74}$
8. $\sqrt{208}$
9. 10
10. $\sqrt{89}$
11. a) $\sqrt{320}$ b) no
12. a) $\sqrt{148}$ b) no
13. $\sqrt{29}$
14. $\sqrt{26}$
15. $\sqrt{10}$
16. a) 5   b) $n = \pm4$
17. a) 13   b) $m = \pm13$
18. a) 5   b) $p = 0$
19. a) 9   b) 6   c) 5
20. a) 30   b) 5   c) $\sqrt{50}$ d) 4

Exercise 10 page 302

1. a) $2\mathbf{a}$; $3\mathbf{b}$ b) $-\mathbf{b} + \mathbf{a}$ c) $-3\mathbf{b} + 2\mathbf{a}$ d) $4\mathbf{a} - 3\mathbf{b}$
   e) $4\mathbf{a} - 6\mathbf{b}$ f) $\overrightarrow{EC} = 2\overrightarrow{ED}$

2. a) $2\mathbf{b}$; $\frac{5}{2}\mathbf{a}$ b) $-\mathbf{a} + \mathbf{b}$ c) $-\frac{5}{2}\mathbf{a} + 2\mathbf{b}$ d) $-5\mathbf{a} + 6\mathbf{b}$
   e) $-\frac{15}{2}\mathbf{a} + 6\mathbf{b}$ f) $\overrightarrow{XC} = 3\overrightarrow{XY}$

3. a) $-\mathbf{b} + \mathbf{a}$; $-3\mathbf{b} + 3\mathbf{a}$ b) $-2\mathbf{b} + \frac{3}{2}\mathbf{a}$ c) $-\frac{1}{2}\mathbf{a}$; $-2\mathbf{b} + \frac{3}{2}\mathbf{a}$ d) Since $\overrightarrow{RQ}$ and $\overrightarrow{QP}$ are equal and share a common point, R, Q and P lie on a straight line.

4. a) $-\mathbf{a} + \mathbf{b}$; $-\frac{2}{3}\mathbf{a} + \frac{2}{3}\mathbf{b}$ b) $\frac{1}{2}\mathbf{a}$; $-\frac{1}{6}\mathbf{a} + \frac{2}{3}\mathbf{b}$ c) $-\frac{1}{2}\mathbf{a} + 2\mathbf{b}$ d) $\overrightarrow{MX} = 3\overrightarrow{MP}$

5. a) $-\mathbf{b} + \mathbf{a}$; $-3\mathbf{a} + \mathbf{b}$ b) $-\frac{3}{2}\mathbf{a} + \frac{1}{2}\mathbf{b}$ c) $\left(k - \frac{3}{2}\right)\mathbf{a} + \left(\frac{1}{2} - k\right)\mathbf{b}$ d) $k = \frac{3}{2}$

6. a) $-\mathbf{a} + \mathbf{b}$ b) $-\frac{1}{4}\mathbf{a} + \frac{1}{4}\mathbf{b}$ c) $\mathbf{a} + (m - 1)\mathbf{b}$ d) $m = \frac{4}{3}$

7. a) $-\mathbf{c} + \mathbf{d}$ b) $-\frac{1}{5}\mathbf{c} + \frac{1}{5}\mathbf{d}$ c) $\frac{4}{5}\mathbf{c} + \frac{1}{5}\mathbf{d}$ d) $\mathbf{c} + (n - 1)\mathbf{d}$
   e) $n = \frac{5}{4}$

8. a) $-\mathbf{a} + \mathbf{b}$; $-\frac{1}{2}\mathbf{a} + \frac{1}{2}\mathbf{b}$; $\frac{1}{2}\mathbf{a} + \frac{1}{2}\mathbf{b}$ b) $\frac{1}{3}\mathbf{a} + \frac{1}{3}\mathbf{b}$ c) $-\frac{2}{3}\mathbf{a} + \frac{1}{3}\mathbf{b}$
   d) $-\mathbf{a} + \frac{1}{2}\mathbf{b}$ e) $m = \frac{2}{3}$

9. a) $-\mathbf{a} + \mathbf{b}$ b) $\frac{1}{2}\mathbf{b}$ c) $-\mathbf{a} + \mathbf{c}$ d) $-\frac{1}{2}\mathbf{a} + \frac{1}{2}\mathbf{c}$
   e) $\frac{1}{2}\mathbf{a} + \frac{1}{2}\mathbf{c}$ f) $-\frac{1}{2}\mathbf{b} + \frac{1}{2}\mathbf{a} + \frac{1}{2}\mathbf{c}$ g) $\mathbf{a} + \mathbf{c} = \mathbf{b}$

10. a) $-\mathbf{b} + \mathbf{a}$ b) $m\mathbf{a} + (1 - m)\mathbf{b}$ c) $4\mathbf{a} + 2\mathbf{b}$ d) $n = \frac{1}{6}$, $m = \frac{2}{3}$

11. a) $-\mathbf{c} + \mathbf{d}$; $-\frac{1}{4}\mathbf{c} + \frac{1}{4}\mathbf{d}$; $\frac{3}{4}\mathbf{c} + \frac{1}{4}\mathbf{d}$ b) $-\mathbf{c} + \frac{1}{2}\mathbf{d}$
   c) $(1 - h)\mathbf{c} + \frac{h}{2}\mathbf{d}$ d) $(1 - h)\mathbf{c} + \frac{h}{2}\mathbf{d} = k$; $\frac{3}{4}\mathbf{c} + \frac{k}{4}\mathbf{d}$; $h = \frac{2}{5}$, $k = \frac{4}{5}$

Exercise 11 page 305

1. a) 5, 10, 1   b) 21, 101, −29
2. $x \to \boxed{\times 5} \to \boxed{+4} \to 5x + 4$
3. $x \to \boxed{-4} \to \boxed{\times 3} \to 3(x - 4)$
4. $x \to \boxed{\times 2} \to \boxed{+7} \to \boxed{\text{square}} \to (2x + 7)^2$
5. $x \to \boxed{\times 5} \to \boxed{+9} \to \boxed{\div 4} \to \dfrac{5x + 9}{4}$
6. $x \to \boxed{\times -3} \to \boxed{\text{subtract from 4}} \to \boxed{\div 5} \to \dfrac{4 - 3x}{5}$

7. $x \rightarrow \boxed{\text{square}} \rightarrow \boxed{\times 2} \rightarrow \boxed{+1} \rightarrow 2x^2 + 1$

8. $x \rightarrow \boxed{\text{square}} \rightarrow \boxed{\times 3} \rightarrow \boxed{\div 2} \rightarrow \boxed{+5} \rightarrow \dfrac{3x^2}{2} + 5$

9. $x \rightarrow \boxed{\times 4} \rightarrow \boxed{-5} \rightarrow \boxed{\text{square root}} \rightarrow \sqrt{(4x - 5)}$

10. $x \rightarrow \boxed{\text{square}} \rightarrow \boxed{+10} \rightarrow \boxed{\text{square root}} \rightarrow \boxed{\times 4} \rightarrow 4\sqrt{(x^2 + 10)}$

11. $x \rightarrow \boxed{\times 3} \rightarrow \boxed{\text{subtract from 7}} \rightarrow \boxed{\text{square}} \rightarrow (7 - 3x)^2$

12. $x \rightarrow \boxed{\times 3} \rightarrow \boxed{+1} \rightarrow \boxed{\text{square}} \rightarrow \boxed{\times 4} \rightarrow \boxed{+5} \rightarrow 4(3x + 1)^2 + 5$

13. $x \rightarrow \boxed{\text{square}} \rightarrow \boxed{\text{subtract from 5}} \rightarrow 5 - x^2$

14. $x \rightarrow \boxed{\text{square}} \rightarrow \boxed{+1} \rightarrow \boxed{\text{square root}} \rightarrow \boxed{\times 10} \rightarrow \boxed{+6} \rightarrow \boxed{\div 4} \rightarrow \dfrac{10\sqrt{(x^2 + 1)} + 6}{4}$

15. $x \rightarrow \boxed{\text{cube}} \rightarrow \boxed{\div 4} \rightarrow \boxed{+1} \rightarrow \boxed{\text{square}} \rightarrow \boxed{\text{subtract 6}} \rightarrow \left(\dfrac{x^3}{4} + 1\right)^2 - 6$

16. a) $-9, 11, \frac{1}{2}$ **b)** $0.8, -2.7, \frac{1}{80}$ **c)** $4, 1.2, 36$

17. a) 0 **b)** 6 **c)** 12

18. a) 10 **b)** $\frac{1}{2}$ **c)** 2

19. a) $6, 24, 6$ **b)** $0, \sqrt{2}, \sqrt{6}$ **c)** $-6, 6, 9\frac{3}{4}$

20. a) ± 3 **b)** ± 3 **c)** ± 2 **d)** ± 6

21. a) i) 10 **ii)** 21 **b) i)** 111 **ii)** 411 **iii)** 990 **iv)** 112

22. a) 7 **b)** 10 **c)** 5 **d)** 14
    e) 7 **f)** 7

23. a) 3 **b)** 6 **c)** 8 **d)** 10

24. a) 11 **b)** 17 **c)** 7

25. a) 5 **b)** 17 **c)** $1\frac{1}{2}$ **d)** 3

26. $a = 3, b = 5$ **27.** $a = 2, b = -5$ **28.** $a = 7, b = 1$

Exercise 12   *page 308*

1. a) $x \mapsto 4(x + 5)$ **b)** $x \mapsto 4x + 5$ **c)** $x \mapsto (4x)^2$ **d)** $x \mapsto 4x^2$
    e) $x \mapsto x^2 + 5$ **f)** $x \mapsto 4(x^2 + 5)$ **g)** $x \mapsto [4(x + 5)]^2$

2. a) -2.5 **b)** $\pm\sqrt{\frac{5}{3}}$

3. a) $x \mapsto 2(x - 3)$ **b)** $x \mapsto 2x - 3$ **c)** $x \mapsto x^2 - 3$ **d)** $x \mapsto (2x)^2$
    e) $x \mapsto (2x)^2 - 3$ **f)** $x \mapsto (2x - 3)^2$

4. a) 2 **b)** 11 **c)** 6 **d)** 2
    e) 1 **f)** 64

5. a) -3 **b)** 2 **c)** $1\frac{1}{2}$ **d)** 5

6. a) $x \mapsto 2(3x - 1) + 1$ **b)** $x \mapsto 3(2x + 1) - 1$ **c)** $x \mapsto 2x^2 + 1$ **d)** $x \mapsto (3x - 1)^2$
    e) $x \mapsto 2(3x - 1)^2 + 1$ **f)** $x \mapsto 3(2x^2 + 1) - 1$

7. a) 11 **b)** 9 **c)** 11 **d)** 14
    e) 81 **f)** -1

8. a) 2 **b)** $0, 2$ **c)** $\pm\sqrt{2}$

9. $x \mapsto \dfrac{x + 2}{5}$ **10.** $x \mapsto \dfrac{x}{5} + 2$ **11.** $x \mapsto \dfrac{x}{6} - 2$ **12.** $x \mapsto \dfrac{3x - 1}{2}$

13. $x \mapsto \dfrac{4x}{3} + 1$ **14.** $x \mapsto \dfrac{x - 2}{6}$ **15.** $x \mapsto \dfrac{2x - 24}{5}$ **16.** $x \mapsto \dfrac{x - 3}{-7}$

17. $x \mapsto \dfrac{3x - 12}{-5}$ **18.** $x \mapsto 10 - 3x$ **19.** $x \mapsto \dfrac{4(5x + 3) + 1}{2}$ **20.** $x \mapsto \dfrac{7x - 30}{6}$

21. $x \mapsto 20x - 164$

22. a) $\sqrt{x}$ **b)** log **c)** $x!$ **d)** x^2 **e)** $\dfrac{1}{x}$ **f)** tan **g)** $\dfrac{1}{x}$ **h)** $\sqrt{}$ **i)** cos

  j) log or ln **k)** tan **l)** $x!$ **m)** cos **n)** sin **o)** cos **p)** $\dfrac{1}{x}$ **q)** $x!$ **r)** log

Exercise 13 *page 311*

1.   **2.**   **3.**   **4.**

5.   **6.**   **7.**

8.   **9.**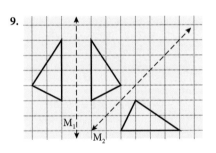

Exercise 14 *page 312*

1. c) i) $(-6, 8)$ **ii)** $(6, -4)$ **iii)** $(8, 6)$
2. c) i) $(8, 8)$ **ii)** $(8, -6)$ **iii)** $(-8, 6)$
3. c) i) $(3, -1)$ **ii)** $(4, 2)$ **iii)** $(-1, 1)$
4. b) i) $y = 1$ **ii)** $y = x$ **iii)** $y = -x$ **iv)** $y = 2$
5. f) $(1, -1), (-3, -1), (-3, -3)$
6. f) $(8, -2), (6, -6), (6, -6)$

Exercise 15   *page 314*

1.

2.

3.

4.

5.
90° clockwise

6.
90° clockwise

7.
180°

8.
90° clockwise

Exercise 16   *page 314*

1. a) A′(3, −1) B′(6, −1) C′(6, −3)
   b) D′(3, −3) E′(3, −6) F′(1, −6)
   c) P′(−7, −4) Q′(−5, −4) R′(−5, −1)

2. b) i) (4, −1), (7, −1), (7, −3)
   ii) (−1, −4), (−1, −7), (−3, −7)
   iii) (−4, 1), (−7, 1), (−7, 3)

3. c) (−2, 1), (−2, −1), (1, −2)

4. e) (−5, 2), (−5, 6), (−3, 5)

5. b) i) 90° anticlockwise, centre (0, 0)
   ii) 180°, centre (2, 1)
   iii) 90° clockwise, centre (2, 0)
   iv) 180°, centre $\left(3\frac{1}{2}, 2\frac{1}{2}\right)$
   v) 90° anticlockwise, centre (6, 1)
   vi) 90° clockwise, centre (1, 3)

6. e) i) 180°, centre $\left(\frac{1}{2}, \frac{1}{2}\right)$
   ii) 90° anticlockwise, centre (−2, 4)

Exercise 17   *page 316*

1. a) $\begin{pmatrix} 7 \\ 3 \end{pmatrix}$ **b)** $\begin{pmatrix} 0 \\ -9 \end{pmatrix}$ **c)** $\begin{pmatrix} 9 \\ 10 \end{pmatrix}$ **d)** $\begin{pmatrix} -10 \\ 3 \end{pmatrix}$ **e)** $\begin{pmatrix} -1 \\ 13 \end{pmatrix}$ **f)** $\begin{pmatrix} 10 \\ 0 \end{pmatrix}$ **g)** $\begin{pmatrix} -9 \\ -4 \end{pmatrix}$ **h)** $\begin{pmatrix} -10 \\ 0 \end{pmatrix}$

2. (5, 2)   **3.** (5, 6)   **4.** (8, −5)   **5.** (0, 6)   **6.** (4, −7)   **7.** (−3, 4)

8. (−3, −5)   **9.** (−1, −8)   **10.** (5, 2)   **11.** (−2, 1)

1.

2.

3.

4.

5.

6.

7. (4, 8), (8, 4), (10, 10)
8. (3, 6), (7, 2), (9, 8)
9. (1, 1), (10, 4), (4, 7)

10. (1, 4), (7, 8), (11, 2)
11. (2, 1), +3
12. (11, 9), $+\frac{1}{2}$

13. (5, 4), −2
14. (6, 6), −1
15. $\left(\frac{1}{2}, 1\right), \left(6\frac{1}{2}, 1\right), \left(\frac{1}{2}, 5\right)$

16. (3, 4), (3, 3), (5, 3)
17. (3, 7), (1, 7), (3, 3)
18. (10, 7), (6, 7), (6, 5)

19. (6, 5), $\left(3\frac{1}{2}, 5\right), \left(3\frac{1}{2}, 3\right)$

1. b) i) Rotation 90° clockwise, centre (0, −2)
    ii) Reflection in $y = x$
    iii) Translation $\begin{pmatrix} 3 \\ 7 \end{pmatrix}$
    iv) Enlargement, scale factor 2, centre (−5, 5)
    v) Translation $\begin{pmatrix} -7 \\ -3 \end{pmatrix}$
    vi) Reflection in $y = x$

2. a) Rotation 90° clockwise, centre (4, −2)
    b) Translation $\begin{pmatrix} 8 \\ 2 \end{pmatrix}$
    c) Reflection in $y = x$
    d) Enlargement, scale factor $\frac{1}{2}$, centre (7, −7)
    e) Rotation 90° anticlockwise, centre(−8, 0)
    f) Enlargement, scale factor 2, centre (−1, −9)
    g) Rotation 90° anticlockwise, centre (7, 3)

3. a) Enlargement, scale factor $1\frac{1}{2}$, centre (1, −4)
    b) Rotation 90° clockwise, centre (0, −4)
    c) Reflection in $y = -x$
    d) Translation $\begin{pmatrix} 11 \\ 10 \end{pmatrix}$
    e) Enlargement, scale factor $\frac{1}{2}$, centre (−3, 8)
    f) Rotation 90° anticlockwise, centre $\left(\frac{1}{2}, 6\frac{1}{2}\right)$
    g) Enlargement, scale factor 3, centre (−2, 5)

1. (2, −3)
2. (5, −1)
3. (6, 4)
4. (4, −6)
5. (0, 0)
6. (−6, 4)
7. (3, −2)
8. (3, 2)
9. (−2, 3)
10. (0, 0)
11. (−3, 2)
12. (−3, −2)
13. (−3, −2)
14. (−6, −4)
15. (6, 0)
16. (−2, 3)
17. (0, 4)
18. (6, 8)
19. (3, 2)
20. (0, 0)

1. a) $(-4, 4)$ **b)** $(2, -2)$ **c)** $(0, 0)$ **d)** $(0, 4)$ **e)** $(0, 0)$
2. a) $(-2, 5)$ **b)** $(-4, 0)$ **c)** $(2, -2)$ **d)** $(1, -1)$
3. a) reflection in y-axis **b)** rotation 180°, centre $(-2, 2)$
  c) rotation 90° clockwise, centre $(2, 2)$
4. a) rotation 90° anticlockwise, centre $(0, 0)$ **b)** translation $\begin{pmatrix} -2 \\ 5 \end{pmatrix}$

  c) rotation 90° anticlockwise, centre $(2, -4)$ **d)** rotation 90° anticlockwise, centre $(-\frac{1}{2}, 3\frac{1}{2})$

5. a) rotation 90° anticlockwise, centre $(2, 2)$ **b)** enlargement, scale factor $\frac{1}{2}$, centre $(8, 6)$

  c) rotation 90° clockwise, centre $(-\frac{1}{2}, -3\frac{1}{2})$
6. $\mathbf{A}^{-1}$: reflection in $x = 2$

  $\mathbf{B}^{-1} : \mathbf{B}$ $\quad$ $\mathbf{C}^{-1}$: translation $\begin{pmatrix} 6 \\ -2 \end{pmatrix}$ $\quad$ $\mathbf{D}^{-1} : \mathbf{D}$ $\quad$ $\mathbf{E}^{-1} : \mathbf{E}$ $\quad$ $\mathbf{F}^{-1}$: translation $\begin{pmatrix} -4 \\ -3 \end{pmatrix}$

  $\mathbf{G}^{-1}$: 90° rotation anticlockwise, centre $(0, 0)$

  $\mathbf{H}^{-1}$: enlargement, scale factor 2, centre $(0, 0)$

7. a) $(4, 0)$ **b)** $(-6, -1)$ **c)** $(-2, -2)$ **d)** $(2, -2)$ **e)** $(6, 2)$
8. a) $(1, -6)$ **b)** $(4, -2)$ **c)** $(2, 7)$ **d)** $(4, -6)$ **e)** $(2, -4)$
9. a) $(-1, -2)$ **b)** $(8, 2)$ **c)** $(4, -6)$ **d)** $(0, -3)$
10. b) rotation, 180°, centre $(4, 0)$ **c)** translation $\begin{pmatrix} 12 \\ -4 \end{pmatrix}$

1. a) $\{5\}$ **b)** $\{1, 3, 5, 6, 7\}$ **c)** $\{2, 4, 6, 7, 8\}$ **d)** $\{2, 4, 8\}$ **e)** $\{1, 2, 3, 4, 5, 8\}$ **2.** 32

3. a) **b)** **c)**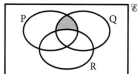

4. a) $(A \cup B)' \cap C$ **b)** $(A \cup B) \cap C'$
5. a) i) $S \subset T$ **ii)** $S \cap M' \neq \phi$ **b)** There are no women on the train over 25 years old.

6. a) 4 **b)** 11 **c)** 17 **7. a)** $\mathbf{r} - \mathbf{p}$ **b)** $\frac{1}{2}\mathbf{r} - \frac{1}{2}\mathbf{p}$ **c)** $\frac{1}{2}\mathbf{r} + \frac{1}{2}\mathbf{p}$

8. a) 5 **b)** $\sqrt{68}$ **c)** $\sqrt{41}$ **9.** $n = 2, m = -15$

10. a) $\begin{pmatrix} -1 \\ 4 \end{pmatrix}$ **b)** $\begin{pmatrix} 4 \\ 4 \end{pmatrix}$ **c)** $\begin{pmatrix} 6 \\ -4 \end{pmatrix}$ **d)** $\begin{pmatrix} 2 \\ 2 \end{pmatrix}$

11. a) $\mathbf{a} - \mathbf{c}$ **b)** $\frac{1}{2}\mathbf{a} + \mathbf{c}$ **c)** $\frac{1}{2}\mathbf{a} - \frac{1}{2}\mathbf{c}$ $\quad$ CA is parallel to NM and CA = 2NM.

12. $m = 3, n = 2$ **13. a)** $\begin{pmatrix} -3 \\ 2 \end{pmatrix}$ **b)** $\begin{pmatrix} -1\frac{1}{2} \\ 1 \end{pmatrix}$ **c)** $\begin{pmatrix} 1\frac{1}{2} \\ 3 \end{pmatrix}$

14. a) -5 **b)** 0 **c)** -3 **d)** 8; ff : $x \mapsto 4x - 9$

15. $f^{-1} : x \mapsto \dfrac{(x - 4)}{3}$; $h^{-1} : x \mapsto 5x + 2$ **a)** 3 **b)** $5\frac{1}{3}$ **16. a)** 3 **b)** 0, 5

17. a) $(4, -1)$ **b)** $(4, 1)$ **c)** $(-3, 2)$
18. a) $A'(-3, -1)\ B'(1, -1)\ C'(-3, -7)$ **b)** $A'(2, -2)\ B'(6, -2)\ C'(2, -8)$

  c) $A'(1, 1)\ B'(2, 1)\ C'(1, -\frac{1}{2})$ **d)** $A'(4, 2)\ B'(3, 2)\ C'\ (4, 3\frac{1}{2})$ **e)** $A'(-2, 2)\ B'(-6, 2)\ C'(-2, 8)$

19. a) reflection in y-axis **b)** reflection in $y = x$ **c)** rotation, $-90°$, centre $(0, 0)$
  d) reflection in $y = -x$ **e)** rotation, 180°, centre $(0, 0)$ **f)** rotation, $-90°$, centre $(0, 0)$

20. a) reflection in $x = \frac{1}{2}$ **b)** reflection in $y = -x$ **f)** rotation, 180°, centre $(1, 1)$

21. a) $(-1, -3)$ **b)** $(-1, 3)$ **c)** $(6, 2)$ **d)** $(-3, 1)$ **e)** $(-2, 6)$ **f)** $(0, 2)$
22. a) $(-1, 2)$ **b)** $(1, -2)$ **c)** $(10, -2)$ **d)** $(6, -2)$ **e)** $(-10, 2)$ **f)** $(12, 2)$

1. a)   **b)**   **c)**

2. a)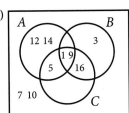

b) 1   **3. a)** ϕ **b)** ε **c)** ε

4. a) $2a - g$ **b)** $\frac{5}{2}a + \frac{1}{2}g$ **5. b)** $\frac{1}{2}a + \frac{2}{3}b$ **c)** $-\frac{1}{2}a + \frac{2}{3}b$

6. a) i) $c - d$ **ii)** $d - 0.5c$ **iii)** $1.5c - d$
  b) i) $120°$ **ii)** 27.7 cm²   **iii)** 13.9 cm   **iv)** 166 to 167 cm²

7. a) -14 **b)** $2x^3 - 6x^2 + 12x - 9$ **c)** $\dfrac{x+1}{2}$

8. a) 8 **b)** $\dfrac{5-x}{3}$ **c)** 8

9. a) 0.5 **b)** 0 **c)** $\dfrac{\sin x - 6}{3}$

10. a) 2 **b)** $\dfrac{2+2x}{2x-1}$ **c)** $\dfrac{3}{x-1}$ **d)** 256 **e)** -3

11. c) i) $(5, -7)(8, -7)(8, -5)$ **ii)** $(-4, 2)(-7, 2)(-7, 4)$ **iii)** $(-2, -2)(-5, -2)(-5, -4)$

12. c) $(1, 2)(1, 5)(3, 3)$ **d)** $(-2, 1)(-5, 1)(-3, 3)$ **e)** Reflection in y-axis

9 Statistics

Exercise 1   *page 333*

1. a) Squash   **b)** 160   **c)** 10
3. a) $3000   **b)** $4000   **c)** $6000   **d)** $11 000
4. red 50°; green 70°; blue 110°; yellow 40°; pink 90°
5. eggs 270°; milk 12°; butter 23.4°; cheese 54°; salt/pepper 0.6°
6. a) A 60°; B 100°; C 60°; D 140°; E 0°
  b) A 50°; B 75°; C 170°; D 40°; E 25°
  c) A 48.5°; B 76.2°; C 62.3°; D 96.9°; E 76.2°
7. 18°, 54°, 54°, 234°   **8.** 80°, 120°, 160°   **9.** $x = 8$ **10.** 100
11. a) 22.5%   **b)** $x = 45°, y = 114°$ **12. a)** 144°   **b)** posters 5%, cinema 1%
13. Area of second apple looks much more than twice area of first.
14. Vertical axis starts at 130.

Exercise 2   *page 337*

1. a)   **b)** 53   **c)** 55

Stem	Leaf
2	1 6 9
3	3 6 7
4	2 5 5 8 8
5	2 3 3 6
6	0 2 2 2 4 6 8
7	1 4 6

2. a) 12 **b)** 14.35 **c)** 2.8 **d)** 15.2

3. a)

Girls		Boys
7 5 1	16	
4	17	5 7
8 5	18	2 8
4 3	19	3
8	20	
0	21	0 9
	22	2 7
	23	1

b) Median: Boys = 20.15, Girls = 18.65
c) Range: Boys = 5.6, Girls = 4.9

4. a)

Action		Horror
8	8	5 8 9
9 3 0	9	0 2 4 5 9
6 0	10	0 5
9 0 0	11	
1	12	

b) Median: Action = 103 , Horror = 93
c) Action films

Exercise 3 *page 339*

1.

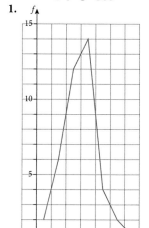

2. P – spend smaller amounts because probably visit more often since live closer.

3. Genetic engineering has little effect on weight. Genetic engineering makes a big difference to life span, extending it significantly.

Exercise 4 *page 341*
Frequency densities for histograms are given here.

1. 1, 1.4, 0.3
2. 1, 0.6, 1.2, 1.7, 1.3, 0.25
3. 0.5, 1.4, 2, 1, 0.2
4. 1.8, 9.2, 7, 1.3, 0.8
5. 0.55, 1.8, 0.7, 0.25
6. 1.6, 3.4, 2.8, 0.73
7. 8, 11, 6, 4, 1, 0.5

Exercise 5 *page 345*

1. a) mean = 6;   median = 5;   mode = 4.   **b)** mean = 9;   median = 7;   mode = 7.
   c) mean = 6.5;   median = 8;   mode = 9.   **d)** mean = 3.5;   median = 3.5;   mode = 4.
2. a) mean = 7.82;   median = 8;   mode = 8.   **b)** mean = 5;   median = 4;   mode = 4.
   c) mean = 2.1;   median = 2.5;   mode = 4.   **d)** mean = $\frac{13}{18}$;   median = $\frac{1}{2}$;   mode = $\frac{1}{2}$.
3. 78 kg   **4.** 35.2 cm   **5. a)** 2   **b)** 9

6. a) 20.4 m   **b)** 12.8 m   **c)** 1.66 m   **7.** 55 kg   **8.** 12

9. mean = 17, median = 3. The median is more representative.

10. the median.   **11.** 15, 20, 31   **12.** 3.38   **13.** 3.475

14. a) mean = 3.025;   median = 3;   mode = 3.   **b)** mean = 17.75;   median = 17;   mode = 17.
    c) mean = 3.38;   median = 4;   mode = 4.

15. a) 5.17   **b)** 5

16. a) 9   **b)** 9   **c)** 15   **17. a)** 5   **b)** 10   **c)** 10

18. 12   **19.** $3\frac{2}{3}$ **20.** 4.68

21. $\dfrac{ax + by + cz}{a + b + c}$

Exercise 6   *page 348*

1. a)

Number of words	Frequency f	Midpoint x	fx
1–5	6	3	18
6–10	5	8	40
11–15	4	13	52
16–20	2	18	36
21–25	3	23	69
Totals	20	—	215

b) 10.75

2. a) 68.25   **b)** The raw data is unavailable and an assumption has been made using the midpoint of each interval.

3. 68.25   **4.** 3.77

5. a) 181 cm
    b) The raw data is unavailable and an assumption has been made using the midpoint of each interval.
    c) 180–90 cm

Exercise 7   *page 352*

2. a) strong positive correlation   **b)** no correlation
    c) weak negative correlation

3. 11   **4.** 9   **5.** no correlation   **6. c)** about 26   **d)** about 46

7. b) 33 m.p.g.   **c)** 63 m.p.h.

Exercise 8   *page 355*

1. a)

Median = 8, Interquartile range = 4.5

b)

Median = 9, Interquartile range = 8

c)

Median = 11, Interquartile range = 12.5

2. a)

Test score

Median = 9, Interquartile range = 10.5

b) Interquartile range = 8

Exercise 9   *page 357*
1. **a)** 47   **b)** 30, 63   **c)** 33   **d)** 37   **e)** 23
2. **a)** 32   **b)** 26, 43   **c)** 17   **d)** 30   **e)** 80
3. **a)** 20 kg   **b)** 10.5 kg   **4. a)** 80.5 cm   **b)** 22 cm
5. **a)** 71 s   **b)** 20 s   **6. a)** 45   **b)** 14
7. **a)** 36.5 g   **b)** 20 g   **c)** 25
8. **a)** 26   **b)** 25.2   **c)** 26.1

9. Average marks are very similar but school B had a much larger spread of marks.
10. People in the town were on average taller but had a greater spread of heights.

Exercise 10   *page 360*
1. **a)** Lucy   **b)** 20   **c)** 22
2. **a)** Median: Class 1 = 42, Class 2 = 36
   b) IQR: Class 1 = 14, Class 2 = 10
   c) On average, Class 1 did better, because they have a higher median.
   d) Class 2 was more consistent, because their interquartile range was smaller.
3. **a)** Median: Children = 62, Adults = 71
      IQR: Children = 78 − 49 = 29, Adults = 83 − 57 = 26
   b) The adults were better at guessing.
4. On average, the waiting times were longer at surgery B because the median is higher.
   There is a greater spread of waiting times at surgery A because the interquartile range is larger.

Revision exercise 9A   *page 362*
1. 162°   **2.** 41.7%   **3.** 54°
4. **a)** 84   **b)** 19.2   **5. a)** 3.4   **b)** 3   **c)** 3
6. **a)** 5.45   **b)** 5   **c)** 5   **7.** 1.552 m   **8.** 3
9. **a)**

Stem	Leaf	Key
1	1 4 6 7 8	1 | 4 means 14
2	2 6 8	
3	4 9	
4	1 2 4 4 6 6 8 9 9	
5	0	

b) Median = 40, Interquartile range = 26
c)

Scores for Class 1

d) Class 2 have a Median of 36 and an IQR of 14.
   On average, Class 1 have higher scores, because their median is bigger.
   However, the scores from Class 2 are more consistent, because their IQR is smaller.

1. a) 3.365 to 3.375   **b)** 0.26 to 0.27   **c)** 55, 56 or 57

2. a) i) 30   **ii)** 30, 30.5, 31   **iii)** 3
    b) i) 20.93 or 20.9   **ii)** 0.7 cm, 2.6 cm, 0.8 cm

3. a) i) 46.5 km/h   **ii)** 9.5   **iii)** 48   **b) i)** $n = 32$ **ii)** 46.4 km/h
    c) Horizontal scale correct. 3 correct widths on their scale (ft). For each block of correct width: 2.7 cm, 7.1(3) or
    7.2 cm, 3.2 cm

4. a)

Age in years

b) On average, the people who took part in 2010 were older.
    There was a greater spread of ages in 2010.

10 Probability

Exercise 1   page 368

1. a) $\frac{1}{6}$ **b)** $\frac{1}{2}$ **c)** $\frac{1}{2}$ **d)** $\frac{1}{3}$

2. a) $\frac{1}{4}$ **b)** $\frac{1}{2}$

3. a) i) $\frac{3}{5}$ **ii)** $\frac{2}{5}$ **b) i)** $\frac{5}{9}$ **ii)** $\frac{4}{9}$

4. a) $\frac{1}{11}$ **b)** $\frac{2}{11}$ **c)** 0   **d)** $\frac{1}{11}$

5. a) $\frac{1}{8}$ **b)** $\frac{3}{8}$ **c)** $\frac{1}{8}$ **d)** $\frac{7}{8}$

6. a) $\frac{5}{11}$ **b)** $\frac{7}{22}$ **c)** $\frac{15}{22}$ **d)** $\frac{17}{22}$

7. a) $\frac{1}{2}$ **b)** $\frac{3}{25}$ **c)** $\frac{9}{100}$ **d)** $\frac{2}{25}$

8. a) $\frac{1}{12}$ **b)** $\frac{1}{36}$ **c)** $\frac{5}{18}$ **d)** $\frac{1}{6}$ **e)** $\frac{1}{6}$; most likely total $= 7$

9. a) $\frac{1}{12}$ **b)** $\frac{5}{36}$ **c)** $\frac{2}{3}$ **d)** $\frac{1}{12}$ **e)** $\frac{1}{36}$

10. a) 1   **b)** 0   **c)** 1   **d)** 0

11. a) $\frac{3}{8}$ **b)** $\frac{1}{16}$ **c)** $\frac{15}{16}$ **d)** $\frac{1}{4}$

12. $\frac{271}{1000}$ **13. a)** $\frac{x}{12}$ **b)** 3

14. a) $\frac{1}{144}$ **b)** $\frac{1}{18}$ **c)** $\frac{1}{72}$; head, tail and total of 7

15. a) $\frac{1}{216}$ **b)** $\frac{1}{72}$ **c)** $\frac{1}{8}$ **d)** $\frac{5}{108}$ **e)** $\frac{5}{72}$ **f)** $\frac{1}{36}$

Exercise 2   page 371

2. Mike. With a large number of spins, we would expect him get zero on about $\frac{1}{10}$ of the spins.

Exercise 3   page 373

1. a) $\frac{1}{2}$ **b)** $\frac{1}{2}$ **c)** $\frac{1}{4}$ **2. a)** $\frac{1}{16}$ **b)** $\frac{25}{144}$

3. a) $\frac{1}{121}$ **b)** $\frac{9}{121}$ **4. a)** $\frac{1}{288}$ **b)** $\frac{1}{72}$

5. a) $\frac{1}{125}$ **b)** $\frac{1}{125}$ **c)** $\frac{1}{10\,000}$ **d)** $\frac{3}{500}$ **e)** $\frac{3}{500}$

6. a) $\frac{1}{9}$ **b)** $\frac{4}{27}$ **c)** $\frac{4}{9}$

Exercise 4   page 374

1. a) $\frac{49}{100}$ **b)** $\frac{9}{100}$ **2. a)** $\frac{9}{64}$ **b)** $\frac{15}{64}$ **3. a)** $\frac{7}{15}$ **b)** $\frac{1}{15}$

4. a) $\frac{2}{9}$ **b)** $\frac{2}{15}$ **c)** $\frac{1}{45}$ **d)** $\frac{14}{45}$

5. a) $\frac{1}{12}$ **b)** $\frac{1}{6}$ **c)** $\frac{1}{3}$ **d)** $\frac{2}{9}$

6. a) $\frac{1}{216}$ **b)** $\frac{125}{216}$ **c)** $\frac{25}{72}$ **d)** $\frac{91}{216}$

7. a) $\frac{1}{6}$ **b)** $\frac{1}{30}$ **c)** $\frac{1}{30}$ **d)** $\frac{29}{30}$

8. a) $\frac{27}{64}$ **b)** $\frac{1}{64}$ **9. a)** 6   **b)** $\frac{1}{3}$

10. a) $\frac{1}{64}$ **b)** $\frac{27}{64}$ **c)** $\frac{9}{64}$ **d)** $\frac{27}{64}$; Sum = 1

11. a) $\frac{6}{6840}$ **b)** $\frac{60}{6840}$

   c) $\frac{1080}{6840}$ **d)** $\frac{120}{116\,280}$

12. a) $\dfrac{1}{10\,000}$ **b)** $\dfrac{523}{10\,000}$ **c)** $\dfrac{9^4}{10^4}$

13. a) $\dfrac{x}{x+y}$ **b)** $\dfrac{x(x-1)}{(x+y)(x+y-1)}$ **c)** $\dfrac{2xy}{(x+y)(x+y-1)}$ **d)** $\dfrac{y(y-1)}{(x+y)(x+y-1)}$

14. a) $\frac{1}{5}$ **b)** $\frac{18}{25}$ **c)** $\frac{1}{20}$ **d)** $\frac{2}{25}$ **e)** $\frac{77}{100}$

15. $\frac{3}{10}$ **16.** $\frac{9}{140}$ **17. a)** 5   **b)** $\frac{1}{64}$

18. a) $\frac{1}{220}$ **b)** $\frac{1}{22}$ **c)** $\frac{3}{11}$ **d)** 5   **e)** 300

19. a) $\dfrac{10 \times 9}{1000 \times 999}$ **b)** $\dfrac{990 \times 989}{1000 \times 999}$ **c)** $\dfrac{2 \times 10 \times 990}{1000 \times 999}$

20. a) $\frac{3}{20}$ **b)** $\frac{7}{20}$ **c)** $\frac{1}{2}$

21. a) 0.00781   **b)** 0.511   **22. a)** $\frac{21}{506}$ **b)** $\frac{455}{2024}$ **c)** $\frac{945}{2024}$

Exercise 5   page 379

1. a) $\dfrac{16}{25}$ **b)** $\dfrac{7}{25}$ **c)** $\dfrac{3}{25}$ **d)** $\dfrac{6}{25}$

2. a) i) $\dfrac{14}{30}$ **ii)** $\dfrac{7}{30}$ **iii)** $\dfrac{9}{30}$

   b) Children who like carrots but do not eat them

3. a)

   b) i) $\dfrac{9}{50}$ **ii)** $\dfrac{38}{50}$ **iii)** $\dfrac{29}{50}$

4. a)

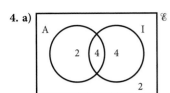

b) i) $\dfrac{4}{12}$ **ii)** $\dfrac{8}{12}$ **iii)** $\dfrac{4}{12}$

5. a) $\dfrac{17}{30}$ **b)** $\dfrac{7}{30}$ **c)** $\dfrac{8}{30}$ **d)** $\dfrac{16}{30}$ **e)** $\dfrac{5}{30}$

6. a) $x = 12$ **b) i)** $\dfrac{66}{120}$ **ii)** $\dfrac{25}{120}$ **iii)** $\dfrac{38}{120}$ **iv)** $\dfrac{69}{120}$

7. a)

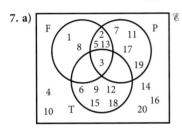

b) i) $\dfrac{4}{20}$ **ii)** $\dfrac{11}{20}$ **iii)** $\dfrac{7}{20}$ **iv)** $\dfrac{16}{20}$ **v)** $\dfrac{15}{20}$

Exercise 6   *page 382*

1. $\dfrac{26}{51}$ **2. a) i)** $\dfrac{4}{8}$ **ii)** $\dfrac{4}{8}$ **b)** $\dfrac{12}{72}$

3. a) $\dfrac{24}{50}$ **b)** $\dfrac{23}{50}$ **c)** $\dfrac{17}{26}$ **d)** $\dfrac{14}{23}$ **e)** $\dfrac{14}{24}$

4. a)

     Kebe   Lilian

                             0.7   late

           0.2   late

                             0.3   not late

                             0.2   late

           0.8   not late

                             0.8   not late

b) 0.3 **c)** 0.3

5. a) 0.62 **b)** 0.632 **6. a)** $\dfrac{23}{37}$ **b)** $\dfrac{20}{43}$ **c)** $\dfrac{3}{23}$

7. a) $\dfrac{5}{7}$ **b)** $\dfrac{5}{8}$ **c)** 1 **d)** 0

Revision exercise 10A   *page 384*

1. $\frac{1}{6}$ **2. a)** 5 **b)** $\frac{4}{25}$ **3.** $\frac{8}{27}$ **4.** $\frac{5}{16}$

5. a) $\frac{1}{28}$ **b)** $\frac{15}{28}$ **c)** $\frac{3}{7}$

6. a) $\dfrac{x}{x+5}$ **b)** $\left(\dfrac{x}{x+5}\right)^2$ **c)** $\dfrac{x(x-1)}{(x+5)(x+4)}$

7. $\frac{1}{19}$ **8. a)** $\frac{1}{32}$ **b)** $\frac{1}{256}$ **9. a)** $\frac{1}{8}$ **b)** $\frac{1}{2}$

10. $\frac{35}{48}$ **11. a)** $\frac{1}{9}$ **b)** $\frac{1}{12}$ **c)** 0   **12.** $\frac{1}{20^3}$

13. a) $\frac{3}{5}$ **b)** $\frac{1}{3}$ **c)** $\frac{2}{15}$ **d)** $\frac{2}{21}$ **e)** $\frac{1}{7}$ **f)** $\frac{1}{35}$

Examination-style exercise 10B   *page 385*

1. a) $\frac{8}{19}$ **b)** $\frac{7}{18}$

2. a) i) 6   **ii)** 4.5   **iii)** 4.54   **iv)** $\frac{1}{63}$ **v)** $\frac{1}{35}$ **vi)** $\frac{92}{819}$

b) i) 0.08   **ii)** 0.125   **iii)** 7

3. a) $p = \frac{1}{20}$, $q = \frac{19}{20}$ **b) i)** $\frac{1}{400}$ **ii)** $\frac{38}{400}$ **c)** $\frac{38}{8000}$ **d)** $\frac{58}{8000}$ **e)** 7.25

4. a) i) 12   **ii)** 3   **iii)** 21   **iv)** 2   **v)** $\frac{14}{24}$ **vi)** $\frac{12}{19}$

b) i) $\frac{132}{462}$ **ii)** $\frac{240}{462}$

5. a)

b) i) $\frac{36}{100}$ **ii)** $\frac{38}{100}$ **iii)** $\frac{26}{100}$ **c)** $\frac{36}{58}$

11 Investigations, Practical Problems, Puzzles

11.1 Investigations   *page 389*

Note: It must be emphasised that the *process* of obtaining reliable results is far more important than these few results. It is not suggested that 'obtaining a formula' is the only aim of these investigations. The results are given here for some of the investigations merely as a check for teachers or students working on their own.

It is not possible to summarise the enormous number of variations which students might think of for themselves. Obviously some original thoughts will be productive while many others will soon 'dry up'.

1. With the numbers written in c columns, the difference for a $(n \times n)$ square is $(n-1)^2 \times c$.

8. a) For n blacks and n whites, number of moves $= \dfrac{n(n+1)}{2}$.

b) For n blacks and n whites, number of moves $= \dfrac{n(n+2)}{2}$.

c) For n of each colour, number of moves $= \frac{3}{2} n(n+1)$.

9. 4×4 : There are 30 squares (i.e. $16 + 9 + 4 + 1$)
8×8 : There are 204 squares $(64 + 49 + 36 + 25 + 16 + 9 + 4 + 1)$
$n \times n$: Number of squares $= 1^2 + 2^2 + 3^2 + \ldots + n^2$
$$= \frac{n}{6}(n+1)(2n+1)$$

14. For $n \times n \times n$:   3 green faces $= 8$
2 green faces $= 12(n-2)$
1 green face $= 6(n-2)^2$
0 green face $= (n-2)^3$

18. a) For a square card, corner cut out $= \frac{1}{6}$ (size of card).

 b) For a rectangle $a \times 2a$, corner cut out $\cong \dfrac{a}{4.732}$.

20. For diagram number n, number of squares $= 2n^2 - 2n + 1$.

21. a) Another Fibonacci sequence.

 b) Terms are alternate terms of original sequence.

 c) Ratio tends towards 1.618 (to 4 s.f.), the 'Golden Ratio'.

 d) (first $\times$ fourth) = (second $\times$ third) + 1

 e) (first $\times$ third) ± 1 = (second)^2, alternating + and $-$

 f) For six terms $a\ b\ c\ d\ e\ f$ let $x = e \times f - (a^2 + b^2 + c^2 + d^2 + e^2)$

 g) sum of 10 terms = $11 \times$ seventh term.

The numbers in the first difference column are the squares of the terms in the original Fibonacci sequence.

22. For n names, maximum possible number of interchanges $= \dfrac{n(n-1)}{2}$.

24. Consider three cases of rectangles $m \times n$

 a) m and n have no common factor. Number of squares $= m + n - 1$.

 e.g. 3×7, number $= 3 + 7 - 1 = 9$

 b) n is a multiple of m. Number of squares $= n$ e.g. 3×12, number $= 12$

 c) m and n share a common factor a

 so $m \times n = a(m' + n')$

 number of squares $= a(m' + n' - 1)$

 e.g. $640 \times 250 = 10(64 \times 25)$, number of squares $= 10(64 + 25 - 1) = 880$.

26. For smallest surface area, height of cylinder $= 2 \times$ radius.

27. Pick's theorem: $A = i + \frac{1}{2}p - 1$

	x	First difference
First six	0	
		1
Second six	1	
		1
Third six	2	
		4
Fourth six	6	
		9
Fifth six	15	
		25
Sixth six	40	
		64
Seventh six	104	
		169
Eighth six	279	

12 Revision tests

Test 1 page 412

1. C	**2.** D	**3.** D	**4.** B	**5.** A
6. C	**7.** A	**8.** C	**9.** C	**10.** B
11. C	**12.** A	**13.** D	**14.** C	**15.** C
16. D	**17.** A	**18.** C	**19.** B	**20.** D
21. A	**22.** C	**23.** B	**24.** B	**25.** C

Test 2 page 414

1. B	**2.** C	**3.** A	**4.** B	**5.** D
6. C	**7.** A	**8.** D	**9.** B	**10.** C
11. B	**12.** D	**13.** A	**14.** D	**15.** C
16. D	**17.** B	**18.** A	**19.** B	**20.** B
21. C	**22.** D	**23.** A	**24.** A	**25.** B

Test 3 page 417

1. D	**2.** D	**3.** D	**4.** B	**5.** A
6. C	**7.** A	**8.** D	**9.** D	**10.** B
11. C	**12.** D	**13.** D	**14.** B	**15.** A
16. B	**17.** C	**18.** A	**19.** D	**20.** D
21. C	**22.** A	**23.** B	**24.** B	**25.** D

Test 4 page 419

1. B	**2.** B	**3.** A	**4.** C	**5.** D
6. A	**7.** B	**8.** C	**9.** D	**10.** B
11. C	**12.** A	**13.** B	**14.** B	**15.** D
16. A	**17.** C	**18.** B	**19.** B	**20.** D
21. A	**22.** C	**23.** C	**24.** C	**25.** A

Examination-style Paper 2

page 422

1. $\frac{4}{5}$ **2.** 265   **3.** $x < 6$

4. $n^2 + 1$ **5.** 1.4×10^{-3} **6.** 15   **7.** $400

8. a) 0.45   **b)** $\frac{33}{74}$

9. a) −3   **b)** $y = \frac{1}{3}x + \frac{2}{3}$

10. a) 4.25 m, 3.75 m   **b)** 11.7 m², 8.44 m²
11. $x = 4, y = -1$ **12.** 4000
13. a) 30 | 2 3
        31 | 5 7 7 9
        32 | 0 1 5 9   Key: 31 | 2 represents 312 bees
    b) 318
14. a) i) 54   **ii)** 57   **b)** $C = 8N + 1$
15. (−3, −12)
16. a) A triangle with vertices (2, −2), (−4, −4) and (−4, −8)   **b)** 12 square units
    c)   **d)** Reflection in the line $y = x$

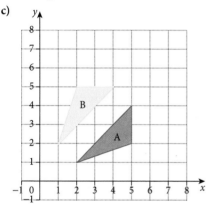

17. a) $xy = k$ or $y = \dfrac{k}{x}$ **b)** y increases by 25%

18. $y = \dfrac{6}{x}$ A, $y = -3 + 2^x$ C   **19.** $\frac{31}{90}$

20. a) XY = XW = 5 cm, YZ = WZ = 10.4 cm   **b)** ∠YZW = 33.4°
21. a) 9.60 cm   **b)** 24.0 cm²   **c)** 19.6 cm
22. $a = 38°, b = 71°, c = 64°$
23. 0.216   **24. a)** $3x^2 - 6x$ **b)** $x = 0, x = 2$

Examination-style Paper 4

page 427

1. a) i) 36   **ii)** −8   **b)** $4\frac{1}{2}$ **c)** +5, −5

d) ×9   **e)** $p = \sqrt{\dfrac{r(q-3)}{2}}$

2. a) i) $2\mathbf{x}$ **ii)** $\overrightarrow{EC} = \overrightarrow{ED} + \overrightarrow{DC}$ **iii)** $\overrightarrow{AE} = 2\mathbf{y} - \mathbf{z}$ $\overrightarrow{CA} = 2\mathbf{z} - \mathbf{x}$

    b) $\mathbf{x} + \mathbf{y} + \mathbf{z}$ **c)** $\mathbf{x} + \mathbf{y} + \mathbf{z} = 0$ **d)** $\overrightarrow{BE} = 2\mathbf{y} - \mathbf{x} - \mathbf{z} = 2\mathbf{y} + \mathbf{y}$ (using c)) $= 3\mathbf{y}$ BE and CD are parallel.

3. a) i) 94.2 cm³　　**ii)** 104 cm²　　　　**b)** 268 g

4. a) $f^{-1}(x) = \frac{x+1}{3}$　　**b)** 2　　　　　**c)** −2　　　　　　**e)** −0.19, 1.19　　　　**f)** $(\frac{1}{3}, -4)$

5. a) i) 14.4 cm　　　　**ii)** 24.8 cm²　　**b) i)** 31.6°　　　　**ii)** 17.9°

6. a) $10x - 30$　　　**b)** $(3x - 8)(2x - 7)$

　　d) i) $(6x + 5)(x - 7)$　　**ii)** $x = -\frac{5}{6}$ or 7

　　e) length 13 cm, width 7 cm

7. a) ii) $\frac{1}{36}$　　　**iii)** $\frac{5}{36}$　　　**iv)** 11　　**b) i)** 0.42　　　**ii)** 0.16　　　　**iii)** 0.34

8. a) 6.10 hours　　**b) i)** $10 < N \leqslant 12$　　**ii)** 5 h 30 m　　**c)** Mode

d)

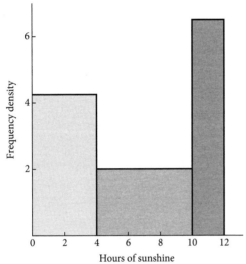

Hours of sunshine

9. a)

Selling price	Number of bicycles sold	Sales revenue ($)
60	6000	360 000
70	5500	385 000
80	5000	400 000
90	4500	405 000
100	4000	400 000
110	3500	385 000
120	3000	360 000

　　c) i) $90　　**ii)** 4500

10. a) 194.5°, 345.5°　　**b)**

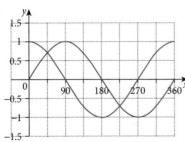

11. a) Accept 606–610　　**b)** Accept 50–54　　　**c)** Accept 620–624　　　**d)** Accept 39–43

Index